Introduction to
Chemical Engineering
and
Computer Calculations

PRENTICE-HALL INTERNATIONAL SERIES
IN THE PHYSICAL AND CHEMICAL ENGINEERING SCIENCES

NEAL R. AMUNDSON, EDITOR, *University of Minnesota*

ADVISORY EDITORS

ANDREAS ACRIVOS, *Stanford University*
JOHN DAHLER, *University of Minnesota*
THOMAS J. HANRATTY, *University of Illinois*
JOHN M. PRAUSNITZ, *University of California*
L. E. SCRIVEN, *University of Minnesota*

PRENTICE-HALL, INC.
PRENTICE-HALL INTERNATIONAL, INC.,
UNITED KINGDOM AND EIRE
PRENTICE-HALL OF CANADA, LTD., CANADA

Introduction to

Chemical Engineering

and

Computer Calculations

ALAN L. MYERS and WARREN D. SEIDER

Department of Chemical and Biochemical Engineering
University of Pennsylvania

PRENTICE-HALL, INC.
Englewood Cliffs, New Jersey

Library of Congress Cataloging in Publication Data

MYERS, ALAN L
    Introduction to chemical engineering and computer
calculations.

    (Prentice-Hall international series in the phys-
ical and chemical engineering sciences)
    Includes bibliographical references.
    1. Chemical engineering. 2. Chemical engineer-
ing—Mathematics. 3. Chemical engineering—Data
processing. I. Seider, Warren D., joint author.
II. Title.
TP155.M9   660.2   75-15984
ISBN 0-13-479238-6

10 9 8 7 6 5 4 3 2 1

Printed in the United States of America

PRENTICE-HALL INTERNATIONAL, INC., *London*
PRENTICE-HALL OF AUSTRALIA, PTY. LTD., *Sydney*
PRENTICE-HALL OF CANADA, LTD., *Toronto*
PRENTICE-HALL OF INDIA PRIVATE LIMITED, *New Delhi*
PRENTICE-HALL OF JAPAN, INC., *Tokyo*
PRENTICE-HALL OF SOUTHEAST ASIA (PTE.) LTD., *Singapore*

To

Irmgard
and
Diane

Contents

Appendices

Index   *518*

Preface

This book is an introduction to chemical engineering for students with a background of differential and integral calculus, physics, and general chemistry. The first nine chapters are appropriate for a one-semester course, usually offered in the sophomore year.

The first three chapters introduce the terminology of chemical processing and describe the operation of individual units like reactors, heat exchangers, and distillation columns. Particular processes such as desalination of seawater and coal gasification are studied qualitatively in preparation for a discussion of process synthesis in Chapter 3, where it is explained how efficient utilization of raw materials and energy, environmental considerations, and economics affect the design of chemical processes.

Chemical process calculations are based upon theories of conservation, thermodynamics, and numerical analysis, and we have tried to develop these theories in a logical and unified manner. Properties of materials and how they are calculated from equations, tables, and graphs are the subject of Chapter 4, which leads naturally into methods of data processing including correlation, interpolation, and information retrieval in Chapter 5.

Material and energy balances are studied in Chapters 6 through 9. These chapters are organized so that material balances are considered before energy balances; individual process units before complete processes with recycling; and physical transformations before chemical reactions. Emphasis is upon analysis: writing equations, selecting design variables, and preparing solution algorithms. Important new concepts are accompanied with examples

intended to develop skill in solving problems. The modular approach described in Chapter 8 reduces the analysis of a process to separate analyses
of its units and is an excellent way of introducing complications of recycling
and countercurrent flow. It is assumed that the reader of Chapter 9 on
energy balances has no background in thermodynamics.

A more advanced treatment of material and energy balances is contained
in Chapter 10. Equations of phase and chemical equilibrium, which enter
into these calculations, are summarized in Appendix IV. Temperature is
introduced as a tear variable for coupled material and energy balance equations. Worked examples include adiabatic chemical reactions, adiabatic flash
vaporization, and distillation columns.

Computer methods of solution are emphasized throughout the book,
particularly in Chapters 5, 8, and 10. Before the age of computers, chemical
engineers relied upon graphical and approximate methods to solve material
and energy balances. These techniques are less important today because of
the number-crunching capacity of computers. Engineers are no longer forced
into making unrealistic assumptions in order to simplify the problem; instead,
the computer makes it possible to simulate the actual process by varying key
parameters and observing the effect.

Chapters 11 through 13 contain mathematical methods of greatest value
for chemical process calculations. Solution of single equations is the subject
of Chapter 11. Matrix algebra, the language of stoichiometry, is introduced
in Chapter 12. Finally, Chapter 13 covers solution of simultaneous nonlinear
equations by methods of precedence ordering, tearing, and iterative techniques with and without derivatives. Chapters 11-13 are intended as references
to be consulted as the need arises to solve problems in previous chapters.
It is desirable that the reader have some knowledge of FORTRAN programming language.

Chemical process calculations are rather like piano playing in that practice
is essential. Worked examples are sprinkled liberally throughout the text to
assist the student in developing the confidence and accuracy that comes
with experience.

ALAN L. MYERS
WARREN SEIDER

Acknowledgments

We express our gratitude to our colleagues at the University of Pennsylvania, particularly Professors Stuart Churchill, David Graves, Noam Lior, and Ronald Klaus, for many ideas and valuable suggestions. We are particularly indebted to Dean Arthur E. Humphrey, whose enthusiastic support helped to launch this book. Professor Brice Carnahan at University of Michigan and Professor J. D. Seader at University of Utah provided valuable collaboration. Useful comments and suggestions were offered by Professor Allen Barduhn at Syracuse University, Professor Robert C. Reid at Massachusetts Institute of Technology, and Professor Imre Zwiebel at Worcester Polytechnic Institute. Financial support from the Exxon Education Foundation enabled us to create computer programs, property information systems, and U.P. PACER. Many students, especially Sezer Soylemez, Daniel Poznanovic, Michael Hanyak, Richard Whittall, William Moore, John Brady, Roy Ginsberg, Greg Powers, and Robert Smith, contributed ideas and helped to assemble the computer programs. We were fortunate to have the skillful assistance of Mary Jane Potter and Elizabeth Davis to translate our sketches into drawings.

List of Symbols

1. Capitals

A	area
	atomic weight
B	second virial coefficient
	flow rate of bottoms stream
C_p	heat capacity at constant pressure
D	flow rate of distillate stream
$\mathcal{E}$	electromotive force
E	energy
F	flow rate, moles per unit time
F'	flow rate, mass per unit time
$\mathbf{F}$	force
G	Gibbs free energy ($H - TS$)
H	enthalpy
	Henry's constant
I	electrical current
K	equilibrium constant of chemical reaction
L	flow rate of liquid stream
M	molecular weight

$\bar{M}$ average molecular weight of mixture

N_A Avogadro's number

N_c number of components

N_d number of design variables

N_e number of equations

N_p number of equipment parameters

N_q number of heat terms

N_s number of streams

N_v number of variables

N_w number of work terms

P pressure

P^s vapor pressure

P_c critical pressure

P_r reduced pressure $= P/P_c$

Q quantity of heat

R gas constant
     radius
     reflux ratio

S entropy

T thermodynamic temperature

T_b normal boiling point

T_c critical temperature

T_r reduced temperature $= T/T_c$

T_0 reference temperature

U internal energy

V volume
     flow rate of vapor stream

W quantity of work

Z quantity of electrical charge

2. Lowercase

a acceleration

c_p molar heat capacity at constant pressure

c_v molar heat capacity at constant volume

d differential operator

e base of natural logarithms

f	fugacity
f_{ij}	fugacity in stream i of component j
g	molar Gibbs free energy
g_c	constant in Eqn. (1.2)
g	acceleration of gravity
h	molar enthalpy
h'	enthalpy per unit mass
k	vapor-liquid equilibrium constant
	liquid-liquid equilibrium constant
	Boltzmann's constant
	reaction rate constant
m	mass
m_{jk}	number of atoms in component j of element k
n	number of moles
q	heat per mole
q'	heat per unit mass
r	rate of chemical reaction
s	molar entropy
s'	entropy per unit mass
t	time
u	molar internal energy
u'	internal energy per unit mass
v	molar volume
v'	specific volume (volume per unit mass)
v_c	molar volume at critical point
v	velocity
w	work per mole
w'	work per unit mass
x	mole fraction in general
	mole fraction in liquid phase
	distance
x'	mass fraction in general
x_{ij}	mole fraction in stream i of component j
y	mole fraction in gas phase
z	compressibility factor ($z = Pv/RT$)
	height
	mole fraction in mixed (i.e., liquid and vapor) feed to a distillation column
z_c	compressibility factor at critical point

3. Greek Letters

Γ	intermolecular potential energy
γ	ratio of specific heats $= c_p/c_v$
	activity coefficient in liquid phase
	fractional conversion of reactants into products
Δ	finite difference
ϵ	convergence tolerance
θ	angular displacement, radians
λ	latent heat of vaporization of a liquid
ν	stoichiometric coefficient
π	ratio of circumference to diameter of circle
ρ	density, mass per unit volume
τ	torque
	time
ω	acentric factor
	angular velocity, radians per unit time

4. Subscripts

c	refers to critical state
i	refers to stream number
j	refers to component number
m	refers to mixture
r	refers to reduced property

5. Superscripts

e	thermodynamic excess quantity
f	refers to formation of a compound from its elements
m	refers to isothermal mixing process
0	refers to limit of zero pressure where gases are ideal
	refers to reference state
$'$	refers to first derivative of function of single variable
	refers to mass basis (as opposed to molar basis)
$*$	refers to guess value of an unknown

6. Abbreviations and Special Conventions

{ }	braces enclose argument of a function, e.g., $f\{x\}$
$\bigcirc$	design variables (known quantities) are circled
—	Bar-over symbol indicates molal average value
(g), (l), (s)	refers to state (gas, liquid, or solid) of substance in a chemical reaction
atm	atmosphere
Btu	British thermal unit
°C	degrees Centigrade
cal	calorie
cm	centimeter
°F	degrees Fahrenheit
ft	foot
g	gram
hp	horsepower
hr	hour
in.	inch
J	joule
°K	degrees Kelvin
K.E.	kinetic energy
kg	kilogram
kw-hr	kilowatt-hour
lb	pound of mass
lb_f	pound of force
ln	natural logarithm
$\log_{10}$	logarithm to base 10
m	meter
min	minute
mm	millimeter
mole	gram-mole
N	newton
P.E.	potential energy
psi	pounds force per square inch
°R	degrees Rankine
rpm	revolutions per minute
sec	second
V	volt
w	watt

Introduction 1

1.1 The Chemical Engineering Profession

The goal of the engineering professions is translation of scientific knowledge into tangible improvements in the quality of life.

Chemical engineering is the design, construction, and operation of processes in which the essential operations are chemical reactions.

What kinds of problems will chemical engineers work on in the year 2000? No one really knows, but some possibilities are life-support systems for interplanetary travel, chemical plants on earth which recycle consumer goods and therefore conserve natural resources, and processes for making still-undiscovered substances. Chemical processes of the future, whatever they may be, must obey the physical and chemical laws of nature. The purpose of this book is to discuss those laws, principles, skills, and practices which give the profession of chemical engineering its name.

Computers have replaced the slide rule for making engineering calculations. The precise language of computer programming has forced engineers to examine more carefully the basic principles of engineering. In this textbook we shall try to present a balanced viewpoint of the capabilities and limitations of computers.

1.2 Process Units, the Building Blocks of Chemical Processes

A chemical engineer divides an entire manufacturing process into separate *unit operations* whose performance characteristics can be studied independently. These unit operations include flow of fluids, transfer of heat, condensation and boiling, chemical reactions, crystallization, gaseous diffusion, sedimentation, filtration, size reduction and classification of solids, absorption, adsorption, extraction, and drying.

A *process unit* is an apparatus or part of a chemical process which accomplishes some changes, physical or chemical or both, on the material which passes through it. Most process units perform more than one unit operation.

A typical process unit is the tubular reactor shown in Fig. 1-1. This reactor was designed for exothermic chemical reactions of gases which require the

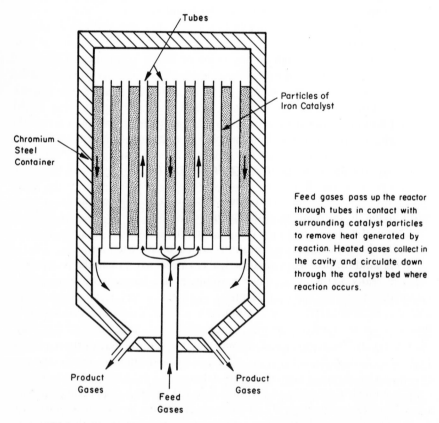

Feed gases pass up the reactor through tubes in contact with surrounding catalyst particles to remove heat generated by reaction. Heated gases collect in the cavity and circulate down through the catalyst bed where reaction occurs.

Figure 1-1 Tubular reactor. [R. F. Baddour, P. L. T. Brian, B. A. Logeais, and J. P. Eymery, "Steady-State Simulation of an Ammonia Synthesis Converter," *Chem. Eng. Sci. 20*, 281 (1965).]

presence of a solid catalyst. The feed gas enters at a steady flow rate and is heated to the reaction temperature as it passes through tubes surrounded by hot catalyst particles. The hot mixture of gases begins to react as soon as it contacts the catalyst; heat given off by the chemical reaction is transferred to the feed gas. The product gases flow out of the bed and finally out of the reactor at a steady flow rate. The tubular reactor combines three unit operations: heat transfer, flow of fluids, and chemical reaction.

An absorber is shown in Fig. 1-2. This process unit removes a condensable vapor (ammonia, for example) from a gas stream (air, for example) by absorbing it in a liquid stream (water, for example). The transfer of the condensable vapor is promoted by intimate, prolonged contact of the gas and liquid streams. Contact is achieved by pumping the gas upward through a bed of small, hollow, ceramic cylinders over which the liquid trickles downward. The gas stream entering at the bottom of the absorber is heavily laden with condensable vapor, but by the time the gas leaves the top of the column most of this vapor has been absorbed into the liquid stream.

A distillation tower is shown in Fig. 1-3(a). The function of this process unit is to purify a feed stream by separating the low-boiling-point or light components from the high-boiling-point or heavy components. The light product stream is called the *distillate*, and the heavy product stream is called the *bottoms*. The feed may be a liquid or a condensable vapor. The tower is composed of a series of identical trays, two of which are shown in Fig. 1-3(b). Liquid flows downward by gravity from the tray above and then across the tray, which is perforated with an array of bubble caps. Vapor from the tray below passes upward through the caps and bubbles through the liquid. In each tray, the liquid stream from above is mixed thoroughly with the vapor stream from below. Some of the light component (the one with the lower boiling point) moves upward with the vapor, while some of the heavy component moves downward with the liquid. This transfer of material, incomplete in each tray, is multiplied by staging. A reboiler at the bottom of the column supplies heat to vaporize the liquid. A condenser at the top of the column supplies liquid reflux. The overall effect is separation of a feed (A + B) into a distillate (A) and a bottoms (B). Distillation combines the unit operations of fluid flow, heat transfer, condensation, and boiling.

A cyclone separator is shown in Fig. 1-4. This process unit is designed to remove small solid particles or liquid droplets from a gas stream using centrifugal forces. The dust- or mist-laden gas is introduced tangentially at a high but subsonic velocity so that the dust or mist particles are thrown outward against the cylindrical wall. The solid or liquid is collected at the bottom, and the gas, free of dust or mist, passes upward and out through a central outlet at the top.

A heat exchanger is shown in Fig. 1-5. The objective is to heat one fluid by cooling another. The fluids never touch but exchange heat through the walls of metal tubes. Fluid 1, which passes through the headers and the *insides* of

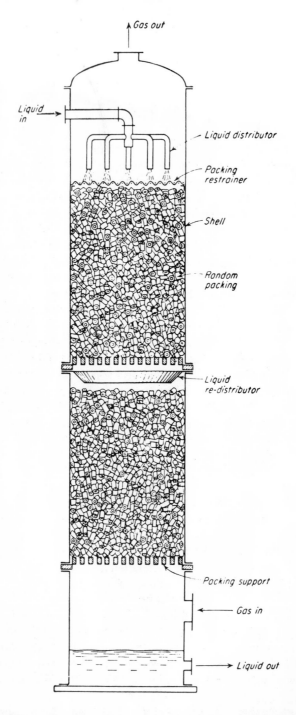

Gas out

Liquid in

Liquid distributor

Packing restrainer

Shell

Random packing

Liquid re-distributor

Packing support

Gas in

Liquid out

Figure 1-2 Gas absorber. (R. E. Treybal, *Mass Transfer Operations*, McGraw-Hill, New York, 1955, p. 134.)

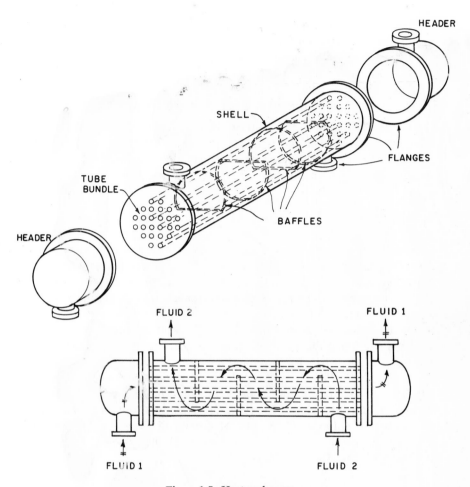

Figure 1-5   Heat exchanger.

the tubes, is called the tube-side fluid; fluid 2, which flows over the outside of the tubes, is called the shell-side fluid. A series of baffles is introduced to improve the circulation of the shell-side fluid. A well-designed heat exchanger can heat the cold fluid to a temperature only slightly below the temperature of the entering hot fluid.

These are some of the process units which have been invented by chemical engineers. We shall next consider certain general principles which apply to any process unit.

1.3 Material and Energy Balances

Each process unit performs a different change on the materials which pass through it. All process units, no matter how complex, obey the conservation principles of physics and chemistry:

1. Conservation of mass (in nonnuclear processes).
2. Conservation of atoms (in chemical reactions).
3. Conservation of energy (i.e., the first law of thermodynamics).
4. Conservation of momentum.
5. Conservation of charge.
6. Conservation of certain families of elementary particles

The application of the first three of these to a chemical process is called a *material and energy balance*. Material balances are introduced in Ch. 6; energy balances are introduced in Ch. 9; simultaneous material and energy balances are treated in Ch. 10.

1.4 Design of Process Units

Emphasis in this book is on *analysis* of chemical process units, that is, application of conservation laws to study performance of process units under varying operating conditions. The complementary role of process design should be clearly understood. The process designer invents new kinds of process units to accomplish desired physical and chemical transformations. The laws of thermodynamics set definite limitations on what a process unit can do. Within these limits there are practical considerations such as the state of existing technology which set even more severe restrictions on the capabilities of process units. The current state of the art may be found in *Chemical Engineering*, Volumes 1 and 2, by J. M. Coulson and J. F. Richardson, Pergamon, Elmsford, N.Y., 1961; *Unit Operations of Chemical Engineering* by W. L. McCabe and J. C. Smith, McGraw-Hill, New York, 1956; and *Chemical Engineers' Handbook*, edited by R. H. Perry and C. H. Chilton, 5th ed., McGraw-Hill, New York, 1973.

1.5 The Chemical Process:
A System of Process Units

A diagram of an ammonia manufacturing plant is shown in Fig. 1-6 (see also Example 8.5). The feed stream is a gaseous mixture of nitrogen and hydrogen containing various impurities. These gases are fed to the process at a constant flow rate, mixed with a low-pressure recycle stream, compressed, and mixed with a high-pressure recycle stream. The reactor performs the double function (see Sec. 1.2) of heating the gases to reaction temperature and reacting nitrogen and hydrogen according to the reaction

$$N_2 + 3H_2 \rightleftharpoons 2NH_3$$

This reaction does not go to completion; the product contains leftover nitrogen and hydrogen. The heat exchanger cools the gaseous product stream

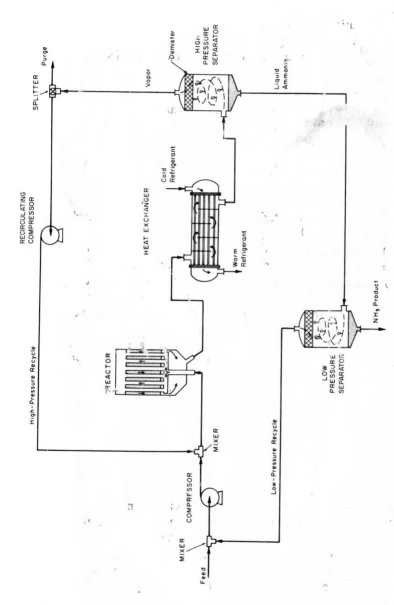

Figure 1-6 Ammonia process.

and liquefies the ammonia, which is separated from the gases in a high-pressure separator. Liquid ammonia is then liberated of dissolved gases in a low-pressure flash drum and removed as product. A portion of the high-pressure stream must be purged to prevent excessive buildup of impurities in the reactor.

Quantitative description of this or any other chemical process is a problem of *systems analysis*. Physical laws, in the form of mathematical equations, describe the working and interactions of process units. To be specific, consider the ammonia process shown in Fig. 1-6 (see also the flow diagram in Fig. 1-8), which consists of 9 process units and 13 process streams. Suppose that there are 5 components: nitrogen, hydrogen, ammonia, and two impurities. For each stream there are 8 variables: flow rate, temperature, pressure, and 5 variables for composition. There is a total of 104 ($13 \times 8 = 104$) stream variables. In addition to stream variables there are equipment parameters which characterize the operation of individual process units; suppose that there are 20 equipment parameters in all. The total number of variables is 124 ($104 + 20 = 124$). The equations are conservation laws (conservation of mass, conservation of energy) and equipment-constraint equations which model the working of process units. If there are 85 equations, 39 ($124 - 85 = 39$) variables must be specified by the design engineer. After the set of 39 design variables is assigned numerical values, the 85 equations may be solved for the 85 unknowns. Methods of systems analysis using computers are described in Ch. 8.

1.6 Economics

The usual objective of designing a new process is to make a profit. If there are several options or alternative processes, all of which satisfy environmental and other societal regulations, then the objective is to create a process that maximizes the net profit over the expected life of the process. The net profit (P) is calculated by the equation

$$\underset{\text{net profit}}{P} = \underset{\text{gross profit}}{(S - C)} - \underset{\substack{\text{federal income} \\ \text{taxes}}}{(S - C - dI)t} - \underset{\substack{\text{depreciation of} \\ \text{equipment}}}{eI} \qquad (1.1)$$

where

P = net profit, \$/year

S = sales, \$/year

C = manufacturing costs (raw materials, cooling water, steam, electricity, labor, etc.), \$/year

I = capital investment for equipment, \$

d = fraction of capital investment that is deducted from taxes each year due to depreciation; if n is the expected life of the process in years, then $d = 1/n$

t = rate for federal income tax (currently 0.5)

e = fraction of capital investment deducted each year to allow for depreciation of equipment; if n is the life of the process in years, then $e = 1/n$

Gross profit is the difference between sales revenues and manufacturing costs. Deduction of taxes and depreciation from gross profit gives the net profit realized by a company and its stockholders. Comparisons of tentative new processes are based upon estimates of markets and costs.

1.7 Control of Chemical Processes

Models of chemical processes are often based upon the idealization that chemicals flow at continuous, fixed rates with negligible variation in their flow rate, composition, temperature, and pressure. Few processes manage to achieve this desirable smoothness of operation. Fluctuations in flow rate of feed stock, feed-stock composition, or cooling-water temperature induce variations in reactor performance and product quality. Chemical plants respond to disturbances in various ways ranging from minor deviations of process variables to severe overheating and explosions. The response is a complicated function of the strength of the disturbance and the stability of the process.

If fluctuations are large or can lead to instabilities, it is essential to monitor the process carefully. Conventionally, men observe recorders displayed on a control panel and search for unusual or large fluctuations. When recorders indicate that an upset is developing, the operator responds by adjusting process conditions to counter the upset. For example, if a stream from a heat exchanger is overheating, the operator responds by adjusting a valve to increase the flow rate of cooling water to the heat exchanger. The operator may intervene with the aid of semiautomatic controls such as push buttons or levers which transmit analog signals to transducers and activate servo-mechanisms that automatically open or close valves or perform other tasks. See, for example, *Introduction to Chemical Process Control* by D.D. Perlmutter, Wiley, New York, 1965.

In some cases the operator is excluded; the *control loop* is closed using electronic circuitry and computers which are programmed to make decisions.

A control panel for a cement-making process is shown in Fig. 1-7. The dials, which report process variables such as flow rate and temperature, are fitted into a *flow diagram* of the actual process. The flow diagram makes it easier for the operator to visualize the effect of adjustments in process variables upon the process. In a flow diagram, each process unit is represented as a circle or block. A flow diagram for the ammonia process is shown in Fig. 1-8, which should be compared with Fig. 1-6. The solid lines in Fig. 1-8 connect the process units and trace the path of material through the process.

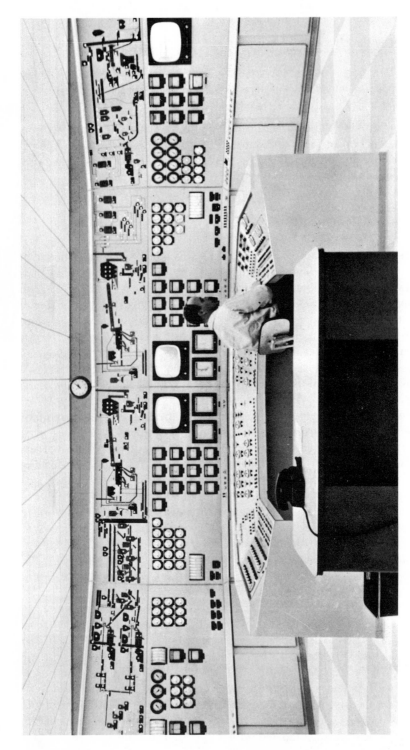

Figure 1-7 Process control panel at the Catskill plant of Alpha Portland Cement Company. (Courtesy Leeds and Northrup Company and Kellogg Company)

12

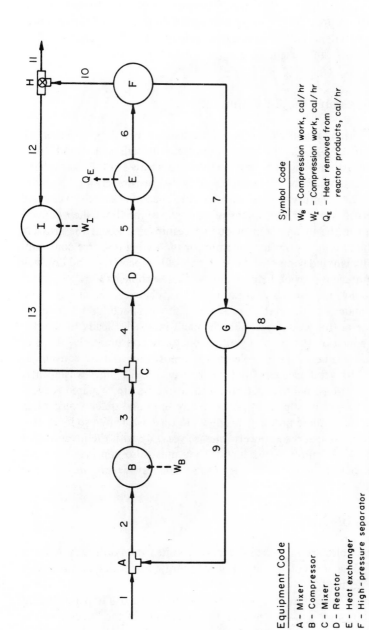

Figure 1-8 Flow diagram of ammonia process.

Equipment Code

A - Mixer
B - Compressor
C - Mixer
D - Reactor
E - Heat exchanger
F - High-pressure separator
G - Low-pressure separator
H - Splitter
I - Recirculating compressor

Symbol Code

W_B – Compression work, cal/hr
W_I – Compression work, cal/hr
Q_E – Heat removed from reactor products, cal/hr

13

Dashed lines account for the exchange of energy in the form of heat and work. The flow diagram provides a concise and useful description of the chemical process. Many students will recognize the analogy between the chemical flow diagram of Fig. 1-8 and schematic diagrams used for electronic circuits.

1.8 Resources and the Environment

One can view inhabitants of earth as passengers traveling together on "spaceship earth." As the journey progresses through space and time, inhabitants of earth use and consume the limited resources of the atmosphere, land, and waters. W. Robert Marshall said*: "As we travel into the latter decades of the 20th century, we, the travelers, are becoming acutely aware and deeply concerned about the resources of our spaceship, about their conversion to wastes in the living room of our spaceship, and about the growing appetite of the passengers of the spaceship for increasing resource consumption. How will mankind cope with the problems of his spaceship, and how will chemical engineering provide help in solving these problems?"

This analogy is especially meaningful to chemical engineers who convert raw materials, the earth's resources, into products useful to mankind. A glance at the products of the chemical industries leads to the disconcerting recognition that virtually all products are consumed shortly after their preparation. Fuels from petroleum are almost immediately consumed; soaps, detergents, and cleaners find their way rapidly into waste-water streams; foods, drugs, pharmaceuticals, and cosmetics are prepared for fast consumption; paper, plastics, and polymers are used and quickly discarded. Processes that make these products produce, in turn, waste by-products. It is not sufficient for engineers to concern themselves only with the invention of new processes and improved products: They must also consider the environmental impact of the products *after their usefulness is realized*.

1.9 Systems of Units

All process variables are expressed in terms of units: units of length, units of mass, units of time, units of velocity, units of energy. For each quantity a base unit must be defined.

Definitions of base units of length which led to the British imperial system of units are shown in Fig. 1-9. The inch was the length of the knuckle of the thumb; the foot was 36 barleycorns from the middle of the ear; the yard was the distance from King Edgar's nose to the tip of the middle finger of his

*W. R. Marshall, "Chemical Engineering in the Last Three Decades of the 20th Century" *CEP*, *69* (No. 2), 25 (1973).

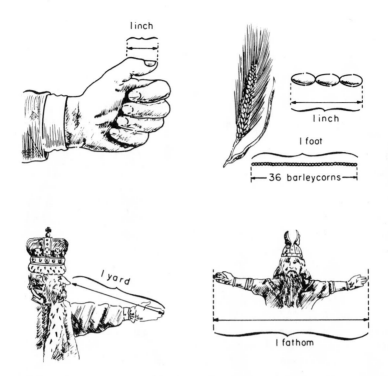

Figure 1-9 British system of units of length.

outstretched hand; a fathom was the length of a Viking's embrace. The units of length were not precise but served well as measurements in medieval times.

Modern measurements would be impossible without precise definitions of base units. The International System of Units is based upon the metric system and has base units for length, mass, time, and temperature. Other nonelectrical quantities (velocity, density, pressure, etc.) may be expressed in terms of these four. The basic units of the primary quantities are the kilogram (mass), the meter (length), the second (time), and the degree Kelvin (temperature). These basic units are defined in Table 1.1. The definitions are not static; for example, the meter used to be defined as the distance between two marks on a platinum-iridium bar stored in France.

Mass, length, time, and temperature are called *primary* quantities. All other quantities (velocity, density, etc.) are called *secondary* quantities. Any secondary quantity may be expressed in terms of primary quantities: velocity in meters per second (m/sec); force in kilogram-meters per square second (kg-m/sec^2); density in kilograms per cubic meter (kg/m^3); etc. Some of these combinations of primary quantities are named. For example, 1 kg-m/sec^2 is called a newton (N), and 1 kg-m^2/sec^2 is called a joule (J). The names of secondary quantities used in this book are listed in Table 1.2.

TABLE 1.1
DEFINED VALUES OF PRIMARY QUANTITIES

Quantity	Standard
Meter (m)	Equal in length to 1,650,763.73 wavelengths in vacuum corresponding to the transition between the levels $2p_{10}$ and $5d_5$ of the krypton-86 atom (the orange-red line)
Second (sec)	The duration of 9,192,631,770 periods of the radiation corresponding to the transition between the two hyperfine levels of the ground state of the cesium-133 atom
Degree Kelvin (°K)	1/273.16 of the temperature of the triple point of water (0.01°C)
Kilogram (kg)	Mass of the international kilogram at Sèvres, France (in time the kilogram will probably be defined in terms of atomic mass)

TABLE 1.2
KEY UNIT EQUIVALENTS

Length	1 foot (ft) = 30.48 centimeters (cm) 1 inch (in.) = 2.54 centimeters (cm) 1 kilometer (km) = 0.62137 miles (mi) 1 meter (m) = 39.37 inches (in.) 1 millimeter (mm) = 0.03937 inches (in.)
Mass	1 pound-mass (lb) = 453.59 grams (g) 1 kilogram = 1000 grams = 2.2046 pounds-mass (lb) 1 gram-mole (g-mole) = amount of substance containing the same number of molecules as the number of atoms in 12 g of pure C^{12}. 1 pound-mole (lb-mole) = 453.59 gram-moles (g-mole)
Volume	1 liter (liter) = 1000 cubic centimeters (cm^3) = 0.2642 gallon (U.S. gal) 1 gallon (U.S. gal) = 231 cubic inches ($in.^3$)

Temperature	(a) Temperature differences:
	   1 Kelvin degree (K°) = 1 Centigrade degree (C°)
	                     = 1.8 Fahrenheit degrees (F°)
	                     = 1.8 Rankine degrees (R°)
	(b) Values of temperature:
	   0°C = 32°F = 273.15°K = 491.67°R
	   −273.15°C = −459.67°F = 0°K = 0°R

Acceleration	Standard acceleration of free fall = 980.665 cm/sec² = 32.174 ft/sec²
Force	1 pound-force (lb_f) = 4.448 newtons (N) 1 newton (N) = 0.22481 pound-force (lb_f) = 1 kg-m/sec² 1 dyne = 1 g-cm/sec²
Pressure	1 newton per square meter (N/m²) = 1.4504×10^{-4} pound-force per square inch (psi) 1 normal atmosphere (atm) = 1.01325×10^6 dynes/cm² = 14.696 psi = 760 mm of mercury (mm Hg)

TABLE 1.2   (continued)

Energy	1 joule (J) $= 10^7$ ergs $= 0.7376$ ft-lb$_f$ $= 1$ kg-m^2/sec^2
	1 calorie (cal) $= 4.184$ joules (J)
	1 kilocalorie (kcal) $= 4184$ joules (J)
	1 British thermal unit (Btu) $= 251.996$ calories (cal)
	1 liter-atm (liter-atm) $= 24.217$ calories (cal)
	1 ft^3-psi $= 0.1852$ Btu
	1 erg $= 1$ g-cm^2/sec^2 $= 1$ dyne-cm
Power	1 watt (w) $= 1$ joule/sec $= 1$ kg-m^2/sec^3
	1 horsepower (hp) $= 550$ ft-lb$_f$/sec $= 745.7$ watt (w)

The metric system is based upon powers of 10. For example, 1 km $=$ 10^3 m. Conversions from one unit to another are made by moving the decimal point. For example, 2.36 km $= 2360$ m. A conversion in the British imperial system (for example, 2.36 mi $= 12,460.8$ ft) is awkward by comparison.

Multiplying prefixes used in the metric system are listed in Table 1.3. The names of these prefixes (giga for 10^9, nano for 10^{-9}, etc.) should be memorized.

TABLE 1.3
MULTIPLYING PREFIXES USED IN THE METRIC SYSTEM*

Prefix	Symbol	Power	Example	Proposed, More Logical Prefix
Giga	G	10^9	Gigahertz (GHz)	Plonine
Mega	M	10^6	Megawatt (Mw)	Plosix
Kilo	k	10^3	Kilometer (km)	Plothree
Hecto	h	10^2		Plotwo
Centi	c	10^{-2}	Centimeter (cm)	Mitwo
Milli	m	10^{-3}	Millimeter (mm)	Mithree
Micro	μ	10^{-6}	Microsecond (μsec)	Misix
Nano	n	10^{-9}	Nanometer (nm)	Minine
Pico	p	10^{-12}	Picofarad (pF)	Mitwelve

*The accepted names for the prefixes are awkward. The proposed system is more logical and may eventually be adopted.

A simpler and more logical system of prefixes has been suggested by Professor Richard Feynman. His idea is to write and name numbers by the floating-decimal-point method. For example, 2,450,000 is written 2.45_{+6} and read 2.45 plosix; 0.00000714 is written 7.14_{-6} and read 7.14 misix. In this system 7.2 angstrom units (Å) $= 7.2_{-10}$ m (read 7.2 mitenmeters). There is no ambiguity whether the -10 symbol belongs to the number or the unit because it makes no difference: 7.2×10^{-10} m $= 7.2$ mitenmeters. If Feynman's suggestion is adopted, it will take years for it to filter down to common usage.

Like a bilingual person, engineers in the United States must learn both the metric and the British imperial system of units and be able to translate units from one "language" to the other. Conversions of units from metric to British or British to metric are not difficult, but they are a nuisance. A systematic procedure for making conversions helps to avoid mistakes.

Key unit equivalents are listed in Table 1.2. More complete lists are given in handbooks (see, for example, the *Handbook of Chemistry and Physics**). The procedure is to write any of these equivalents (for example, 1 lb = 453.59 g) in the form of a ratio equal to unity:

$$\left[\frac{1 \text{ lb}}{453.59\text{g}}\right] = 1$$

A conversion of any quantity is made by multiplying or dividing that quantity by the appropriate ratio so that unwanted units cancel. The following example illustrates the procedure.

Example 1.1

The density of ethyl alcohol at 60°F is 0.793 g/cm³. What is the density in pounds per cubic foot?

Solution:

$$\frac{0.793\,g}{cm^3}\left[\frac{30.48\,cm}{ft}\right]^3\left[\frac{lb}{453.59\,g}\right] = 49.51 \text{ lb/ft}^3$$

Notice that the procedure is
1. Write down the quantity to be converted from one system of units to another.
2. Multiply this quantity successively by factors of unity:

$$\left[\frac{30.48 \text{ cm}}{ft}\right] = 1$$

$$\left[\frac{lb}{453.59 \text{ g}}\right] = 1$$

Each factor may be taken to an arbitrary power. The process is continued until the required units are obtained by cancellation.

It is difficult to make a mistake using this procedure. If the last factor had been written upside down, the result would have been

$$\frac{0.793 \text{ g}}{cm^3}\left[\frac{30.48\,cm}{ft}\right]^3\left[\frac{453.59 \text{ g}}{lb}\right] = 1.018 \times 10^7 \text{ g}^2/\text{lb-ft}^3$$

This answer has incorrect units for density.

An alternative procedure is to look up the conversion factor in a handbook. For example, using the conversion factor given in Perry's handbook,†

$$\frac{0.793\,g}{cm^3}\left[\frac{62.43 \text{ lb/ft}^3}{g/cm^3}\right] = 49.51 \text{ lb/ft}^3$$

Whichever procedure is used, mistakes can be avoided by checking the units of the answer.

---

*R.C. Weast, ed., 55th edition, CRC Press, Cleveland, Ohio, 1974-1975.
†R. H. Perry and C. H. Chilton, eds., *Chemical Engineers' Handbook*, 5th ed., McGraw-Hill, New York, 1973.

A conscious effort to memorize conversion factors is unnecessary; a conversion table is more dependable. But the more frequently used conversion factors are usually memorized, in the end, by repetition.

Force

Newton's second law is as follows: "The acceleration of a body is proportional to the resultant force exerted on the body, is inversely proportional to the mass of the body, and is in the same direction as the resultant force." Mathematically,

$$\mathbf{F} = \frac{1}{g_c} ma \qquad (1.2)$$

where $\mathbf{F}$ = force, m = mass, a = acceleration, and g_c is a constant. Values of g_c in different systems of units are

Systems of Units	Unit of Force	Unit of Mass	Unit of Acceleration	Value of g_c
English	lb_f	lb	ft/sec²	32.174 ft-lb/lb$_f$-sec²
mks	Newton (N)	kg	m/sec²	1 kg-m/N-sec²
cgs	Dyne	g	cm/sec²	1 g-cm/dyne-sec²

It is important to distinguish the English unit of mass (lb) from the English unit of force (lb_f); see Example 1.2.

Example 1.2

Compute the force necessary to impart an acceleration of 5 ft/sec² to 20 lb (pounds of mass) lying on a flat, frictionless surface (see Fig. 1-10).

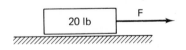

Figure 1-10

Solution:

$$\mathbf{F} = \frac{1}{g_c} ma$$

$$= \frac{1}{[32.174 \text{ ft-lb/lb}_f\text{-sec}^2]} (20 \text{ lb})\left(5 \frac{\text{ft}}{\text{sec}^2}\right)$$

$$= 3.108 \text{ lb}_f$$

The force of gravitational attraction which the earth exerts on a body is called the *weight* of the body. The weight of a body is different on other planets. g_c is a constant, but local acceleration of gravity, **g**, varies even on the earth's surface.

Example 1.3

What is the weight of an astronaut, of mass 200 lb, on the surface of the moon where the acceleration due to gravity is 5.47 ft/sec² ?

Solution:

$$\mathbf{F} = \frac{200 \text{ lb} \times 5.47 \text{ ft/sec}^2}{32.174 \text{ ft lb/lb}_f\text{-sec}^2} = 34.0 \text{ lb}_f$$

The value of g_c is unity in the cgs and mks systems. For this reason it is customary to omit g_c in the mks and cgs systems so that the unit of force is defined by means of Newton's second law:

$$\mathbf{F} = ma$$

cgs: 1 dyne $=$ 1 g-cm/sec²

mks: 1 N $=$ 1 kg-m/sec²

Since g_c is omitted from formulas in the cgs and mks systems, it is useful to adopt the point of view that g_c is unity in the English system as well. Accepting this viewpoint, the English unit of force is given by

English: 1 lb$_f$ $=$ 32.174 lb-ft/sec²

Example 1.4

If g_c is taken as unity in the English system, Example 1.3 is worked in the following way:

$$\mathbf{F} = ma = 200 \text{ lb} \times 5.47 \text{ ft/sec}^2 \left[\frac{\text{lb}_f\text{-sec}^2}{32.174 \text{ ft lb}}\right] = 34.0 \text{ lb}_f$$

The *standard* acceleration of free fall on earth, $\mathbf{g}_n$, is defined as 980.665 cm/sec² $=$ 32.174 ft/sec². The actual acceleration of gravity depends on latitude, height above sea level, and local variations in the composition of the earth's crust.

Pressure

Pressure (P) is defined as force per unit area acting in a direction perpendicular to a surface, which may be real or imaginary. If the component of the force normal to the surface is $\mathbf{F}$,

$$P = \frac{\mathbf{F}}{A} \tag{1.3}$$

System of Units	Unit of Pressure
English	lb$_f$/ft²
mks	N/m²
cgs	dyne/cm²

The pressure gradient (dP/dz) at any point in a fluid at rest is given by the hydrostatic pressure equation,

$$\frac{dP}{dz} = -\rho g \tag{1.4}$$

where ρ is the density of the fluid at that point and z is distance measured upward from a datum plane. For an incompressible fluid (constant density), Eqn. (1.4) can be integrated (see Fig. 1-11) if variation of g with height is neglected.

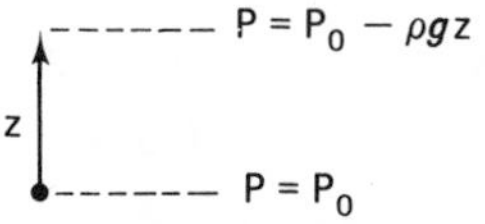

$$P = P_0 - \rho g z \tag{1.5}$$

$$P = P_0$$

Figure 1-11

Example 1.5

A pressure of *one atmosphere* (1 atm), called normal atmospheric pressure, is the pressure necessary to support a column of mercury 76 cm long when the temperature is 0°C and g has its standard value. See Fig. 1-12. Calculate the value of 1 atm in cgs units.

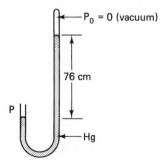

$P_0 = 0$ (vacuum)

76 cm

P

Hg

Figure 1-12

Solution:

The density of mercury at 0°C is 13.5955 g/cm³.

$$P = P_0 - \rho g z$$

$$= 0 - \left[13.5955 \frac{g}{cm^3}\right]\left[980.665 \frac{cm}{sec^2}\right](-76 \text{ cm})\left[\frac{dyne\text{-}sec^2}{g\text{-}cm}\right]$$

$$= 1.013 \times 10^6 \frac{dyne}{cm^2}$$

By international agreement, one normal atmosphere is defined in cgs units by

$$\text{one normal atmosphere} \equiv 1.01325 \times 10^6 \text{ dynes/cm}^2$$

and, in the English system,

$$\text{one normal atmosphere} = 14.696 \text{ lb}_f/\text{in}^2$$

Work and energy

Mechanical work is the product of force ($\mathbf{F}$) times displacement (x):

$$W = \mathbf{F}x \tag{1.6}$$

If force varies with position, then work is defined as a differential,

$$dW = \mathbf{F}\,dx \tag{1.7}$$

where $\mathbf{F}$ is the component of force in the direction of displacement. Units of work in the various systems of units are:

System of Units	Unit of Work
mks	N-m or J
cgs	Dyne-cm or erg
English	ft-lb$_f$

It is often necessary to convert units from one system to another.

Example 1.6

Compute the work in joules if a steady force of 3 lb$_f$ is needed to push a 5-lb mass a distance of 100 ft.

Solution:

$$W = \mathbf{F}x = 3 \text{ lb}_f(100 \text{ ft}) = 300 \text{ ft lb}_f$$

$$= (300 \text{ ft lb}_f)\left(\frac{0.3048 \text{ m}}{\text{ft}}\right)\left(\frac{4.448 \text{ N}}{\text{lb}_f}\right)\left(\frac{\text{J}}{\text{N-m}}\right)$$

$$= 407 \text{ J}$$

One calorie is the amount of heat that must be supplied to 1 g of liquid water in order to raise its temperature by 1°C. In English units, the Btu (British thermal unit) is defined as the amount of heat needed to raise the temperature of 1 lb of water by 1°F. Heat can be generated by performing work, as was first demonstrated by Benjamin Thompson (Count Rumford) in his famous gun-boring experiment reported in 1798. The first accurate measurement of heat generated from mechanical energy by friction was made by James Prescott Joule in about 1845. Since heat and work are different forms of energy, the modern approach is simply to define the basic unit of heat energy (calorie, Btu) in terms of mechanical work:

System of Units	Unit of Heat	Equivalent Amount of Mechanical Work
mks	cal	4.184 J
English	Btu	777.65 ft lb$_f$

The modern definitions of heat units were chosen to correspond fairly closely to the older definitions based upon heating water. A useful conversion factor is

$$1 \text{ Btu} = 252 \text{ cal}$$

Example 1.7

Show that 1 Btu is equal to 252 cal.

Solution:

$$1 \text{ Btu}\left(\frac{777.65 \text{ ft lb}_f}{\text{Btu}}\right)\left(\frac{4.448 \text{ N}}{\text{lb}_f}\right)\left(\frac{0.3048 \text{ m}}{\text{ft}}\right)\left(\frac{\text{J}}{\text{N-m}}\right)\left(\frac{\text{cal}}{4.184 \text{ J}}\right) = 252.0 \text{ cal}$$

Temperature

Temperature is defined on the thermodynamic scale by assigning 273.16°K to the triple point of water. On the Centigrade scale the triple point of water is at 0.01°C, so that the freezing point of water is at 273.15°K = 0°C.

Four temperature scales are in common use:

Scale	Temp. of Absolute Zero	Temp. of Normal Freezing Point of Water	Temp. of Normal Boiling Point of Water
Centigrade (Celsius)	−273.15°C	0°C	100°C
Kelvin	0°K	273.15°K	373.15°K
Fahrenheit	−459.67°F	32°F	212°F
Rankine	0°R	491.67°R	671.67°R

Temperatures on the Centigrade (T_C), Kelvin (T_K), Fahrenheit (T_F), and Rankine (T_R) scales are related by simple linear equations:

$$T_C = \tfrac{5}{9}(T_F - 32) \tag{1.8}$$

$$T_F = \tfrac{9}{5}T_C + 32 \tag{1.9}$$

$$T_K = T_C + 273.15 \tag{1.10}$$

$$T_R = T_F + 459.67 \tag{1.11}$$

$$T_R = 1.8T_K \tag{1.12}$$

Temperature *differences* are related by

$$\Delta T_F = \Delta T_R = 1.8\Delta T_C = 1.8\Delta T_K$$

The Centigrade and Kelvin scales are associated with the mks and cgs systems of units, and the Fahrenheit and Rankine scales are associated with the English system of units. The Kelvin and Rankine scales are called absolute scales. In thermodynamic calculations only absolute scales of temperature are used.

Example 1.8

The normal boiling point of oxygen is $-182.96°C$. Express this temperature in the other scales.

Solution:

$$T_K = T_C + 273.15 = -182.96 + 273.15 = 90.19°K$$
$$T_R = 1.8T_K = (1.8)(90.19) = 162.34°R$$
$$T_F = T_R - 459.67 = 162.34 - 459.67 = -297.33°F$$

Gram-atom and mole

Natural carbon is composed of 98.9% of C^{12} isotope and 1.1% of C^{13} isotope. A gram-atom of an element is defined as the amount of that element containing the same number of atoms as 12 g of pure carbon 12 isotope. This number of atoms, called Avogadro's number, is equal to 6.0225×10^{23}. The mass of one gram-atom of an element is called its atomic weight. Values of atomic weights are tabulated in Appendix II.

A mole (or mol) of a chemical compound means Avogadro's number of molecules (6.0225×10^{23} molecules per mole). The molecular weight (M) of a compound is the mass of 1 mole and is equal to the sum of masses of its atoms:

$$M = \sum_{k=1}^{N_e} m_k A_k \tag{1.13}$$

m_k is the number of atoms of the kth element in the compound, A_k is the atomic weight of the kth element, and the summation is over the N_e elements contained in the compound.

Example 1.9

Compute the molecular weight of sulfuric acid, H_2SO_4.

Solution:

From Appendix II,

k	Element	Atomic Weight, A_k
1	H	1.008
2	S	32.064
3	O	15.999

Substituting in Eq. (1.13),

$$M = \sum_{k=1}^{3} m_k A_k = m_1 A_1 + m_2 A_2 + m_3 A_3$$
$$= 2(1.008) + 1(32.064) + 4(15.999)$$
$$= 98.076 \text{ g/mole}$$

It is important to distinguish the gram-mole (or g-mole or mole) from the pound-mole (or lb-mole). A pound-mole is the amount of a compound containing the same number of molecules as the number of atoms in 12 lb of pure C^{12}. Therefore,

$$1 \text{ lb-mole} = 453.59 \text{ g-mole}$$

Example 1.10

Compute the molecular weight of H_2SO_4 in pounds per pound-mole.

Solution:

From Example 1.9,

$$M = 98.076 \left(\frac{g}{\text{g-mole}}\right)\left(\frac{lb}{453.59 \text{ g}}\right)\left(\frac{453.59 \text{ g-mole}}{\text{lb-mole}}\right)$$
$$= 98.076 \text{ lb/lb-mole}$$

Therefore, molecular weights of a compound in grams per gram-mole and pounds per pound-mole have the same value.

A chemical reaction specifies the number of moles of each species that participates in the reaction. For example,

$$Sb_2S_3 + 3Fe \longrightarrow 3FeS + 2Sb$$

means that 1 mole of stibnite (Sb_2S_3) reacts with 3 moles of iron to yield 3 moles of iron sulfide and 2 moles of antimony. The mass of each compound is equal to the number of moles of that compound multiplied by its molecular weight.

Example 1.11

Calculate how much scrap iron is needed to reduce 500 lb of stibnite to pure antimony.

Solution:

	Sb_2S_3	+	$3Fe$	$\longrightarrow$	$3FeS$	+	$2Sb$
Mol. wt.	339.69		55.85		87.91		121.75
lb-mole	1.472		4.416		4.416		2.944
lb	500		246.6		388.2		358.4

The table was prepared by first calculating the number of pound-moles of stibnite:

$$n = \frac{500}{339.69} = 1.472$$

The number of moles of each reactant and product is a simple multiple of this number; for iron,

$$n = 3 \times 1.472 = 4.416$$

and

$$\text{mass of iron} = n \times M = (4.416)(55.85) = 246.6 \text{ lb}$$

The calculation is checked by comparing the masses of reactants and products:

$$500 + 246.6 = 388.2 + 358.4$$
$$746.6 = 746.6$$

Mole fraction or mass fraction

The composition of a mixture is the mole fraction or mass fraction of each component.

Example 1.12

Calculate the mass fraction and mole fraction of each component in the following mixture of hydrocarbons:

$$100 \text{ g of } CH_4$$
$$100 \text{ g of } C_2H_6$$
$$200 \text{ g of } C_3H_8$$

Solution:

Component	Mass, g	Mass Fraction	M (g/mole)	Moles	Mole Fraction	Mole Percent
CH_4	100	0.25	16.04	6.234	0.442	44.2
C_2H_6	100	0.25	30.07	3.326	0.236	23.6
C_3H_8	200	0.50	44.09	4.536	0.322	32.2
	400	1.00		14.096	1.000	100.0

Methods for converting from mass fractions to mole fractions and vice versa are given in Sec. 6.6.

Gas constant, *R*

The gas constant, R, appears frequently in formulas for properties such as density and energy. R has units of energy per mole per degree; some useful values for various sets of units are

$$R = 8.3143 \text{ J/mole-}°K$$
$$= 1.9872 \text{ cal/mole-}°K$$
$$= 82.06 \text{ cm}^3\text{-atm/mole-}°K$$
$$= 10.73 \text{ ft}^3\text{-psi/(lb-mole)}°R$$
$$= 0.7302 \text{ ft}^3\text{-atm/(lb-mole)}°R$$

Notice that R may also be expressed in units of (pressure $\times$ volume) per mole per degree.

Example 1.13

Convert the units of R from J/mole-°K to cm³-atm/mole-°K.

Solution:

$$R = \frac{8.3143 \text{ J}}{\text{mole-}°K}\left(\frac{10^7 \text{ erg}}{\text{J}}\right)\left(\frac{\text{dyne-cm}}{\text{erg}}\right)\left(\frac{\text{atm-cm}^2}{1.01325 \times 10^6 \text{ dynes}}\right)$$
$$= 82.06 \text{ cm}^3\text{-atm/mole-}°K$$

R appears in equations of state (see Sec. 4.1) such as the perfect gas law:

$$Pv = RT \tag{1.14}$$

P is pressure, T is absolute temperature, and v is molar volume,

$$v = \frac{V}{n}$$

where V is the total volume occupied by n moles of gas. The units of P, v, and T depend on the units of R. For example, for $R = 82.06 \text{ cm}^3\text{-atm/mole-}°K$, P is in atmospheres, v is in cubic centimeters per mole, and T is in degrees Kelvin.

Combining the last two equations,

$$PV = nRT \tag{1.15}$$

The number of moles (n) is equal to the mass (W) of gas divided by its molecular weight (M):

$$n = \frac{W}{M}$$

Therefore,

$$PVM = WRT \tag{1.16}$$

The density (ρ) of a mass W of gas occupying volume V is

$$\rho = \frac{W}{V}$$

so that

$$\rho = \frac{PM}{RT} \tag{1.17}$$

Equations (1.14)–(1.17) are different forms of the perfect gas law for calculating the total volume, molar volume, and density of a gas at low pressure.

Example 1.14

Calculate the molar volume (ft³/lb-mole) and density (lb/ft³) of methane gas at 60°F (519.67°R) and a pressure of 3.5 atm.

Solution:

From Eqn. (1.14),

$$v = \frac{RT}{P} = \left(\frac{0.7302 \text{ ft}^3\text{-atm}}{(\text{lb-mole})(°R)}\right)\left(\frac{519.67°R}{3.5 \text{ atm}}\right) = 108.4 \text{ ft}^3/\text{lb-mole}$$

The molecular weight of methane is 16.04. From Eqn. (1.17),

$$\rho = \frac{PM}{RT} = \frac{3.5 \text{ atm} \times 16.04 \text{ lb/lb-mole}}{0.7302 \text{ ft}^3\text{-atm}/(\text{lb-mole})(°R) \times 519.67(°R)} = 0.148 \text{ lb/ft}^3$$

The next example is a typical calculation requiring selection of appropriate units for R.

Example 1.15

The velocity of sound, a, in a gas at low pressure is given by

$$a = \sqrt{\frac{\gamma RT}{M}}$$

Calculate the speed of sound in air at 80°F in units of feet per second. For air, $\gamma = 1.4$ and the molecular weight is $M = 29$ g/mole.

Solution:

The absolute temperature is 539.67°R.

$$a^2 = \frac{\gamma RT}{M} = \frac{1.4 \times 10.73 \text{ ft}^3\text{-psi/lb-mole-}°R \times 539.67°R}{29 \text{ lb/lb-mole}}\left[\frac{144 \text{ in.}^2}{\text{ft}^2}\right]\left[\frac{32.174 \text{ ft lb}}{\text{lb}_f\text{-sec}^2}\right]$$

$$= 1.295 \times 10^6 \text{ ft}^2/\text{sec}^2$$

$$a = 1138 \text{ ft/sec}$$

PROBLEMS

1.1. (a) Which race is farther, 440 yards or 400 m?
    (b) What is the average speed in miles per hour of an Olympic runner who runs the 100-m race in 9.9 sec?
    (c) Which mass is greater, 5 kg or 11 lb?

1.2. Liquid oxygen is delivered to a rocket engine at the mass velocity of 452,000 lb/(ft²)(sec). Calculate the mass velocity in g/(cm²)(sec).

1.3. A man weighing 175 lb_f on the earth has a weight of 460 lb_f on the planet Jupiter. What is the value, on Jupiter, of the acceleration of gravity (**g**) and the gravitational constant (g_c)?

1.4. How far down must one go into the ocean to double the pressure at the surface?

1.5. (a) How many gallons of water are contained in a swimming pool that is 32 ft long, 16 ft wide, and 8 ft deep?
  (b) What is the weight of the water?
  (c) How heavy is the pool? It is made of Portland cement (specific gravity approximately 2.5) and its walls and floor are 4 in. thick.
  (d) Suppose that the soil outside the pool is flooded when the pool is empty. What is the upward pressure on the bottom of the pool in psi? (*Hint:* Use Archimedes' principle.)

1.6. Stainless steel, type 304 (18% Cr, 8% Ni, 0.08% C max.), has a thermal conductivity of 162 Btu/(hr)(ft)(F°). Convert this value of thermal conductivity into units of cal/(sec)(cm)(C°).

1.7. The specific heat of water at 50°C is 1 Btu/lb-F°. Calculate the specific heat in cal/g-C°.

1.8. The rate at which solar radiation is intercepted by the earth is 1.7×10^{17} watts. How many kilowatt-hours of energy are received in 1 yr?

1.9. A forest or a field receives, on a typical summer day in the United States, 500 cal of solar energy per square centimeter per day. What is the average energy flux in watts per square meter?

1.10. Show that the product $P \times v$ has units of energy per unit mass if v is specific volume.

1.11. Tidal friction is gradually slowing down the rate of rotation of the earth. As an exercise in handling units, calculate the rate of decrease of the earth's rotational kinetic energy in watts using the formula

$$\frac{d(KE)}{dt} = \frac{2}{5} MR^2 \omega \alpha$$

where

M = mass of earth = 5.975×10^{27} g

R = radius of earth = 6.38×10^6 m

ω = rate of rotation of earth = $2\pi/86{,}400$ sec^{-1}

α = rate of angular acceleration of earth

   = -1.33×10^{-20} sec^{-2}

1.12. Convert $-40°$F to degrees Centigrade.

1.13. Show that $T_R = 1.8 T_K$ using Eqns. (1.8)–(1.11).

1.14. Compute the molecular weight of methyl vinyl ketone:

$$
\begin{array}{ccccc}
 & H & O & H & H \\
 & | & \| & | & | \\
H- & C & -C & -C= & C-H \\
 & | & & & \\
 & H & & &
\end{array}
$$

1.15. Calculate the composition in mass fractions for the following mixture:

	Mole Percent
C_2H_3Cl	22
$C_2H_4Cl_2$	17
HCl	28
C_2H_4	33

1.16. The heat liberated when iron pyrites (FeS_2) is formed from its elements at 25°C is 42.52 kcal/mole of pyrites. Convert these units to calories per gram of pyrites.

1.17. Calculate the density of air in grams per cubic centimeter at 200°C and 5 atm using the perfect gas law. Assume that the molecular weight of air = 29.

1.18. What is the density of argon gas in pounds per cubic foot at 0°F and 1 atm? Use the perfect gas law.

1.19. Steam at 300°F and 1 atm is flowing through a pipeline at the rate of 4.52 $\times$ 10^5 ft^3/hr. Assuming that steam molecules are flowing down the pipe at a uniform velocity of 10 ft/sec, what is the diameter of the pipe?

1.20. The velocity of sound is given by

$$
a = \sqrt{\frac{1}{\rho \kappa}}
$$

For liquid water at 30°C,

$$\rho = \text{density} = 1 \text{ g/cm}^3$$

$$\kappa = \text{adiabatic compressibility} = 4.5 \times 10^{-5} \text{ atm}^{-1}$$

Calculate the velocity of sound in liquid water in feet per second.

Chemical Processes 2

2.1 History of Chemical Processing

Chemical engineers design, build, and operate chemical processes that convert raw materials into useful products. Chemical engineering as a profession can be traced back to the 1800s when advances in the chemical industry created special engineering problems.

At first chemical processes were designed by trial and error, and engineers learned from their own mistakes. Formal chemical engineering education, based upon principles of science and mathematics, was not introduced in the United States until the first part of the twentieth century. The first course in chemical engineering was offered at Massachusetts Institute of Technology in 1888, and the first department of chemical engineering was established at the University of Pennsylvania in 1892. By 1910 there were nearly 1000 chemical engineering students in attendance at engineering schools in the United States.

It is difficult to overestimate the dependence of modern achievements in chemical engineering on the pioneering developments of the past few hundred years. Some of the landmarks* include

1. Preparation of artificial soda (sodium carbonate) by Nicolas Leblanc (France) in 1791.
2. Large-scale gas lighting system (coal gas) in London in 1814.

*The World Book Encyclopedia, Field Enterprises Educational Corporation, Chicago, 1972.

3. Synthetic dye from coal tar by William H. Perkin (Great Britain) in 1856.
4. Development of rayon synthetic fabric by Hilaire Chardonnet (France) in 1884.
5. Petroleum cracking process by George L. Benton (United States) in 1885.
6. Synthetic ammonia by Fritz Haber (Germany) in 1908.
7. Synthetic rubber (Germany and United States) in the 1920s.
8. Large-scale desalting of sea water (United States) during the 1960s.

The modern petrochemical industry is a logical outgrowth of the development of synthetic dye (1856) and a process for cracking petroleum (1885). The inorganic chemicals industry goes back to the preparation of sulfuric acid (about 1500), artificial soda (1791), and synthetic ammonia (1908). The synthesis of rayon (1884) led to the modern polymer and plastics industry. Coal gasification, described in this chapter, is a highly advanced version of the coal gas process used in London in 1814. Systematic development of chemical engineering unit operations such as distillation and crystallization during the 1940s and 1950s made possible the desalting of seawater on a commercial scale in the 1960s.

On the one hand, there is no such thing as a typical chemical process; each process represents a particular engineering solution of a unique problem. On the other hand, it is impossible to give in a single chapter or even in a single volume a comprehensive survey of chemical engineering. As a compromise, two particular chemical processes will be examined in an attempt to reveal the flavor if not the breadth of chemical process technology:

1. Manufacture of synthetic natural gas from petroleum or coal.
2. Preparation of fresh water from sea water.

Knowledge of how these particular processes work motivates further study of scientific laws and principles that govern the operation of all chemical processes.

2.2 Synthetic Natural Gas (Methane) from Petroleum or Coal

Natural gas is found in porous rock (limestone, sandstone), where it is trapped by nonporous cap rock (shale, marble) folded in the shape of a dome or inverted container (see Fig. 2-1). The gas can be removed by drilling through the overlying strata and cap rock and tapping the porous rock containing the gas. Natural gas is mostly methane, but ethane, nitrogen, carbon dioxide, and other gases are usually mixed with the methane, which is burned to generate heat:

$$CH_4 + 2O_2 \longrightarrow CO_2 + 2H_2O + \text{heat} \qquad (2.1)$$

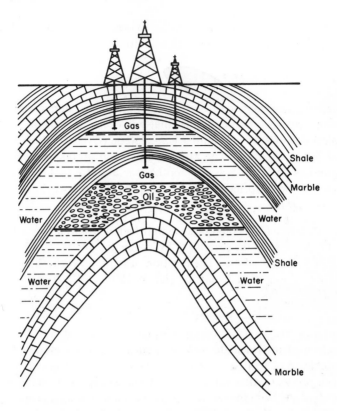

Figure 2-1 Oil well field producing gas from the upper zone and oil and gas from the lower zone.

The flame temperature (see Example 10.6) of pure methane burned in air is about 3400°F (1870°C). Complete combustion of pure methane gas to gaseous carbon dioxide and liquid water yields 976 Btu of heat per cubic foot of methane gas (volumes of gas are conventionally measured at ambient temperature and at atmospheric pressure). In practice the heating value is less because of incomplete cooling of the combustion products, incomplete condensation of water vapor, and partial combustion to CO instead of complete combustion to CO_2.

If the natural gas contains ethane, which has a molar heat of combustion considerably higher than that of methane, then the theoretical heating value may be over 1000 Btu/ft³ of natural gas. Known global reserves of natural gas are estimated* to be about 10^{15} ft³. If these reserves continue to be used at the present rate, they will last about 50 more years. Since the United States produces 58% and consumes 63% of the total worldwide production of

*D. H. Meadows, D. L. Meadows, J. Randers, and W. W. Behrens III, *The Limits to Growth*, Universe Books, New York, 1972.

natural gas, it will be necessary either to switch to another fuel or to make methane from other materials such as petroleum or coal.

Methane from naphtha

Methane can be made from naphtha, one of the derivatives of crude oil containing hydrocarbon molecules that boil in the range from 100° to 300°F. A typical constituent of naphtha is *n*-heptane (C_7H_{16}), which has a normal boiling point of 209°F. The ratio of hydrogen atoms to carbon atoms in methane is 4 to 1, whereas in naphtha it is about 2 to 1. The deficiency of hydrogen could, in principle, be made up by the following reaction:

$$C_7H_{16} + 6H_2 \longrightarrow 7CH_4 \tag{2.2}$$

Even if Reaction (2.2) could be accomplished, it would not be attractive commercially because of the scarcity of hydrogen gas. Water is a more abundant source of hydrogen atoms. The reaction of naphtha with water, called steam reforming of naphtha, is carried out at 850°F and 30 atm over a nickel catalyst:

$$4C_7H_{16} + 14H_2O \longrightarrow 21CH_4 + 7CO_2 + 4H_2 \tag{2.3}$$

[The overall reaction (2.3) does not explain the detailed mechanism involving production of intermediate molecules such as carbon monoxide.] Reaction (2.3) yields an unwanted by-product (CO_2) which must be removed from the methane product. After removal of carbon dioxide and excess water vapor, the product gas from the reformer would consist of methane and hydrogen in the molar ratio 21:4, or 84% methane and 16% hydrogen (mole percentages). Since heats of combustion of methane and hydrogen are 976 and 313 Btu/ft³, respectively, the theoretical heating value of the product gas is

$$976(0.84) + 313(0.16) = 870 \text{ Btu/ft}^3$$

Since most commercial and domestic gas burners are designed for gas with a heat of combustion of about 1000 Btu/ft³, the product from steam reforming must be "upgraded" in energy content. This can be accomplished (see Fig. 2-2) by converting carbon dioxide and hydrogen, the by-products of steam reforming, into more methane in a two-step process:

$$CO_2 + H_2 \rightleftharpoons CO + H_2O \tag{2.4}$$

$$CO + 3H_2 \rightleftharpoons CH_4 + H_2O \tag{2.5}$$

Reaction (2.4) is called the water-gas shift reaction, and the object is to get a 3-to-1 molar ratio of hydrogen to carbon monoxide in preparation for the actual methanation [Reaction (2.5)]. Reactions (2.4) and (2.5), unlike Reaction (2.3), are reversible: They can be forced in either the forward or reverse direction by manipulation of temperature and pressure. For example, high temperature shifts Reaction (2.4) in the forward direction as written, and low temperature favors the reverse reaction. If the reactants from the reformer

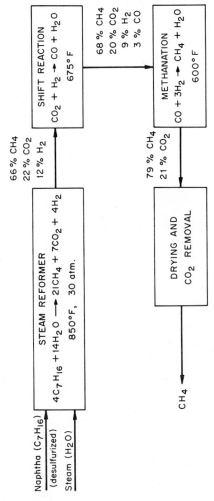

Figure 2-2 Flowsheet for conversion of naphtha to methane. Mole percentages are on dry basis.

are 7 moles of carbon dioxide and 4 moles of hydrogen, then at 675°F, 1 mole
of carbon dioxide will react with 1 mole of hydrogen as shown in Table 2.1.
Notice that both reactants, carbon dioxide and hydrogen, are only partially
consumed and that after the reaction, hydrogen and carbon monoxide are in
the desired molar ratio of 3 to 1 for Reaction (2.5), which goes practically to
completion at 600°F. Reactions (2.4) and (2.5), like Reaction (2.3), require a
catalyst to speed up the rate of the desired reaction.

TABLE 2.1
WATER-GAS SHIFT REACTION AT 675°F

			Moles		
	CH_4	CO_2	H_2	CO	H_2O
Before Reaction (2.4)	21	7	4	0	0
Reaction (2.4)		−1	−1	+1	+1
After Reaction (2.4)	21	6	3	1	1

The overall process* is the sum of Reactions (2.3), (2.4), and (2.5):

$$\text{steam reforming:} \quad 4C_7H_{16} + 14H_2O = 21CH_4 + 7CO_2 + 4H_2 \qquad (2.3)$$

$$\text{water-gas shift:} \quad CO_2 + H_2 = CO + H_2O \qquad (2.4)$$

$$\text{methanation:} \quad CO + 3H_2 = CH_4 + H_2O \qquad (2.5)$$

$$\text{overall process:} \quad 4C_7H_{16} + 12H_2O = 22CH_4 + 6CO_2 \qquad (2.6)$$

After drying and removal of carbon dioxide, the process yields a substitute
natural gas composed of about 98% methane. Four moles of n-heptane give
22 moles of methane. Theoretically the gasification of naphtha could be
accomplished by Reaction (2.6) with practically no loss of chemical energy,
because the heat of combustion of liquid heptane is 1150 kcal/mole × 4 moles
= 4600 kcal and the heat of combustion of methane product is 212.8 kcal/
mole × 22 moles = 4680 kcal. In practice there is a net loss of energy
represented by process requirements of heat for generating steam and
electricity for operating pumps and compressors.

Methane from coal

Production of methane from petroleum products such as naphtha is only
a temporary solution to the problem of shortage of natural gas because our
reserves of petroleum are limited. The United States has a comparatively vast
supply of coal, enough to last hundreds of years at present rates of energy
consumption. Coal is a dirty fossil fuel which, when burned for generation of

*S. A. Bresler and J. D. Ireland, "Substitute Natural Gas: Processes, Equipment,
Costs," *Chem. Eng.*, *79* (No. 23), 94 (1972).

electric power or for heating buildings, pollutes the air with smoke and sulfur oxides. Therefore, conversion of coal to sulfur-free methane, called coal gasification, is likely to be one of the major developments in chemical engineering for the twentieth century.

Coal is a complex mixture of hydrocarbons, and the composition depends not only on the type of coal (anthracite, bituminous, lignite) but also on the particular location of the coal deposits. The weight percentage of carbon is as low as 40% in lignite and nearly 90% in anthracite. The composition of a typical bituminous coal mined in the United States is shown in Table 2.2. The heat of combustion of this coal is about 12,600 Btu/lb. The ratio of hydrogen atoms to carbon atoms is less than unity. Ash, the inorganic residue left after burning coal, consists principally of silica (SiO_2), alumina (Al_2O_3), lime (CaO), and ferric oxide (Fe_2O_3) with smaller amounts of magnesia (MgO), titanium dioxide (TiO_2), and alkali and sulfur compounds.

TABLE 2.2
ANALYSIS OF TYPICAL BITUMINOUS COAL MINED IN THE UNITED STATES

Substance	Weight %	Mole % (Ash-Free Basis)
C	70	50
H	5	42
O	12	6.5
N	1.4	0.9
S	2.3	0.6
Ash	9.3	—

Carbon and hydrogen atoms make up more than 90 mole % of the combustible material of typical bituminous coal. Using CH as an approximate chemical formula for coal, the overall reaction for coal gasification is

$$2CH + \tfrac{1}{2}O_2 + H_2O \longrightarrow CH_4 + CO_2 \qquad (2.7)$$

The basic objective is to react coal with oxygen and steam to produce methane and carbon dioxide. The purpose of the oxygen is to supply heat to the gasification reaction, which would otherwise be endothermic, by burning a portion of the coal. A practical method for carrying out this reaction in a single step has not yet been invented; existing processes for making methane from coal require at least three reaction steps. For example, the process* developed by Bituminous Coal Research, Inc. and Air Products and Chemicals, Inc., which has not yet been operated at full scale, is shown in Fig. 2-3. Coal is received from the mine in sizes up to 10 in. In sequential steps the coal is crushed, separated from the refuse (about 40% by weight), dried, and finally pulverized. The pulverized coal is transported by pneumatic

*W. P. Hegarty and B. E. Moody, "Coal Gasification: Evaluating the Bi-Gas SNG Process," *Chem. Eng. Progr.*, *69* (No. 3), 37 (1973).

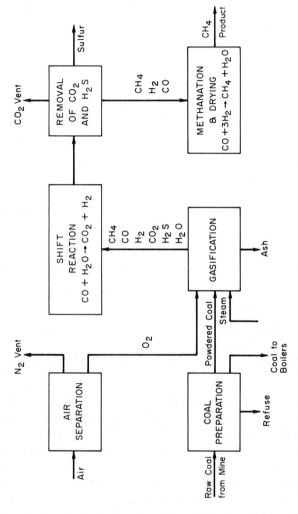

Figure 2-3 Flowsheet of Bituminous Coal Research, Inc. (BCR) process for coal gasification as performed by Air Products and Chemicals, Inc.

conveyors to storage hoppers from which it is charged to the gasifier using piston feeders.

Pure oxygen for the gasification is obtained from low-temperature distillation of air, and superheated steam for the gasification is generated in a boiler heated by burning a portion of the coal.

The key step in the process is gasification. The most important reactions occurring in the gasifier are

$$2CH \longrightarrow 2C + H_2 \tag{2.8}$$

$$C + O_2 \longrightarrow CO_2 \tag{2.9}$$

$$C + H_2O \longrightarrow CO + H_2 \tag{2.10}$$

$$CO + H_2O \longrightarrow CO_2 + H_2 \tag{2.11}$$

$$C + 2H_2 \longrightarrow CH_4 \tag{2.12}$$

The product from the gasifier is a mixture of methane, carbon monoxide, carbon dioxide, hydrogen, water, and hydrogen sulfide impurity. The molar ratio of hydrogen to carbon monoxide in this gas mixture is about $\frac{1}{2}$ to 1. This is far below the ratio of 3 to 1 needed for methanation [see Reaction (2.5)]. Therefore, the gas mixture is subjected to a shift reaction using an iron oxide catalyst,

$$CO + H_2O \longrightarrow CO_2 + H_2 \tag{2.11}$$

with adjustment of temperature to increase the ratio of hydrogen to carbon monoxide to 3 to 1. Notice that the shift reaction is used to generate more hydrogen in the coal gasification process but that the same reaction in reverse [see Reaction (2.4)] produces more carbon monoxide in the naphtha gasification process.

After removal of carbon dioxide and hydrogen sulfide, hydrogen and carbon monoxide in approximately stoichiometric proportion (3 to 1) are reacted to yield more methane. Methanation is accomplished in a fixed-bed reactor packed with aluminum-supported nickel catalyst. After drying, the product is 90 to 95 mole % methane mixed with unreacted carbon monoxide and hydrogen and inerts.

At present there are several alternative designs under consideration for the gasifier. The oldest is the Lurgi gasifier,* originally designed to produce power gas from coal, shown in Fig. 2-4. Coal gravitates downward against a rising flow of air and steam introduced through slots in a rotating grate. Directly above the grate oxygen in the air is consumed in a shallow combustion zone that converts the last of the char (carbon) in the descending solid to carbon dioxide. Ash is discharged below the grate. Hot gases (carbon dioxide, steam, nitrogen) rise upward from the combustion zone through the coal bed, giving up heat to sustain the endothermic reaction (2.10) of steam with carbon to yield hydrogen and carbon monoxide. When the rising gases have cooled

---

*A. M. Squires, "Clean Power from Dirty Fuels," *Sci. Am.*, *227* (No. 4), 26 (1972).

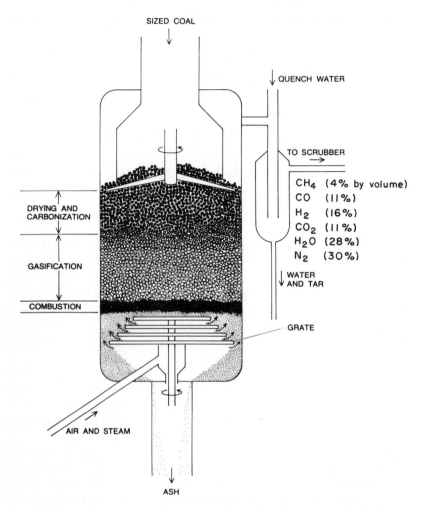

Figure 2-4 Lurgi gasifier for production of crude power gas from coal.
[A. M. Squires, "Clean Power from Dirty Fuels," *Sci. Am.*, *227* (No. 4),
26 (1972).]

to 1300°F these reactions effectively cease. Further exchange of heat with the
incoming raw coal drives methane and tars from the coal and cools the gases
to about 900°F. The composition of the product gas from the Lurgi gasifier
is shown in Fig. 2-4.

The major problem with the Lurgi gasifier is that the methane content is
low and the product gas contains about 60% by volume of water vapor and
nitrogen. Nitrogen can be eliminated by substituting pure oxygen for air (see
Fig. 2-3). New gasifier designs must cope with the following problems:

1. Mechanical difficulty of introducing coal at atmospheric pressure into
   high-pressure gasifiers.

2. Severe refractory service caused by operating temperatures in the gasifier as high as 2700°F.

3. Freezing and plugging of gasifier outlet during slag removal.

In modern gasifiers the coal, instead of gravitating to the bottom, is entrained in the steam feed or fluidized in a bed in which rising gases buoy up the coal and set it in motion. The gasifier designed by Bituminous Coal Research, Inc. (see Fig. 2-5) has two stages: The first is operated at 2700°F to produce synthesis gas (carbon monoxide, hydrogen) from the last of the char, and the second stage runs at 1700°F to partially volatilize the coal to methane and char, which is cycled to the first stage. The product gas from the two-stage gasifier, compared to the old Lurgi gasifier, contains more methane, less steam, and almost no nitrogen.

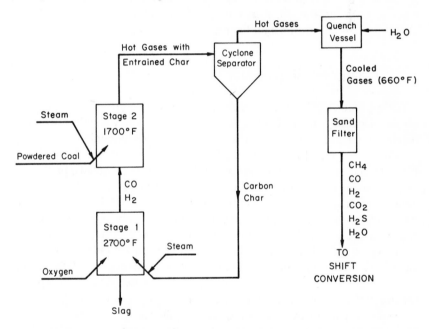

Figure 2-5 Flow diagram of two-stage coal gasifier designed for Bituminous Coal Research, Inc.

There is inevitably a net loss of chemical energy when coal is gasified. For example, the process designed by Bituminous Coal Research converts about 110 lb of bituminous coal (heat of combustion = 12,600 Btu/lb) into 1000 standard ft³ of gas (heat of combustion = 950 Btu/ft³). Therefore,

$$12,600 \times 110 = 1,386,000 = \text{heat of combustion of coal}$$
$$950 \times 1,000 = \underline{950,000} = \text{heat of combustion of gas}$$
$$436,000 = \text{loss of chemical energy due to coal gasification, Btu}$$

The efficiency of the process in conserving chemical energy is

$$\frac{950,000}{1,386,000} \times 100 = 69\%$$

Loss of chemical energy is 31%, but reduction in air pollution and ease and convenience of transportation of gas compared to coal compensate for the loss.

In summary, coal gasification is feasible, but there is practically no agreement on the best and most economical process. No commercial plants that produce methane from coal have yet been built, and it is possible that there will be major breakthroughs in process design as a result of intensive research and developmental work. Like all other chemical processes, the final selection of the best process will be based upon a careful balance of capital costs (equipment and construction), operating costs (fuel, raw materials, electricity), and environmental factors.

2.3 Desalination of Seawater

The freshwater needs of an average person for domestic consumption are about 70 gal/day in the United States. Industrial and agricultural requirements, on a per-capita basis, are about 20 times this amount.

Freshwater for human consumption is normally obtained from rainfall. If the annual precipitation in the United States were distributed equally, each man, woman, and child would get about 25,000 gal/day.* The apparent abundance of freshwater is deceptive because most rainfall later evaporates from soil, rivers, lakes, and the leaves of plants. Only about one-fourth of the rainfall is actually available for use by tapping runoff in streams and rivers. Moreover, these values are averages and therefore do not reflect geographical variations or seasonal fluctuations in rainfall. Arid regions of the United States such as the Southwest must ration freshwater carefully, and even regions with moist climates experience shortages of water during dry spells.

Since supplies of freshwater are often insufficient for human needs, man has always been fascinated by the possibility of augmenting his supply of freshwater by desalting, or desalination, of seawater.

Seawater contains suspended particles of inorganic matter, living organisms, and organic detritus. After removal of suspended particles, seawater contains dissolved gases such as oxygen, nitrogen, and carbon dioxide at low concentration (less than 0.01% by weight) and large amounts of almost completely ionized salts. The average concentration of dissolved salts is about 3.5% by weight, but concentrations vary from 0.7% in the Baltic Sea to 4.3% in the Red Sea. Water for drinking should contain less than 500 parts per

*L. B. Leopold and W. B. Langbein, *A Primer on Water*, U.S. Government Printing Office, Washington, D.C., 1960.

million (ppm) (0.05% by weight) of salt. The composition of dissolved salt is given in Table 2.3.

TABLE 2.3
TYPICAL COMPOSITION OF DISSOLVED SALTS IN SEAWATER

Ions	Weight %
Positive	
Na^+	30.6
Mg^{++}	3.7
Ca^{++}	1.2
K^+	1.1
Negative	
Cl^-	55.0
SO_4^{--}	7.7
HCO_3^-	0.4
Br^-	0.2
	99.9

We shall consider next the most important methods of desalination.

Simple distillation

The oldest method for getting freshwater from seawater or brackish water (1500–10,000 ppm salts) is distillation. A simple laboratory distilling apparatus is shown in Fig. 2-6. At normal atmospheric pressure, pure water boils at 100°C, and seawater boils at a slightly higher temperature, 100.5°C. The small increase in temperature due to dissolved salts, 0.5°C, is called boiling-point elevation. A source of heat, at some temperature higher than 100.5°C to provide a driving force for heat transfer, vaporizes water, which is condensed

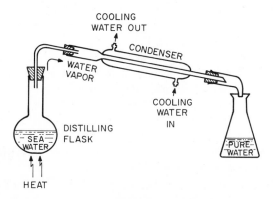

Figure 2-6 Simple laboratory distillation apparatus for desalting seawater.

in the side arm by a stream of cooling water and runs into a receiver. Since salt ions do not evaporate, the condensate is pure water. The concentration of brine in the distilling flask increases as more and more water is evaporated. As the concentration of salt increases with evaporation, the boiling point is continuously elevated and thus increasingly higher temperatures are needed to continue the boiling process. Eventually the concentrated brine must be removed and replaced by a new sample of seawater. Since seawater is added intermittently, it is a batch operation.

The heat requirement for simple distillation is equal to the heat of vaporization of water, which is 970 Btu/lb of water evaporated. In units of kilowatt hours per 1000 gal of water,

$$\frac{970 \text{ Btu}}{\text{lb of } H_2O} \times \frac{\text{kw-hr}}{3410 \text{ Btu}} \times \frac{8340 \text{ lb of } H_2O}{1000 \text{ gal of } H_2O}$$
$$= 2{,}370 \text{ kw-hr of heat energy}/1000 \text{ gal}$$

This heating requirement is far too high for large-scale desalination. For example, if heat were supplied by combustion of fuel oil (about 20,000 Btu/lb of oil), then 1 lb of oil would desalt only 20 lb of water:

$$\frac{20{,}000 \text{ Btu/lb of oil}}{970 \text{ Btu/lb of } H_2O} = 20 \text{ lb of water/lb of oil}$$

The cost would be too great, to say nothing of the waste of a valuable energy resource. However, distillation gives a clean separation of freshwater from seawater, and because of its simplicity, engineers have designed and perfected schemes to reduce its inherent inefficiency. The basic problem with simple distillation is that the heat energy, after conversion to latent heat of evaporated water, is wasted when it is transferred to cooling water in the condenser.

Multiple-effect evaporation

A more efficient process for evaporating water is the triple-effect evaporator shown in Fig. 2-7, which is a large-scale, continuous process in contrast to the small-scale, batch operation in Fig. 2-6. Seawater is fed continuously to evaporator 1, concentrated brine flows continuously out of evaporator 3, and freshwater is obtained continuously from all but the first evaporator.

Heat energy is conserved because latent heat in the vapor from evaporator 1, instead of being wasted in a condenser, is used to evaporate more water from brine in the second evaporator, and the latent heat in the vapor from evaporator 2 is used in turn to evaporate still more water from brine in evaporator 3. For the process to work, vapor from evaporator 1 must be hotter than the boiling point of the brine in evaporator 2. Likewise the vapor from evaporator 2 must be hotter than the boiling point of the brine in evaporator 3. Since the boiling point of the brine is reduced by lowering the

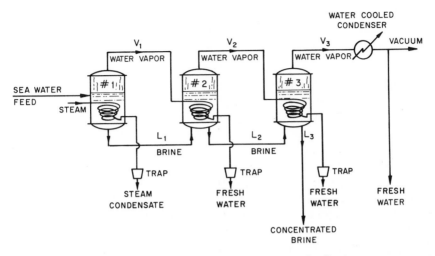

Figure 2-7 Triple-effect evaporator for water desalination.

pressure, a vacuum applied to evaporator 3 produces a series of decreasing pressures $P_1 > P_2 > P_3$ and a corresponding set of decreased boiling points.

Since the system operates under vacuum, it must be sealed against outside air. Air also enters the plant dissolved in the saltwater stream and is released during heating and lowering of pressure. Even in minute concentrations, air reduces condensation rates significantly and increases rates of corrosion. Considerable technical effort is devoted to the removal of air and other noncondensable gases from distillation plants.

In each evaporator unit the amount of water evaporated from the brine is approximately equal to the amount of water vapor condensed within the heating tubes so that $V_1 = V_2 = V_3$.

The driving force for the system is heat energy in the form of steam at about 105°C introduced in evaporator 1. Since each pound of steam condensed in evaporator 1 gives 3 lb of freshwater, a triple-effect evaporator reduces consumption of heat energy by a factor of 3. Similarly an *n*-effect evaporator reduces consumption of heat energy by a factor of *n* (certain complications have been neglected, but the statement is essentially correct).

In practice the total number of effects is limited by capital cost (see Fig. 2-20 and accompanying discussion). Minimum total cost, which is the sum of capital and operating costs, corresponds to about 10 effects. Therefore, neglecting heat losses and electrical power for operation of pumps, the heat energy requirement for a 10-effect evaporator is about

$$\frac{2370}{10} = 237 \text{ kw-hr of heat energy per 1000 gal of water}$$

This energy requirement is one order of magnitude less than that of simple distillation, but it is still high and can be justified only under certain special circumstances of unusual scarcity of freshwater and availability of energy in the form of steam at 105°C.

Multistage flash distillation

Although there are many important applications for multiple-effect evaporators, most desalting plants use an entirely different method called multistage flash distillation.

A simplified flow diagram for a typical large-scale plant composed of 50 stages and producing 2.5 million gal of freshwater per day is shown in Fig. 2-8. Seawater is first degassed and treated chemically to reduce formation of scale on heat transfer surfaces. This makeup seawater, after being mixed with a much larger volume of recycle brine, is preheated to 240°F as it is pumped through condenser tubes inside each stage. The recycle brine is heated from 240° to 250°F by steam from a power plant and then passes back through the stages in the opposite direction, flashing a small portion of water vapor in each stage. As water evaporates, the concentration of the brine increases. Vapor is condensed in each stage by exchanging heat with slightly cooler recycle brine. Freshwater from trays in each stage is collected as product. Part of the brine from the last stage (50) is returned to the ocean.

Since the boiling point of brine decreases with decreasing pressure, the brine in stage 1 is the hottest (246°F) and the brine in stage 50 is the coldest (96°F).

Operation of a single stage is shown in Fig. 2-9. Warm brine enters from the previous stage, which is at a higher pressure, through an orifice or weir and flashes (evaporates) a small fraction of water, cooling about 3°F in the process. Water vapor rises from the flashing brine and condenses on the outside of tubes containing recycle brine. Latent heat released by the vapor as it condenses warms the recycle brine. Pure, condensed water drips into a tray from which freshwater product is collected. Small drops of brine carried upward with the water vapor from the flashing brine are removed by entrainment separators (not shown in Fig. 2-9).

Multistage flash distillation differs from multiple-effect evaporation in several important ways. In multistage flash distillation, vapor is formed and condensed in the same stage, thus eliminating the need for evaporator heating surfaces. Scale composed of calcium sulfate and other substances deposits in the flash tank instead of fouling heat exchange tubing. Another difference is the manner in which heat energy, in the form of steam from a power plant, is used to operate the process. In multiple-effect evaporation, the external source of heat energy evaporates water in the first effect. In multistage flash distillation, heat energy supplies the last increment (from 240° to 250°F) of preheating for the recycle brine before it is flashed.

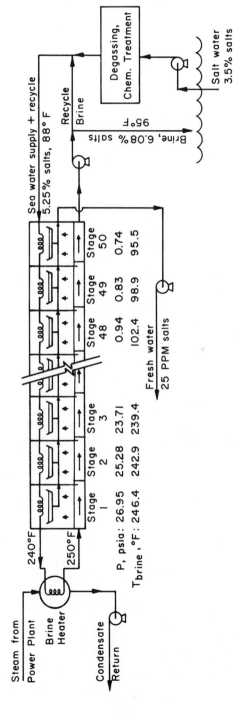

Figure 2-8 Multistage flash evaporator for desalination of seawater.

47

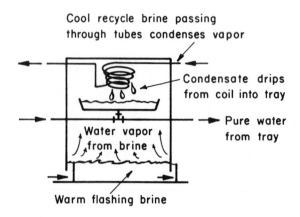

Cool recycle brine passing
through tubes condenses vapor

Condensate drips
from coil into tray

Pure water
from tray

Water vapor
from brine

Warm flashing brine

Figure 2-9 Operation of one stage in multistage flash distillation plant.

Flashing brine, as it passes from stage to stage in the direction of decreasing pressure, cools about 150°F as it gives up the energy needed to evaporate water. Since cooling of the brine supplies about 150 Btu of energy per pound of brine and evaporation of water requires 970 Btu/lb of vapor, an energy balance (see problem 9.21) shows that the recycle ratio is

$$\frac{(970) \text{ Btu/lb of fresh water}}{(150) \text{ Btu/lb of recycle brine}} = 6.5 \text{ lb recycle brine/lb of fresh water}$$

if heat losses are neglected. For the process shown on Figure 2.8, the actual recycle ratio is 7.33 pounds of brine per pound of fresh water. High flow rates of recycle brine are an unavoidable feature of multistage flash distillation.

Neglecting energy for operating pumps and other auxiliary equipment, the energy requirement of a flash desalting plant is mainly the cost of energy in the form of steam from a power plant (at about 255°F) for heating recycle brine from 240 to 250°F. Since heating water 10°F requires 10 Btu of energy:

$$\frac{10 \text{ Btu}}{\text{lb recycle}} \times \frac{(7.33) \text{ lb recycle}}{\text{lb water}} \times \frac{(8340) \text{ lb water}}{1000 \text{ gal}} \times \frac{\text{kw-hr}}{3410 \text{ Btu}}$$

$$= 179 \text{ kw-hr of heat energy/1000 gal of water}$$

This energy requirement, which neglects work consumed in pumping, is lower than that of multiple-effect evaporation. Multistage flash distillation has simpler construction and less severe problems of scale formation. Indeed, one of the most annoying problems associated with operation of an evaporator is scale formation: sea water deposits insoluble solids such as $CaSO_4 \cdot \frac{1}{2}H_2O$, $CaCO_3$ and $Mg(OH)_2$ on metal surfaces. Accumulation of these solids on metal surfaces of heating tubes significantly reduces the capacity of the evaporator by lowering the rate of heat transfer.

Freezing

Distillation exploits the difference in salt concentration of two coexisting phases, liquid and vapor, to separate water from brine. There are other types of phase equilibria involving brine which could serve as a basis for desalination and the most important one is the equilibrium between brine and ice, formed by freezing.

Water desalination by freezing has the important advantage over distillation that scale formation and corrosion are reduced. Compounds such as calcium carbonate and calcium sulfate form scale on surfaces in contact with warm brine but remain in solution at low temperature. Rates of corrosion are slow at 30°F compared to 250°F. Heat is transferred during freezing and melting by direct contact, thus providing high rates of heat transfer. On the other hand, the freezing process does not allow a clean separation of phases like distillation. Separation of ice crystals from brine is difficult. Although individual ice crystals are free of dissolved salts, brine adheres to their surface with a tenacity that is abnormally high compared to adherence of mother liquor to crystals in other systems (for example, crystallization of para-xylene from solution in n-heptane).

Figure 2-10 shows a schematic diagram of a simple freezing process consisting of a freezer, a wash column for separating ice from brine, and a melter. The freezer coils are cooled by a refrigeration unit. Pure water freezes at 0°C, and seawater freezes at a slightly lower temperature, -1.9°C. This small lowering of temperature due to dissolved salts is called freezing-point depression. Refrigerant liquid, at a temperature below -1.9°C to set up a driving force for heat transfer, is pumped through the cooling coils. 144 Btu of heat energy, called latent heat of freezing, must be removed from the brine for each pound of ice formed. The energy requirement is the work needed to run the compresser of the refrigeration unit.

There are several serious flaws in the process shown in Fig. 2-10. First, it is very difficult to separate ice from brine because of the strong adherence of brine to the ice crystals. Second, potentially useful refrigeration capacity is wasted when ice is melted.

Vacuum freezing-vapor compression

Both of the flaws in the simple freezing process are solved by the vacuum freezing-vapor compression process shown in Fig. 2-11. Since water itself is the refrigerant fluid, heating coils in the melter and cooling coils in the freezer are eliminated. The heart of the process is a separation column in which ice is washed clean of brine by a recycled portion of freshwater from the melter.

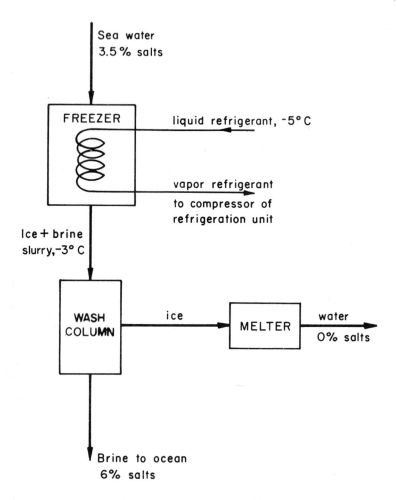

Figure 2-10 Flow diagram of simple (and impractical) freezing process for desalination of seawater.

Seawater is cooled almost to its freezing point by heat exchange with outgoing streams of brine and freshwater. Some of the cooled seawater evaporates as it is sprayed into the freezer, which is evacuated to a pressure of 3 mm Hg by a vacuum pump. Evaporation of water causes the brine to cool and partially freeze to a slurry of ice and brine. The energy released by water as it freezes is equal to its latent heat of fusion, 144 Btu/lb of ice. The energy absorbed by water as it evaporates, the latent heat of vaporization, is 1075 Btu/lb at 0°C. An energy balance (see Example 9.22) shows that the ratio of ice to vapor generated in the freezer is

$$\frac{1075 \text{ Btu/lb of vapor}}{144 \text{ Btu/lb of ice}} = 7.5 \text{ lb of ice per lb of vapor}$$

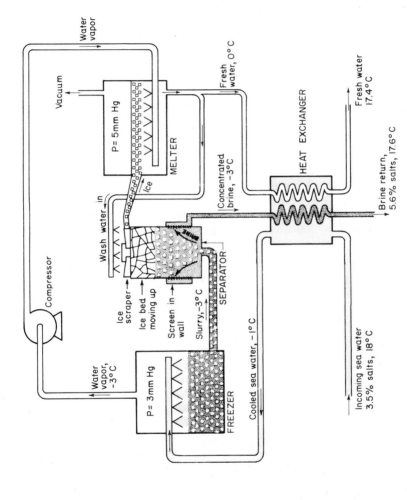

Figure 2-11 Vacuum freezing-vapor compression process for desalination of seawater.

Slurry from the freezer goes to the separator where it enters at the bottom. Since ice is less dense than brine, it floats upward as ice-free brine flows downward and out the sides through a screen. The ice cake, as it moves upward to the top of the separator, is washed by a small stream of freshwater which flows downward over the ice cake, washing off the brine. Only about 5% of the product water is needed for washing the ice. Salt-free ice is scraped off the top of the ice cake and goes into the melter, where condensing water vapor pumped in from the freezer gives off heat to melt the ice. Neglecting heat leaks and other inefficiencies, each pound of vapor condensed in the melter provides enough energy to melt 7.5 lb of ice.

The melter operates close to the triple point of water (0.01°C, 4.6 mm Hg) at which liquid water, water vapor, and ice are in equilibrium. At equilibrium, however, nothing happens, so the operating point is set at a slightly higher pressure (5 mm Hg) to provide a driving force for condensing vapor and melting ice. The freezer, on the other hand, operates near the point (−1.9°C, 3.9 mm Hg) at which ice, seawater brine, and water vapor are in equilibrium. The actual operating point is at a slightly lower pressure (3.2 mm Hg) so that water simultaneously evaporates and freezes in the ratio of 7.5 lb of ice per pound of vapor.

About half of the energy requirement for the vacuum freezing-vapor compression process is the work of running the compressor. The rest is for operating auxiliary pumps and motors and an auxiliary refrigeration unit (not shown in Fig. 2-11) that makes up for inefficiencies in the process. Total energy consumption is about 40 kw-hr of electricity per 1000 gal of freshwater.

Recall that the heat energy requirement for flash distillation is 179 kw-hr/ 1000 gal of water. In comparing these processes it should be borne in mind that the efficiency of conversion of heat energy to electricity in modern power plants is about 33% so that the heat energy requirement is

$$\frac{40}{0.33} = 120 \text{ kw-hr of heat energy per 1000 gal of water}$$

for desalination by freezing. Also, the distillation process uses less valuable or "lower-grade" heat energy in the form of steam at 255°F.

Since distillation and freezing processes have comparable energy requirements, the economics of converting energy from one form to another will affect the selection of the optimum process. Distillation requires low-temperature (about 250°F) steam, which is obtained from steam plants or perhaps in the future from geothermal sources, while freezing processes run on electrical power derived from fuel-burning, hydroelectric, or nuclear power plants.

Reverse osmosis

Certain types of polymeric membranes such as cellulose acetate permit water molecules to pass through in either direction but are relatively impermeable to salt ions. The membrane forms an effective but imperfect barrier to the passage of salt. If pure water and saltwater are divided by a membrane of this type, as shown in Fig. 2-12, water will flow spontaneously through the membrane into the saltwater side.

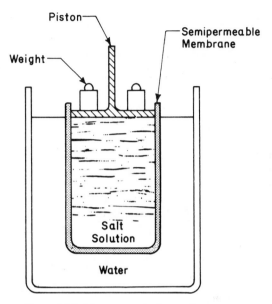

Figure 2-12 Measurement of osmotic pressure.

The phenomenon of diffusion of a solvent through a semipermeable membrane into the more concentrated solution is called osmosis. Suppose that the compartment holding the salt solution is sealed by a piston as shown in Fig. 2-12. Water that enters the salt solution through the membrane forces the piston upward, but this upward force is opposed by the weight of the piston. Osmotic pressure is defined as the total weight per unit area of the piston when these forces are equal and the piston remains motionless. For seawater containing 3.5% salts by weight, osmotic pressure is equal to about 25 atm.

If the hydrostatic pressure on the saltwater side is increased to a value greater than the osmotic pressure ($\Delta P > 25$ atm), then the natural flow into the saltwater side is reversed, as shown in Fig. 2-13. During reverse osmosis, water flows into the pure-water side and salt is left behind. Flow of saltwater parallel to the membrane sweeps away salt ions which would otherwise accumulate at the surface. The decrease in efficiency due to salt buildup in the boundary next to the membrane is called concentration polarization, a problem which also arises in electrodialysis. Polarization problems are alleviated and flow rates are enhanced by proper design of water passages to promote mixing.

The energy consumed in desalination of seawater by reverse osmosis is the work done by the pump in overcoming osmotic pressure plus frictional losses

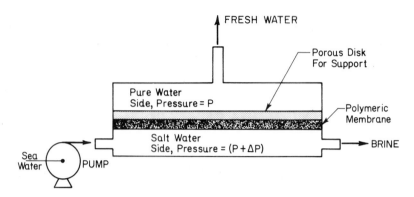

Figure 2-13 Principle of desalination of water by reverse osmosis through a membrane impermeable to salts.

within the module. Under typical operating conditions of 60 atm pressure at the pump outlet, the work is about 30 kw-hr of electrical energy per 1000 gal of freshwater product. This may be compared to 40 kw-hr/1000 gal required for operation of the freezing process. In terms of energy consumption, reverse osmosis has an advantage over distillation and freezing. Also, scale and corrosion problems are minimized because reverse osmosis is performed at ambient temperature.

Is there an absolute lower limit to the energy requirement for desalination of seawater? Imagine a perfect membrane which rejects all salt but passes water freely. Let the pressure difference ΔP (Fig. 2-13) be increased an infinitesimal amount over the osmotic pressure (25 atm), just enough to force a small amount of water through the membrane. The production rate of freshwater would be infinitesimal, but work would be at a minimum because concentration polarization and friction would be virtually eliminated. Therefore, the minimum work is the work of compressing seawater feed from atmospheric pressure to 26 atm. For a perfect compressor operating with no friction, the work is 2.6 kw-hr/1000 gal of fresh water. It can be shown that this is the minimum work for any desalination process, including those not yet invented.

The overall efficiency of reverse osmosis, at the present state of development, in the use of electrical energy to desalinate seawater is the ratio of minimum work to actual work:

$$\frac{2.6 \text{ kw-hr}/1000 \text{ gal}}{30 \text{ kw-hr}/1000 \text{ gal}} \times 100 = 9\%$$

There is considerable room for improvement. It is not unreasonable to expect an efficiency as high as 25% for carefully designed, large-scale reverse osmosis plants of the future.

Scale-up of reverse osmosis from laboratory devices to commercial production units is a challenging problem. The rate of production of freshwater by reverse osmosis is directly proportional to the surface area of the membrane. Therefore, the ratio of surface area to volume is a major factor in engineering design. Another important factor is the useful lifetime of the membrane, which should be at least 1 year and preferably several years. Other design considerations are ease of replacement of membranes, hydraulics (pressure drop), and ruggedness.

Several different membrane configurations are currently being evaluated; one of them is the Dupont hollow-fiber module shown in Fig. 2-14. Each module contains a bundle of millions of hollow fibers, the ends of which are encapsulated in an epoxy resin. Salt water enters the module in the space

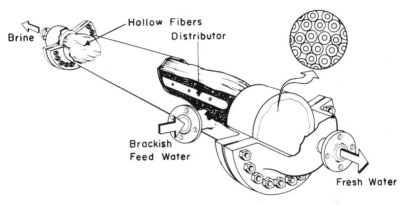

Figure 2-14 Hollow-fiber desalination module. [*Dupont Innovation, 1* (No. 1), 1 (1969).]

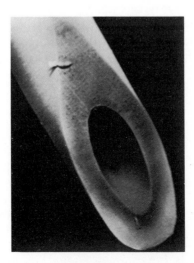

Figure 2-15 Photograph of hollow-fiber membrane. Outer diameter = 0.0050 cm, inner diameter = 0.0025 cm.

outside the fibers at high pressure. Water diffuses through the walls of the polyamide (nylon) fibers into the bores by reverse osmosis, and freshwater is collected from the open ends of the fibers in a manifold at one end of the module. Figure 2-15 shows a photograph of a single hollow fiber (outer diameter 0.05 mm, inner diameter 0.025 mm). The relatively thick walls of the fibers prevent their collapse under the hydrostatic pressure outside the fibers.

Ion exchange

Desalination processes may be grouped into two categories:

1. Water is removed from the brine, as in distillation, freezing, and reverse osmosis.
2. Salt is removed from the brine leaving freshwater behind, as in ion exchange and electrodialysis.

Ion exchange resins are solid substances which possess exchangeable cations or anions. An example of a cation exchanger is a crosslinked polystyrene with sulfonic acid groups ($-SO_3H$) introduced after polymerization by treatment with concentrated sulfuric acid. The structure of this resin is shown in Fig. 2-16; the proton of the sulfonic acid group may be replaced by a univalent ion (Na^+) from aqueous solution. Divalent ions such as Ca^{2+} replace two protons.

Anion exchange resins are prepared, for example, by attaching ammonium hydroxide groups $[-(NH_3)^+(OH)^-]$ to the framework of giant polymer molecules. The $(OH)^-$ may be exchanged with a univalent ion (Cl^-) from aqueous solution.

Removal of dissolved salt (NaCl) can be accomplished in a two-step process, shown in Fig. 2-17 and represented by the following equations:

Cation exchange:

$$\text{resin—H(solid)} + \text{NaCl(aq)} = \text{resin—Na(solid)} + \text{HCl(aq)}$$

Anion exchange:

$$\text{resin—OH(solid)} + \text{HCl(aq)} = \text{resin—Cl(solid)} + H_2O$$

Cation and anion exchange resins in the form of small beads about 1 mm in diameter are placed in separate fixed beds connected in series (an alternative is to mix the resins and pack them into a single bed). Salt water is added at the top of each bed, and ion exchange occurs as the solution flows past the resin particles. At first the exchange is at the top of the bed, and then the exchange zone moves downward as the cation and anion resins become saturated with Na^+ and Cl^- ions, respectively. Eventually both beds become

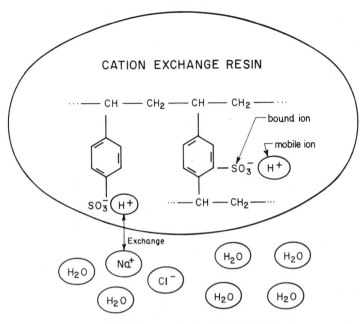

Figure 2-16 Cation exchange resin composed of a sulfonated copolymer of styrene and divinylbenzene.

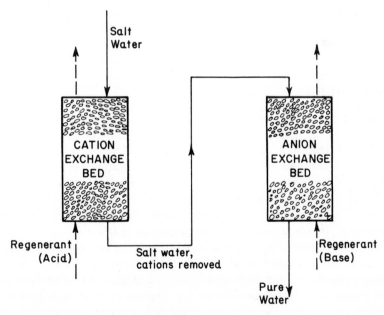

Figure 2-17 Schematic of fixed-bed process for removal of dissolved salts from water by ion exchange.

saturated when the exchange zone reaches the bottom of the bed, at which time both beds must be removed from service and regenerated as follows:

Regeneration of cation exchanger:

$$resin—Na(solid) + HCl(aq, concentrated)$$
$$= resin—H(solid) + NaCl(aq, concentrated)$$

Regeneration of anion exchanger:

$$resin—Cl(solid) + NaOH(aq, concentrated)$$
$$= resin—OH(solid) + NaCl(aq, concentrated)$$

Every molecule of NaCl removed from aqueous solution must in turn be removed from the resins by treatment with one molecule each of HCl and NaOH. Since acid and base is the major operating cost, the cost of desalination by ion exchange is directly proportional to the concentration of salt. Ion exchange is not competitive with other processes such as distillation for desalting seawater, but ion exchange is often the most economical method of purifying solutions containing less than 100 ppm of salt. Also, ion exchange is the final step in the preparation of ultrapure water (containing less than 50 parts per billion of salt) used by semiconductor and pharmaceutical manufacturers, nuclear power plants, and other industries.

New ion exchange processes are designed for continuous regeneration during water treatment. Fixed beds of resins are replaced by countercurrent flow of resin (downward) and salt water (upward). Continuous processes may extend the range of application of ion exchange to purification of slightly brackish water ($<$ 2000 ppm of salt).

Electrodialysis

Electrodialysis is based upon the development of membranes permeable to positive or negative ions and impermeable to ions of opposite charge. These membranes are prepared by mixing ion exchange resins with inert polymeric binders. In electrodialysis the ion exchange resin serves as a conductor of electrical current in the form of ions, which are removed from solution and pass though the membrane to the other side. Membranes permeable to cations only are made of cation exchange resins; membranes permeable to anions are made of anion exchange resins.

The basic principle of electrodialysis is illustrated in Fig. 2-18. Brackish water is pumped through stacks of alternating anion-permeable (A) and cation-permeable (C) membranes. The stack is closely spaced to form thin (1-mm) compartments and thus lower the resistance of the stack to flow of electrical current between the two electrodes. Cations (principally Na^+) migrate toward the cathode, and anions (principally Cl^-) migrate toward the

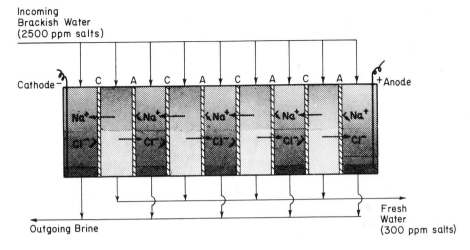

Figure 2-18 Stacking of cation-permeable and anion-permeable membranes for electrodialysis of brackish water.

anode so that flow of positive electricity through the stack is from right to left.

Consider a single cation-permeable membrane (C). Electric current carries sodium ions to the left through C. Chloride ions are simultaneously transferred from the right side of C, and these are not replaced by transport through C. The net result is accumulation of salt (NaCl) on the left side of C and removal of the same amount of salt from the right side of C. A similar separation, but with the roles of the cation and anion reversed, occurs across each anion-permeable membrane (A). Alternating compartments form brine and product (freshwater) passages as shown in Fig. 2-18.

Electric current is carried by electrons in the external circuit and by ions in the electrodialysis cell as shown in Fig. 2-19. Electrons are removed from the cathode by chemical reduction and delivered to the anode by chemical oxidation. Important electrode reactions for acidic brackish water are shown in Fig. 2-19: Chloride ion is oxidized to chlorine gas at the anode, and hydrogen ions are reduced to hydrogen gas at the cathode. One of the problems of desalination by electrodialysis is disposal of unwanted products generated by electrochemical reactions. Another difficulty, also found in reverse osmosis, is scaling of membranes and thus the need to clean them occasionally. Careful pretreatment of feed water is needed to prevent membrane fouling.

dc power for electrodialysis is generated by an ac to dc converter. A small amount of additional electrical power is needed for pumping water. The total energy cost, in the form of electricity, needed for desalination of brackish water with 2500-ppm dissolved salts is about 15 kw-hr/1000 gal of freshwater. The energy cost for desalination of brackish water containing 5000-ppm dissolved salts is twice as much, or about 30 kw-hr/1000 gal. The latter value is equal to the energy cost of desalination by reverse osmosis, which is almost independent of salt concentration. Therefore, electrodialysis loses its advantage over distillation, freezing, and reverse osmosis when the salt concentration exceeds about 5000 ppm.

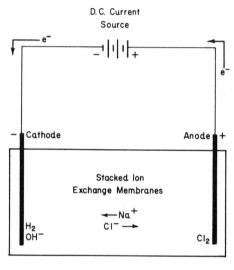

$$\text{Cathode:} \quad 2 H_2O + 2e^- \rightarrow H_2 \qquad + 2OH^-$$
$$\text{Anode:} \qquad 2Cl^- \rightarrow Cl_2 + 2e^-$$
$$\text{Overall reaction:} \quad 2 H_2O + 2Cl^- \rightarrow H_2 + Cl_2 + 2OH^-$$

Figure 2-19 Electrode reactions during electrodialysis of brackish water.

Summary

Almost all desalination of seawater is carried out at present by distillation, especially multistage flash distillation. One of the advantages of distillation is that it delivers freshwater of high purity (5–25 ppm of dissolved salts). Desalination by distillation is coupled to the availability and cost of steam. Other processes (reverse osmosis, freezing, and electrodialysis) require electrical power. Most desalting of brackish water is now done by electrodialysis. The appeal of reverse osmosis is its potentially low energy cost, but large-scale processes are still under development. Most applications of reverse osmosis in the early 1970s were limited to desalting of brackish water containing less than 1% salt, although membranes capable of desalting seawater have been developed. Electrodialysis is superior to other processes for desalination of slightly brackish water, and ion exchange is applied to the preparation of ultrapure water.

It is interesting to classify desalination processes* according to the type of transport and driving force employed, as shown in Table 2.4. There is no known process based upon transport of salt to the vapor phase.

Comparisons of known methods of making freshwater from seawater show that each scheme has its advantages and disadvantages. Selection of the "best" desalting process for a particular task is based upon minimum cost.

TABLE 2.4
CLASSIFICATION OF SEPARATION PROCESSES FOR DESALINATION
OF SEAWATER

Process	Substance Removed from Salt Water	Phase to Which Transported	Driving Force
Distillation	Water	Vapor	Temperature: Heating
Freezing	Water	Solid (ice)	Temperature: Cooling
Reverse osmosis	Water	Liquid	Pressure
Ion exchange	Salt	Solid (resin)	Chemical
Electrodialysis	Salt	Liquid	Electrical

Important factors which must be weighed in cost comparisons include†

1. Salt concentration and temperature of feedwater.
2. Maximum acceptable concentration of salt in product water.
3. Difficulty in disposing of waste brine.
4. Commercial state of development of the process.
5. Size and location of the plant.
6. Type and cost of energy sources available.

For a particular process, the total cost is a sum of the two costs shown in Fig. 2-20: operating cost (mainly energy for desalination) and capital cost (plant equipment). Capital cost increases with the size of the equipment (area available for heat and mass transfer), but the operating cost decreases because of improved efficiency. For example, in multiple-effect evaporation, increasing the number of effects lowers the energy cost but raises the equipment cost. In reverse osmosis, increasing the membrane area lowers the energy cost for

---

*"Desalination Research and the Water Problem," *National Research Council Publication 941*, National Academy of Sciences, Washington, D.C., 1962.

†"Special Report on Status of Desalting," U.S. Department of the Interior, Office of Saline Water, U.S. Government Printing Office, Washington, D.C., Nov. 1970.

pumping and raises the capital or investment cost. Since operating cost decreases and capital cost increases with area, there is an optimum design which minimizes the total cost, as shown in Fig. 2-20.

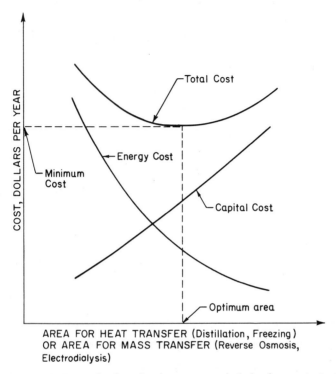

AREA FOR HEAT TRANSFER (Distillation, Freezing) OR AREA FOR MASS TRANSFER (Reverse Osmosis, Electrodialysis)

Figure 2-20 Determination of optimum economic design for constant rate of desalination.

Process Synthesis 3

Process flow sheets for coal gasification and desalination of sea water were presented in Ch. 2 as a *fait accompli*. Historical development of a process, although quite interesting, was neglected in order to focus attention on how a process works. As the student becomes familiar with some of the similarities and distinctive features of chemical processes, it is natural to begin to question their origin and to explore alternatives.

Designing or inventing chemical processes is a skill that cannot easily be taught. Intuition and experience are as important to the design engineer as to the artist. Nevertheless, it is worthwhile to examine some of the steps that accompany the synthesis of a new chemical process.

Chemical processes are represented by flow sheets, which show basic process units and how they are connected by streams of mass and energy. In this chapter we shall discuss methods of synthesizing flow sheets, given desired products and available raw materials.

Invention of a chemical process often begins with the discovery of a phenomenon or new substance. Often the discovery opens up a new field of chemical technology. If the discovery or idea can be applied to make new substances with improved properties or to reduce the cost of existing products by using less valuable raw materials, then the first step in the process development is the preparation of a flow sheet. As shown in Ch. 2, chemical reactions and separations can be accomplished in a variety of ways, and the trick is to find a method with desirable features such as safety, low cost, and reliability in an optimum combination set by the designer.

3.1 Process Operations

A chemical process is an assembly of process units such as reactors and heat exchangers. Each process unit carries out one or more of the following operations:

1. Chemical reaction.
2. Separation or purification.
3. Change of temperature.
4. Change of pressure.
5. Change of phase.
6. Mixing.

These are the most important operations, but there are many others (grinding, for example).

Chemical reaction is, of course, the nucleus of a chemical process. Feasibility of a chemical reaction depends on many factors such as equilibrium yield,* reaction rate, and the ability to control or eliminate unwanted side reactions. A low equilibrium yield can often be increased by appropriate adjustment of temperature and pressure. Reactions which have high equilibrium yields but occur slowly can sometimes be accelerated by catalysts or enzymes; the catalyst is selected so that it accelerates the desired reaction while simultaneously suppressing unwanted side reactions. Degree of conversion, rates, and equilibrium yields of chemical reactions are discussed in Ch. 7.

Separation in chemical engineering means breakdown of a mixture of two or more chemicals into its pure or nearly pure constituents. Separation usually implies physical separation, carried out without chemical reaction. Examples include distillation of air at low temperature to get oxygen and nitrogen, desalination of seawater, and chromatographic separation of complex mixtures of amino acids dissolved in water. In addition to separation of molecules of different species, separation is applied to heterogeneous mixtures containing more than one phase; examples are separation of cream from milk and removal of slate from coal.

Separation processes are based upon differences in physical properties of the chemicals to be separated. For example, distillation is based upon differences in volatility or boiling points, crystallization upon differences in melting points, and solvent extraction upon differences in solubility of a substance in two immiscible liquids. Separation processes are discussed in Chs. 6 and 10, and properties of materials are discussed in Ch. 4.

Temperature is the most important variable in chemical processing. Change of temperature is a driving force for adjusting rates and yields of chemical reactions; phase changes such as condensation of vapors, solidifica-

---

*Equilibrium yield is the amount of feed chemical converted to product in a reacting system at equilibrium.

tion and vaporization of liquids, and melting of solids; and changes in properties such as viscosity, solubility, and surface tension. Change of temperature is accomplished by transferring heat from a hot fluid to a cold fluid in a heat exchanger (see Fig. 1.5). The surface separating the two fluids is made of a substance with high thermal conductivity such as copper; the amount of heat transferred depends on the temperature difference of the fluids, their contact time, and their relative flow rates. Since heating or cooling requires expenditure of energy, considerable economy can be achieved by heat recovery. For example, energy necessary to heat materials to their reaction temperature can be partially recovered by preheating reactants with hot products.

Change of pressure is a driving force for phase changes such as condensation of vapors or vaporization of liquids. Pressure has only a small effect upon properties of liquids and solids such as melting point and solubility (however, it has an important effect upon the solubility of gases in liquids). Pressure is applied to fluids by pumps and compressors to overcome friction in process equipment and pipelines. When some of the reactants or products of a chemical reaction are gases, raising or lowering of the pressure has an effect upon the equilibrium yield according to the principle of Le Chatelier; an important example is the reaction

$$N_2 + 3H_2 \rightleftharpoons 2NH_3$$

for which increase of pressure increases the equilibrium yield of ammonia (see Ch. 7).

Change of phase is brought about by changes in temperature and pressure: solidification of a liquid by lowering its temperature, and vaporization of a liquid by raising its temperature or lowering its pressure. In separation processes, temperature and pressure are adjusted so that two phases exist simultaneously in contact with one another (liquid and vapor, solid and liquid, solid and vapor, two immiscible liquids, etc.); small differences in concentration between two phases are multiplied by staging techniques to effect a complete separation (see, for example, multistage flash distillation of seawater in Ch. 2). Change of phase from a gas to a liquid or solid is a method of reducing volume for transportation, as in the liquefaction of natural gas. Energy required to produce a phase change is called latent heat, for example, latent heat of fusion (melting) of a solid or latent heat of vaporization of a liquid. The amount of energy necessary to produce a phase change is liberated when the phase change occurs in the opposite direction, and therefore phase changes provide a method of storing energy (production of steam, for example).

Mixing is the reverse of separation and, by definition, occurs without chemical reaction. It is interesting that there is an energy requirement for separating a solution into its pure constituents, but mixing can be accomplished with no expenditure of energy other than the small amount of energy required when an agitator is used to speed up the mixing process. Mixing includes the formation of a homogeneous solution of two or more substances (mixing of salt and water to form salt water) and the formation of hetero-geneous suspensions and colloidal dispersions (mixing of chocolate syrup and milk to make chocolate milk).

3.2 Chemical State

The state of a substance or mixture of substances is defined by the values of the following properties:

1. Mass.
2. Composition (mole or mass fraction of each chemical species).
3. Phase (solid, liquid, gas).
4. Form (crystalline modification—applies only to solids).
5. Temperature.
6. Pressure.

Once the state of a substance is fixed by giving values to these properties, all the other properties including viscosity, thermal conductivity, color, refractive index, and density, have definite values. For example, the volume of a mixture of alcohol and water depends on its state (mass, composition, phase, temperature, pressure).

The state of a substance is independent of its position in a gravitational field and its velocity. Although there are other properties (magnetic field strength, surface area) whose values must be specified under certain conditions, the set of properties listed above is usually sufficient to fix the state of a substance.

Two kinds of properties should be distinguished: intensive properties, which are independent of the mass of the substance (temperature, pressure, density, refractive index), and extensive properties, whose values are directly proportional to the quantity of substance (mass, volume).

3.3 Process Synthesis

Process synthesis is the design of a sequence of process operations that converts raw materials to products by changing their chemical state. It was shown in Ch. 2 that there are always several practical alternatives for accomplishing a given conversion or separation. These different methods must be compared in terms of their safety features, reliability, capital and operating costs, and estimated net profit. Selection of the optimum process proceeds in the following order:

1. *Process synthesis.* This step, the selection of a sequence of process units and the preparation of a flow sheet specifying flow rates of mass and energy, is the most creative aspect of design. Sometimes process units (reactors, pumps, distillation columns) with proven operating char-

acteristics can be incorporated in the design without modification, but usually a new process requires extensive modification of previous equipment and invention of new process units.

2. *Process analysis and optimization.* For each process whose development appears promising, important adjustable operating conditions or parameters such as temperature, pressure, and recycle rate are varied to minimize the total cost (equipment cost plus operating cost) of the process.

3. *Process selection.* Alternative processes, each of them optimized to minimize costs, are compared, and the "best" process is selected for development and construction. If all of the constraints imposed by society such as product desirability, conservation of resources, and antipollution regulations have been satisfied, then maximum net profit is the criterion for process selection.

There are no rules for discovering new chemical reactions or for inventing new chemical processes. However, the art of process design can be reduced to manageable proportions by assuming that equipment for accomplishing any of the process operations in Sec. 3.1 exists or can be developed (subject, of course, to the laws of conservation of mass and energy). Let us consider the more modest task of combining these process operations in an appropriate scheme to produce a flow sheet. Rules of thumb or heuristics* for synthesis of flow sheets have been developed. The basic idea is to create the flow sheet by assembling its process operations in the following order:

1. Chemical reaction.
2. Distribution of chemicals.
3. Physical separation.
4. Temperature, pressure, and phase change.
5. Task integration.

For illustration, these steps will be applied consecutively to the preparation of a flow sheet for the production of vinyl chloride.

3.4 Example of Process Synthesis: Manufacture of Vinyl Chloride

Vinyl chloride,

$$\begin{array}{ccc} H & & Cl \\ \diagdown & & \diagup \\ & C{=}C & \\ \diagup & & \diagdown \\ H & & H \end{array}$$

*D. F. Rudd, J. Siirola, and G. J. Powers, *Process Synthesis*, Prentice Hall, Englewood Cliffs, N.J., 1973.

is a monomer intermediate for production of polyvinyl chloride,

$$
\begin{array}{ccccc}
& \text{CHCl} & & \text{CHCl} & & \text{CHCl} \\
\diagdown\diagup & & \diagdown\diagup & & \diagdown\diagup & \diagdown \\
\text{CH}_2 & & \text{CH}_2 & & \text{CH}_2 &
\end{array}
$$

an important plastic. Vinyl chloride was discovered in 1835 in the laboratory of the French chemist Regnault, and the first practical method for polymerizing vinyl chloride was developed in 1917 by the German chemists Klatte and Rollett.* Since then, growth of production of polyvinyl chloride in industrialized countries has been almost continuous. Vinyl chloride monomer is an extremely toxic substance and therefore industrial plants that manufacture or process it must be carefully designed to satisfy governmental health regulations.

The objective is to design a flow sheet for Fig. 3.1. The first and most important step in synthesizing a flow sheet is selection of promising chemical reaction paths. We shall examine five schemes, all of which have been successfully performed in laboratory experiments. Chemicals that participate in the reactions are listed in Table 3.1.

TABLE 3.1
CHEMICALS THAT PARTICIPATE IN
REACTIONS TO PRODUCE VINYL CHLORIDE

Chemical	Molecular weight	Chemical formula	Chemical structure
Acetylene	26.04	C_2H_2	$H-C\equiv C-H$
Chlorine	70.91	Cl_2	$Cl-Cl$
1,2-Dichloroethane	98.96	$C_2H_4Cl_2$	$\begin{array}{c} Cl\ \ Cl \\ |\ \ \ | \\ H-C-C-H \\ |\ \ \ | \\ H\ \ H \end{array}$
Ethylene	28.05	C_2H_4	$\begin{array}{c} H \qquad H \\ \diagdown\ \ \ \diagup \\ C=C \\ \diagup\ \ \ \diagdown \\ H \qquad H \end{array}$
Hydrogen chloride	36.46	HCl	$H-Cl$
Vinyl chloride	62.50	C_2H_3Cl	$\begin{array}{c} H \qquad Cl \\ \diagdown\ \ \ \diagup \\ C=C \\ \diagup\ \ \ \diagdown \\ H \qquad H \end{array}$

*E. C. Leonard, ed., *Vinyl and Diene Monomers*, Part 3, Wiley-Interscience, New York, 1971.

Figure 3-1 The process synthesis problem.

Chemical reactions

1. *Direct chlorination of ethylene:*

$$C_2H_4 + Cl_2 \longrightarrow C_2H_3Cl + HCl \qquad (3.1)$$

Although this reaction occurs spontaneously at a few hundred degrees Centigrade, it is difficult to get a high yield of vinyl chloride without simultaneous production of large amounts of by-products such as dichloroethylene.

2. *Hydrochlorination of acetylene:*

$$C_2H_2 + HCl \longrightarrow C_2H_3Cl \qquad (3.2)$$

This exothermic reaction gives good conversion (98%) of acetylene to vinyl chloride at 150°C in the presence of mercuric chloride ($HgCl_2$) catalyst impregnated in activated carbon.

3. *Thermal cracking of dichloroethane from chlorination of ethylene:*

$$C_2H_4 + Cl_2 \longrightarrow C_2H_4Cl_2 \qquad (3.3)$$
$$\underline{C_2H_4Cl_2 \longrightarrow C_2H_3Cl + HCl \qquad (3.4)}$$
$$C_2H_4 + Cl_2 \longrightarrow C_2H_3Cl + HCl \quad \text{(overall)} \qquad (3.1)$$

The sum of Reactions (3.3) and (3.4) is equal to Reaction (3.1). The two-step reaction path has the advantage that conversion of ethylene to 1,2-dichloroethane in exothermic reaction (3.3) is about 98% at 90°C with a Friedel-Crafts catalyst such as ferric chloride ($FeCl_3$). Dichloroethane intermediate is then converted to vinyl chloride by thermal cracking according to endothermic reaction (3.4), which occurs spontaneously at 500°C with conversions as high as 65%.

4. *Thermal cracking of dichloroethane from oxychlorination of ethylene:*

$$C_2H_4 + 2HCl + \tfrac{1}{2}O_2 \longrightarrow C_2H_4Cl_2 + H_2O \qquad (3.5)$$
$$\underline{C_2H_4Cl_2 \longrightarrow C_2H_3Cl + HCl \qquad (3.4)}$$
$$C_2H_4 + HCl + \tfrac{1}{2}O_2 \longrightarrow C_2H_3Cl + H_2O \quad \text{(overall)} \qquad (3.6)$$

Reaction (3.5) is called oxychlorination of ethylene to produce 1,2-dichloroethane, which is converted to vinyl chloride by thermal cracking as before in Reaction (3.4). The source of chlorine for the overall

reaction is hydrogen chloride. Reaction (3.5), which is highly exothermic, has a conversion of ethylene to dichloroethane of 95% at 250°C
in the presence of cupric chloride ($CuCl_2$) catalyst.

5. *Balanced process for chlorination of ethylene:* Comparison of path 3
   for chlorination and path 4 for oxychlorination shows that hydrogen
   chloride is a by-product in one path and a raw material in the other.
   Therefore, reaction paths 3 and 4 can be combined to form a new path
   in which hydrogen chloride appears only as an intermediate:

$$C_2H_4 + Cl_2 \longrightarrow C_2H_4Cl_2 \qquad (3.3)$$

$$C_2H_4 + 2HCl + \tfrac{1}{2}O_2 \longrightarrow C_2H_4Cl_2 + H_2O \qquad (3.5)$$

$$2C_2H_4Cl_2 \longrightarrow 2C_2H_3Cl + 2HCl \qquad (3.4)$$

$$\overline{2C_2H_4 + Cl_2 + \tfrac{1}{2}O_2 \longrightarrow 2C_2H_3Cl + H_2O} \text{ (overall)} \quad (3.7)$$

There are no new reactions, but this path has the distinction that all of
the chlorine is converted to vinyl chloride: There are no by-products
containing chlorine.

At this point it is helpful to estimate the gross profit for each reaction path.
Prices of chemicals on the open market fluctuate constantly; suppose for
purposes of discussion that chemical costs are those given in Table 3.2. Let

TABLE 3.2
ASSUMED COST OF CHEMICALS PURCHASED
OR SOLD IN BULK QUANTITIES

Chemical	Cost (cents/lb)
Ethylene	4
Acetylene	9
Chlorine	3
Vinyl chloride	6
Hydrogen chloride	4
Water	0
Oxygen (air)	0

us estimate gross profit as the total income derived from sales of product
less the cost of raw materials. For the first reaction path, gross profit is calculated by converting to a mass basis:

	C_2H_4	$+$	Cl_2	$=$	C_2H_3Cl	$+$	HCl
lb-mole	1		1		1		1
Molecular weight	28.05		70.91		62.50		36.46
lb	28.05		70.91		62.50		36.46
lb/lb of vinyl chloride	0.449		1.134		1		0.583
cents/lb	4		3		6		4

The gross profit is $6(1) + 4(0.583) - 4(0.449) - 3(1.134) = 3.13$ cents/lb of vinyl chloride. Gross profit is estimated for each reaction path in Table 3.3. Observe that reaction paths 1 and 3 have the same gross profit because their overall reactions are identical.

TABLE 3.3
GROSS PROFIT FOR PRODUCTION OF VINYL CHLORIDE
(BASED UPON CHEMICAL PRICES IN TABLE 3.2)

Reaction path no.	Overall reaction	Gross profit (cents/lb of vinyl chloride)
1	$C_2H_4 + Cl_2 = C_2H_3Cl + HCl$	3.13
2	$C_2H_2 + HCl = C_2H_3Cl$	-0.08
3	$C_2H_4 + Cl_2 = C_2H_3Cl + HCl$	3.13
4	$C_2H_4 + HCl + \frac{1}{2}O_2 = C_2H_3Cl + H_2O$	1.87
5	$2C_2H_4 + Cl_2 + \frac{1}{2}O_2 = 2C_2H_3Cl + H_2O$	2.50

In calculating gross profit, we have ignored operating costs (labor, steam, electricity, etc.) and capital costs (construction of plant, depreciation, etc.). Since net profit is less than the values in Table 3.3, reaction path 2 (hydrochlorination of acetylene) can be dropped from further consideration unless there is a drastic decrease in the cost of acetylene relative to ethylene. The other reaction paths all show a positive gross profit and therefore merit further study. Notice that the competitive advantage of paths 1 and 3 depends strongly on the market for hydrogen chloride.

Figure 3-2 shows the first step toward creating a process flow sheet for reaction path 3. Each reaction is shown with arrows representing its feed and product chemicals. The "sources" and "sinks" for these chemicals are not shown because they depend on the distribution of chemicals, the next step in

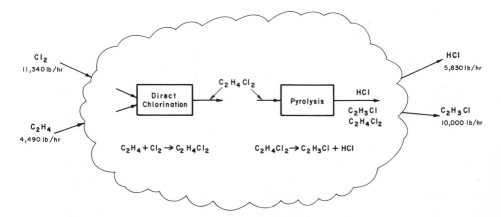

Figure 3-2 Thermal cracking of dichloroethane from chlorination of ethylene (reaction path 3).

process synthesis. External flow rates are computed by assuming that raw materials are completely converted to 10,000 lb/hr of vinyl chloride according to the overall reaction. Unreacted raw materials are separated from the reaction products and recycled.

Distribution of chemicals

In the next step, sources and sinks for each of the chemical species in Fig. 3-2 are matched up. When a single sink is supplied by one or more sources, a mixer operation is inserted. Often a single source is divided among several sinks. The objective is to distribute chemicals so as to eliminate differences in quantity between sources and sinks, as shown in Fig. 3-3. Ethylene and chlorine are fed to the chlorination reactor in stoichiometric ratio (1 mole of C_2H_4/mole of Cl_2). At 90°C and 1.5 atm, 98% of the ethylene is converted to dichloroethane; the remainder is converted to unwanted by-products such as trichloroethane. This small fraction is neglected in the preliminary flow sheet. Dichloroethane is mixed with recycle and fed to the pyrolysis furnace, where at 500°C and 26 atm, 60% of the feed (including recycle) is converted to vinyl chloride. The product stream from the reactor must be separated into three streams: vinyl chloride product, hydrogen chloride by-product, and recycle dichloroethane.

Figure 3-3 also shows heats of reaction. The chlorination reaction is exothermic: at 90°C and 1.5 atm, 15 million Btu of heat are released per hour and must be removed from the reactor to prevent overheating. The pyrolysis reaction is endothermic: at 500°C and 26 atm, 5.2 million Btu/hr must be added to the reactor to prevent cooling below 500°C. Sources and sinks for energy will be added to the flow sheet later during the task integration step.

The distribution of chemicals shown in Fig. 3-3 implies the existence of a practical separation scheme, which is considered next.

Physical Separations

Figure 3-3 shows a mixture of hydrogen chloride, vinyl chloride, and dichloroethane to be separated into its pure components. Distillation is a prospective separation process because boiling points of these chemicals differ significantly, as illustrated in Table 3.4. (Operation of distillation columns was discussed in Sec. 1.2 and illustrated in Fig. 1-3.)

Figure 3-4 shows two distillation columns in series. Column 1 removes the most volatile chemical, hydrogen chloride, as distillate and leaves only trace quantities of hydrogen chloride in the bottoms product. It is operated at 12 atm so that the temperature in the reboiler is below the critical temperature of vinyl chloride (158°C), above which it is difficult to achieve a good

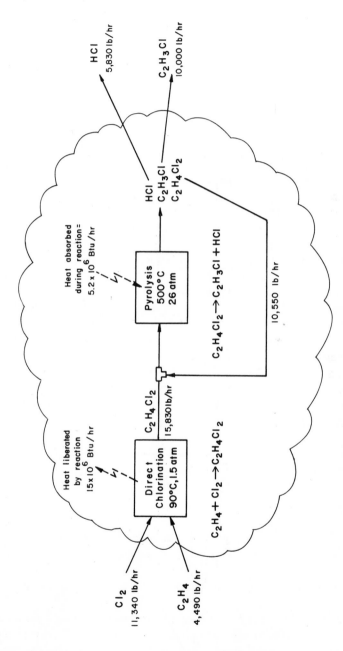

Figure 3-3 Flow sheet showing distribution of chemicals for thermal cracking of dichloroethane from chlorination of ethylene (reaction path 3).

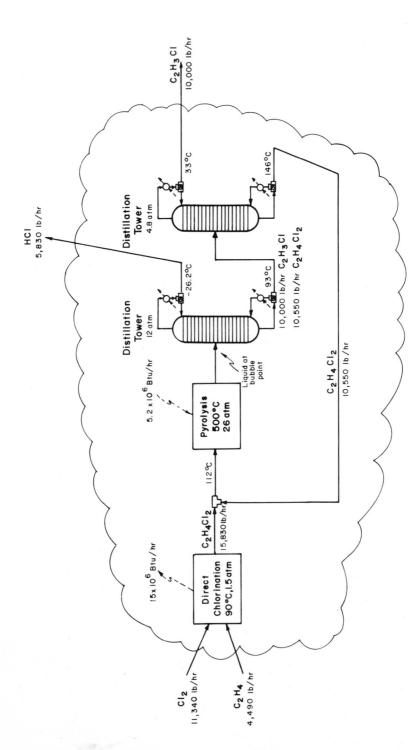

Figure 3-4 Flow sheet showing separation scheme for vinyl chloride process.

TABLE 3.4
BOILING POINTS

Chemical	Normal boiling point (1 atm, °C)	Boiling point (°C)		
		4.8 atm	12 atm	26 atm
HCl	−84.8	−51.7	−26.2	0
C_2H_3Cl	−13.8	33.1	70.5	110
$C_2H_4Cl_2$	83.7	146	193	242

separation. The distillate is at its boiling point (−26.2°C at 12 atm); hence, the condenser must be cooled by refrigeration.

Column 2 produces nearly pure vinyl chloride as distillate and nearly pure dichloroethane as bottoms product. The temperature of distillate and bottoms depends on the pressure (see Table 3.4). The pressure in this column is fixed at 4.8 atm, just high enough so that cooling water at 25°C will condense the reflux portion of vinyl chloride emerging at 33°C.

Figure 3-4 does not show how changes of temperature and pressure and phase changes are to be accomplished; these are considered next.

Temperature, pressure, and phase changes

Operations to heat and compress dichloroethane to its pyrolysis temperature and pressure and operations to cool and liquefy the pyrolysis products in transit to the first distillation column are missing in Fig. 3.4. The necessary transformations are shown in Fig. 3-5. Liquid dichloroethane from the recycle mixer at 112°C and 1.5 atm undergoes the following operations:

1. Its pressure is increased to 26 atm.
2. Its temperature is raised to the boiling point, which is 242°C at 26 atm.
3. Dichloroethane liquid is vaporized at 242°C.
4. Its temperature is raised to the pyrolysis temperature, 500°C.

Hot vapor mixture from the pyrolysis furnace (at 500°C and 26 atm) is operated upon as follows:

1. Its temperature is lowered to its dew point, 170°C at 26 atm (the dew point is the temperature at which the first drop of liquid forms from its vapor upon cooling).
2. Vapor mixture is condensed to liquid at its bubble point (the bubble point is the temperature at which the last bubble of vapor condenses) by cooling and removal of latent heat of condensation.

Figure 3-5 does not show what kinds of process units will accomplish temperature, pressure, and phase changes. These are identified in the last step of process synthesis: task integration.

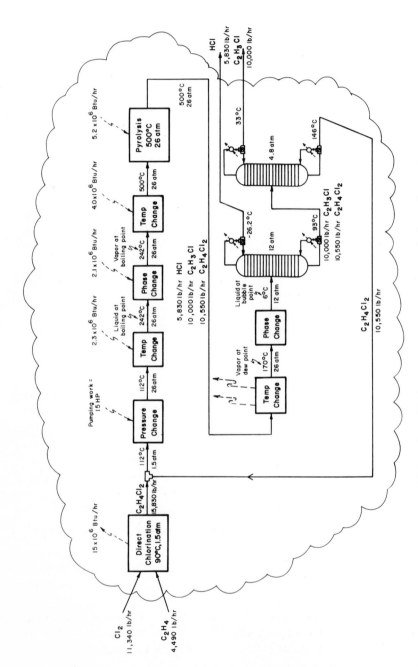

Figure 3-5 Flow sheet showing temperature, pressure, and phase change operations in the vinyl chloride process.

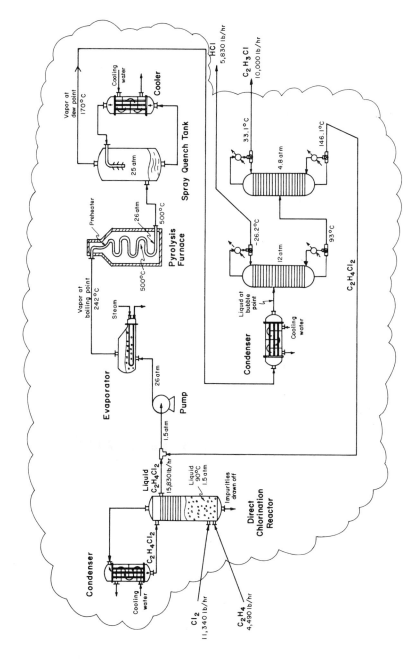

Figure 3-6 Flow sheet showing task integration for the vinyl chloride process.

TABLE 3.5
VINYL CHLORIDE PROCESS UNITS

Process unit	Operations performed
1. *Direct chlorination reactor with condenser.** Feed Cl_2 and C_2H_4 vapors bubble through a dilute liquid solution of $FeCl_3$ catalyst in product $C_2H_4Cl_2$, where reaction occurs. Heat of reaction vaporizes some of the $C_2H_4Cl_2$, which rises into the tray section of the reactor, where it is separated from heavier by-products (such as $C_2H_3Cl_3$). Cooling water pumped through the condenser removes the heat of reaction and produces cold liquid reflux for the separation. Nearly pure $C_2H_4Cl_2$ is removed as liquid from the top tray.	Chlorination reaction, removal of exothermic heat of reaction, and separation of impurities produced by unwanted side reactions
2. *Pumps.* Two or more pumps are placed in series to compress liquid $C_2H_4Cl_2$ from 1.5 to 26 atm. The pumps are operated by electric motors.	Pressure change
3. *Evaporator.* Liquid $C_2H_4Cl_2$ is heated to its boiling point and vaporized as it passes through tubes which are heated on the outside by superheated steam.	Temperature change, phase change
4. *Pyrolysis furnace.*† Vapor $C_2H_4Cl_2$ is heated to 500°C in the preheater section, at which temperature the pyrolysis reaction occurs. The vapors pass through a bundle of stainless steel tubes (6 cm in diameter and approximately 300 m long). Heat energy to preheat the vapors and to supply the heat of reaction is obtained from a gas-fired heater.	Temperature change, pyrolysis reaction
5. *Spray quench tower with heat exchanger.*† Pyrolysis reaction products are cooled to the dew point, 170°C, by contact with a shower of cold liquid dichloroethane. Warm liquid falls to the bottom of the tower and is recirculated through a water-cooled heat exchanger.	Temperature change
6. *Condenser.* Gaseous mixture cooled to its dew point is expanded to a lower pressure and liquefied. Latent heat released by condensation is removed by cooling water.	Phase change, temperature change
7. *Distillation columns.*† See the discussion above.	Separation

*D.B. Benedict, "Process for the Preparation of Olefin Dichlorides," U.S. Patent 2,929,852, March 22, 1960.
†B.F. Goodrich Co., "Preparation of Vinyl Chloride," British Patent 938,824, October 9, 1963.

Task integration

Task integration is the combination of process operations into process units. Figure 3-6 shows one possible solution. Important features of each process unit are summarized in Table 3-5. Notice that both the evaporator and pyrolysis furnace combine two of the operations in Fig. 3-5.

It may seem strange that the pyrolysis reaction products at 500°C are not used, rather than steam, to evaporate liquid $C_2H_4Cl_2$. Two reasons are that (1) hydrogen chloride is corrosive and (2) the carbonaceous reaction products would deposit coke that is difficult and costly to remove from the evaporator tubes.

In summary, a tentative process flow sheet for production of vinyl chloride has been prepared (Fig. 3-6). This particular flow sheet is a direct result of explicit and implicit decisions made in each step of the process synthesis. There are many other practical solutions to the problem, and the selection of the best method is basically an optimization problem.

Physical and Chemical Properties of Substances

4

The basis for design of chemical processing units is the set of physical and chemical properties (boiling point, heat capacity, etc.) of the substances that undergo transformation. These properties are obtained from

1. Direct measurement in the laboratory or pilot plant.
2. Previously published data in the scientific literature.
3. Estimation procedures.

Direct experimental measurements are the most reliable. Published data in the scientific literature are extremely useful but often incomplete and occasionally incorrect. Estimation of data is a last resort when previous data have not been published and new experimental work is considered to be either too costly or too time-consuming.

In principle, it should be possible to calculate properties of substances by applying fundamental laws of physics and chemistry. In practice, molecular properties needed for these calculations (dipole moment, polarizability, interatomic distances, etc.) are often unknown. Even when molecular properties are known, calculations of properties are extremely complicated, particularly for substances in the condensed state. Therefore, engineers have developed methods of combining theory with empiricism to estimate physical and chemical properties of substances. A summary of methods for estimating vapor pressure, heat of vaporization, heat capacity, critical constants, density, thermochemical constants, surface tension, viscosity, thermal conductivity, diffusion coefficients, and other properties of fluids and their mixtures is given in *The Properties of Gases and Liquids.**

*R. C. Reid and T. K. Sherwood, *The Properties of Gases and Liquids*, 2nd ed., McGraw-Hill, New York, 1966.

4.1 Volumetric Properties of Pure Fluids

The relation between pressure (P), molar volume (v), and temperature (T) of a substance is called a PVT equation. For a pure substance there are two independent variables, and the equation may be written in three explicit forms: $P = P\{v, T\}$, $v = v\{P, T\}$, and $T = T\{P, v\}$.

Experimental PVT data

As an example, let us examine the volumetric behavior of pure carbon dioxide. The function $P = P\{v, T\}$, obtained from experimental measurements, is plotted as $P = P\{v\}$ for four values of temperature in Fig. 4-1. The curve for each temperature is called an isotherm.

The dashed curve AGCFB is the boundary of the two-phase region. Any point such as J under this curve consists of two phases: liquid and vapor.

Suppose that pure gaseous carbon dioxide at 0°C is compressed isothermally by immersing it in a bath of melting ice. Starting at point E, the specific

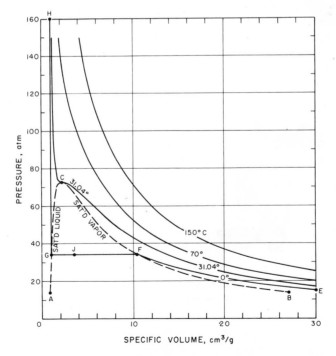

Figure 4-1 Experimental PVT data for carbon dioxide. Dashed line is boundary of two-phase region. (F. Din, *Thermodynamic Functions of Gases*, Vol. 1, Butterworths, London, 1962.)

volume at 15 atm is 30.0 cm³/g. As pressure is increased, specific volume decreases along line EF. At point F the first drop of liquid forms, and the pressure is constant at 34.4 atm as the two-phase mixture is compressed at 0°C. This pressure, 34.4 atm, is called the vapor pressure of carbon dioxide at 0°C. Condensation occurs isothermally and isobarically (constant pressure) along line FG. The intermediate point J, with *overall* specific volume of liquid plus vapor equal to 3.5 cm³/g, consists of two phases: liquid of specific volume 1.1 cm³/g, and vapor of specific volume 10.4 cm³/g. Eventually, compression at 0°C and 34.4 atm proceeds to point G where the last bubble of vapor condenses to liquid. Further decrease of specific volume below 1.1 cm³/g at 0°C requires a large increase of pressure, as indicated by the steepness of the line GH. The liquid, compared to the gas, is nearly incompressible.

Condensation of carbon dioxide along line FG at 0°C and 34.4 atm is accompanied by evolution of its latent heat of condensation, which is 56 cal/g at 0°C (see Example 4.1).

As temperature is increased, the intersection of isotherms with the two-phase region under the curve AGCFB moves upward until a temperature is reached at which the isotherm is tangent to the curve at point C. This isotherm, 31.04°C for carbon dioxide, is the temperature above which it is impossible to obtain a two-phase mixture of liquid plus vapor regardless of the pressure. Notice that the critical isotherm has a horizontal point of inflection (first and second derivatives vanish) at point C. Each pure substance is characterized by its critical properties at point C. For carbon dioxide the critical constants are critical temperature $(T_c) = 31.0°C$, critical pressure $(P_c) = 72.85$ atm, and critical volume $(v_c) = 2.14$ cm³/g.

At the critical point the density and other properties of liquid and vapor become identical and the meniscus separating the two phases disappears. Experimentally the critical point of a substance is located by observing the disappearance of the meniscus when the sample is heated with adjustment of pressure at each temperature so that the sample contains equal volumes of liquid and vapor. Critical constants of several hundred pure substances are given in Table 4.1. The critical temperature is roughly proportional to the boiling point:

$$\frac{\text{critical temperature (°K)}}{\text{normal boiling point (°K)}} = 1.5 \text{ to } 1.74 \tag{4.1}$$

Inspection of Table 4.1 shows that critical pressures of pure substances vary from 2.3 atm for helium to 218 atm for water. There is an interesting relationship between the critical temperature (T_c), critical pressure (P_c), and critical volume (v_c):

$$z_c = \frac{P_c v_c}{R T_c} \simeq 0.27 \tag{4.2}$$

This remarkable relation is a consequence of the principle of corresponding states discussed later in this section. Values of z_c, called the critical compress-

ibility factor, vary from 0.20 for acetic acid to 0.30 for helium, but the value
0.27 applies to a large class of organic substances, as shown in Table 4.1.

Vapor at any of the states lying on dashed curve BC of Fig. 4-1 is called
saturated because it is on the verge of condensing and will do so if heat is
removed. Similarly, liquid at any state on dashed curve AC is called saturated
because it is on the verge of boiling and will do so if heat is added. Vapor to
the right of curve BC is called superheated vapor to emphasize the fact that
it is not on the verge of condensation, and liquid to the left of curve AC is
called subcooled liquid to indicate that it is not on the verge of boiling. The
term fluid applies to states in the region above point C where the distinction
between liquid and vapor vanishes.

Properties of solid carbon dioxide are not shown in Fig. 4-1. Regimes of
pressure and temperature for the existence of all three phases (solid, liquid,
and vapor) are shown in Fig. 4-2. Each two-phase region appears as a curve:
AP for solid + vapor, PD for solid + liquid, and PC for liquid + vapor.
Curve AP is called the vapor pressure of the solid, and curve PC is called the

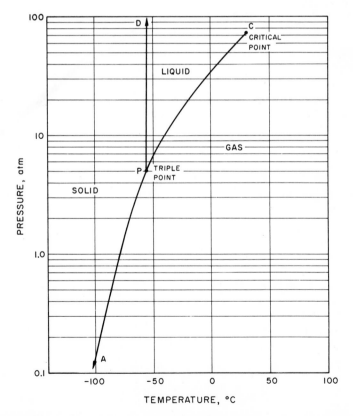

Figure 4-2 *PT* diagram for carbon dioxide. (F. Din, *Thermodynamic
Functions of Gases*, Vol. 1, Butterworths, London, 1962.)

TABLE 4.1
CRITICAL CONSTANTS*

Substance	Molecular weight	Critical temperature, T_c (°K)	Critical pressure, P_c (atm)	Critical density (g/cm³)	Critical volume, v_c (cm³/mole)	Critical compressibility factor, z_c
A. Inert gases						
Helium	4.00	5.3	2.26	0.0693	57.8	0.300
Helium³	3.00	3.34	1.15			
Neon	20.18	44.5	26.9	0.484	41.7	0.307
Argon	39.94	151	48.0	0.531	75.2	0.291
Krypton	83.7	209.4	54.3	0.908	92.2	0.291
Xenon	131.3	289.75	58.0	1.105	118.8	0.290
B. Elementary gases						
Chlorine	70.91	417	76.1	0.573	124	0.276
Bromine	159.83	584	102	1.18	144	0.306
Iodine	253.81	826				
Hydrogen (normal)	2.02	33.3	12.80	0.0310	65.0	0.304
Hydrogen (equilibrium)	2.02	33.0	12.8	0.0326	61.8	0.292
Nitrogen	28.02	126.2	33.5	0.311	90.1	0.291
Oxygen	32.00	154.8	50.1	0.41	78	0.308
Ozone	48.00	268	67	0.537	89.4	0.272
C. Aliphatic hydrocarbons						
1. Paraffins						
Methane	16.04	191.1	45.8	0.162	99.0	0.289
Ethane	30.07	305.5	48.2	0.203	148	0.284
Propane	44.09	370.0	42.0	0.220	200	0.277
n-Butane	58.12	425.2	37.5	0.228	255	0.274
Isobutane	58.12	408.1	36.0	0.221	263	0.283
n-Pentane	72.15	469.8	33.3	0.232	311	0.269

Compound						
Isopentane	72.15	461.0	32.9	0.234	308	0.268
Neopentane	72.15	433.8	31.6	0.238	303	0.269
n-Hexane	86.17	507.9	29.9	0.234	368	0.264
2-Methylpentane	86.17	497.9	29.9	0.235	367	0.268
3-Methylpentane	86.17	504.7	30.8	0.235	367	0.273
2,2-Dimethylbutane	86.17	489.4	30.7	0.240	359	0.274
2,3-Dimethylbutane	86.17	500.3	30.9	0.241	358	0.269
n-Heptane	100.20	540.2	27.0	0.235	426	0.259
2-Methylhexane	100.20	531.1	27.2	0.234	428	0.267
3-Methylhexane	100.20	535.6	28.1	0.240	417	0.267
3-Ethylpentane	100.20	540.8	28.6	0.241	416	0.268
2,2-Dimethylpentane	100.20	520.9	28.4	0.248	404	0.268
2,3-Dimethylpentane	100.20	537.8	29.2	0.247	406	0.269
2,4-Dimethylpentane	100.20	520.3	27.4	0.239	419	0.269
3,3-Dimethylpentane	100.20	536	30			0.269
2,2,3-Trimethylbutane	100.20	531.5	29.75			
n-Octane	114.22	569.4	24.6	0.254	394	0.258
2-Methylheptane	114.22	561	24.8	0.233	490	0.263
3-Methylheptane	114.22	565	25.6	0.234	488	0.264
4-Methylheptane	114.22	563	25.6	0.239	478	0.264
3-Ethylhexane	114.22	567	26.4	0.240	476	0.264
2,2-Dimethylhexane.	114.22	552	25.6	0.245	466	0.263
2,3-Dimethylhexane.	114.22	566	26.6	0.245	466	0.263
2,4-Dimethylhexane.	114.22	555	25.8	0.248	460	0.264
2,5-Dimethylhexane.	114.22	550.0	24.6	0.245	466	0.263
3,3-Dimethylhexane.	114.22	564	27.2	0.237	482	0.264
3,4-Dimethylhexane.	114.22	571	27.4	0.254	450	0.264
3-Ethyl-2-methylpentane	114.22	568	27.4	0.253	451	0.264
3-Ethyl-3-methylpentane.	114.22	578	28.9	0.263	450	0.264
2,2,3-Trimethylpentane	114.22	576	29.0	0.264	434	0.266
2,2,4-Trimethylpentane	114.22	544.1	25.4	0.243	433	0.267
2,3,4-Trimethylpentane	114.22	568	27.6	0.256	470	0.264

TABLE 4.1 (Continued)

Substance	Molecular weight	Critical temperature T_c (°K)	Critical pressure P_c (atm)	Critical density (g/cm³)	Critical volume, v_c (cm³/mole)	Critical compressibility factor, z_c
2,2,3,3-Tetramethylbutane	114.22	544	24.5	0.238	480	0.263
2. Olefins						
Ethylene	28.05	282.4	50.0	0.227	124	0.268
Propene	42.08	365.0	45.6	0.233	181	0.276
1-Butene	56.10	419.6	39.7	0.234	240	0.277
2-Butene	56.10	430	41	0.238	236	0.274
Isobutylene (2-methylpropene)	56.10	417.9	39.5	0.235	239	0.275
1-Pentene	70.13	474	40			
2-Pentene	70.13	475.6	40.4			
Isoamylene	70.13	464.8	33.9			
2-Methyl-2-butene	70.13	470	34			
Hexene	84.16	516.7				
Octene	112.21	578.0				
3. Diolefins						
Propadiene	40.06	393				
1,3-Butadiene	54.09	425	42.7	0.245	221	0.270
1,5-Hexadiene	82.14	507.6				
4. Acetylenes						
Ethyne	26.04	309	61.6	0.231	113	0.274
Propyne	40.06	401	52.8			
Ethylacetylene	54.09	463.7				
Dimethylacetylene	54.09	488.7				
Propylacetylene	68.11	493.5				
D. Cycloparaffins						
Cyclopentane	70.13	511.8	44.6	0.27	260	0.276

Methylcyclopentane	84.16	532.8	37.4	0.264	319	0.273
Ethylcyclopentane	98.18	569.5	33.5	0.262	375	0.269
Cyclohexane	84.16	553	40.0	0.273	308	0.272
Methylcyclohexane	98.18	572.3	34.32	0.285	344	0.251
E. Aromatic hydrocarbons						
Benzene	78.11	562	48.6	0.300	260	0.274
Toluene	92.13	594.0	41.6	0.29	320	0.273
o-Xylene	106.16	631.6	36.9			
m-Xylene	106.16	619	36			
p-Xylene	106.16	618	35			
Ethylbenzene	106.16	619.6	38			
1,2,3-Trimethylbenzene	120.19	668	31	0.28	430	0.243
1,2,4-Trimethylbenzene	120.19	654.4	33	0.28	430	0.264
1,3,5-Trimethylbenzene	120.19	641	33	0.28	430	0.270
2-Ethyl-1-methylbenzene	120.19	653	31	0.28	430	0.249
3-Ethyl-1-methylbenzene	120.19	636	31	0.28	430	0.255
4-Ethyl-1-methylbenzene	120.19	636	31	0.28	430	0.255
Propylbenzene	120.19	638.8	32	0.28	430	0.262
Isopropylbenzene	120.19	635.9	32	0.28	430	0.264
Cymene	134.21	658				
Isobutylbenzene	134.21	650	31			
F. Substituted aromatic compounds						
Fluorobenzene	96.10	559.8	44.6	0.354	271	0.263
Chlorobenzene	112.56	632.4	44.6	0.365	308	0.265
Bromobenzene	157.02	670	44.6	0.458	343	0.278
Iodobenzene	204.02	721	44.6	0.581	351	0.265
Phenol	94.11	692.4	60.5			
o-Cresol	108.13	695	49.4			
m-Cresol	108.13	705	45.0	0.35	310	0.241
p-Cresol	108.13	699	50.8			
Aniline	93.12	698.8	52.3	0.340	274	0.250
Methylaniline	107.15	701.6	51.3			

TABLE 4.1 (Continued)

Substance	Molecular weight	Critical temperature, T_c (°K)	Critical pressure, P_c (atm)	Critical density (g/cm³)	Critical volume, v_c (cm³/mole)	Critical compressibility factor, z_c
Dimethylaniline	121.18	687.9	35.8			
G. Alcohols						
Methyl alcohol	32.04	513.2	78.5	0.272	118	0.220
Ethyl alcohol	46.07	516	63.0	0.276	167	0.248
n-Propyl alcohol	60.09	537	50.2	0.273	220	0.251
Isopropyl alcohol	60.09	508.8	53	0.274	219	0.278
n-Butyl alcohol	74.12	561	49			
sec-Butyl alcohol	74.12	538				
tert-Butyl alcohol	74.12	508				
H. Ethers						
Dimethyl ether	46.07	400.1	53	0.242	190	0.307
Ethyl methyl ether	60.09	437.9	43.4	0.272	221	0.267
Diethyl ether	74.12	467	35.6	0.264	281	0.261
Ethyl propyl ether	88.15	500.6	32.1	0.260	339	0.265
Dioxane	88.10	585	50.7	0.36	240	0.253
I. Ketones						
Acetone	58.08	508.7	46.6	0.273	213	0.238
Ethyl methyl ketone	72.10	533	39.5	0.25	290	0.262
J.						
Acetaldehyde	44.05	461				
K. Organic acids						
Acetic acid	60.05	594.8	57.1	0.351	171	0.200
Acetic anhydride	102.09	569	46.2			
Propionic acid	74.08	612	53	0.32	230	0.243
n-Butyric acid	88.10	628	52	0.304	290	0.293
Isobutyric acid	88.10	609	40	0.302	292	0.234

n-Valeric acid	102.13	651				
Isovaleric acid	102.13	634				
L. Esters						
Methyl formate	60.05	487.2	59.2	0.349	172	0.254
Ethyl formate	74.08	508.5	46.8	0.323	229	0.257
Propyl formate	88.10	538.1	40.1	0.309	285	0.259
Isobutyl formate	102.13	551.4	38.3			
Methyl acetate	74.08	506.9	46.3	0.325	228	0.254
Ethyl acetate	88.10	523.3	37.8	0.308	286	0.252
n-Propyl acetate	102.13	549.4	32.9	0.296	345	0.252
Methyl butyrate	102.13	554.5	34.3	0.300	340	0.256
Methyl isobutyrate	102.13	540.8	33.9	0.301	339	0.259
Ethyl isobutyrate	116.16	553	30	0.276	421	0.278
M. Nitrogen compounds						
Ammonia	17.03	405.5	111.3	0.235	72.5	0.242
Hydrazine	32.05	653	145			
Cyanogen	52.02	400	59			
Hydrogen cyanide	27.03	456.7	53.2	0.195	139	0.197
Methylamine	31.06	430.1	73.6			
Dimethylamine	45.08	437.7	52.4			
Trimethylamine	59.11	433.3	40.2	0.233	254	0.287
Ethylamine	45.08	456	55.5			
Diethylamine	73.14	496	36.6			
Triethylamine	101.19	532	30			
Propylamine	59.11	507.0	46.8			
Dipropylamine	101.19	550	31			
Acetonitrile	41.05	547.9	47.7	0.237	173	0.184
Propionitrile	55.08	564.4	41.3	0.240	230	0.205
Butyronitrile	69.10	582.3	37.4			
Capronitrile	125.21	622.0	32.1			
Benzonitrile	103.12	699.4	41.6			

TABLE 4.1 (Continued)

Substance	Molecular weight	Critical temperature, T_c (°K)	Critical pressure, P_c (atm)	Critical density (g/cm³)	Critical volume, v_c (cm³/mole)	Critical compressibility factor, z_c
N. Inorganic halides						
Hydrogen fluoride	20.01	503.4	81.5	0.42	48	0.147
Hydrogen chloride	36.47	324.6	84.0			
Hydrogen bromide	80.92	363.2	81			
Hydrogen iodide	127.93	423				
Boron trifluoride	67.82	260.9	49.2			
Boron trichloride	117.19	452.0	38.2			
Boron tribromide	250.57	573		0.90	280	
Phosgene	98.92	455	56	0.52	190	0.285
Germanium tetrachloride	214.43	550.1	38			
Silicon tetrafluoride	104.06	259.1	36.7			
Chlorotrifluorosilane	120.52	307.7	34.2			
Dichlorodifluorosilane	136.97	369.0	34.5			
Trichlorofluorosilane	153.43	438.5	35.3			
Silicon tetrachloride	169.89	506				
Stannic chloride	260.53	591.9	37.0	0.742	351	0.267
Sulfur hexafluoride	146.06	318.71	37.11	0.752	194	0.275
O. Aliphatic organic halides						
Methyl fluoride	34.03	317.8	58.0	0.300	113	0.251
Methyl chloride	50.49	416.3	65.9	0.353	143	0.276
Methyl bromide	94.95	464				
Methyl iodide	141.95	528				
Methylene chloride	84.94	510	60			
Chloroform	119.39	536.6	54	0.50	240	0.294

Carbon tetrachloride	153.84	556.4	45.0	0.558	276	0.272
Ethyl fluoride	48.06	375.4	46.6			
Ethyl chloride	64.52	460.4	52	0.507	215	0.320
Ethyl bromide	108.98	503.9	61.5	0.44	220	0.253
1,1-Dichloroethane	98.97	523	50			
1,2-Dichloroethane	98.97	561	53			
Dibromomethane	173.86	583.0	70.6			
Chlorodifluoromethane	86.48	369.6	48.5	0.525	165	0.264
Dichlorofluoromethane	102.93	451.7	51.0	0.522	197	0.271
Chlorotrifluoromethane	104.47	302.0	39	0.58	180	0.283
Dichlorodifluoromethane (Freon 12)	120.92	384.7	39.6	0.555	218	0.273
Trichlorofluoromethane (Freon 11)	137.38	471.2	43.2	0.554	248	0.277
Chlorotrifluoroethylene	116.48	379	40	0.55	210	0.270
Dichlorotetrafluoroethane	170.93	418.9	32.3			
Trichlorotrifluoroethane (Freon 113)	187.39	487.3	33.7	0.576	325	0.274
Perfluoro-n-butane	238.04	386.5	23			
Perfluoro-n-heptane	388.07	474.8	16.0	0.584	664	0.273
Perfluoromethylcyclohexane	350.07	486.6	24			
P. Oxides						
Carbon dioxide	44.01	304.2	72.9	0.468	94.0	0.274
Carbon monoxide	28.01	133	34.5	0.301	93.1	0.294
Ethylene oxide	44.05	468	71.0	0.32	138	0.255
Nitrous oxide	44.02	309.7	71.7	0.457	96.3	0.272
Nitric oxide	30.01	180	64	0.52	58	0.251
Nitrogen peroxide	46.01	431	100	0.56	82	0.232
Sulfur dioxide	64.06	430.7	77.8	0.524	122	0.268
Sulfur trioxide	80.06	491.4	83.8	0.633	126	0.262
Water	18.02	647.4	218.3	0.32	56	0.230

TABLE 4.1 (Continued)

Substance	Molecular weight	Critical temperature, T_c (°K)	Critical pressure, P_c (atm)	Critical density (g/cm^3)	Critical volume, v_c (cm^3/mole)	Critical compressibility factor, z_c
Q. Sulfur and sulfides						
Sulfur................	32.06	1313	116			
Carbonyl sulfide.....	60.07	378	61			
Carbon disulfide.....	76.13	552	78	0.44	170	0.293
Hydrogen selenide ...	81.22	411	88			
Hydrogen sulfide.....	34.08	373.6	88.9	0.349	97.7	0.283
Methyl sulfide	62.13	503.1	54.6	0.309	201	0.266
Ethyl mercaptan	62.13	499	54.2	0.300	207	0.274
Ethyl sulfide........	90.18	557	39.1	0.279	323	0.276
R. Miscellaneous compounds						
Phosphine............	34.00	324.5	64.5			
Phosphonium chloride .	70.47	322.3	72.7			
Pyridine	79.10	617.4	60.0			
Silane	32.09	269.7	47.8			
Thiophene	84.13	590	48			
Nitromethane	61.04	588	62.3	0.352	173	0.223

*From K. A. Kobe and R. E. Lynn, Jr., "The Critical Properties of Elements and Compounds," *Chem. Rev. 52*, 117 (1953).

vapor pressure of the liquid. Although it may not be apparent in Fig. 4-2, curves AP and PC intersect at point P with different slopes; the slope of the vapor pressure curve for the solid is always steeper than that for the liquid. Curve PD, which shows the variation of the melting point with pressure, has a positive slope of 48 atm/°K (see Example 4.2) that appears to be vertical in Fig. 4-2. The three curves intersect at the triple point where all three phases can exist simultaneously. The triple point of carbon dioxide is at $-56.6°C$ and 5.11 atm; for water it is 0.01°C and 0.0060 atm. Carbon dioxide has the peculiarity that its triple-point pressure is above atmospheric pressure. Therefore, solid carbon dioxide, if heated at atmospheric pressure, sublimes without melting (at $-78°C$). For most substances, the triple-point pressure is less than 1 atm, and there exists a normal melting point at which the solid melts under atmospheric pressure.

The slopes of all three curves in Fig. 4-2 obey the Clapeyron equation,

$$\frac{dP}{dT} = \frac{\Delta h}{T \, \Delta v} \tag{4.3}$$

where Δh and Δv are latent heat and volume change, respectively, for transformation from one state to another. For curve PD, Δh is the heat of fusion of the solid and Δv is the change in volume upon melting. Both Δh and Δv refer to the same amount (e.g., 1 g or 1 mole). For curve AP, Δh is the heat of sublimation of the solid and Δv is the change in volume upon sublimation. For curve PC, Δh is the heat of vaporization of the liquid and Δv is the change in volume upon vaporization. Equation (4.3) is a rigorous equation describing change in pressure with temperature for any combination of two phases of the same pure substance.

Example 4.1

Calculate the latent heat of vaporization of liquid carbon dioxide at 0°C using the Clapeyron equation.

Solution:

From Fig. 4-2, the slope of the vapor pressure curve PC at 0°C is 0.91 atm/°K. From Fig. 4-1, specific volumes of liquid and vapor are 1.08 and 10.38 cm³/g, respectively. From Eqn. (4.3),

$$\Delta h = T \Delta v \frac{dP}{dT} = (273.15)(10.38 - 1.08)(0.91)(°K)\left(\frac{cm^3}{g}\right)\left(\frac{atm}{°K}\right)\left(\frac{0.0242 \, cal}{cm^3\text{-}atm}\right)$$

$$= 56 \, cal/g$$

Example 4.2

What does the Clapeyron equation predict for the slope of curve PD in Fig. 4-2?

Solution:

At the triple point ($-56.6°C$), the latent heat of fusion of solid carbon dioxide is 47.54 cal/g, and the specific volumes of solid and liquid are 0.661 and 0.849 cm^3/g, respectively.* Therefore,

$$\frac{dP}{dT} = \frac{\Delta h}{T \Delta v} = \frac{(47.54)}{(216.55)(0.849 - 0.661)} \frac{(cal/g)}{(°K)(cm^3/g)} \left(\frac{cm^3\text{-atm}}{0.0242 \text{ cal}} \right)$$

$$= 48 \text{ atm/°K}$$

For curves AP and PC in Fig. 4-2, the Clapeyron equation may be integrated if two assumptions are made:

1. The pressure is low so that the vapor obeys the perfect gas law. This assumption is better for curve AP than for curve PC and breaks down as the critical point C is approached.
2. Δh, heat of sublimation for curve AP and heat of vaporization for curve PC, is a constant.

It is apparent from Fig. 4-1 that at low pressure the volume in the condensed state (solid or liquid) is negligible compared to the volume of the vapor. Therefore,

$$\Delta v = v^{gas} - v^{condensed} \simeq v^{gas} = \frac{RT}{P} \tag{4.4}$$

Δv in Eqn. (4.4) is the change in molar volume due to sublimation or vaporization. Substituting Eqn. (4.4) in (4.3),

$$d \ln P^s = \frac{\Delta h}{RT^2} dT \tag{4.5}$$

Integration of Eqn. (4.5) using assumption 2 gives

$$\ln P^s = -\frac{\Delta h}{RT} + B \tag{4.6}$$

where P^s means vapor pressure of solid or liquid and B is an integration constant. Actually, neither of the assumptions leading to Eqn. (4.6) is very good. Both heat of fusion and heat of vaporization are functions of temperature, and heat of vaporization is zero at the critical point. Nevertheless the formula

$$\ln P^s = -\frac{A}{T} + B \tag{4.7}$$

based upon Eqn. (4.6) but used with empirical constants A and B, fits vapor pressure data with reasonable accuracy. The reason is a cancellation of errors in the two assumptions, neither of which is very good by itself.

For example, for $A = 1997°K$, $B = 10.853$, T in $°K$, and P^s in atmospheres, Eqn. (4.7) reproduces curve PC in Fig. 4-2 within $\pm 1\%$ from the triple point to the critical point of carbon dioxide.

---

*F. Din, *Thermodynamic Functions of Gases*, Vol. 1, Butterworths, London, 1962.

Use of the two-parameter equation (4.7) for interpolation of vapor pressures is discussed in Ch. 5. For wide ranges of temperature and high accuracy, a three-parameter equation is needed.*

A few of the most important theories and equations of state for fluids are examined next.

Perfect gas law

Many theories of fluids have been proposed. Of these, the simplest is the theory of perfect gases (see Ch. 1). Molecules are assumed to be point centers of mass that collide with the walls of the container, and therefore exert a pressure, but that neither attract nor repel one another. The PVT equation of state for a perfect gas is

$$Pv = RT \qquad\qquad (4.8)$$

Three isotherms calculated by Eqn. (4.8) are shown in Fig. 4-3. These isotherms should be compared with the real isotherms for carbon dioxide in Fig. 4-1. For high temperature and low pressure the agreement is good; at low tempera-

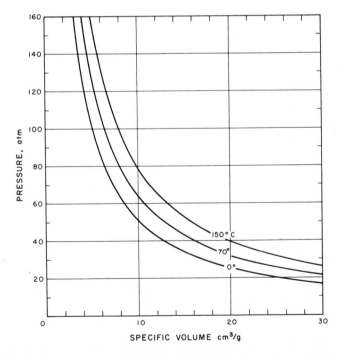

Figure 4-3 Isotherms calculated for carbon dioxide using the perfect gas law.

*R. C. Reid and T. K. Sherwood, *The Properties of Gases and Liquids*, 2nd ed., McGraw-Hill, New York, 1966, Ch. 4.

ture and high pressure the agreement is bad. Since the theory of perfect gases does not take into account the forces of attraction between molecules, it does not predict condensation: Compare the 0°C isotherms in Figs. 4-1 and 4-3.

Van der Waals' equation

Johannes van der Waals (1837–1923), a Dutch physicist who was awarded the Nobel Prize in 1910, formulated a theory of the fluid state that is remarkable for its simplicity. Van der Waals' famous equation of state is

$$\left(P + \frac{a}{v^2}\right)(v - b) = RT \tag{4.9}$$

where a and b are constants, different for each gas. Equation (4.9) reduces to Eqn. (4.8) in the limit as v goes to infinity. The equation takes into account two major characteristics of molecular interactions: Molecules attract one another (with force proportional to a), and molecules have finite volume (proportional to b).

The constants a and b can be calculated from critical properties. At the critical point there is a horizontal point of inflection (see Fig. 4-1) so that

$$\left[\frac{\partial P}{\partial v}\right]_{T_c} = 0 = \frac{-RT_c}{(v_c - b)^2} + \frac{2a}{v_c^3} \tag{4.10}$$

$$\left[\frac{\partial^2 P}{\partial v^2}\right]_{T_c} = 0 = \frac{2RT_c}{(v_c - b)^3} - \frac{6a}{v_c^4} \tag{4.11}$$

Equations (4.10) and (4.11) may be solved for a and b in terms of P_c, v_c, and T_c. If Eqn. (4.9) evaluated at the critical point is combined with (4.10) and (4.11), a and b can be expressed in terms of any pair of the critical properties P_c, v_c, and T_c:

$$a = 3P_c v_c^2 = \frac{9}{8}RT_c v_c = \frac{27R^2 T_c^2}{64P_c} \tag{4.12}$$

$$b = \frac{v_c}{3} = \frac{RT_c}{8P_c} \tag{4.13}$$

Example 4.3

Calculate the pressure needed to compress carbon dioxide gas to a density of 0.08 g/cm³ at 0°C. Use van der Waals' equation.

Solution:

P_c and T_c are chosen as the pair of critical constants for calculating values of a and b. From Table 4.1 and Eqns. (4.12) and (4.13),

$$a = \frac{27R^2 T_c^2}{64P_c} = \frac{(27)(82.06)^2(304.2)^2}{(64)(72.9)} = 3.60 \times 10^6 \text{ atm}\left(\frac{cm^3}{gmole}\right)^2$$

$$b = \frac{RT_c}{8P_c} = \frac{(82.06)(304.2)}{(8)(72.9)} = 42.8 \frac{cm^3}{gmole}$$

molar volume $= \dfrac{1}{0.08} = 12.5 \text{ cm}^3/\text{g} = 550.1 \text{ cm}^3/\text{gmole}$

van der Waals' equation can be solved explicitly for pressure:

$$P = \frac{RT}{v - b} - \frac{a}{v^2} = \frac{(82.06)(273.15)}{550.1 - 42.8} - \frac{3.60 \times 10^6}{(550.1)^2}$$

$$= 44.18 - 11.90 = 32.3 \text{ atm}$$

The experimental value* is 30.5 atm.

Four complete isotherms for carbon dioxide calculated from T_c and P_c in the same manner as in Example 4.3 are plotted in Fig. 4-4. It is instructive to compare the calculated isotherms with the real isotherms in Fig. 4-1. Since values of critical pressure and critical temperature are experimental, the test of van der Waals' equation is its ability to predict specific volume. The actual critical volume of carbon dioxide (Fig. 4-1) is 2.14 cm³/g, and the calculated value (Fig. 4-4) is 2.92 cm³/g, an error of almost 40%.

The inaccuracy of van der Waals' equation is apparent from the value that it predicts for the critical compressibility factor. From Eqn. (4.12),

$$z_c = \frac{P_c v_c}{RT_c} = \frac{a/3v_c}{8a/9v_c} = \frac{3}{8} = 0.375$$

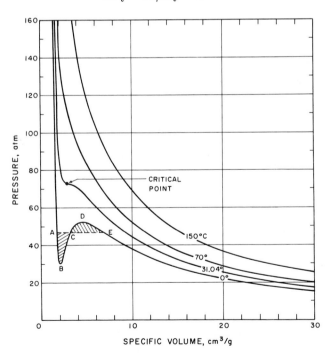

Figure 4-4 PVT behavior of carbon dioxide predicted by van der Waals' equation.

*F. Din, *Thermodynamic Functions of Gases*, Vol. 1, Butterworths, London, 1962.

Inspection of Table 4.1 shows that the predicted value of z_c is about 40% larger than the typical experimental value of 0.27.

Figure 4-4 shows a loop in the 0°C isotherm predicted for carbon dioxide. There are three values of volume (A, C, and E) corresponding to each pressure because van der Waals' equation is cubic in volume. Observe that on the isotherm path BCD, van der Waals' equation predicts that pressure increases as volume increases! A fluid behaving in this manner, if it existed, would be highly unstable. The homogeneous, unstable fluid would condense to a stable mixture of liquid and vapor. It can be shown* that the stable equilibrium state corresponds to a horizontal line ACE drawn so that area ABC = area CDE.

After removal of the unstable loop in the 0°C isotherm, the vapor pressure predicted by van der Waals' equation (horizontal line AE) is 47 atm. This is an error of nearly 40%; the experimental value of vapor pressure at 0°C is 34.4 atm.

Study of Figs. 4-1, 4-3, and 4-4 leads to the conclusion that van der Waals' equation is a considerable improvement over the perfect gas law because it predicts liquefaction. However, van der Waals' equation is only qualitatively correct: Errors for predicted properties in the liquid state (density, vapor pressure) are of the order of 50%.

Redlich-Kwong equation

The Redlich-Kwong equation,† an empirical modification of van der Waals' equation, is

$$\left[P + \frac{a}{T^{1/2} v(v + b)} \right][v - b] = RT \tag{4.14}$$

Like van der Waals' equation, the Redlich-Kwong equation has two constants, a and b. Using as before the fact that the critical point is a horizontal point of inflection, it is found that

$$a = \frac{0.4278 \, R^2 T_c^{2.5}}{P_c} \tag{4.15}$$

$$b = \frac{0.0867 \, R T_c}{P_c} \tag{4.16}$$

Example 4.4

Repeat the calculation in Example 4.3, but use the Redlich-Kwong equation instead of van der Waals' equation.

---

*I. Prigogine, R. Defay, and D. H. Everett, *Chemical Thermodynamics*, Longmans, Green & Co. Ltd., London, 1954, p. 229.

†O. Redlich and J. N. S. Kwong, "On the Thermodynamics of Solutions. V. An Equation of State for Fugacities of Gaseous Solutions," *Chem. Rev.*, *44*, 233 (1949).

Solution:

The constants of the Redlich-Kwong equation for carbon dioxide are

$$a = \frac{(0.4278)R^2 T_c^{2.5}}{P_c} = \frac{(0.4278)(82.06)^2(304.2)^{2.5}}{(72.9)}$$

$$= 6.377 \times 10^7 \text{ atm-}^\circ\text{K}^{0.5}\left(\frac{cm^3}{gmole}\right)^2$$

$$b = \frac{(0.0867)RT_c}{P_c} = \frac{(0.0867)(82.06)(304.2)}{(72.9)} = 29.7 \text{ cm}^3/\text{gmole}$$

From Eqn. (4.14),

$$P = \frac{RT}{v - b} - \frac{a}{T^{0.5}v(v + b)}$$

$$= \frac{(82.06)(273.15)}{550.1 - 29.7} - \frac{6.377 \times 10^7}{(273.15)^{0.5}(550.1)(550.1 + 29.7)}$$

$$= 43.07 - 12.10$$

$$= 31.0 \text{ atm}$$

Agreement with experiment (30.5 atm) is somewhat better than for van der Waals' equation.

Four isotherms for carbon dioxide calculated using Eqns. (4.14)–(4.16) are shown in Fig. 4-5. The Redlich-Kwong equation, like van der Waals'

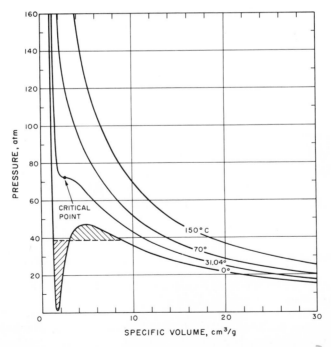

Figure 4-5 PVT behavior of carbon dioxide predicted by Redlich-Kwong equation.

equation, is cubic in volume and gives the same kind of loop in the two-phase region of liquid and vapor. Corrected for instability using the equal-area rule as shown in Fig. 4-5, the Redlich-Kwong equation predicts a vapor pressure of 39 atm at 0°C; the experimental value is 34.4 atm, and therefore the error is 13%.

The critical volume of carbon dioxide is 2.14 cm³/g, whereas the value predicted by the Redlich-Kwong equation is 2.59 cm³/g, an error of 21%.

In summary, the Redlich-Kwong equation is more accurate than van der Waals' equation, but the error in calculated volumetric properties is about 20% in the critical region.

Virial equation for gases

Van der Waals' theory agrees qualitatively with experiment but is still crude in the sense that it does not show how the constants (a and b) are related to intermolecular forces. The virial equation of state is based upon molecular collisions in groups of 2, 3, 4, . . . , shown in Eqn. (4.17) and Fig. 4-6.

$$\frac{Pv}{RT} = 1 + \frac{B\{T\}}{v} + \frac{C\{T\}}{v^2} + \frac{D\{T\}}{v^3} + \cdots \tag{4.17}$$

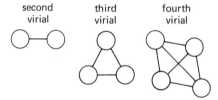

second virial   third virial   fourth virial

Figure 4-6

Notice that the virial equation reduces to the perfect gas law in the limit as volume goes to infinity. B is called the second virial coefficient, C is called the third virial coefficient, etc. B, C, D, . . . are functions of temperature alone. Each virial coefficient is related to intermolecular potential energies in terms of explicit *collision integrals*. The collision integral for B is

$$B\{T\} = 2\pi N_A \int_0^\infty [1 - e^{-\Gamma\{r\}/kT}]r^2 \, dr \tag{4.18}$$

where $\Gamma\{r\}$ is the intermolecular potential energy of a pair of molecules as a function of the distance r between molecular centers, k is the Boltzmann constant, and N_A is Avogadro's number.

For example, $\Gamma\{r\}$ is plotted in Fig. 4-7 for interactions of carbon dioxide molecules in pairs. Since carbon dioxide molecules have a cylindrical shape, the energy depends on their mutual orientation. The intermolecular-potential

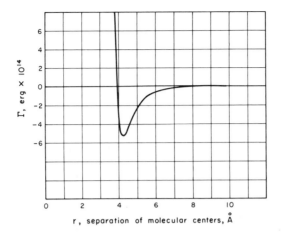

Figure 4-7 Intermolecular potential energy for pairwise interactions of carbon dioxide molecules.

curve plotted in Fig. 4-7 is an average over all possible orientations. The slope of the curve, $d\Gamma/dr$, is the force of attraction between a molecular pair. At distances of 10 Å, the force of attraction is almost negligible. At 5 Å the force of attraction is very strong, and at 4 Å there is a very strong repulsion ($d\Gamma/dr$ negative). In between at the point where the slope is equal to zero, forces of attraction and repulsion exactly balance.

The intermolecular potential energy $\Gamma\{r\}$ is obtained from theories of intermolecular forces or from molecular beam experiments. Calculation of virial coefficients from potential energy functions is discussed in *Molecular Theory of Gases and Liquids*.* Substitution of an equation for $\Gamma\{r\}$ into Eqn. (4.18) followed by integration over r yields the second virial coefficient $B\{T\}$ of carbon dioxide, shown in Fig. 4-8.†

An empirical equation, (4.29), for calculating the second virial coefficient is given in the next section. A method for calculating virial coefficients from experimental *PVT* data is described in Examples 5.3 and 5.4.

The virial equation can be made as accurate as desired for gases by including more terms in Eqn. (4.17). The virial equation terminated after B by setting all higher-order terms equal to zero is particularly useful for calculating properties of vapors. Unfortunately the virial equation does not predict condensation and therefore cannot be used to calculate properties of liquids.

*J. O. Hirschfelder, C. F. Curtiss, and R. B. Bird, *Molecular Theory of Gases and Liquids*, Wiley, New York, 1954.

†J. M. Prausnitz and A. L. Myers, "Kihara Parameters and Second Virial Coefficients for Cryogenic Fluids and their Mixtures," *A.I.Ch.E. J.*, *9*, 5 (1963).

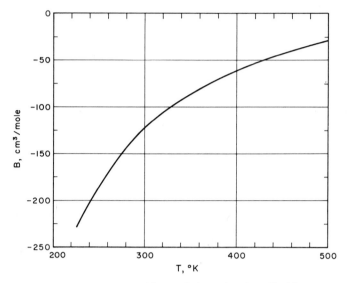

Figure 4-8 Second virial coefficient of carbon dioxide.

Example 4.5

Repeat the calculation in Example 4.3, but use the virial equation terminated after B instead of van der Waals' equation.

Solution:

The problem is to calculate the pressure exerted by carbon dioxide at 0°C and at a density of 0.08 g/cm³ (molar volume = 550.1 cm³/mole). The second virial coefficient of carbon dioxide at 0°C (from Fig. 4-8) is −151 cm³/mole. From Eqn. (4.17),

$$P = \frac{RT}{v}\left(1 + \frac{B}{v}\right) = \frac{(82.06)(273.15)}{(550.1)}\left(1 - \frac{151}{550.1}\right) = 29.6 \text{ atm}$$

The experimental value is 30.5 atm.

Each additional coefficient in Eqn. (4.17) extends the range of applicability to a higher pressure. For example, Fig. 4-9 shows the pressure of carbon dioxide as a function of its specific volume at 40°C. Since the temperature is above the critical temperature, there is no liquefaction and the virial equation applies if enough terms are included. The one-term series (i.e., the perfect gas law, $B = C = D = \cdots = 0$) begins to show substantial error at 20 atm. The two-term series terminated after the second virial coefficient ($C = D = \cdots = 0$) begins to exhibit appreciable error at about 50 atm.

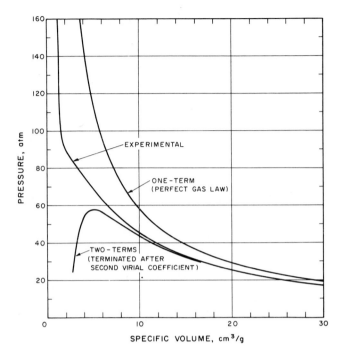

Figure 4-9 Comparison of virial equation with 40°C isotherm of carbon dioxide.

More accurate equations of state

The failure of two-constant equations of state, such as those of van der Waals and Redlich-Kwong, to give good agreement with experimental *PVT* data has instigated the development of more accurate equations. Although these equations are more accurate, they are complicated and contain a large number of constants that must be determined for each substance. A typical equation of this type is the Benedict-Webb-Rubin equation, which contains eight constants:

$$\frac{Pv}{RT} = 1 + \frac{(B_0 - A_0/RT - C_0/RT^3)}{v} + \frac{(b - a/RT)}{v^2} + \frac{a\alpha}{RTv^5}$$
$$+ \frac{c(1 + \gamma/v^2)}{RT^3 v^2} e^{-\gamma/v^2} \tag{4.19}$$

Values of the constants may be estimated* from experimental critical constants:

*J. Joffe, "Prediction of P-V-T Properties of Gases from Critical Data," *Chem. Eng. Progr.*, *45* (No. 2), 160 (1949).

$$A_0 = 0.31315 \frac{R^2 T_c^2}{P_c}$$

$$B_0 = 0.13464 \frac{RT_c}{P_c}$$

$$C_0 = 0.1692 \frac{R^2 T_c^4}{P_c}$$

$$a = 0.059748 \frac{R^3 T_c^3}{P_c^2}$$

$$b = 0.04307 \frac{R^2 T_c^2}{P_c^2}$$ (4.20)

$$c = 0.059416 \frac{R^3 T_c^5}{P_c^2}$$

$$\alpha = 0.0016081 \frac{R^3 T_c^3}{P_c^3}$$

$$\gamma = 0.042113 \frac{R^2 T_c^2}{P_c^2}$$

These equations should be used only for substances whose critical compressibility factor (z_c) is equal to about 0.27 (see Table 4.1).

Example 4.6

Calculate the pressure exerted by gaseous propane at a density of 5 mole/liter and at 400°K using the Benedict-Webb-Rubin equation; compare with the experimental value of 66.4 atm.

Solution:

The eight constants for propane are calculated from Eqn. (4.20) using $R = 0.08206$ liter-atm/mole-°K and critical constants from Table 4.1: $T_c = 370°K$ and $P_c = 42$ atm. The values are

$$A_0 = 6.8727$$
$$B_0 = 0.09733$$
$$C_0 = 5.0837 \times 10^5$$
$$a = 0.9479$$
$$b = 0.0225$$
$$c = 1.29 \times 10^5$$
$$\alpha = 6.074 \times 10^{-4}$$
$$\gamma = 0.0220$$

The units of these constants give P in atmospheres for v in liters per mole and T in °K.

Substituting in Eqn. (4.19),

$$\frac{Pv}{RT}$$
$$= 1 + \frac{[(0.09733) - (6.8727)/(0.08206)(400) - (5.0837 \times 10^5)/(0.08206)(400)^3]}{(0.2)}$$
$$+ \frac{[(0.0225) - (0.9479)/(0.08206)(400)]}{(0.2)^2} + \frac{(0.9479)(6.074 \times 10^{-4})}{(0.08206)(400)(0.2)^5}$$
$$+ \frac{(1.29 \times 10^5)[1 + (0.022)/(0.2)^2]}{(0.08206)(400)^3(0.2)^2} e^{-(0.022)/(0.2)^2}$$
$$= 1 - 1.0443 - 0.1595 + 0.0548 + 0.5492$$
$$= 0.4002$$

Therefore,

$$P = \frac{(0.4002)RT}{v} = \frac{(0.4002)(0.08206)(400)}{(0.2)} = 65.7 \text{ atm}$$

The error in the calculated pressure is about 1%.

For equations of this complexity, PVT properties are usually calculated with the aid of a computer.

Principle of corresponding states

None of the PVT equations for pure fluids (van der Waals, Redlich-Kwong, Benedict-Webb-Rubin, and others) is in quantitative agreement with experimental data. The frustration of trying to find a suitable equation led K. S. Pitzer to say[*]: "The failure to find a really satisfactory analytical equation of state arises not from any lack of skill in selecting the appropriate combination of common mathematical functions, but rather from nonexistence of any suitable function. Consequently it is best, in effect, to let nature generate mathematical functions. . . ."

The basic idea is to use experimental PVT data of one substance, or group of substances, to predict PVT properties of other substances. This procedure, which works remarkably well, is called the principle of corresponding states.

The reduced property (I_r) of a property (I) is defined relative to its value at the critical point (I_c) by

$$I_r = \frac{I}{I_c} \tag{4.21}$$

For example, there are reduced temperature ($T_r = T/T_c$), reduced pressure ($P_r = P/P_c$), reduced volume ($v_r = v/v_c$), and reduced density ($\rho_r = \rho/\rho_c$).

[*]G. N. Lewis, M. Randall, K. S. Pitzer, and L. Brewer, *Thermodynamics*, 2nd ed., McGraw-Hill, New York, 1961, Appendix 1.

Two pure substances are said to be in corresponding states when they share the same values of reduced properties.

The principle of corresponding states is that if two reduced properties coincide for any pair of pure fluids, then the other reduced properties will coincide too.

Example 4.7

Use the experimental PVT data for carbon dioxide in Fig. 4-1 and the principle of corresponding states to estimate the density of n-butane at 206.5°C and 40 atm.

Solution:

Critical constants are given in Table 4.1.
The reduced properties of n-butane are

$$T_r = \frac{T}{T_c} = \frac{479.6}{425.2} = 1.128$$

$$P_r = \frac{P}{P_c} = \frac{40}{37.5} = 1.067$$

At the same values of T_r and P_r, for carbon dioxide we have

$$T = T_r T_c = (1.128)(304.2) = 343.13°K = 70°C$$
$$P = P_r P_c = (1.067)(72.9) = 77.8 \text{ atm}$$

At this temperature and pressure, the molar volume of carbon dioxide (from Fig. 4-1) is 5.88 cm³/g = 259 cm³/mole. Therefore, for carbon dioxide

$$v_r = \frac{v}{v_c} = \frac{259}{94} = 2.75$$

According to the principle of corresponding states, the reduced volume of n-butane must be the same. Therefore, for n-butane at 206.5°C and 40 atm,

$$v = v_r v_c = (2.75)(255) = \underline{701 \text{ cm}^3/\text{mole}}$$

The calculated molar volume of n-butane is in quantitative agreement with the experimental value because carbon dioxide and n-butane obey the principle of corresponding states to a very high accuracy.

This example shows that much time could be saved by tabulating the function $v_r = v_r\{T_r, P_r\}$, which, according to the principle of corresponding states, should be the same function for all substances. Instead it is more convenient to tabulate the compressibility factor z defined by

$$z = \frac{Pv}{RT} \tag{4.22}$$

According to Eqn. (4.8), z is unity for a perfect gas. Therefore, the difference between z and unity is a measure of the deviation from the perfect gas law.

The principle of corresponding states may be restated:

$$z = z\{T_r, P_r\} \tag{4.23}$$

is a universal function for all substances. The function of Eqn. (4.23), derived from actual volumetric behavior of pure fluids, has been tabulated by A. L. Lydersen, R. A. Greenkorn, and O. A. Hougen (*University of Wisconsin Engineering Experimental Station Report 4*, Oct. 1955) and is reproduced in Table 4.2. For $P_r < 1$, each column is divided by a horizontal line into two regions: liquid (above the line) and vapor (below the line). Notice that the entry at the top of each column gives the reduced temperature at saturation (T_r^s) and the compressibility factors of saturated gas and saturated liquid.

The values of z tabulated in Table 4.2 are for fluids with $z_c = 0.27$. It was pointed out before (see Table 4.1) that z_c is close to 0.27 for many fluids. Table 4.3 shows that the value of 0.27 applies to many simple, nonpolar, non-hydrogen-bonding molecules. Nevertheless, deviations of the critical compressibility factor from this average value are significant, and, in practical applications of the principle of corresponding states, it is necessary to include z_c as a third parameter such that

$$z = z\{T_r, P_r, z_c\} \qquad (4.24)$$

The value of the compressibility factor (z) at values of z_c other than 0.27 is calculated by

$$z = z_{0.27} + D(z_c - 0.27) \qquad (4.25)$$

If $z_c > 0.27$, $D = D_a$; if $z_c < 0.27$, $D = D_b$.

A graph of the function $z = z\{P_r, T_r\}$ is shown in Fig. 4-10 for gases and vapors with $z_c = 0.27$. The value of z along the envelope for saturated vapors

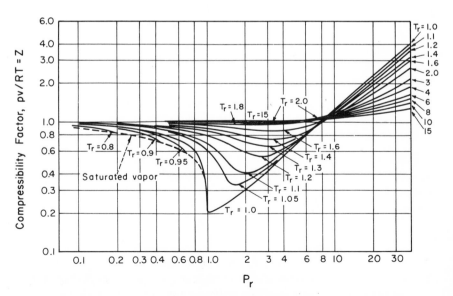

Figure 4-10 Compressibility factors of gases. (J. H. Perry, ed., *Chemical Engineers' Handbook*, 3rd ed., McGraw-Hill, New York, 1950, p. 353.)

TABLE 4.2
COMPRESSIBILITY FACTORS* OF PURE GASES AND LIQUIDS, z

	$P_r = 0.01$			$P_r = 0.05$			$P_r = 0.10$			$P_r = 0.2$			$P_r = 0.3$		
	D_b	z	D_a	D_b	z	D_a	D_b	z	D_a	D_b	z	D_a	D_b	z	D_a
$T_r^s \rightarrow$		0.59			0.690			0.740			0.804			0.847	
z sat. gas $\rightarrow$		0.985			0.942			0.898			0.833			0.783	
z sat. liquid $\rightarrow$		0.002			0.009			0.015			0.030			0.045	
T_r															
0.50	0.01	0.002	0.01	0.05	0.009	0.07	0.11	0.0184	0.14	0.22	0.0367	0.27	0.35	0.0551	0.40
0.60	0.20	0.990	0.02	0.05	0.008	0.07	0.10	0.0164	0.12	0.20	0.0328	0.25	0.31	0.0491	0.37
0.70	0.07	0.992	0.02	0.33	0.943	0.35	0.09	0.0152	0.12	0.19	0.0304	0.23	0.29	0.0456	0.34
0.80	0.01	0.993	0.02	0.13	0.960	0.18	0.28	0.920	0.40	0.18	0.0295	0.20	0.28	0.0441	0.31
0.90	0.01	0.994	0.02	0.07	0.973	0.10	0.14	0.947	0.20	0.28	0.890	0.36	0.44	0.825	0.50
0.92	0.01	0.995	0.02	0.07	0.975	0.10	0.13	0.951	0.19	0.26	0.900	0.34	0.40	0.840	0.47
0.94	0.01	0.995	0.02	0.06	0.977	0.10	0.12	0.954	0.18	0.24	0.908	0.33	0.37	0.854	0.44
0.96	0.01	0.995	0.02	0.05	0.978	0.09	0.11	0.958	0.17	0.22	0.915	0.30	0.33	0.868	0.40
0.98	0.01	0.996	0.02	0.05	0.980	0.09	0.10	0.961	0.16	0.21	0.921	0.28	0.31	0.879	0.37
1.00	0.01	0.996	0.02	0.04	0.982	0.09	0.10	0.964	0.15	0.21	0.927	0.24	0.28	0.889	0.34
1.01	0.01	0.996	0.02	0.04	0.983	0.08	0.10	0.966	0.15	0.20	0.930	0.24	0.26	0.894	0.33
1.02	0.01	0.996	0.02	0.04	0.983	0.08	0.10	0.967	0.15	0.19	0.933	0.23	0.25	0.897	0.34
1.03	0.01	0.996	0.02	0.04	0.984	0.08	0.09	0.968	0.14	0.18	0.935	0.22	0.24	0.902	0.32
1.04	0.01	0.996	0.02	0.04	0.985	0.08	0.09	0.970	0.14	0.18	0.938	0.21	0.24	0.905	0.29

1.05	0.28	0.909	0.23	0.20	0.940	0.17	0.14	0.971	0.08	0.08	0.985	0.04	0.02	0.996	0.00
1.06	0.26	0.913	0.22	0.20	0.942	0.17	0.14	0.972	0.08	0.08	0.986	0.04	0.02	0.996	0.00
1.07	0.25	0.916	0.21	0.19	0.944	0.16	0.14	0.973	0.08	0.07	0.986	0.04	0.02	0.996	0.00
1.08	0.24	0.918	0.20	0.18	0.946	0.16	0.13	0.974	0.08	0.07	0.987	0.04	0.02	0.996	0.00
1.09	0.24	0.922	0.19	0.17	0.948	0.15	0.12	0.975	0.07	0.07	0.987	0.04	0.01	0.997	0.00
1.10	0.21	0.924	0.18	0.17	0.950	0.14	0.12	0.976	0.07	0.07	0.988	0.04	0.01	0.997	0.00
1.12	0.20	0.928	0.17	0.16	0.953	0.13	0.12	0.977	0.06	0.06	0.988	0.04	0.01	0.997	0.00
1.14	0.19	0.933	0.16	0.14	0.956	0.12	0.11	0.979	0.06	0.06	0.989	0.03	0.01	0.997	0.00
1.16	0.16	0.937	0.14	0.13	0.960	0.12	0.09	0.980	0.06	0.05	0.990	0.03	0.01	0.997	0.00
1.18	0.15	0.942	0.12	0.12	0.962	0.12	0.09	0.982	0.06	0.04	0.991	0.03	0.01	0.997	0.00
1.20	0.13	0.945	0.11	0.10	0.965	0.09	0.07	0.983	0.06	0.03	0.991	0.03	0.01	0.998	0.00
1.30	0.10	0.960	0.07	0.08	0.974	0.07	0.05	0.987	0.04	0.02	0.993	0.03	0.01	0.998	0.00
1.40	0.07	0.971	0.06	0.05	0.982	0.05	0.03	0.990	0.03	0.01	0.995	0.02	0.00	0.998	0.00
1.50	0.04	0.980	0.02	0.03	0.986	0.03	0.02	0.991	0.01	0.01	0.995	0.01	0.00	0.999	0.00
1.60	0.02	0.986	0.01	0.02	0.988	0.01	0.00	0.992	0.00	0.00	0.996	0.01	0.00	0.999	0.00
1.70	0.01	0.989	0.00	0.01	0.989	0.00	0.00	0.992	0.00	0.00	0.996	0.00	0.00	0.999	0.00
1.80	0.01	0.991	0.00	0.01	0.991	0.00	0.00	0.993	0.00	0.00	0.996	0.00	0.00	0.999	0.00
1.90	0.00	0.993	0.00	0.00	0.992	0.00	0.00	0.993	0.00	0.00	0.997	0.00	0.00	1.000	0.00
2.00		0.995		0.00	0.994			0.994						1.000	

TABLE 4.2 (Continued)

P_r	0.4	0.5	0.6	0.7	0.8
T_r^s →	0.879	0.909	0.929	0.950	0.967
z sat. gas →	0.738	0.693	0.641	0.583	0.519
z sat. liquid →	0.060	0.077	0.096	0.114	0.136

T_r	$P_r = 0.4$			$P_r = 0.5$			$P_r = 0.6$			$P_r = 0.7$			$P_r = 0.8$		
	D_b	z	D_a	D_b	z	D_a	D_b	z	D_a	D_b	z	D_a	D_b	z	D_a
0.50	0.46	0.0734	0.53	0.57	0.0918	0.66	0.70	0.110	0.81	0.81	0.128	0.95	0.93	0.147	1.07
0.60	0.41	0.0654	0.49	0.52	0.0817	0.60	0.63	0.0980	0.71	0.74	0.113	0.82	0.84	0.130	0.95
0.70	0.39	0.0605	0.45	0.49	0.0758	0.55	0.59	0.0906	0.65	0.69	0.106	0.77	0.79	0.121	0.88
0.80	0.37	0.0588	0.40	0.47	0.0735	0.52	0.57	0.0879	0.62	0.66	0.102	0.73	0.76	0.116	0.85
0.90	0.73	0.763	0.63	0.45	0.0761	0.50	0.55	0.0908	0.60	0.64	0.105	0.71	0.74	0.120	0.82
0.92	0.60	0.783	0.59	0.81	0.710	0.70	0.55	0.0929	0.60	0.65	0.108	0.70	0.74	0.122	0.82
0.94	0.50	0.800	0.55	0.63	0.735	0.64	0.77	0.660	0.73	0.65	0.111	0.70	0.74	0.126	0.82
0.96	0.44	0.817	0.51	0.53	0.760	0.59	0.65	0.700	0.67	0.75	0.613	0.76	0.76	0.133	0.82
0.98	0.39	0.832	0.47	0.46	0.781	0.54	0.54	0.729	0.62	0.62	0.665	0.68	0.70	0.580	0.76
1.00	0.34	0.845	0.42	0.41	0.800	0.48	0.47	0.755	0.54	0.52	0.704	0.60	0.60	0.636	0.65
1.01	0.33	0.852	0.42	0.38	0.809	0.47	0.44	0.765	0.51	0.50	0.718	0.56	0.55	0.659	0.61
1.02	0.30	0.858	0.39	0.36	0.817	0.44	0.41	0.775	0.48	0.45	0.732	0.52	0.50	0.678	0.56
1.03	0.29	0.863	0.37	0.34	0.825	0.42	0.38	0.786	0.46	0.42	0.745	0.50	0.46	0.696	0.54
1.04	0.28	0.869	0.34	0.32	0.832	0.38	0.35	0.794	0.40	0.39	0.755	0.44	0.43	0.710	0.46

1.05	0.27	0.873	0.30	0.30	0.838	0.33	0.33	0.802	0.35	0.36	0.765	0.38	0.39	0.723	0.39
1.06	0.26	0.878	0.29	0.29	0.845	0.32	0.31	0.810	0.33	0.34	0.773	0.35	0.35	0.735	0.36
1.07	0.25	0.883	0.27	0.27	0.850	0.28	0.29	0.817	0.30	0.32	0.781	0.31	0.33	0.745	0.33
1.08	0.24	0.886	0.26	0.26	0.856	0.27	0.28	0.824	0.28	0.30	0.790	0.28	0.31	0.755	0.29
1.09	0.22	0.890	0.25	0.24	0.862	0.25	0.26	0.830	0.25	0.23	0.798	0.25	0.28	0.764	0.25
1.10	0.21	0.894	0.22	0.23	0.867	0.22	0.24	0.836	0.22	0.25	0.805	0.22	0.25	0.773	0.23
1.12	0.19	0.900	0.20	0.21	0.876	0.20	0.21	0.848	0.20	0.22	0.818	0.20	0.22	0.789	0.20
1.14	0.18	0.907	0.20	0.18	0.884	0.20	0.19	0.859	0.20	0.19	0.830	0.20	0.19	0.803	0.20
1.16	0.15	0.913	0.19	0.16	0.891	0.20	0.17	0.868	0.20	0.17	0.842	0.20	0.17	0.816	0.18
1.18	0.13	0.918	0.16	0.14	0.898	0.17	0.15	0.877	0.18	0.15	0.852	0.18	0.15	0.830	0.17
1.20	0.12	0.924	0.15	0.13	0.905	0.15	0.13	0.885	0.15	0.14	0.862	0.14	0.14	0.841	0.15
1.30	0.09	0.944	0.11	0.10	0.931	0.11	0.10	0.916	0.11	0.10	0.900	0.11	0.10	0.888	0.12
1.40	0.06	0.959	0.08	0.07	0.949	0.08	0.07	0.937	0.09	0.07	0.928	0.09	0.07	0.920	0.09
1.50	0.04	0.970	0.05	0.04	0.963	0.06	0.05	0.952	0.07	0.05	0.948	0.07	0.05	0.945	0.07
1.60	0.02	0.978	0.03	0.02	0.973	0.04	0.03	0.965	0.05	0.03	0.964	0.06	0.03	0.960	0.06
1.70	0.01	0.983	0.02	0.01	0.980	0.03	0.02	0.974	0.03	0.02	0.974	0.03	0.02	0.970	0.04
1.80	0.00	0.987	0.02	0.00	0.985	0.02	0.01	0.982	0.02	0.01	0.982	0.02	0.01	0.980	0.02
1.90	0.00	0.991	0.01	0.00	0.989	0.01	0.00	0.987	0.01	0.00	0.987	0.01	0.00	0.987	0.02
2.00	0.00	0.994	0.00	0.00	0.993	0.00	0.00	0.992	0.01	0.00	0.992	0.01	0.00	0.989	0.02

TABLE 4.2 (Continued)

T_r	$P_r = 0.9$			$P_r = 1.0$			$P_r = 1.05$			$P_r = 1.1$			$P_r = 1.2$		
	D_b	z	D_a	D_b	z	D_a	D_b	z	D_a	D_b	z	D_a	D_b	z	D_a
$T_r^s \rightarrow$		0.984			1.000										
z sat. gas $\rightarrow$		0.443			0.270										
z sat. liquid $\rightarrow$		0.164			0.270										
0.50	1.05	0.165	1.20	1.17	0.183	1.35	1.22	0.192	1.40	1.28	0.201	1.48	1.40	0.220	1.62
0.60	0.95	0.147	1.05	1.05	0.163	1.17	1.11	0.171	1.23	1.16	0.179	1.28	1.27	0.195	1.39
0.70	0.90	0.136	0.99	1.00	0.151	1.10	1.05	0.158	1.15	1.10	0.165	1.20	1.20	0.180	1.30
0.80	0.86	0.131	0.95	0.95	0.145	1.05	1.00	0.152	1.10	1.05	0.159	1.15	1.15	0.173	1.25
0.90	0.83	0.134	0.92	0.92	0.148	1.02	0.97	0.155	1.07	1.01	0.162	1.11	1.10	0.176	1.20
0.92	0.83	0.137	0.92	0.92	0.151	1.02	0.97	0.158	1.06	1.01	0.165	1.11	1.10	0.179	1.19
0.94	0.83	0.141	0.92	0.93	0.155	1.01	0.98	0.162	1.06	1.01	0.169	1.10	1.10	0.183	1.18
0.96	0.85	0.147	0.92	0.94	0.161	1.01	0.99	0.169	1.05	1.03	0.176	1.09	1.13	0.189	1.17
0.98	0.87	0.161	0.92	0.97	0.174	1.00	1.02	0.182	1.05	1.07	0.189	1.09	1.16	0.202	1.16
1.00	0.70	0.520	0.82	1.00	0.270	1.00	1.06	0.230	1.05	1.14	0.224	1.09	1.20	0.220	1.15
1.01	0.60	0.568	0.68	0.65	0.424	0.75	0.67	0.365	0.79	0.68	0.256	0.83	0.70	0.242	0.88
1.02	0.55	0.600	0.62	0.58	0.509	0.67	0.59	0.447	0.70	0.60	0.374	0.73	0.60	0.295	0.77
1.03	0.49	0.627	0.57	0.51	0.555	0.60	0.52	0.505	0.62	0.52	0.461	0.63	0.52	0.369	0.66
1.04	0.44	0.642	0.49	0.45	0.585	0.51	0.45	0.546	0.53	0.45	0.505	0.54	0.45	0.422	0.56

1.05	0.46	0.478	0.41	0.45	0.541	0.41	0.44	0.577	0.41	0.43	0.611	0.41	0.41	0.670	0.40
1.06	0.40	0.517	0.38	0.40	0.568	0.38	0.40	0.603	0.38	0.39	0.633	0.38	0.38	0.687	0.37
1.07	0.36	0.548	0.35	0.35	0.594	0.35	0.35	0.627	0.35	0.35	0.654	0.35	0.34	0.700	0.34
1.08	0.30	0.573	0.32	0.30	0.616	0.32	0.30	0.647	0.32	0.30	0.671	0.32	0.29	0.715	0.32
1.09	0.25	0.600	0.28	0.25	0.637	0.28	0.25	0.662	0.28	0.25	0.686	0.28	0.25	0.726	0.28
1.10	0.23	0.620	0.25	0.23	0.655	0.25	0.23	0.678	0.25	0.23	0.700	0.25	0.23	0.738	0.25
1.12	0.21	0.654	0.22	0.21	0.686	0.22	0.21	0.704	0.22	0.21	0.723	0.22	0.21	0.756	0.22
1.14	0.20	0.683	0.19	0.20	0.712	0.19	0.20	0.731	0.19	0.20	0.745	0.19	0.20	0.773	0.19
1.16	0.20	0.707	0.18	0.18	0.735	0.18	0.18	0.750	0.18	0.18	0.764	0.18	0.18	0.790	0.18
1.18	0.18	0.730	0.17	0.17	0.756	0.17	0.17	0.771	0.17	0.17	0.780	0.17	0.17	0.805	0.17
1.20	0.15	0.751	0.15	0.15	0.775	0.15	0.15	0.787	0.15	0.15	0.795	0.15	0.15	0.818	0.15
1.30	0.13	0.827	0.11	0.13	0.841	0.11	0.12	0.849	0.11	0.12	0.857	0.11	0.12	0.874	0.11
1.40	0.10	0.875	0.07	0.10	0.888	0.07	0.10	0.890	0.07	0.10	0.899	0.07	0.10	0.912	0.07
1.50	0.08	0.911	0.05	0.08	0.918	0.05	0.08	0.922	0.05	0.08	0.927	0.05	0.08	0.938	0.05
1.60	0.08	0.935	0.03	0.08	0.940	0.03	0.07	0.944	0.03	0.07	0.948	0.03	0.06	0.955	0.03
1.70	0.07	0.951	0.03	0.06	0.956	0.03	0.05	0.958	0.02	0.05	0.964	0.02	0.04	0.968	0.01
1.80	0.06	0.963	0.02	0.05	0.968	0.02	0.04	0.968	0.00	0.03	0.974	0.00	0.03	0.976	0.00
1.90	0.05	0.974	0.01	0.03	0.978	0.01	0.02	0.978	0.00	0.02	0.983	0.00	0.02	0.985	0.00
2.00	0.03	0.981	0.01	0.03	0.984	0.01	0.02	0.986	0.00	0.02	0.988	0.00	0.02	0.990	

TABLE 4.2 (Continued)

T_r	$P_r = 1.4$ z	$P_r = 1.6$ z	$P_r = 1.8$ z	$P_r = 2.0$ z	$P_r = 4.0$ z	$P_r = 6.0$ z	$P_r = 8.0$ z	$P_r = 10.0$ z	$P_r = 20.0$ z	$P_r = 30.0$ z
0.50	0.256	0.293	0.329	0.365	0.726	1.083	1.439	1.791	3.551	5.28
0.60	0.227	0.259	0.291	0.323	0.640	0.952	1.262	1.568	3.098	4.59
0.70	0.210	0.239	0.268	0.297	0.584	0.862	1.139	1.413	2.769	4.08
0.80	0.201	0.229	0.257	0.284	0.549	0.804	1.056	1.305	2.525	3.70
0.90	0.203	0.230	0.257	0.283	0.532	0.768	1.005	1.233	2.341	3.40
0.92	0.206	0.233	0.259	0.284	0.530	0.763	0.997	1.222	2.310	3.35
0.94	0.210	0.237	0.262	0.287	0.530	0.760	0.991	1.201	2.278	3.30
0.96	0.217	0.242	0.267	0.291	0.531	0.757	0.985	1.202	2.250	3.25
0.98	0.228	0.253	0.276	0.298	0.532	0.755	0.980	1.195	2.224	3.20
1.00	0.234	0.254	0.279	0.306	0.536	0.756	0.975	1.193	2.200	3.15
1.01	0.246	0.262	0.287	0.312	0.538	0.757	0.974	1.188	2.188	3.14
1.02	0.264	0.276	0.296	0.318	0.540	0.758	0.973	1.184	2.175	3.11
1.03	0.288	0.289	0.307	0.326	0.543	0.759	0.972	1.181	2.164	3.08
1.04	0.323	0.305	0.317	0.333	0.546	0.760	0.972	1.177	2.153	3.06
1.05	0.366	0.323	0.332	0.341	0.548	0.761	0.972	1.174	2.142	3.04
1.06	0.403	0.347	0.347	0.351	0.552	0.762	0.971	1.171	2.130	3.02
1.07	0.438	0.370	0.365	0.361	0.554	0.763	0.970	1.168	2.119	3.00
1.08	0.472	0.396	0.380	0.372	0.558	0.764	0.970	1.165	2.109	2.96
1.09	0.507	0.424	0.398	0.386	0.562	0.766	0.970	1.162	2.098	2.95

1.10	0.534	0.455	0.416	0.400	0.565	0.768	0.970	1.160	2.088	2.93
1.12	0.577	0.505	0.454	0.432	0.572	0.772	0.970	1.156	2.068	2.89
1.14	0.615	0.549	0.494	0.466	0.581	0.776	0.970	1.153	2.049	2.85
1.16	0.647	0.588	0.540	0.503	0.589	0.780	0.972	1.151	2.030	2.81
1.18	0.677	0.622	0.583	0.542	0.599	0.786	0.973	1.150	2.013	2.78
1.20	0.705	0.653	0.620	0.573	0.609	0.792	0.975	1.148	1.995	2.74
1.30	0.795	0.768	0.742	0.716	0.687	0.824	0.984	1.144	1.921	2.63
1.40	0.855	0.837	0.819	0.801	0.763	0.863	0.996	1.144	1.862	2.56
1.50	0.894	0.882	0.869	0.852	0.813	0.893	1.012	1.146	1.818	2.49
1.60	0.923	0.914	0.904	0.888	0.852	0.918	1.028	1.150	1.790	2.44
1.70	0.945	0.934	0.929	0.915	0.883	0.940	1.041	1.154	1.767	2.39
1.80	0.960	0.950	0.946	0.935	0.909	0.960	1.052	1.156	1.744	2.33
1.90	0.972	0.965	0.960	0.952	0.932	0.977	1.061	1.158	1.714	2.29
2.00	0.979	0.974	0.971	0.966	0.952	0.993	1.070	1.159	1.691	2.24
3.00	1.000	0.997	0.995	0.986	0.990	1.008	1.068	1.130	1.500	1.84
4.00	1.000	1.000	0.997	0.992	1.000	1.014	1.065	1.120	1.400	1.66
6.00	1.004	1.003	1.000	1.000	1.013	1.024	1.064	1.100	1.300	1.50
8.00	1.008	1.008	1.005	1.005	1.016	1.030	1.063	1.085	1.250	1.40
10.00	1.010	1.010	1.008	1.010	1.020	1.035	1.062	1.080	1.185	1.30
15.00	1.020	1.020	1.020	1.020	1.030	1.045	1.061	1.070	1.140	1.20

*A.L. Lydersen, R. A. Greenkorn, and O. A. Hougen, *University of Wisconsin Experimental Station Report 4*, Oct. 1955.

TABLE 4.3
CRITICAL COMPRESSIBILITY FACTORS

	z_c
Simple, nearly spherical molecules	
Helium	0.300
Argon	0.290
Xenon	0.290
Methane	0.289
Nitrogen	0.291
Carbon monoxide	0.294
Hydrocarbons and small polar molecules	
Ethane	0.284
Propane	0.277
Acetylene	0.274
Cyclohexane	0.272
Isobutane	0.283
Neopentane	0.269
n-Butane	0.274
Benzene	0.274
Carbon dioxide	0.274
n-Pentane	0.269
Toluene	0.273
n-Heptane	0.259
Polar molecules	
Ammonia	0.242
Water	0.230
Methanol	0.220
Ethanol	0.248

is shown by a solid line. Notice that $z < 1$ in the critical region and that $z > 1$ for large values of P_r and T_r.

Example 4.8

Calculate the compressibility factor of acetone at 250°C and 30 atm using the principle of corresponding states.

Solution:

From Table 4.1, for acetone, $T_c = 508.7°K$, $P_c = 46.6$ atm, and $z_c = 0.238$.

$$T_r = \frac{T}{T_c} = \frac{523.15}{508.7} = 1.028$$

$$P_r = \frac{P}{P_c} = \frac{30}{46.6} = 0.644$$

Table 4.2 gives $z_{0.27}$ at

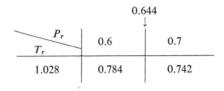

	P_r	0.644↓	
T_r		0.6	0.7
1.028 →	1.02	0.775	0.732
	1.03	0.786	0.745

We interpolate linearly with respect to temperature first:

	P_r	0.644↓	
T_r		0.6	0.7
1.028		0.784	0.742

Linear interpolation with respect to pressure yields

$$z_{0.27} = 0.766$$

Table 4.2 gives D_b at

	P_r	0.644↓	
T_r		0.6	0.7
1.028 →	1.02	0.41	0.45
	1.03	0.38	0.42

Following a similar interpolation procedure,

$$D_b = 0.40$$

The corrected compressibility factor, z, is computed with Eqn. (4.25):

$$z = z_{0.27} + D_b(z_c - 0.27) = 0.766 + 0.40(0.238 - 0.27)$$
$$= 0.766 - 0.013$$
$$= 0.753$$

In summary, the two-parameter principle of corresponding states is that $z = z\{T_r, P_r\}$ is a universal function for all pure substances. The two-parameter principle is only an approximation; introduction of a third parameter improves the correlation. In the tables of Lydersen, Greenkorn, and Hougen the third parameter is z_c so that $z = z\{T_r, P_r, z_c\}$. In the next section we shall discuss another application of the principle of corresponding states in which the third parameter is the so-called acentric factor, ω.

Pitzer's theory of corresponding states

According to the two-parameter theory of corresponding states, the reduced vapor pressure of a pure liquid $P_r^s = P^s/P_c$ should be a universal function of the reduced temperature $T_r = T/T_c$. Figure 4-11 shows that this

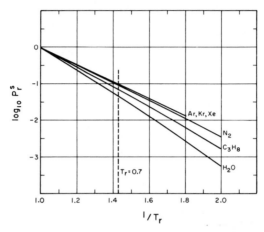

Figure 4-11 Reduced vapor pressure of several liquids.

is true only for monatomic molecules such as Ar, Kr, and Xe; these so-called simple fluids conform to the two-parameter principle of corresponding states. Pitzer et al.* proposed as a third parameter the deviation of the reduced vapor pressure from the value for a simple fluid, ω:

$$\omega = -\log_{10}[P_r^s]_{T_r=0.7} - 1.000 \qquad (4.26)$$

P_r^s in Eqn. (4.26) is the reduced vapor pressure at $T_r = 0.7$. By this definition, the value of ω is approximately zero for Ar, Kr, and Xe. For molecules more complicated than single atoms, there are noncentral forces due to the non-spherical shape of the molecules—hence the name acentric factor. Values of the acentric factor for several substances, calculated using Eqn. (4.26), are listed in Table 4.4.

Example 4.9

Calculate the acentric factor of propane.

Solution:

At $T_r = 0.7$, $T = T_r T_c = (0.7)(370) = 259°K$. At this temperature the vapor pressure of liquid propane is 2.96 atm, so

*K. S. Pitzer, D. Z. Lippmann, R. F. Curl, Jr., C. M. Huggins, and D. E. Petersen, "The Volumetric and Thermodynamic Properties of Fluids," *J. Am. Chem. Soc.*, 77, 3427 (1955).

$$P_r^s = \frac{P^s}{P_c} = \frac{2.96}{42.0} = 0.07048$$

$$\log_{10} P_r^s = -1.152$$

From Eqn. (4.26),

$$\omega = -(-1.152) - 1 = 0.152$$

TABLE 4.4
ACENTRIC FACTORS, ω

	ω
Simple, nearly spherical molecules	
Argon	-0.002
Xenon	0.002
Methane	0.013
Oxygen	0.021
Nitrogen	0.04
Carbon monoxide	0.041
Hydrocarbons and small nonpolar molecules	
Ethane	0.105
Propane	0.152
Acetylene	0.186
Cyclohexane	0.186
Isobutane	0.192
Neopentane	0.195
n-Butane	0.201
Benzene	0.215
Carbon dioxide	0.225
n-Pentane	0.252
Toluene	0.252
n-Heptane	0.352
Polar molecules	
Ammonia	0.250
Water	0.348
Methanol	0.556
Ethanol	0.635

If the vapor pressure of the liquid at a reduced temperature of 0.7 is unknown, the acentric factor may be estimated* from the normal boiling point of the liquid (T_b),

$$\omega = \frac{3}{7}\left[\frac{\log_{10} P_c}{(T_c/T_b) - 1}\right] - 1 \tag{4.27}$$

*W. C. Edmister, "Applied Hydrocarbon Thermodynamics. Part I. A Review of Fundamentals." *Petrol. Refiner*, 37 (No. 1), 173 (1958).

Table con be
Interpolated not
at demarcation lines.

TABLE 4.5
VALUES OF $z^{(0)}$ FOR COMPRESSIBILITY FACTOR CALCULATION*

T_r	P_r 0.2	0.4	0.6	0.8	1.0	1.2	1.4	1.6	1.8	2.0	2.2	2.4	2.6	2.8	3.0	3.2	3.4	3.6	3.8	4.0	4.5	5.0	6.0	7.0	8.0	9.0
0.80	0.851	0.066	0.100	0.133	0.164	0.192	0.225	0.258	0.287	0.318	0.347	0.376	0.405	0.433	0.461	0.490	0.519	0.547	0.576	0.605	0.675	0.746	0.883	1.017	1.15	1.28
0.85	0.882	0.067	0.101	0.134	0.165	0.194	0.226	0.258	0.287	0.316	0.345	0.374	0.403	0.431	0.459	0.487	0.515	0.542	0.569	0.597	0.663	0.730	0.861	0.990	1.115	1.24
0.90	0.904	0.778	0.102	0.135	0.167	0.198	0.229	0.258	0.288	0.316	0.345	0.373	0.402	0.430	0.458	0.485	0.512	0.538	0.565	0.591	0.655	0.718	0.842	0.966	1.089	1.21
0.95	0.920	0.819	0.697	0.145	0.176	0.205	0.235	0.262	0.292	0.321	0.347	0.375	0.403	0.430	0.457	0.484	0.510	0.536	0.561	0.587	0.647	0.709	0.828	0.947	1.066	1.185
1.00	0.932	0.849	0.756	0.638	0.291	0.231	0.250	0.278	0.304	0.329	0.356	0.381	0.407	0.433	0.458	0.484	0.509	0.534	0.557	0.582	0.642	0.702	0.819	0.932	1.048	1.166
1.05	0.942	0.874	0.800	0.714	0.609	0.470	0.341	0.320	0.332	0.350	0.372	0.393	0.417	0.441	0.466	0.489	0.512	0.535	0.557	0.580	0.639	0.700	0.814	0.923	1.032	1.147
1.10	0.950	0.893	0.833	0.767	0.691	0.607	0.512	0.442	0.408	0.402	0.405	0.420	0.440	0.462	0.484	0.504	0.525	0.547	0.567	0.589	0.643	0.699	0.810	0.916	1.019	1.129
1.15	0.958	0.908	0.858	0.805	0.746	0.684	0.620	0.562	0.514	0.484	0.477	0.478	0.485	0.498	0.513	0.529	0.546	0.563	0.581	0.600	0.651	0.705	0.809	0.911	1.008	1.113
1.20	0.963	0.921	0.879	0.835	0.788	0.737	0.690	0.640	0.598	0.568	0.553	0.545	0.544	0.548	0.554	0.563	0.574	0.587	0.601	0.618	0.664	0.714	0.810	0.907	1.000	1.100
1.25	0.968	0.930	0.896	0.858	0.820	0.778	0.740	0.702	0.664	0.636	0.618	0.606	0.599	0.597	0.598	0.602	0.609	0.618	0.629	0.643	0.682	0.726	0.816	0.907	0.994	1.088
1.30	0.971	0.940	0.909	0.878	0.846	0.811	0.780	0.749	0.718	0.691	0.671	0.657	0.649	0.644	0.642	0.642	0.645	0.651	0.659	0.668	0.701	0.740	0.824	0.910	0.992	1.078
1.4	0.977	0.952	0.929	0.908	0.883	0.859	0.838	0.817	0.795	0.777	0.759	0.745	0.734	0.725	0.720	0.718	0.718	0.722	0.727	0.734	0.754	0.781	0.844	0.921	0.994	1.071
1.5	0.982	0.963	0.945	0.927	0.909	0.892	0.875	0.859	0.844	0.831	0.819	0.808	0.800	0.790	0.794	0.785	0.784	0.784	0.786	0.790	0.805	0.826	0.877	0.934	1.000	1.070
1.6	0.985	0.971	0.957	0.944	0.930	0.917	0.904	0.893	0.882	0.872	0.863	0.855	0.848	0.840	0.843	0.836	0.834	0.833	0.834	0.835	0.844	0.860	0.904	0.953	1.010	1.075
1.7	0.988	0.977	0.966	0.956	0.946	0.936	0.926	0.919	0.911	0.903	0.896	0.889	0.883	0.879	0.875	0.873	0.872	0.872	0.873	0.874	0.882	0.895	0.930	0.972	1.023	1.082
1.8	0.991	0.982	0.974	0.966	0.958	0.950	0.944	0.937	0.931	0.926	0.921	0.916	0.913	0.910	0.908	0.907	0.906	0.906	0.907	0.908	0.914	0.925	0.955	0.993	1.039	1.091
1.9	0.993	0.986	0.980	0.974	0.968	0.962	0.958	0.952	0.948	0.944	0.940	0.936	0.933	0.931	0.930	0.929	0.929	0.930	0.932	0.934	0.941	0.950	0.976	1.010	1.051	1.097
2.0	0.995	0.989	0.984	0.979	0.975	0.971	0.968	0.964	0.961	0.959	0.956	0.954	0.953	0.953	0.952	0.952	0.953	0.954	0.954	0.956	0.962	0.972	0.996	1.027	1.064	1.106
2.5	1.000	0.999	0.999	0.998	0.998	0.998	0.997	0.997	0.999	1.000	1.001	1.001	1.002	1.004	1.006	1.008	1.009	1.012	1.014	1.018	1.026	1.035	1.055	1.079	1.105	1.136
3.0	1.001	1.002	1.003	1.004	1.005	1.007	1.008	1.010	1.012	1.014	1.016	1.019	1.022	1.025	1.028	1.030	1.033	1.036	1.038	1.041	1.049	1.058	1.077	1.10	1.124	1.150
3.5	1.002	1.004	1.006	1.008	1.011	1.013	1.015	1.018	1.020	1.022	1.024	1.027	1.030	1.033	1.036	1.039	1.042	1.045	1.048	1.051	1.058	1.067	1.086	1.105	1.126	1.148
4.0	1.003	1.005	1.008	1.010	1.013	1.015	1.017	1.020	1.022	1.024	1.026	1.029	1.032	1.035	1.038	1.041	1.044	1.047	1.050	1.053	1.060	1.068	1.086	1.104	1.124	1.143

*K. S. Pitzer, D. Z. Lippmann, R. F. Curl, Jr., C. M. Huggins, and D. E. Petersen, "The Volumetric and Thermodynamic Properties of Fluids," *J. Am. Chem. Soc.*, 77, 3427 (1955).

TABLE 4.6
VALUES OF $z^{(1)}$ FOR COMPRESSIBILITY FACTOR CALCULATION*

P_r

T_r	0.2	0.4	0.6	0.8	1.0	1.2	1.4	1.6	1.8	2.0	2.2	2.4	2.6	2.8	3.0	4.0	5.0	6.0	7.0	8.0	9.0
0.80	-0.095	-0.028	-0.044	-0.058	-0.07	-0.08	-0.10	-0.11	-0.12	-0.13	-0.14	-0.15	-0.16	-0.17	-0.18	-0.23	-0.26	-0.29	-0.32	-0.35	-0.37
0.85	-0.067	-0.031	-0.049	-0.064	-0.08	-0.09	-0.11	-0.12	-0.13	-0.14	-0.15	-0.16	-0.17	-0.18	-0.18	-0.22	-0.25	-0.28	-0.31	-0.34	-0.36
0.90	-0.042	-0.09	-0.053	-0.068	-0.085	-0.10	-0.11	-0.12	-0.13	-0.14	-0.15	-0.16	-0.17	-0.17	-0.18	-0.21	-0.24	-0.27	-0.30	-0.32	-0.35
0.95	-0.025	-0.050	-0.100	-0.072	-0.091	-0.10	-0.11	-0.12	-0.12	-0.13	-0.14	-0.15	-0.15	-0.16	-0.17	-0.20	-0.22	-0.25	-0.28	-0.31	-0.34
1.00	-0.012	-0.016	-0.020	-0.05	-0.080	-0.090	-0.099	-0.108	-0.115	-0.123	-0.13	-0.13	-0.14	-0.14	-0.15	-0.17	-0.20	-0.23	-0.26	-0.30	-0.33
1.05	0.000	+0.001	+0.005	+0.015	+0.02	+0.01	-0.01	-0.04	-0.06	-0.07	-0.08	-0.09	-0.10	-0.10	-0.11	-0.14	-0.17	-0.20	-0.24	-0.28	-0.31
1.10	+0.002	0.008	0.016	0.030	0.055	0.082	+0.11	+0.082	+0.035	0.000	-0.02	-0.03	-0.05	-0.06	-0.07	-0.10	-0.13	-0.16	-0.21	-0.25	-0.28
1.15	0.004	0.012	0.012	0.040	0.064	0.093	0.12	0.140	0.136	+0.100	+0.07	+0.04	+0.02	0.00	-0.01	-0.04	-0.08	-0.12	-0.16	-0.20	-0.24
1.20	0.009	0.018	0.028	0.044	0.069	0.10	0.13	0.16	0.17	0.17	0.16	0.14	0.12	+0.09	+0.07	0.00	-0.04	-0.08	-0.12	-0.16	-0.19
1.25	0.011	0.023	0.036	0.050	0.069	0.10	0.13	0.16	0.18	0.19	0.19	0.18	0.16	0.14	0.12	+0.05	0.00	-0.03	-0.07	-0.11	-0.13
1.30	0.013	0.027	0.041	0.055	0.072	0.10	0.13	0.16	0.18	0.20	0.20	0.20	0.20	0.19	0.18	0.10	+0.04	0.00	-0.04	-0.07	-0.09
1.4	0.016	0.032	0.049	0.065	0.082	0.10	0.13	0.16	0.18	0.19	0.20	0.21	0.21	0.21	0.20	0.15	0.11	+0.07	+0.04	+0.01	-0.01
1.5	0.017	0.035	0.052	0.070	0.088	0.10	0.13	0.15	0.17	0.18	0.20	0.20	0.21	0.21	0.21	0.20	0.17	0.14	0.11	0.09	+0.07
1.6	0.018	0.036	0.054	0.07	0.08	0.10	0.12	0.14	0.16	0.17	0.18	0.19	0.20	0.20	0.21	0.22	0.21	0.19	0.17	0.15	0.14
1.7	0.018	0.036	0.054	0.07	0.09	0.10	0.11	0.13	0.15	0.16	0.17	0.18	0.19	0.20	0.21	0.24	0.25	0.26	0.25	0.24	0.22
1.8	0.018	0.036	0.054	0.07	0.09	0.10	0.11	0.13	0.15	0.16	0.17	0.18	0.19	0.20	0.21	0.26	0.29	0.31	0.32	0.32	0.30
1.9	0.018	0.035	0.05	0.07	0.09	0.10	0.11	0.13	0.15	0.16	0.17	0.18	0.19	0.20	0.21	0.26	0.30	0.35	0.38	0.40	0.40
2.0	0.016	0.031	0.05	0.07	0.08	0.10	0.11	0.13	0.14	0.15	0.16	0.17	0.18	0.20	0.21	0.26	0.30	0.35	0.40	0.43	0.45
2.5	0.01	0.02	0.04	0.05	0.07	0.08	0.10	0.11	0.12	0.13	0.15	0.16	0.18	0.19	0.20	0.25	0.30	0.35	0.40	0.45	0.50
3.0	0.01	0.02	0.03	0.05	0.06	0.07	0.08	0.09	0.10	0.11	0.13	0.14	0.15	0.16	0.17	0.23	0.28	0.34	0.38	0.45	0.50
3.5	0.01	0.02	0.03	0.04	0.05	0.06	0.07	0.08	0.08	0.09	0.10	0.11	0.12	0.13	0.14	0.19	0.24	0.28	0.33	0.38	0.42
4.0	0.01	0.02	0.02	0.03	0.04	0.05	0.06	0.06	0.07	0.08	0.09	0.10	0.10	0.11	0.12	0.16	0.20	0.23	0.27	0.31	0.35

*K. S. Pitzer, D. Z. Lippmann, R. F. Curl, Jr., C. M. Huggins, and D. E. Petersen, "The Volumetric and Thermodynamic Properties of Fluids," *J. Am. Chem. Soc.*, 77, 3427 (1955).

TABLE 4.7
VALUES OF $z^{(0)}$ NEAR THE TWO-PHASE REGION*

T_r	\multicolumn{7}{c}{P_r}						
	0.4	0.5	0.6	0.7	0.8	0.9	1.0
0.90	0.778	0.701	0.102	0.118	0.135	0.151	0.167
0.91	0.787	0.715	0.104	0.120	0.136	0.152	0.168
0.92	0.796	0.728	0.650	0.122	0.138	0.153	0.169
0.93	0.805	0.740	0.666	0.124	0.140	0.155	0.170
0.94	0.812	0.751	0.681	0.125	0.142	0.157	0.173
0.95	0.819	0.762	0.697	0.612	0.145	0.160	0.176
0.96	0.826	0.772	0.711	0.632	0.149	0.164	0.180
0.97	0.832	0.782	0.724	0.652	0.56	0.170	0.186
0.98	0.838	0.791	0.735	0.669	0.591	0.177	0.193
0.99	0.844	0.800	0.746	0.685	0.616	0.514	0.205
1.00	0.849	0.807	0.757	0.699	0.638	0.554	0.291
1.01	0.854	0.813	0.767	0.713	0.654	0.583	0.476
1.02	0.860	0.820	0.776	0.726	0.672	0.608	0.525
1.03	0.865	0.826	0.784	0.737	0.687	0.630	0.558
1.04	0.870	0.833	0.793	0.748	0.701	0.648	0.586
1.05	0.874	0.838	0.800	0.758	0.714	0.665	0.609

*K. S. Pitzer, D. Z. Lippmann, R. F. Curl, Jr., C. M. Huggins, and D. E. Petersen, "The Volumetric and Thermodynamic Properties of Fluids," *J. Am. Chem. Soc.*, 77, 3427 (1955).

TABLE 4.8
VALUES OF $z^{(1)}$ NEAR THE TWO-PHASE REGION*

T_r	\multicolumn{4}{c}{P_r}			
	0.4	0.6	0.8	1.0
0.90	−0.09	−0.053	−0.068	−0.085
0.91	−0.08	−0.053	−0.069	−0.087
0.92	−0.072	−0.18	−0.070	−0.089
0.93	−0.066	−0.15	−0.071	−0.090
0.94	−0.058	−0.12	−0.072	−0.091
0.95	−0.050	−0.10	−0.072	−0.091
0.96	−0.042	−0.08	−0.072	−0.091
0.97	−0.035	−0.065	−0.14	−0.091
0.98	−0.027	−0.050	−0.11	−0.090
0.99	−0.021	−0.033	−0.08	−0.087
1.00	−0.016	−0.020	−0.05	−0.080
1.01	−0.012	−0.012	−0.02	−0.02
1.02	−0.008	−0.006	0.00	−0.01
1.03	−0.005	−0.001	+0.005	0.00
1.04	−0.002	+0.002	+0.010	+0.01
1.05	+0.001	+0.005	+0.015	+0.02

*K. S. Pitzer, D. Z. Lippmann, R. F. Curl, Jr., C. M. Huggins, and D. E. Petersen, "The Volumetric and Thermodynamic Properties of Fluids," *J. Am. Chem. Soc.*, 77, 3427 (1955).

where the critical pressure P_c is expressed in atmospheres and T_c and T_b are in degrees Kelvin.

The compressibility factor is given by the following equation:

$$z = z^{(0)} + \omega z^{(1)} \tag{4.28}$$

$z^{(0)}$ and $z^{(1)}$, which are functions of reduced temperature and reduced pressure, are tabulated in Tables 4.5 to 4.8. Notice that the tables contain a solid line separating the vapor region from the liquid region. One cannot interpolate between two values separated by this line because of the discontinuity corresponding to condensation. Table 4.7 for $z^{(0)}$ and Table 4.8 for $z^{(1)}$ should be used to estimate compressibility factors near the two-phase region.

Example 4.10

Calculate the molar volume of propane at $440°K$ and 150 atm and compare the result with the experimental value.

Solution:

The acentric factor of propane (Table 4.4) is 0.152. The reduced properties (see Table 4.1) are

$$T_r = \frac{T}{T_c} = \frac{440}{370} = 1.189$$

$$P_r = \frac{P}{P_c} = \frac{150}{42} = 3.571$$

Using Eqn. (4.28) and linear interpolation of Tables 4.5 and 4.6,

$$z = z^{(0)} + \omega z^{(1)} = (0.580) + (0.152)(0.017) = 0.582$$

so

$$v = \frac{zRT}{P} = \frac{(0.582)(82.06)(440)}{(150)} = 140.1 \text{ cm}^3/\text{mole}$$

The calculated value is within 1% of the experimental value (*Thermodynamic Functions of Gases*, Vol. 2, by F. Din, Butterworths, London, 1962).

Another useful part of the Pitzer correlation is that the second virial coefficient $B\{T\}$ may be estimated from the acentric factor and the critical properties:

$$\frac{BP_c}{RT_c} = (0.1445 + 0.073\omega) - (0.330 - 0.46\omega)T_r^{-1} - (0.1385 + 0.50\omega)T_r^{-2}$$

$$- (0.0121 + 0.097\omega)T_r^{-3} - 0.0073\omega T_r^{-8} \tag{4.29}$$

Example 4.11

Calculate the second virial coefficient of carbon dioxide gas at $0°C$ and compare with the experimental value of $-151 \text{ cm}^3/\text{mole}$.

Solution:

The acentric factor of carbon dioxide is 0.225 (Table 4.4). The reduced temperature is $T_r = T/T_c = 273.15/304.2 = 0.898$. From Eqn. (4.29),

$$\frac{BP_c}{RT_c} = [0.1445 + 0.073(0.225)] - \frac{[0.330 - 0.46(0.225)]}{(0.898)} - \frac{[0.1385 + 0.50(0.225)]}{(0.898)^2}$$

$$- \frac{[0.0121 + 0.097(0.225)]}{(0.898)^3} - \frac{0.0073(0.225)}{(0.898)^8}$$

$$= 0.161 - 0.252 - 0.311 - 0.047 - 0.004 = -0.453$$

$$B = \left[\frac{BP_c}{RT_c}\right]\frac{RT_c}{P_c} = \frac{(-0.453)(82.06)(304.2)}{72.9} = -155 \ \text{cm}^3/\text{mole}$$

TABLE 4.9
DATA FOR COEXISTING LIQUID AND VAPOR PHASES*

	$-(\log_{10} P_r^s)^x$		cal/mole-°K		Vapor		Liquid	
T_r	$x = (0)$	$x = (1)$	$\Delta s^{(0)}$	$\Delta s^{(1)}$	$z^{(0)}$	$z^{(1)}$	$z^{(0)}$	$z^{(1)}$
1.00	0.000	0.000	0.00	0.00	0.291	−0.080	0.291	−0.080
0.99	0.025	0.021	2.57	2.83	0.43	−0.030	0.202	−0.090
0.98	0.050	0.042	3.38	3.91	0.47	0.000	0.179	−0.093
0.97	0.076	0.064	4.00	4.72	0.51	+0.020	0.162	−0.095
0.96	0.102	0.086	4.52	5.39	0.54	0.035	0.148	−0.085
0.95	0.129	0.109	5.00	5.96	0.565	0.045	0.136	−0.095
0.94	0.156	0.133	5.44	6.51	0.59	0.055	0.125	−0.094
0.92	0.212	0.180	6.23	7.54	0.63	0.075	0.108	−0.092
0.90	0.270	0.230	6.95	8.53	0.67	0.095	0.0925	−0.087
0.88	0.330	0.285	7.58	9.39	0.70	0.110	0.0790	−0.080
0.86	0.391	0.345	8.19	10.3	0.73	0.125	0.0680	−0.075
0.84	0.455	0.405	8.79	11.2	0.756	0.135	0.0585	−0.068
0.82	0.522	0.475	9.37	12.1	0.781	0.140	0.0498	−0.062
0.80	0.592	0.545	9.97	13.0	0.804	0.144	0.0422	−0.057
0.78	0.665	0.620	10.57	13.9	0.826	0.144	0.0360	−0.053
0.76	0.742	0.705	11.20	14.9	0.846	0.142	0.0300	−0.048
0.74	0.823	0.800	11.84	16.0	0.864	0.137	0.0250	−0.043
0.72	0.909	0.895	12.49	17.0	0.881	0.131	0.0210	−0.037
0.70	1.000	1.00	13.19	18.1	0.897	0.122	0.0172	−0.032
0.68	1.096	1.12	13.89	19.3	0.911	0.113	0.0138	−0.027
0.66	1.198	1.25	14.62	20.5	0.922	0.104	0.0111	−0.022
0.64	1.308	1.39	15.36	21.8	0.932	0.097	0.0088	−0.018
0.62	1.426	1.54	16.12	23.2	0.940	0.090	0.0068	−0.015
0.60	1.552	1.70	16.92	24.6	0.947	0.083	0.0052	−0.012
0.58	1.688	1.88	17.74	26.2	0.953	0.077	0.0039	−0.009
0.56	1.834	2.08	18.64	27.8	0.959	0.070	0.0028	−0.007

*K. S. Pitzer, D. Z. Lippmann, R. F. Curl, Jr., C. M. Huggins, and D. E. Petersen, "The Volumetric and Thermodynamic Properties of Fluids," *J. Am. Chem. Soc.*, 77, 3427 (1955).

The special merit of the principle of corresponding states tabulated by Pitzer et al. is that, since the third parameter is based upon the vapor pressure, the correlation is particularly accurate for properties at saturation. Table 4.9 gives the vapor pressure, entropy of vaporization, and compressibility factor of the liquid and the gas at saturation. Formulas for P_r^s and Δs are analogous to Eqn. (4.28). Δs, entropy of vaporization, is equal to latent heat of vaporization divided by absolute temperature. Use of this table is illustrated in the next example.

Example 4.12

For propane, calculate the vapor pressure of the liquid, the latent heat of vaporization of the liquid, and the molar volumes of saturated liquid and vapor at 300.44°K.

Solution:

For propane the acentric factor is 0.152 (Table 4.4). The reduced temperature is $T_r = T/T_c = 300.44/370 = 0.812$. From Table 4.9, using linear interpolation,

1. $$\log_{10} P_r^s = [\log_{10} P_r^s]^{(0)} + \omega[\log_{10} P_r^s]^{(1)}$$

$$= -0.550 + 0.152(-0.503) = -0.6265$$

$$P_r^s = 0.2363$$

$$P^s = \left[\frac{P_s}{P_c}\right]P_c = (0.2363)(42) = 9.95 \text{ atm}$$

2. $$\Delta s = \Delta s^{(0)} + \omega\,\Delta s^{(1)}$$

$$= 9.61 + 0.152(12.46) = 11.50 \text{ cal/mole-}°\text{K}$$

$$\Delta h = T\Delta s = (300.44)(11.50) = 3456 \text{ cal/mole}$$

3. For the vapor,

$$z = z^{(0)} + \omega z^{(1)} = 0.790 + 0.152(0.142) = 0.812$$

$$v = \frac{zRT}{P} = \frac{(0.812)(82.06)(300.44)}{9.95} = 2010 \text{ cm}^3/\text{mole}$$

4. For the liquid,

$$z = z^{(0)} + \omega z^{(1)} = 0.0468 + 0.152(-0.06) = 0.0377$$

$$v = \frac{zRT}{P} = \frac{(0.0377)(82.06)(300.44)}{9.95} = 93.4 \text{ cm}^3/\text{mole}$$

These results may be compared with experimental data (*Thermodynamic Functions of Gases*, Vol. 2, by F. Din, Butterworths, London, 1962):

	Corres. States	Experi- mental	Error (%)
Vapor pressure, atm	9.95	10.0	0.5
Heat of vaporization, cal/mole	3456	3500	1.3
Molar volume, saturated vapor, cm^3/mole	2010	2003	0.3
Molar volume, saturated liquid, cm^3/mole	93.4	89.9	3.9

Pitzer's correlation gives poor results for molecules which have large dipole moments or form hydrogen bonds, for example, those molecules in the last group in Table 4.4.

4.2 Sources of Data in Scientific Literature

Professor K. A. Kobe* said in 1949: "The organization of information in technical journals is by its nature haphazard. Most scientific journals are reluctant to publish review articles. The result is that the assimilation in usable form of valuable scientific and technical data trails in poor fashion the accumulation of such knowledge. The majority of scientific and technical data is buried in journals—unorganized, barely catalogued and available only after considerable effort." In spite of considerable work by Professor Kobe, his students, and his colleagues (see Table 4.14), the same statement could be made today.

The U.S. National Bureau of Standards (NBS) in Washington, D.C., plays an important role in dissemination of scientific data. For example, *NBS Circular 500*, entitled "Selected Values of Chemical Thermodynamic Properties," contains chemical data such as heats of formation from the elements and latent heats of fusion, transition, and vaporization for a large number of inorganic compounds. NBS also publishes technical notes and monographs containing data on properties of substances. In the NBS Technical Note Series, for example, number 392 is entitled "The Thermodynamic Properties of Compressed Gaseous and Liquid Fluorine." NSRDS (National Standard Reference Data System) is a new series published by NBS; number 19, for example, is entitled "Thermodynamic Properties of Ammonia as an Ideal Gas." Most scientific library collections include the technical notes, monographs, and circulars issued by NBS.

Other agencies of the U.S. government publish useful collections of scientific data. For example, *U.S. Bureau of Mines Bulletin No. 476* (compiled by K. K. Kelley) contains equations for heat capacities of inorganic compounds at high temperature. *National Aeronautics and Space Administration*

*K. A. Kobe, "Thermochemistry for the Petroleum Industry," *Petrol. Refiner*, **28** (No. 1), 83 (1949).

(NASA) *Bulletin SP-3001* contains thermodynamic properties up to 6000°K for 210 substances involving the first 18 elements in the periodic table. There are many other useful sources of property data; the intention here is only to point out a few representative examples.

The series of tables by Landolt-Börnstein* in German is an important source of data on physical and chemical properties of substances. The International Critical Tables (McGraw-Hill, New York, 1933, seven volumes) is a similar but less extensive compilation.

A useful reference for properties of hydrocarbons is *American Petroleum Institute* (API) *Research Project 44*, entitled "Selected Values of Properties of Hydrocarbons." This reference contains boiling points, refractive indices, densities, freezing points, vapor pressures, enthalpies, free energies, etc.

The Chemical Engineers' Handbook (edited by R. H. Perry and C. H. Chilton, McGraw-Hill, New York), contains tables and graphs of data on properties of materials. *The Handbook of Chemistry and Physics* (edited by R. C. Weast, Chemical Rubber Publishing Company, Cleveland) is a handy reference book of chemical and physical data. Most chemical engineers have one or both of these handbooks in their personal library.

Technical magazines, journals, and periodicals such as the *Journal of the American Chemical Society, Science,* the *Journal of Physical Chemistry,* and hundreds of others are primary sources of property information. An engineer looking for specific information that is not available in handbooks has to make a search in these journals for data which may or may not exist. Literature searches are simplified by the *Chemical Abstracts,* where published information is indexed by author, subject, and chemical formula. A useful supplement to the *Chemical Abstracts* is the *Engineering Index,* which is an annual index of information and data published in the fields of engineering.

In the future computers will play a pivotal role in the storage and retrieval of information. In Ch. 5 we shall discuss the computer's role in data processing.

4.3 Constants for Pure Substances

Constants are tabulated in textbooks for thousands of pure substances. For example, the *Handbook of Chemistry and Physics*† contains physical constants for about 17,000 organic and inorganic compounds: molecular weight, normal boiling point, normal melting point, density (usually at room tem-

---

*Landolt-Börnstein, *Zahlenwerte und Funktionen aus Physik, Chemie, Astronomie, Geophysik und Technik,* Springer-Verlag, Berlin.

†Robert C. Weast, ed., *Handbook of Chemistry and Physics,* 55th ed., Chemical Rubber Publishing Company, Cleveland, 1974-1975.

Substance	Melting Point (°C)	Heat of Fusion (cal/gmole)	Boiling Point at 1 atm (°C)	Heat of Vaporization (cal/gmole)
Bromine				
Br_2	−7.2	2,580	58.0	7,420
BrF_5	−61.3	1,355	40.4	7,470
Cadmium				
Cd	320.9	1,460	765	23,870
$CdBr_2$	568	5,000		
$CdCl_2$	568	5,300	967	29,860
CdF_2	1110	5,400		
CdI_2	387	3,660	796	25,400
CdO			1559†	53,820†
$CdSO_4$	1000	4,790		
Carbon				
C (graphite)	3600	11,000		
CBr_4	90	1,050		
CCl_4	−24.0	644	77	7,280
CF_4			−127.9	3,110
CH_4	−182.5	224	−161.4	2,040
C_2N_2	−27.8	1,938	−21.1	5,576
CNBr	52			11,010†
CNCl	−5	2,240	13	6,300
CNF			−72.8†	5,780†
CNI			141†	13,980†
CO	−205.0	200	−191.5	1,444
CO_2	−57.5	1,900	−78.4†	6,030†
COS	−138.8	1,129	−50.2	4,423
$COCl_2$			8.0	5,990
CS_2	−112.0	1,049		
Cerium				
Ce	775	2,120		
Cesium				
Cs	28.4	500	690	16,320
CsBr			1300	35,990
CsCl	642	3,600	1300	35,690
CsF	715	2,450	1251	34,330
CsI			1280	35,930
$CsNO_3$	407	3,250		
Chlorine				
Cl_2	−101.0	1,531	−34.1	4,878
ClF			−101	
ClF_3			11.3	5,890
Cl_2O			2.0	6,280
ClO_2			10.9	7,100
Cl_2O_7			79	8,480

TABLE 4.10 (Continued)

Substance	Melting Point (°C)	Heat of Fusion (cal/gmole)	Boiling Point at 1 atm (°C)	Heat of Vaporization (cal/gmole)
Chromium				
Cr	1550	3,930	2475	
CrO_2Cl_2			117	8,250
Cobalt				
Co	1490	3,660		
$CoCl_2$	727	7,390	1050	27,170
Copper				
Cu	1083.0	3,110	2595	72,810
Cu_2Br_2			1355	16,310
Cu_2Cl_2	430	4,890	1490	11,920
CuI			1336	15,940
$Cu_2(CN)_2$	473	5,400		
Cu_2O	1230	13,400		
CuO	1447	2,820		
Cu_2S	1127	5,500		
Fluorine				
F_2	-223		-188.2	1,640
F_2O			-144.8	2,650
Gallium				
Ga	29.8	1,336	2071	

*R. H. Perry and C. H. Chilton, eds., *Chemical Engineers' Handbook*, 5th ed., McGraw-Hill, New York, 1973.
†Sublimation.

perature), index of refraction, and solubility of the substance in various solvents.

Constants such as latent heat of fusion and latent heat of vaporization (at normal boiling point) are available for selected substances. For example, Table 4.10 is an excerpt from *Chemical Engineers' Handbook*. If experimental data are not available, latent heats of vaporization can be estimated using Pitzer's theory of corresponding states (see Sec. 4.1). A similar correlation for heats of fusion has not been discovered.

Another important set of constants are thermochemical properties of pure substances: standard heat of formation (Δh^f), standard free energy of formation (Δg^f), and entropy at 25°C. These properties are tabulated in the *Handbook of Chemistry and Physics* for about 2000 elements and compounds; a small portion of this important compilation is reproduced in Table 4.11. Notice that values of thermochemical properties depend on the state of the substance (solid, liquid, gas, or dissolved in water). The use of thermochemical constants for calculating equilibrium yields and heats of chemical reactions is explained in Ch. 9 and 10.

TABLE 4.11
THERMOCHEMICAL PROPERTIES*

Substance	State	Δh^f (cal/mole)	Δg^f (cal/mole)	s (cal/mole-°K)
Nitrogen				
N_2	Gas	0	0	45.77
NOBr	Gas	19,560	19,700	65.16
NOCl	Gas	12,570	15,860	63.0
NF_3	Gas	−27,200	—	—
NO	Gas	21,600	20,720	50.34
NO_2	Gas	8,090	12,390	57.47
N_2O_4	Gas	2,310	23,490	72.73
N_2O	Gas	19,490	24,760	52.58
N_2O_5	Gas	3,600	—	—
	Crystalline	−10,000	—	—
HNO_3	Liquid	−41,400	−19,100	37.19
	Aqueous	−49,370	−26,410	35.0
$HNO_3 \cdot H_2O$	Liquid	−112,960	−78,410	51.83
$HNO_3 \cdot 3H_2O$	Liquid	−252,200	−193,700	82.92
Osmium				
Os	Gas	174,000	163,000	45.97
	Crystalline	0	0	7.8
OsO_4 (white)	Gas	−79,900	−67,900	65.6
(yellow)	Crystalline	−91,700	−70,500	34.7
	Crystalline	−93,400	−70,700	29.7
	Aqueous	—	—	—
OsS_2	Crystalline	−35,000	—	—
H_2OsO_5	Aqueous	—	−125,280	—
Oxygen				
O_2	Gas	0	0	49.003
O_3	Gas	34,000	39,060	56.8
OH^-	Aqueous	−54,957	−37,595	−2.519
Palladium				
Pd	Gas	93,000	84,000	39.91
	Crystalline	0	0	8.9

Substance	State	Δh^f (cal/mole)	Δg^f (cal/mole)	s (cal/mole-°K)
$PdBr_2$	Crystalline	−24,900	—	—
	Aqueous	−205,600	—	—
$Pd(CN)_2$	Crystalline	52,100	—	—
$PdCl_2$	Crystalline	−45,400	—	—
$PdCl_4^-$	Aqueous	−128,300	−96,700	41.0
H_2PdCl_4	Aqueous	−129,300	—	—
Pd_2H	Crystalline	−8,900	—	—
PdO	Crystalline	−20,400	—	—
$Pd(OH)_2$	Crystalline	−92,100	—	—
$Pd(OH)_4$	Crystalline	−169,400	—	—
Phosphorus				
P (white)	Gas	75,180	66,710	38.98
	Crystalline	0	0	10.6
(red)	Crystalline	−4,400	—	—
(black)	Crystalline	−10,300	—	—
P_2	Gas	33,820	24,600	52.13
P_4	Gas	13,120	5,820	66.90
PBr_3	Gas	−35,900	−41,200	83.11
PBr_5	Crystalline	−66,000	—	—
$POBr_3$	Crystalline	−114,600	—	—
PCl_3	Gas	−73,220	−68,420	74.49
PCl_5	Gas	−95,350	−77,590	84.3
$POCl_3$	Gas	−141,500	−130,300	77.59
PH_3	Gas	2,210	4,360	50.2
PI_3	Crystalline	−10,900	—	—
PN	Gas	−20,200	−25,300	50.45
HPO_3	Crystalline	−228,200	—	—
H_3PO_2	Aqueous	−234,900	—	—
	Crystalline	−145,500	—	—
H_3PO_3	Aqueous	−145,600	—	—
	Crystalline	−232,200	—	—
H_3PO_4	Aqueous	−232,200	—	—
	Crystalline	−306,200	—	—
$H_4P_2O_7$	Crystalline	−538,000	—	—

*R. C. Weast, ed., Handbook of Chemistry and Physics, 55th ed., Chemical Rubber Publishing Company, Cleveland, 1974-1975.

4.4 Tables, Equations, and Graphs of Smoothed Data

Tables

Progress in technology is based in part upon accumulation, storage, and dissemination of scientific data. The problem of smoothing, digesting, and correlating raw experimental data for distribution to the scientific community has never been solved to everyone's satisfaction. A single experiment may generate hundreds of experimental points. One person may want detailed information on the scatter in the raw experimental data, and another person may be satisfied with an average value for all of the observations.

Tables take up considerable space on printed pages, particularly when there is more than one independent variable. For example, thermodynamic properties of water (specific volume, enthalpy) are each a function of two independent variables (temperature and pressure) so that a complete tabulation of these properties fills a small book. A single page from this book,* called the steam tables, is shown in Table 4.12. The table gives values of specific volume (v), enthalpy (h), and entropy (s) for water as a function of temperature and pressure. Properties in the first two columns following the pressure are for saturated liquid and saturated vapor; the remaining columns are for superheated steam. If the value of a property is desired at an intermediate state (say, at 494°F and 378 psi), then interpolation is necessary. Methods of interpolation are discussed in Ch. 5.

Another example of tabulated data is shown in Table 4.13, which gives the molar volume of ammonia as a function of temperature and pressure. Horizontal lines separate vapor (above) from liquid (below). Since the critical temperature of ammonia is at 405.6°K, isotherms at 420°K and higher do not have a two-phase region.

Equations

Data are tabulated when there is no equation that fits the experimental points within estimated limits of experimental error. For example, none of the PVT equations of state discussed in Sec. 4.1 accurately reproduces the volumetric data for ammonia in Table 4.13.

In some cases values of properties calculated from theoretical equations are more accurate than the best available experimental data. Thermodynamic properties of diatomic molecules and some simple polyatomic molecules at

---

*J. H. Keenan and F. G. Keyes, *Thermodynamic Properties of Steam*, Wiley, New York, 1936.

Table 4.12
THERMODYNAMIC PROPERTIES OF STEAM*

Abs. Press. (lb/in.²) (Sat. Temp.)		Sat. Liquid	Sat. Vapor	Temperature (°F)												
				430°	440°	450°	460°	470°	480°	490°	500°	520°	540°	560°	580°	600°
340 (428.97)	v	0.0191	1.3645	1.3673	1.3941	1.4201	1.4454	1.4700	1.4941	1.5178	1.5410	1.5863	1.6303	1.6733	1.7155	1.7569
	h	406.7	1203.7	1204.5	1212.1	1219.4	1226.4	1233.2	1239.9	1246.4	1252.8	1265.2	1277.2	1288.9	1300.4	1311.6
	s	0.6022	1.4992	1.5000	1.5085	1.5166	1.5243	1.5317	1.5388	1.5457	1.5524	1.5652	1.5773	1.5889	1.6000	1.6108
345 (430.35)	v	0.0191	1.3450		1.3707	1.3964	1.4215	1.4460	1.4699	1.4933	1.5163	1.5612	1.6047	1.6472	1.6889	1.7298
	h	408.2	1203.8		1211.2	1218.5	1225.6	1232.5	1239.2	1245.8	1252.1	1264.6	1276.7	1288.4	1299.9	1311.2
	s	0.6039	1.4979		1.5061	1.5142	1.5220	1.5294	1.5366	1.5435	1.5502	1.5631	1.5753	1.5869	1.5981	1.6089
350 (431.72)	v	0.0191	1.3260		1.3478	1.3734	1.3984	1.4226	1.4463	1.4696	1.4923	1.5368	1.5799	1.6220	1.6631	1.7036
	h	409.7	1203.9		1210.3	1217.7	1224.8	1231.7	1238.5	1245.1	1251.5	1264.1	1276.2	1288.0	1299.5	1310.9
	s	0.6056	1.4966		1.5037	1.5119	1.5197	1.5272	1.5344	1.5414	1.5481	1.5611	1.5733	1.5850	1.5962	1.6070
355 (433.06)	v	0.0191	1.3075		1.3257	1.3511	1.3759	1.3999	1.4234	1.4465	1.4690	1.5130	1.5557	1.5973	1.6381	1.6781
	h	411.2	1204.0		1209.3	1216.8	1224.0	1231.0	1237.8	1244.4	1250.9	1263.5	1275.7	1287.5	1299.1	1310.5
	s	0.6073	1.4953		1.5013	1.5095	1.5174	1.5250	1.5323	1.5393	1.5461	1.5591	1.5714	1.5831	1.5943	1.6052
360 (434.40)	v	0.0192	1.2895		1.3041	1.3294	1.3539	1.3778	1.4012	1.4240	1.4464	1.4900	1.5322	1.5734	1.6137	1.6533
	h	412.7	1204.1		1208.4	1215.9	1223.2	1230.2	1237.1	1243.8	1250.3	1263.0	1275.2	1287.1	1298.7	1310.1
	s	0.6090	1.4941		1.4989	1.5072	1.5152	1.5228	1.5301	1.5372	1.5440	1.5571	1.5694	1.5812	1.5925	1.6033
365 (435.72)	v	0.0192	1.2720		1.2831	1.3082	1.3326	1.3563	1.3795	1.4021	1.4243	1.4675	1.5094	1.5501	1.5900	1.6291
	h	414.1	1204.1		1207.5	1215.1	1222.4	1229.5	1236.4	1243.1	1249.6	1262.4	1274.7	1286.6	1298.2	1309.7
	s	0.6106	1.4928		1.4965	1.5049	1.5129	1.5206	1.5280	1.5351	1.5420	1.5551	1.5675	1.5793	1.5906	1.6015
370 (437.03)	v	0.0192	1.2550		1.2626	1.2876	1.3118	1.3354	1.3584	1.3808	1.4028	1.4457	1.4871	1.5275	1.5670	1.6057
	h	415.6	1204.2		1206.5	1214.2	1221.6	1228.7	1235.7	1242.4	1249.0	1261.8	1274.1	1286.1	1297.8	1309.3
	s	0.6122	1.4916		1.4942	1.5027	1.5107	1.5185	1.5259	1.5330	1.5399	1.5531	1.5656	1.5775	1.5888	1.5997
375 (438.32)	v	0.0192	1.2384		1.2427	1.2675	1.2916	1.3150	1.3378	1.3601	1.3819	1.4244	1.4655	1.5054	1.5445	1.5828
	h	417.0	1204.3		1205.6	1213.3	1220.7	1227.9	1234.9	1241.8	1248.4	1261.2	1273.6	1285.6	1297.4	1308.9
	s	0.6137	1.4904		1.4918	1.5004	1.5085	1.5163	1.5238	1.5310	1.5379	1.5512	1.5637	1.5756	1.5870	1.5980

Steam table (superheated steam). Column temperature headings are not printed on this page; data columns below are, in order: saturated liquid, saturated vapor, then superheat values.

Abs. press. (Sat. temp.)		Sat. liquid	Sat. vapor												
380 (439.60)	v	0.0192	1.2222	1.2232	1.2479	1.2719	1.2951	1.3178	1.3399	1.3616	1.4037	1.4444	1.4840	1.5226	1.5605
	h	418.5	1204.3	1204.6	1212.4	1219.9	1227.2	1234.2	1241.1	1247.7	1260.7	1273.1	1285.2	1297.1	1308.5
	s	0.6153	1.4891	1.4895	1.4981	1.5063	1.5142	1.5217	1.5289	1.5359	1.5493	1.5618	1.5738	1.5852	1.5962
385 (440.86)	v	0.0193	1.2064		1.2289	1.2527	1.2758	1.2983	1.3202	1.3417	1.3835	1.4238	1.4632	1.5013	1.5389
	h	419.9	1204.3		1211.5	1219.1	1226.4	1233.5	1240.4	1247.1	1260.1	1272.6	1284.7	1296.5	1308.1
	s	0.6169	1.4879		1.4959	1.5042	1.5121	1.5196	1.5269	1.5340	1.5474	1.5600	1.5720	1.5835	1.5945
390 (442.12)	v	0.0193	1.1910		1.2102	1.2339	1.2569	1.2793	1.3011	1.3224	1.3638	1.4038	1.4426	1.4806	1.5177
	h	421.3	1204.4		1210.6	1218.2	1225.6	1232.8	1239.7	1246.4	1259.5	1272.1	1284.2	1296.1	1307.7
	s	0.6184	1.4867		1.4937	1.5020	1.5100	1.5176	1.5249	1.5320	1.5455	1.5582	1.5702	1.5817	1.5928
395 (443.36)	v	0.0193	1.1760		1.1921	1.2156	1.2385	1.2607	1.2824	1.3035	1.3446	1.3843	1.4228	1.4603	1.4971
	h	422.7	1204.4		1209.7	1217.4	1224.8	1232.0	1239.0	1245.8	1258.9	1271.5	1283.8	1295.7	1307.3
	s	0.6199	1.4856		1.4914	1.4998	1.5079	1.5156	1.5230	1.5301	1.5436	1.5564	1.5685	1.5800	1.5911
400 (444.59)	v	0.0193	1.1613		1.1744	1.1978	1.2205	1.2426	1.2641	1.2851	1.3259	1.3652	1.4034	1.4406	1.4770
	h	424.0	1204.5		1208.8	1216.5	1224.0	1231.3	1238.3	1245.1	1258.3	1271.0	1283.3	1295.2	1306.9
	s	0.6214	1.4844		1.4892	1.4977	1.5058	1.5135	1.5210	1.5281	1.5417	1.5546	1.5667	1.5783	1.5894
405 (445.81)	v	0.0193	1.1470		1.1571	1.1804	1.2030	1.2249	1.2463	1.2672	1.3076	1.3466	1.3845	1.4214	1.4574
	h	425.4	1204.5		1207.9	1215.7	1223.2	1230.5	1237.6	1244.5	1257.8	1270.5	1282.8	1294.8	1306.5
	s	0.6229	1.4832		1.4870	1.4956	1.5037	1.5115	1.5190	1.5262	1.5399	1.5528	1.5650	1.5766	1.5878
410 (447.01)	v	0.0194	1.1330		1.1401	1.1634	1.1859	1.2077	1.2289	1.2496	1.2898	1.3285	1.3660	1.4026	1.4383
	h	426.8	1204.5		1206.9	1214.8	1222.4	1229.8	1236.9	1243.8	1257.2	1270.0	1282.3	1294.3	1306.1
	s	0.6243	1.4821		1.4848	1.4935	1.5017	1.5095	1.5171	1.5243	1.5381	1.5510	1.5632	1.5749	1.5861
415 (448.21)	v	0.0194	1.1194		1.1236	1.1468	1.1692	1.1908	1.2119	1.2325	1.2724	1.3108	1.3480	1.3842	1.4196
	h	428.1	1204.6		1206.0	1214.0	1221.6	1229.0	1236.2	1243.2	1256.6	1269.4	1281.8	1293.9	1305.7
	s	0.6258	1.4810		1.4826	1.4913	1.4996	1.5075	1.5151	1.5224	1.5363	1.5492	1.5615	1.5733	1.5845
420 (449.39)	v	0.0194	1.1061		1.1075	1.1305	1.1528	1.1744	1.1953	1.2158	1.2554	1.2935	1.3304	1.3663	1.4014
	h	429.4	1204.6		1205.0	1213.1	1220.8	1228.3	1235.5	1242.5	1256.0	1268.9	1281.4	1293.5	1305.3
	s	0.6272	1.4799		1.4804	1.4892	1.4976	1.5056	1.5132	1.5205	1.5345	1.5475	1.5598	1.5716	1.5829
425 (450.57)	v	0.0194	1.0931			1.1146	1.1368	1.1583	1.1791	1.1995	1.2388	1.2766	1.3132	1.3488	1.3836
	h	430.7	1204.6			1212.2	1220.0	1227.5	1234.8	1241.8	1255.4	1268.3	1280.9	1293.0	1304.9
	s	0.6287	1.4788			1.4872	1.4956	1.5036	1.5113	1.5187	1.5327	1.5458	1.5582	1.5700	1.5813

v, volume, ft^3/lb; h, enthalpy, Btu/lb; s, entropy, Btu/lb-°R.
*J. H. Keenan and F. G. Keyes, *Thermodynamic Properties of Steam*, Wiley, New York, 1936.

TABLE 4.13

SPECIFIC VOLUME OF AMMONIA (cm³/gmole)*

Press. (atm)	Temperature (°K)														
	300	310	320	330	340	350	360	370	380	390	400	420	440	460	480
1	24,384		26,069		27,743		29,410		31,072		32,730	34,386	36,040	37,692	39,342
5	4,659		5,037		5,399		5,753		6,102		6,447	6,790	7,130	7,468	7,805
10	2,181		2,402		2,606		2,799		2,985		3,166	3,344	3,520	3,694	3,867
15			1,514		1,666		1,810		1,943		2,070	2,194	2,316	2,436	2,554
20		29.1	30.0		1,196		1,312		1,419		1,521	1,619	1,714	1,807	1,898
25					908.2		1,014		1,106		1,192	1,274	1,353	1,429	1,503
30		29.0	29.9	30.8	704.9		810.1		894.7		972.1	1,044	1,112	1,178	1,242
40		28.9	29.8	30.7	31.8	33.2	549.5		628.7		694.6	753.7	809.0	861.8	912.6
50		28.8	29.7	30.6	31.7	33.0	34.7		463.8		526.5	579.3	627.5	672.7	715.6
60		28.8	29.6	30.5	31.5	32.8	34.5	36.5	350.6		411.0	461.2	505.6	545.9	583.5
70		28.7	29.5	30.4	31.4	32.6	34.2	36.2	253.4		326.8	375.2	417.7	455.7	490.2
80		28.7	29.5	30.3	31.3	32.5	34.0	36.0	38.5		261.5	310.2	351.0	386.5	418.5
90		28.6	29.4	30.2	31.2	32.4	33.8	35.7	38.1	41.9	209.5	262.1	299.7	332.9	363.1
100		28.6	29.3	30.1	31.1	32.2	33.6	35.4	37.7	41.2	138.2	221.1	258.4	291.0	319.9
120		28.5	29.2	30.0	30.9	32.0	33.3	34.9	37.0	39.8	45.1	153.0	195.5	227.9	253.2
140		28.4	29.1	29.9	30.8	31.8	33.0	34.5	36.3	38.7	42.5	85.2	144.9	178.6	204.3
160		28.3	29.0	29.8	30.6	31.6	32.8	34.2	35.8	37.9	40.7	55.4	103.7	141.5	167.5
180		28.3	28.9	29.7	30.5	31.4	32.5	33.8	35.3	37.2	39.5	48.1	74.6	111.8	138.3
200		28.2	28.8	29.5	30.3	31.2	32.3	33.5	34.9	36.5	38.6	45.4	61.7	89.9	115.6

220	28.1	28.7	29.4	30.2	31.1	32.1	33.2	34.5	36.0	37.9	43.7	55.5	75.7	98.4
240	28.0	28.6	29.3	30.1	30.9	31.9	33.0	34.2	35.6	37.3	42.3	51.3	66.2	85.5
260	28.0	28.5	29.2	30.0	30.8	31.7	32.7	33.9	35.3	36.8	41.2	48.3	59.9	75.9
280	27.9	28.5	29.1	29.8	30.6	31.5	32.5	33.6	34.9	36.4	40.4	46.1	55.7	68.9
300	27.8	28.4	29.0	29.7	30.5	31.4	32.3	33.4	34.6	36.1	39.6	44.5	52.6	63.7
320	27.7	28.3	28.9	29.6	30.4	31.2	32.1	33.2	34.4	35.7	38.9	43.3	50.2	59.6
340	27.7	28.2	28.8	29.5	30.2	31.0	31.9	32.9	34.1	35.4	38.4	42.4	48.3	56.4
360	27.6	28.1	28.7	29.4	30.1	30.9	31.8	32.7	33.9	35.1	38.0	41.6	46.8	53.8
380	27.5	28.0	28.6	29.2	29.9	30.7	31.6	32.5	33.6	34.7	37.5	40.9	45.5	51.6
400	27.5	27.9	28.5	29.1	29.8	30.6	31.4	32.3	33.3	34.4	37.1	40.4	44.5	49.9
450	27.3	27.8	28.3	28.9	29.6	30.3	31.1	31.9	32.8	33.8	36.1	39.0	42.3	46.5
500	27.1	27.6	28.1	28.7	29.3	30.0	30.7	31.5	32.4	33.3	35.3	37.8	40.6	44.5
550	27.0	27.5	28.0	28.5	29.1	29.7	30.4	31.2	32.0	32.9	34.7	36.9	39.4	42.7
600	26.8	27.3	27.8	28.3	28.9	29.5	30.2	30.9	31.7	32.5	34.2	36.1	38.4	41.2
650	26.7	27.1	27.6	28.1	28.7	29.3	29.9	30.6	31.3	32.1	33.7	35.4	37.5	40.0
700	26.5	26.9	27.4	27.9	28.5	29.1	29.7	30.3	31.0	31.7	33.2	34.8	36.7	38.9
750	26.4	26.8	27.3	27.8	28.3	28.8	29.4	30.0	30.7	31.4	32.8	34.3	36.0	38.1
800	26.3	26.7	27.1	27.6	28.1	28.6	29.2	29.8	30.4	31.1	32.5	33.9	35.5	37.4
850	26.2	26.6	27.0	27.4	27.9	28.4	29.0	29.6	30.2	30.8	32.1	33.5	35.0	36.7
900	26.1	26.4	26.8	27.2	27.7	28.2	28.8	29.3	29.9	30.5	31.8	33.1	34.5	36.1
950	26.0	26.3	26.7	27.1	27.6	28.1	28.6	29.1	29.7	30.3	31.5	32.8	34.1	35.6
1000	25.9	26.2	26.6	27.0	27.4	27.9	28.4	28.9	29.5	30.0	31.2	32.4	33.7	35.1
1050	25.8	26.1	26.4	26.8	27.2	27.7	28.2	28.7	29.3	29.8	30.9	32.1	33.3	34.6
1100	25.8	26.0	26.3	26.7	27.1	27.6	28.1	28.6	29.1	29.6	30.6	31.7	32.9	34.2

*F. Din, Thermodynamic Functions of Gases, Vol. 1, Butterworths, London, 1962.

low pressure can be calculated from data on molecular structure such as vibrational frequencies, interatomic distances, and moments of inertia. One such property is the heat capacity, or specific heat, of a substance, which is the energy in calories necessary to raise the temperature of 1 mole of the substance $1°C$. As an example, the heat capacity of carbon monoxide gas up to $5000°K$ is given with very high accuracy by the equation

$$c_p^0 = R\left[\frac{7}{2} + \frac{u^2 e^u}{(e^u - 1)^2}\right] + \frac{R}{u}\left\{4x\left[\frac{u^3 e^u(2ue^u - 2e^u + u + 2)}{(e^u - 1)^4}\right]\right.$$
$$\left. + \delta\left[\frac{u^3 e^u(e^u + 1)}{(e^u - 1)^3}\right] + 16\gamma\right\} \tag{4.30}$$

where $u = T_0/T$ and x, δ, and γ are dimensionless constants. For carbon monoxide, $T_0 = 3082.9°K$, $x = 0.00628$, $\delta = 0.00909$, and $\gamma = 0.00089$.* The heat capacity at constant pressure (c_p^0) is strictly for the limit of very low pressure at which the gas behaves as a perfect gas, but the heat capacity at atmospheric pressure differs only slightly from c_p^0.

We shall not consider the derivation† of Eqn. (4.30) except to point out that $\frac{7}{2}R$ is the contribution to heat capacity of translational and rotational kinetic energy. The term $Ru^2 e^u/(e^u - 1)^2$ is the contribution of vibration of the nuclei, and the rest of the equation is a relatively small correction for anharmonicity of vibration and for stretching of the average C—O distance as temperature increases.

Example 4.13

Calculate the heat capacity (c_p^0) of carbon monoxide gas at $3000°K$.

Solution:

$$u = \frac{T_0}{T} = \frac{3082.9}{3000} = 1.0276$$

The functions of u are

$$\frac{u^2 e^u}{(e^u - 1)^2} = 0.9164$$

$$\frac{u^3 e^u(2ue^u - 2e^u + u + 2)}{(e^u - 1)^4} = 0.9307$$

$$\frac{u^3 e^u(e^u + 1)}{(e^u - 1)^3} = 1.9914$$

---

*Thermodynamic Properties to 6000°K for 210 Substances Involving the First 18 Elements, NASA SP-3001, National Aeronautics and Space Administration, Washington, D.C., 1963.

†G. N. Lewis, M. Randall, K. S. Pitzer, and L. Brewer, Thermodynamics, 2nd ed., McGraw-Hill, New York, 1961, Ch. 27.

From Eqn. (4.30),

$$c_p^0 = 1.9872(3.5 + 0.9164) + \frac{1.9872}{1.0276}[4(0.00628)(0.9307) + (0.00909)(1.9914)$$
$$+ 16(0.00089)]$$
$$= 8.7764 + 0.1077$$
$$= 8.884 \text{ cal/mole-}°\text{K}$$

Either tabulated data or complicated expressions like Eqn. (4.30) can be replaced by empirical equations using methods described in Ch. 5. For example, the heat capacity (c_p^0) of carbon monoxide in the temperature range from 300° to 3800°K is given within $\pm 2\%$ by a three-term empirical equation:

$$c_p^0 = a + bT + cT^2 \tag{4.31}$$

The advantage of an empirical equation of this type is that heat capacities of different substances can be written with an equation of the same form so that corresponding terms can be added and subtracted (see Ch. 9). Another advantage of Eq. (4.31) is that it is easy to differentiate and integrate. For carbon monoxide the constants are

$$a = 6.480 \text{ cal/mole-K}$$
$$b = 1.566 \times 10^{-3} \text{ cal/mole-K}^2$$
$$c = -2.387 \times 10^{-7} \text{ cal/mole-K}^3$$

Example 4.14

Calculate the heat capacity (c_p^0) of carbon monoxide gas at 3000°K using empirical equation (4.31).

Solution:

$$c_p^0 = 6.480 + 1.566 \times 10^{-3}(3000) - 2.387 \times 10^{-7}(3000)^2$$
$$= 6.480 + 4.698 - 2.148$$
$$= 9.03 \text{ cal/mole-K}$$

The error is

$$\frac{9.03 - 8.884}{8.884} \times 100 = 1.6\%$$

Coefficients of a four-term empirical equation for heat capacity

$$c_p^0 = a + bT + cT^2 + dT^3 \tag{4.32}$$

were derived by Kobe and his co-workers* for 100 pure gases; these sets of coefficients are given in Table 4.14. Notice that the temperature range of

*K. A. Kobe et al., "Thermochemistry for the Petrochemical Industry," *Petrol. Refiner* (Jan. 1949–Dec. 1959).

TABLE 4.14

MOLAL HEAT CAPACITIES OF GASES* AT ZERO PRESSURE $c_p^0 = a + bT + cT^2 + dT^3$ ($T = °K$)

		a	$b \times 10^2$	$c \times 10^5$	$d \times 10^9$	Temperature Range (°K)	Error Max. (%)	Avg. (%)
Paraffinic hydrocarbons								
Methane	CH_4	4.750	1.200	0.3030	−2.630	273–1500	1.33	0.57
Ethane	C_2H_6	1.648	4.124	−1.530	1.740	273–1500	0.83	0.28
Propane	C_3H_8	−0.966	7.279	−3.755	7.580	273–1500	0.40	0.12
n-Butane	C_4H_{10}	0.945	8.873	−4.380	8.360	273–1500	0.54	0.24
i-Butane	C_4H_{10}	−1.890	9.936	−5.495	11.92	273–1500	0.25	0.13
n-Pentane	C_5H_{12}	1.618	10.85	−5.365	10.10	273–1500	0.56	0.21
n-Hexane	C_6H_{14}	1.657	13.19	−6.844	13.78	273–1500	0.72	0.20
Monoolefinic hydrocarbons								
Ethylene	C_2H_4	0.944	3.735	−1.993	4.220	273–1500	0.54	0.13
Propylene	C_3H_6	0.753	5.691	−2.910	5.880	273–1500	0.73	0.17
1-Butene	C_4H_8	−0.240	8.650	−5.110	12.07	273–1500	0.25	0.18
i-Butene	C_4H_8	1.650	7.702	−3.981	8.020	273–1500	0.11	0.06
cis-2-Butene	C_4H_8	−1.778	8.078	−4.074	7.890	273–1500	0.78	0.14
trans-2-Butene	C_4H_8	2.340	7.220	−3.403	6.070	273–1500	0.54	0.12
Cycloparaffinic hydrocarbons								
Cyclopentane	C_5H_{10}	−12.957	13.087	−7.447	16.41	273–1500	1.00	0.25
Methylcyclopentane	C_6H_{12}	−12.114	15.380	−8.915	20.03	273–1500	0.86	0.23
Cyclohexane	C_6H_{12}	−15.935	16.454	−9.203	19.27	273–1500	1.57	0.37
Methylcyclohexane	C_7H_{14}	−15.070	18.972	−10.989	24.09	273–1500	0.92	0.22
Aromatic hydrocarbons								
Benzene	C_6H_6	−8.650	11.578	−7.540	18.54	273–1500	0.34	0.20
Toluene	C_7H_8	−8.213	13.357	−8.230	19.20	273–1500	0.29	0.18
Ethylbenzene	C_8H_{10}	−8.398	15.935	−10.003	23.95	273–1500	0.34	0.19
Styrene	C_8H_8	−5.968	14.354	−9.150	22.03	273–1500	0.37	0.23
Cumene	C_9H_{12}	−9.452	18.686	−11.869	28.80	273–1500	0.36	0.17

						Temp. range		
Acetylenes and diolefins								
Acetylene	C_2H_2	5.21	2.2008	-1.559	4.349	273–1500	1.46	0.59
Methylacetylene	C_3H_4	4.21	4.073	-2.192	4.713	273–1500	0.36	0.13
Dimethylacetylene	C_4H_6	3.54	5.838	-2.760	4.974	273–1500	0.70	0.16
Propadiene	C_3H_4	2.43	4.693	-2.781	6.484	273–1500	0.37	0.19
1,3-Butadiene	C_4H_6	-1.29	8.350	-5.582	14.24	273–1500	0.91	0.47
Isoprene	C_5H_8	-0.44	10.418	-6.762	16.93	273–1500	0.99	0.43
Combustion gases (low range)								
Nitrogen	N_2	6.903	-0.03753	0.1930	-0.6861	273–1800	0.59	0.34
Oxygen	O_2	6.085	0.3631	-0.1709	0.3133	273–1800	1.19	0.28
Air		6.713	0.04697	0.1147	-0.4696	273–1800	0.72	0.33
Hydrogen	H_2	6.952	-0.04576	0.09563	-0.2079	273–1800	1.01	0.26
Carbon monoxide	CO	6.726	0.04001	0.1283	-0.5307	273–1800	0.89	0.37
Carbon dioxide	CO_2	5.316	1.4285	-0.8362	1.784	273–1800	0.67	0.22
Water vapor	H_2O	7.700	0.04594	0.2521	-0.8587	273–1800	0.53	0.24
Combustion gases (high range)								
Nitrogen	N_2	6.529	0.1488	-0.02271	—	273–3800	2.05	0.72
Oxygen	O_2	6.732	0.1505	-0.01791	—	273–3800	3.24	1.20
Air		6.557	0.1477	-0.02148	—	273–3800	1.64	0.70
Hydrogen	H_2	6.424	0.1039	-0.007804	—	273–3800	2.14	0.79
Carbon dioxide	CO_2	*See footnote for special equation†*				273–3800	2.65	0.54
Carbon monoxide	CO	6.480	0.1566	-0.02387	—	273–3800	1.86	1.01
Water vapor	H_2O	6.970	0.3464	-0.04833	—	273–3800	2.03	0.66
Sulfur compounds								
Sulfur	S_2	6.499	0.5298	-0.3888	0.9520	273–1800	0.99	0.38
Sulfur dioxide	SO_2	6.157	1.384	-0.9103	2.057	273–1800	0.45	0.24
Sulfur trioxide	SO_3	3.918	3.483	-2.675	7.744	273–1300	0.29	0.13
Hydrogen sulfide	H_2S	7.070	0.3128	0.1364	-0.7867	273–1800	0.74	0.37
Carbon disulfide	CS_2	7.390	1.489	-1.096	2.760	273–1800	0.76	0.47
Carbonyl sulfide	COS	6.222	1.536	-1.058	2.560	273–1800	0.94	0.49
Halogens and halogen acids								
Fluorine	F_2	6.115	0.5864	-0.4186	0.9797	273–2000	0.78	0.45

†Equation for CO_2, 273 to 3800°K: $c_p^0 = 18.036 - 0.00004474T - 158.08/\sqrt{T}$.

TABLE 4.14 (Continued)

		a	$b \times 10^2$	$c \times 10^5$	$d \times 10^9$	Temperature Range, (°K)	Error Max. (%)	Error Avg. (%)
Chlorine	Cl_2	6.8214	0.57095	−0.5107	1.547	273–1500	0.50	0.23
Bromine	Br_2	8.051	0.2462	−0.2128	0.6406	273–1500	0.43	0.15
Iodine	I_2	8.504	0.13135	−0.10684	0.3125	273–1800	0.11	0.06
Hydrogen fluoride	HF	7.201	−0.1178	0.1576	−0.3760	273–2000	0.37	0.09
Hydrogen chloride	HCl	7.244	−0.1820	0.3170	−1.036	273–1500	0.22	0.08
Hydrogen bromide	HBr	7.169	−0.1604	0.3314	−1.161	273–1500	0.27	0.12
Hydrogen iodide	HI	6.702	0.04546	0.1216	−0.4813	273–1900	0.92	0.39
Chloromethanes								
Methyl chloride	CH_3Cl	3.05	2.596	−1.244	2.300	273–1500	0.75	0.16
Methylene chloride	CH_2Cl_2	4.20	3.419	−2.3500	6.068	273–1500	0.67	0.30
Chloroform	$CHCl_3$	7.61	3.461	−2.668	7.344	273–1500	0.92	0.42
Carbon tetrachloride	CCl_4	12.24	3.400	−2.995	8.828	273–1500	1.21	0.57
Phosgene	$COCl_2$	10.35	1.653	−0.8408	—	273–1000	0.97	0.46
Thiophosgene	$CSCl_2$	10.80	1.859	−1.045	—	273–1000	0.98	0.71
Cyanogens								
Cyanogen	$(CN)_2$	9.82	1.4858	−0.6571	—	273–1000	0.69	0.42
Hydrogen cyanide	HCN	6.34	0.8375	−0.2611	—	273–1500	1.42	0.76
Cyanogen chloride	CNCl	7.97	1.0745	−0.5265	—	273–1000	0.97	0.58
Cyanogen bromide	CNBr	8.82	0.9084	−0.4367	—	273–1000	0.85	0.54
Cyanogen iodide	CNI	9.69	0.7213	−0.3265	—	273–1000	0.75	0.37
Acetonitrile	CH_3CN	5.09	2.7634	−0.9111	—	273–1200	0.45	0.26
Acrylic nitrile	CH_2CHCN	4.55	4.1039	−1.6939	—	273–1000	0.63	0.41
Oxides of nitrogen								
Nitric oxide	NO	6.461	0.2358	−0.07705	0.08729	273–3800	2.23	0.54
Nitric oxide	NO	7.008	−0.02244	0.2328	−1.000	273–1500	0.97	0.36

Name	Formula					Temp. range		
Nitrous oxide	N_2O	5.758	1.4004	−0.8508	2.526	273–1500	0.59	0.26
Nitrogen dioxide	NO_2	5.48	1.365	−0.841	1.88	273–1500	0.46	0.18
Nitrogen tetroxide	N_2O_4	7.9	4.46	−2.71	—	273–600	0.97	0.36
Oxygenated hydrocarbons								
Formaldehyde	CH_2O	5.447	0.9739	0.1703	−2.078	273–1500	1.41	0.62
Acetaldehyde	C_2H_4O	4.19	3.164	−0.515	−3.800	273–1000	0.40	0.17
Methanol	CH_4O	4.55	2.186	−0.291	−1.92	273–1000	0.18	0.08
Ethanol	C_2H_6O	4.75	5.006	−2.479	4.790	273–1500	0.40	0.22
Ethylene oxide	C_2H_4O	−1.12	4.925	−2.389	3.149	273–1000	0.36	0.14
Ketene	C_2H_2O	4.11	2.966	−1.793	4.22	273–1500	0.48	0.17
Miscellaneous hydrocarbons								
Cyclopropane	C_3H_6	−6.481	8.206	−5.577	15.61	273–1000	0.94	0.35
Isopentane	C_5H_{12}	−2.273	12.434	−7.097	15.86	273–1500	0.34	0.14
Neopentane	C_5H_{12}	−3.865	13.305	−8.018	18.83	273–1500	0.27	0.12
o-Xylene	C_8H_{10}	−3.789	14.291	−8.354	18.80	273–1500	0.52	0.15
m-Xylene	C_8H_{10}	−6.533	14.905	−8.831	20.05	273–1500	0.67	0.16
p-Xylene	C_8H_{10}	−5.334	14.220	−7.984	17.03	273–1500	0.56	0.18
C_3 Oxygenated hydrocarbons								
Carbon suboxide	C_3O_2	8.203	3.073	−2.081	5.182	273–1500	1.22	0.31
Acetone	C_3H_6O	1.625	6.661	−3.737	8.307	273–1500	0.56	0.10
i-Propyl alcohol	C_3H_8O	0.7936	8.502	−5.016	11.56	273–1500	0.35	0.18
n-Propyl alcohol	C_3H_8O	−1.307	9.235	−5.800	14.14	273–1500	0.90	0.30
Allyl alcohol	C_3H_6O	0.5203	7.122	−4.259	9.948	273–1500	0.23	0.14
Chloroethenes								
Chloroethene	C_2H_3Cl	2.401	4.270	−2.751	6.797	273–1500	0.46	0.22
1,1-Dichloroethene	$C_2H_2Cl_2$	5.899	4.383	−3.182	8.516	273–1500	0.81	0.40
cis-1,2-Dichloroethene	$C_2H_2Cl_2$	4.336	4.691	−3.397	9.010	273–1500	0.70	0.39
trans-1,2-Dichloroethene	$C_2H_2Cl_2$	5.661	4.295	−3.022	7.891	273–1500	0.50	0.27
Trichloroethene	C_2HCl_3	9.200	4.517	−3.600	10.10	273–1500	1.17	0.50
Tetrachloroethene	C_2Cl_4	15.11	3.799	−3.179	9.089	273–1500	0.94	0.42
Nitrogen compounds								
Ammonia	NH_3	6.5846	0.61251	0.23663	−1.5981	273–1500	0.91	0.36

TABLE 4.14 (Continued)

		a	$b \times 10^2$	$c \times 10^5$	$d \times 10^9$	Temperature Range, (°K)	Error Max. (%)	Avg. (%)
Hydrazine	N_2H_4	3.890	3.554	−2.304	5.990	273–1500	1.80	0.50
Methylamine	CH_5N	2.9956	3.6101	−1.6446	2.9505	273–1500	0.59	0.07
Dimethylamine	C_2H_7N	−0.275	6.6152	−3.4826	7.1510	273–1500	0.96	0.15
Trimethylamine	C_3H_9N	−2.098	9.6187	−5.5488	12.432	273–1500	0.91	0.18
Fluorochloromethanes								
Carbon tetrachloride	CCl_4	9.288	5.099	−5.729	22.57	273–1000	0.36	0.20
Fluorotrichloromethane	CCl_3F	6.964	5.563	−6.144	24.06	273–1000	0.33	0.21
Dichlorodifluoromethane	CCl_2F_2	5.085	5.685	−5.93	22.15	273–1000	0.25	0.15
Chlorotrifluoromethane	$CClF_3$	3.311	5.829	−5.846	21.24	273–1000	0.18	0.12
Carbon tetrafluoride	CF_4	1.666	5.83	−5.502	18.97	273–1000	0.10	0.05

*K. A. Kobe et al., "Thermochemistry for the Petrochemical Industry," *Petrol. Refiner* (Jan. 1949–Dec. 1959).

142

applicability is furnished for each set of coefficients; extrapolation outside this range is not recommended. Errors do not exceed 1–2% within the range of applicability. Units of a, b, c, and d are cal/mole-K, cal/mole-K^2, cal/mole-K^3, and cal/mole-K^4, respectively, so that substitution of the temperature in °K in Eqn. (4.32) yields c_p^0 in units of cal/mole-K.

Calculation of enthalpy and heats of reaction using data on heat capacity is discussed in Ch. 9.

Example 4.15

Calculate the zero-pressure specific heat, c_p^0, of benzene vapor at 726.8°C. What is the maximum error expected?

Solution:

Absolute temperature $T = t + 273.2 = 1000°K$. Substituting in Eqn. (4.32) with coefficients from Table 4.14,

$$c_p^0 = -8.65 + (11.578 \times 10^{-2})(1000) + (-7.54 \times 10^{-5})(1000)^2$$
$$+ (18.54 \times 10^{-9})(1000)^3$$
$$= -8.65 + 115.78 - 75.4 + 18.54$$
$$= 50.3 \frac{cal}{gmole-°K}$$

The maximum percentage error is 0.34%. Hence, the maximum absolute error expected is $(0.0034)(50.3) = 0.2$. Therefore,

$$c_p^0 = 50.3 \pm 0.2 \frac{cal}{gmole-°K}$$

Graphs

The graph of a function shows its general character, singularities, discontinuities, and other distinguishing features which might not be apparent in a table. For example, Fig. 4-12 is a graph of the heat capacity (c_p) of carbon dioxide gas at three temperatures. Several interesting features of the variation of heat capacity with pressure are immediately apparent. According to the theory of perfect gases, heat capacity is independent of pressure; the lines in Fig. 4-12 would be horizontal for a perfect gas. The zero-pressure heat capacity (c_p^0) at 70°C (9.32 cal/mole-K) is very nearly the same as the value at atmospheric pressure (9.42 cal/mole-K). The higher the temperature, the less the variation of heat capacity with pressure. c_p becomes infinitely large at the critical point (31°C, 72.85 atm) and at 70°C exhibits a large but finite maximum.

Values of heat capacity at intermediate points not plotted on the graph (say, at 95 atm and 100°C) must be interpolated. Visual interpolation is fast but inaccurate. It is difficult to read most graphs with an accuracy greater than two significant figures.

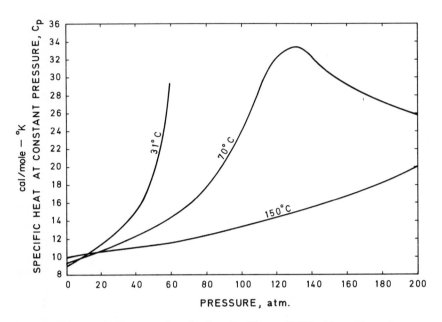

Figure 4-12   Heat capacity of carbon dioxide gas. (F. Din, *Thermodynamic Functions of Gases*, Vol. 1, Butterworths, London, 1962.)

Although a graph gives an overall picture of the behavior of a function, it cannot be used directly for calculations on a computer. Reading values from a graph in preparation for storage in the computer's memory is awkward. This communications problem has been solved by new electronic scanning equipment that automatically takes points from a graph for subsequent correlation, interpolation, and storage in a computer.

Nomographs

A nomograph is a special kind of graph that enables one to read off the value of a dependent variable with a straightedge when the value of the independent variable is given. Figure 4-13 shows a nomograph for specific heat as a function of temperature for about 60 liquids. The nomograph is read by passing a straight line through the point for the liquid and the temperature on the left scale. The intersection of this straight line with the scale on the right gives the value of the specific heat. Other values of specific heat for the liquid of interest are obtained by rotating the straight line about an axis located at the point for the liquid (see Fig. 4-14).

Since both scales in Fig. 4-13 are linear, the equation for specific heat upon which it is based must be linear in temperature,

$$c_p = a + bt \tag{4.33}$$

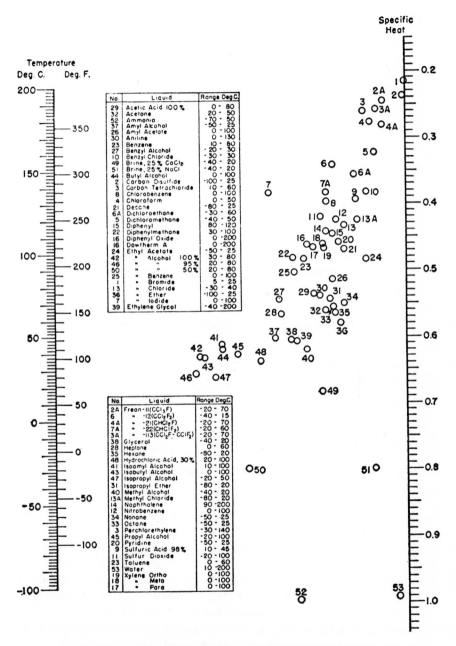

Figure 4-13 Specific heats of liquids in BTU/lb-°F or cal/g-°C. (J. H. Perry, ed., *Chemical Engineers' Handbook*, 4th ed., McGraw-Hill, New York, 1963, p. 3-126.)

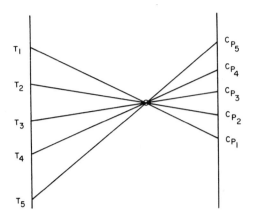

Figure 4-14 Reading data from a nomograph.

where c_p is specific heat in cal/g-°C, t is temperature in °C, and a and b are coefficients, different for each liquid. For example, it may be verified that the nomograph reproduces the specific heat of liquid acetone according to Eqn. (4.33) with

$$a = 0.512 \text{ cal/g-°C} \quad \text{and} \quad b = 7.67 \times 10^{-4} \text{ cal/g-(°C)}^2$$

for the range 20° to 50°C.

A second example of a nomograph is Fig. 4-15, which gives latent heat of vaporization of about 30 liquids as a function of temperature. What is the equation for latent heat upon which Fig. 4-15 is based (see Problem 4.17)?

4.5 Properties of Mixtures

Estimating properties of mixtures is unavoidable because for every set of 100 chemical compounds there are

$$\frac{100!}{2!(100 - 2)!} = 4950 \text{ binary mixtures}$$

$$\frac{100!}{3!(100 - 3)!} = 161,700 \text{ ternary mixtures, etc.}$$

Since it is not feasible to measure properties of every mixture experimentally, it is essential to develop reliable methods for estimating mixture properties using the properties of the pure components.

The simplest relation between mixture and pure-component properties is the molal average: For any property p, the molal average is

$$p = \sum_{j=1}^{N_c} x_j p_j \tag{4.34}$$

where p_j is the value of p for pure compound j (at the temperature and

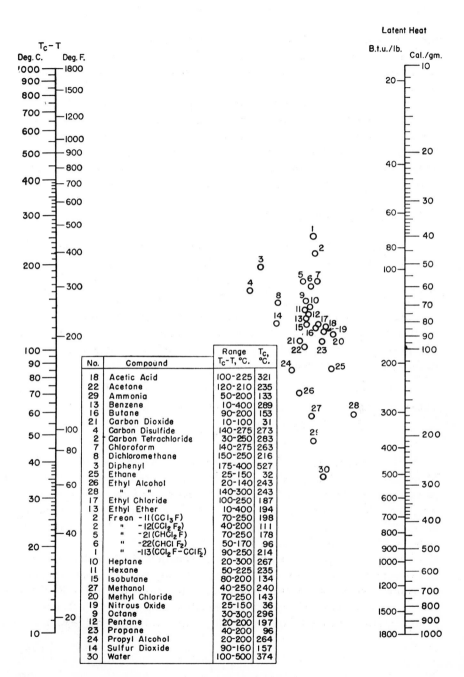

Figure 4-15 Latent heats of vaporization. (J. H. Perry, ed., *Chemical Engineers' Handbook*, 4th ed., McGraw-Hill, New York, 1963, p. 3-114.) The range of the correlation and normal boiling point is tabulated for each compound.

pressure of the mixture). x_j is the mole fraction of component j, and the summation is over all the N_c components of the mixture. The molal average is used only when all the pure substances are in the same state (solid, liquid, or gas).

Equation (4.34) works well for some properties but fails for others. For example, Eqn. (4.34) predicts molar volume of mixtures of liquids at atmospheric pressure with errors seldom exceeding a few percent. On the other hand, the viscosity of a gas mixture is sometimes larger than the viscosity of either pure component, and therefore Eqn. (4.34) is only a crude approximation for viscosity. Thus, it is necessary to discuss each property individually.

Volumetric properties of mixtures

1. *Molal Average.* The molal average, Eqn. (4.34), is correct for the molar volume of gas mixtures only in the limit of low pressure, where

$$v = \sum x_j v_j = \sum x_j \frac{RT}{P} = \frac{RT}{P} \tag{4.35}$$

Equation (4.34) is also a good approximation for molar volume of liquid mixtures at low pressure. For example, the actual molar volume of a mixture of 6 mole % ethanol and 94 mole % water is 20.17 cm³/mole at 20°C; the molal average at the same temperature is

$$v = \sum x_j v_j = 0.06(58.36) + 0.94(18.05) = 20.47 \text{ cm}^3/\text{mole}$$

Thus, the error incurred by using the molal average is

$$\frac{20.47 - 20.17}{20.17} \times 100 = 1.5\%$$

2. *PVT Equations of State.* Equation (4.34), written for the molar volume of gas mixtures, is Amagat's law. Amagat's law is correct in the limit of low pressure and works fairly well at very high pressure. At intermediate pressure (say, from a few atmospheres to a few hundred atmospheres, depending on the temperature) Amagat's law is a poor approximation. A *PVT* equation of state for the mixture is needed for this region of intermediate pressures. Consider, for example, the Redlich-Kwong equation (4.14), which contains two constants, a and b. How do these constants vary with the composition of a mixture? There is no precise answer to this question because the Redlich-Kwong equation is itself an empirical equation and there is no theory for guidance. However, the following "mixing rules" work reasonably well:

$$a_m = \sum_{j=1}^{N_c} \sum_{k=1}^{N_c} x_j x_k a_{jk} \tag{4.36}$$

and

$$b_m = \sum_{j=1}^{N_c} x_j b_j \tag{4.37}$$

The interaction parameter a_{jk} is given by

$$a_{jk} = \sqrt{a_j a_k} \tag{4.38}$$

The mixing rules in Eqns. (4.36) and (4.37) are also used for the constants of the van der Waals equation (4.9). Mixing rules for the eight constants of the Benedict-Webb-Rubin equation are given in Appendix E of *The Properties of Gases and Liquids*, 2nd ed., by R. C. Reid and T. K. Sherwood, McGraw-Hill, New York, 1966.

Example 4.16

Calculate the molar volume of a mixture of 67.4 mole % n-butane and 32.6 mole % carbon dioxide at 190.5 atm and 171.1°C using the Redlich-Kwong equation. Compare the result with the experimental value [R.H. Olds, H.H. Reamer, B.H. Sage, and W.N. Lacey, "Phase Equilibria in Hydrocarbon Systems," *Ind. Eng. Chem.*, **41**, 475 (1949)] of 125.0 cm³/mole.

Solution:

Using Eqs. (4.15) and (4.16) and the critical properties in Table 4.1,

Component	No.	a	b
Carbon dioxide	1	0.638×10^8	29.69
n-Butane	2	2.864×10^8	80.67

The units of a and b are consistent with v in cm³/mole, T in °K, P in atm, and $R = 82.06$ cm³-atm/mole-°K.

From Eqn. (4.38),

$$a_{12} = \sqrt{a_1 a_2} = 1.351 \times 10^8$$

From Eqn. (4.36),

$$a_m = x_1^2 a_1 + 2x_1 x_2 a_{12} + x_2^2 a_2$$
$$= (0.326)^2(0.638 \times 10^8) + 2(0.326)(0.674)(1.351 \times 10^8)$$
$$+ (0.674)^2(2.864 \times 10^8) = 1.962 \times 10^8 (cm^3/mole)^2 atm(°K)^{1/2}$$

From Eqn. (4.37),

$$b_m = x_1 b_1 + x_2 b_2 = (0.326)(29.69) + (0.674)(80.67)$$
$$= 64.05 \text{ cm}^3/\text{mole}$$

The Redlich-Kwong equation (4.14) is written

$$f\{v\} = P - \frac{RT}{v - b} + \frac{a}{T^{1/2}v(v + b)} = 0$$

$$= 190.5 - \frac{(82.06)(444.25)}{v - 64.05} + \frac{1.962 \times 10^8}{(444.25)^{1/2}v(v + 64.05)} = 0$$

Using any of the methods of solving algebraic equations that are described in Ch. 11,

$$v = 128.2 \text{ cm}^3/\text{mole}$$

The error is

$$\frac{128.2 - 125.0}{125.0} \times 100 = 2.6\%$$

3. *Principle of Corresponding States*. The principle of corresponding states discussed in Sec. 4.1 may be extended to mixtures. One needs to know the reduced properties, and hence the critical properties, of the mixture.

If a liquid mixture in equilibrium with an equal volume of vapor is heated with adjustment of pressure so as to maintain equal volumes, as illustrated in Fig. 4-16, then the mixture will eventually reach a point at which the intensive properties (density, composition, etc.) of the liquid and vapor are identical.

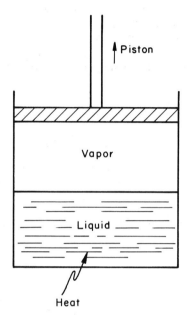

Figure 4-16 Mixture heated and expanded to maintain equal volumes of vapor and liquid.

This point is called the critical point of the mixture and is a function of composition. For example, the critical pressure and critical temperature of a mixture of *n*-butane and carbon dioxide, measured by Olds et al. [*Ind. Eng. Chem.*, *41*, 475 (1949)], is shown in Fig. 4-17.

These real critical properties are measured in the laboratory. Pseudocritical properties are defined by mixing rules, the simplest of which is Kay's rule,*

$$T_{cm} = \sum x_j T_{cj} \tag{4.39}$$

$$P_{cm} = \sum x_j P_{cj} \tag{4.40}$$

where the summation is over all the components of the mixture. Pseudocritical

---

*W. B. Kay, "Density of Hydrocarbon Gases and Liquids," *Ind. Eng. Chem.*, *28*, 1014 (1936).

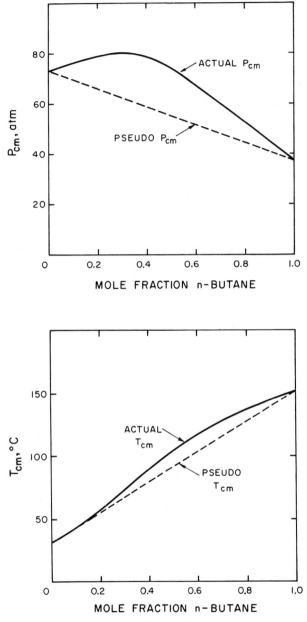

Figure 4-17 Comparison of experimental critical properties and pseudo-critical properties of mixtures of *n*-butane and carbon dioxide. [R. H. Olds, H. H. Reamer, B. H. Sage, and W. N. Lacey, "Phase Equilibria in Hydrocarbon Systems," *Ind. Eng. Chem.*, 41, 475 (1949).]

properties are linear in composition and are shown in Fig. 4-17 as a dashed line.

The principle of corresponding states is extended to mixtures by mixing rules such as Kay's rule. Pseudocritical properties, not real critical properties, are used to compute reduced properties. Reduced properties should not be calculated using actual critical properties of the mixture.

Third parameters (ω, z_c) are also assumed to be linear in composition. For the critical compressibility factor,

$$z_{cm} = \sum x_j z_{cj} \tag{4.41}$$

and for the acentric factor,

$$\omega_m = \sum x_j \omega_j \tag{4.42}$$

Example 4.17

Repeat the calculation of molar volume of a mixture of n-butane and carbon dioxide in Example 4.16. Use the principle of corresponding states and the tables of Pitzer et al.

Solution:

From Tables 4.1 and 4.4,

Component	No.	$T_c(°K)$	$P_c(atm)$	ω
Carbon dioxide	1	304.2	72.9	0.225
n-Butane	2	425.2	37.5	0.201

Pseudocritical properties of the mixture are given by Eqs. (4.39) and (4.40):

$$T_{cm} = \sum x_j T_{cj} = 0.326(304.2) + 0.674(425.2) = 385.75°K$$
$$P_{cm} = \sum x_j P_{cj} = 0.326(72.9) + 0.674(37.5) = 49.04 \text{ atm}$$

The acentric factor of the mixture is given by Eqn. (4.42):

$$\omega_m = \sum x_j \omega_j = 0.326(0.225) + 0.674(0.201) = 0.209$$

Reduced properties of the mixture are

$$T_r = \frac{T}{T_c} = \frac{444.25}{385.75} = 1.152$$

$$P_r = \frac{P}{P_c} = \frac{190.5}{49.04} = 3.884$$

Using Eqn. (4.28) and linear interpolation of Tables 4.5 and 4.6,

$$z = z^{(0)} + \omega z^{(1)} = 0.590 + (0.209)(-0.035) = 0.583$$

Therefore,

$$v = \frac{zRT}{P} = \frac{(0.583)(82.05)(444.25)}{(190.5)} = 112 \text{ cm}^3/\text{mole}$$

The error is

$$\frac{125 - 112}{125} \times 100 = 10\%$$

The principle of corresponding states extended to mixtures gives errors in the density of the order of 10% in the critical region, as compared to a few percent for pure materials.

PROBLEMS

4.1. The following properties of saturated solid acetylene in equilibrium with its own vapor are tabulated in *Thermodynamic Functions of Gases*, Vol. II, by F. Din, Butterworths, London, 1962:

Pressure (atm)	Temperature (°K)	Enthalpy (cal/mole)		Volume (cm³/mole)	
		Solid	Vapor	Solid	Vapor
0.7	184.34				
1.0	189.13	1330	6319	35.7	15,050
1.266	192.4				

Do these data satisfy the Clapeyron equation?

4.2. The specific volume of carbon dioxide is 30 cm³/g and the pressure is 15 atm but the temperature is unknown. Calculate the temperature under these conditions using the perfect gas law and compare your result with the experimental value of 0°C.

4.3. Repeat the calculation of the temperature of carbon dioxide gas in Problem 4.2 using van der Waals' equation of state. Constants for carbon dioxide are given in Example 4.3.

4.4. Carbon dioxide is liquefied and compressed to a density of 1 g/cm³ inside a container at 0°C. Calculate the pressure using the Redlich-Kwong equation and compare your result with the experimental value of 140 atm. Why is the error so large? (*Hint:* See Fig. 4-5.)

4.5. Estimate the molar volume of carbon dioxide gas at 30 atm and 0°C by means of the virial equation of state terminated after the second virial coefficient. At 0°C for carbon dioxide, $B = -151$ cm³/mole.

4.6. Figure 4-1 shows a set of four isotherms and the boundary of the two-phase region for carbon dioxide. Sketch the same figure for *n*-butane using only the data in the figure and critical constants from Table 4.1.

4.7. Plot the compressibility factor (z) for ethane at 320°K as a function of pressure from 0 to 50 atm

a. Using the tables of Lydersen, Greenkorn, and Hougen.
b. Using the tables of Pitzer et al.

Compare your results with experimental values:

Pressure (atm)	$z = Pv/RT$
1	0.994
2	0.988
5	0.969
—10	0.937
20	0.868
30	0.789
40	0.697
50	0.579

4.8. Calculate and prepare a graph of compressibility factor versus pressure for ethylene at 75°C from $P = 0$ to $P = 200$ bars (1 atm = 1.01325 bars) using the following methods:
(a) The perfect gas law.
(b) The virial equation of state terminated after the second virial coefficient. $B = -100$ cm³/mole for ethylene at 75°C.
(c) The van der Waals' equation. Get constants from critical properties of ethylene.
(d) The principle of corresponding states and the tables of Pitzer et al. The acentric factor of ethylene is equal to 0.08.

Make a graphical comparison of these calculated results with experimental data for ethylene at 75°C:

Pressure (bars)	Volume (cm³/g)	Pressure (bars)	Volume (cm³/g)
1	1028.4	80	9.000
2	512.4	100	6.501
5	202.81	120	5.048
10	99.59	140	4.229
20	47.94	160	3.754
40	22.03	180	3.453
60	13.34	200	3.246

Discuss briefly the relative accuracy and computational difficulties of these methods.

4.9. Estimate the second virial coefficient of carbon dioxide at 100°C using Eqn. (4.29) and compare with the experimental value in Fig. 4-8.

4.10. The properties of saturated liquid and vapor acetylene at 240.7°K are

Vapor pressure (atm)	Enthalpy (cal/mole)		Volume (cm³/mole)	
	Liquid	Vapor	Liquid	Vapor
10	3517	6584	48.4	1654

Compare these experimental data to values predicted by the tables of Pitzer et al. The acentric factor of acetylene is equal to 0.186.

4.11. Look up the following properties in the *Handbook of Chemistry and Physics:*
  (a) The melting point of pyridine.
  (b) The solubility of codeine (morphine 3-methyl ether) in ethyl alcohol.
  (c) The normal boiling point of magnesium oxide (MgO).
  (d) The surface tension of chloroform ($CHCl_3$) at room temperature.
  (e) The viscosity of chloroform gas at 100°C.
  (f) The density of 30% aqueous solution of potassium iodide at room temperature.
  (g) The vapor pressure of liquid tin at 1900°C.
  (h) The vapor pressure of subcooled liquid water and the vapor pressure of ice at -15.5°C.

4.12. Estimate the heat capacity (c_p^0) of carbon monoxide at 25°C using empirical equation (4.32); compare your estimate with the precise value from Eqn. (4.30). Does the error lie within the limits given in Table 4.14?

4.13. Determine the heat capacity (c_p) of liquid methanol (methyl alcohol) at -35°C and at 20°C using Fig. 4-13.

4.14. What is the latent heat of vaporization of *n*-octane at its normal boiling point according to the nomograph, Fig. 4-15?

4.15. Estimate, using heat capacities of the pure liquids, the heat capacity (c_p) of an aqueous solution containing 25% ethanol and 45% propanol (mole percentages) at 25°C.

4.16. A gaseous mixture of 72% trichlorofluoromethane (Freon 11) and 28% dichlorodifluoromethane (Freon 12) is compressed to a density of 0.5 g/cm³ at 275°C. Calculate the pressure
  (a) Using the Redlich-Kwong equation extended to mixtures.
  (b) By the principle of corresponding states and Kay's rule.

4.17. Derive an equation for the latent heat of vaporization of methanol as a function of temperature using the data point for methanol in Fig. 4-15. (*Hint:* The scales in Fig. 4-15 are the antilogarithm of the rectangular coordinate.) Compare the constants with those calculated in Example 5.2.

4.18. Calculate and plot the compressibility factor ($z = Pv/RT$) from 0 to 100 atm at 100°C for pure ethane using van der Waals' equation. Calculate a and b using Eqns. (4.12) and (4.13) and the critical constants in Table 4.1. Preparation of the plot is simplified by picking values of molar volume (v) as the independent variable and then calculating P (and z) from van der Waals'

equation. Compare your calculated compressibility factors with experimental
values at 100°C from Perry's *Chemical Engineers' Handbook*:

ρ (mole/liter)	P (atm)	z
0.5	14.43	0.9425
1.0	27.28	0.8909
1.5	38.79	0.8446
2.0	49.03	0.8006
2.5	58.29	0.7615
3.0	66.68	0.7259
3.5	74.36	0.6939
4.0	81.5	0.6654
4.5	88.25	0.6405
5.0	94.73	0.6188

4.19. Estimate the vapor pressure of *n*-butane at 60°C using Table 4.9 and critical
properties from Table 4.1. The acentric factor for *n*-butane is $\omega = 0.202$.

Data Processing   **5**

Invention of the computer has launched a "postindustrial revolution" in which information is a major commodity of the market place.

Before this revolution, accumulation of scientific information was limited by old-fashioned techniques of data processing, which relied heavily upon handbooks, slide rules, graphical correlations, and nomographs. These traditional tools of the engineer are not obsolete but are gradually being supplemented by computers, whose power to store, retrieve, and process information improves with each new generation.

Two major advances in computers were made in the late 1960s. First, the workhorse of the computer, the high-speed control and arithmetic units, was interfaced to disk memory units capable of storing vast quantities of information. For example, a single disk stores over 6 million 10-digit numbers. Second, computers have been interfaced with typewriter and video-display terminals using telephone lines so that information can be exchanged freely between offices, laboratories, and homes.

The capacity to store and retrieve large quantities of information is not necessarily a blessing; one can be overwhelmed by data too voluminous for digestion. In engineering, the essential step is the transformation of raw data into information useful for the solution of a particular problem. This transformation, called data processing, is the subject of this chapter.

5.1 Correlation, Approximation, and
Interpolation

Engineering calculations are based upon functions, especially numerical-valued functions. A numerical-valued function assigns to each point x in its domain a single real number $f\{x\}$ called the value of f at x.

The function $f\{x\}$ may be characterized by a formula, a graph, or a table. For example, Fig. 5-1 shows three different methods of describing the same function. The representation of $f\{x\}$ in a table emphasizes the fact that a function is essentially a mapping. f is the rule or mapping, and $f\{x\}$ is the value of f at x. It is useful to think of a function as a machine into which you can feed points, while the corresponding values emerge from the other end.*

Engineers often work with functions of more than one real variable. The compact notation

$$y = y\{x_1, x_2, \ldots, x_n\}$$

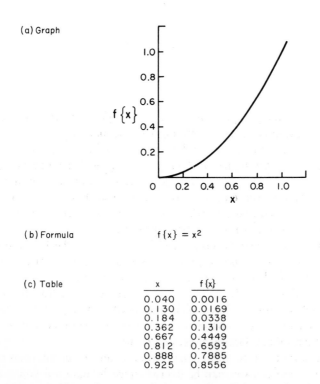

(a) Graph

$f\{x\}$

(b) Formula $f\{x\} = x^2$

(c) Table

x	$f\{x\}$
0.040	0.0016
0.130	0.0169
0.184	0.0338
0.362	0.1310
0.667	0.4449
0.812	0.6593
0.888	0.7885
0.925	0.8556

Figure 5-1 Alternative means of representation of the same function.

*R. C. Buck, *Advanced Calculus*, McGraw-Hill, New York, 1965, p. 16.

refers to a function of n real variables $(x_1, x_2, \ldots, x_n)$, and y is the value that the function assigns to a particular point in the domain. For example, the fact that the heat capacity of air is a function of temperature and pressure is stated concisely by the notation

$$c_p = c_p\{T, P\}$$

Values of this particular function at a few selected points are shown in Table 5.1.

TABLE 5.1
HEAT CAPACITY OF AIR (J/mole-°K)*

T (°K)	P (atm)			
	1	10	20	30
180	29.52	31.24	33.51	36.14
200	29.38	30.59	32.10	33.73
220	29.26	30.14	31.23	32.38
240	29.16	29.88	30.72	31.60

*F. Din, *Thermodynamic Functions of Gases*, Vol. 2, Butterworths, London, 1962.

Data processing is concerned with correlation (finding the formula for a function), approximation (finding an approximate formula or graph of the function), and interpolation (finding the value of a function between two points in its domain). For example, consider the function $c_p\{T, P\}$ of air, for which only a few points are given in Table 5.1. Does there exist an accurate formula for this function? If not, is there an approximate formula for the domain of interest? What are the geometrical properties of the graph of this function? What is the value of the function at the point $T = 210°$K, $P = 15$ atm?

In the following sections we shall examine some of the answers to these questions.

5.2 Graphical Methods

Graphs of experimental data can often be replotted in a form more con-venient for interpolation by a *transformation of coordinates*. Let us consider the set of five data points listed in Table 5.2 and plotted in Fig. 5-2. Assume that the formula for the function is unknown.

Instead of plotting y versus x, transform the coordinates by plotting x/y versus x as shown in Fig. 5-3. The new function $Y\{X\}$ is defined by the

TABLE 5.2
FIVE POINTS OF FUNCTION
$y = f\{x\}$

y	x
0.339	0.146
0.477	0.233
0.694	0.430
0.934	0.825
1.111	1.430

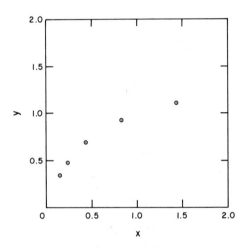

Figure 5-2 Five points of function $y = f\{x\}$.

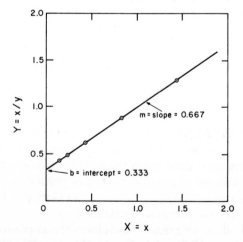

Figure 5-3 Plot of function $y = f\{x\}$ in transformed coordinates.

transformation

$$Y = x/y$$
$$X = x$$

Figure 5-3 shows that the new function is linear, so

$$Y = mX + b \qquad (5.1)$$

where m is the slope of the straight line and b is its Y-intercept. From Fig. 5-3,

$$\frac{x}{y} = (0.667)x + (0.333)$$

Solving for y,

$$y = \frac{3x}{1 + 2x} \qquad (5.2)$$

The formula for $f\{x\}$ is useful for interpolation and, more cautiously, for extrapolation. For example, from Eqn. (5.2),

$$\lim_{x \to \infty} y = 1.5$$

$$\lim_{x \to 0} \frac{dy}{dx} = 3.0$$

Both of these extrapolations are difficult to obtain directly from Fig. 5-2.

Given a nonlinear function such as the one plotted in Fig. 5-2, the objective of the transformation is to find two new functions F_1 and F_2 such that

$$F_1\{x, y\} = mF_2\{x\} + b \qquad (5.3)$$

where m and b are constants for all values of x. Thus, for the function of Eqn. (5.2), a transformation that satisfies Eqn. (5.3) is

$$Y = F_1\{x, y\} = \frac{x}{y}$$

$$X = F_2\{x\} = x$$

The trick of the transformation is to guess the formula of a function from the shape of its curve on a graph. Certain functions such as e^x and x^n occur frequently in engineering problems. Particular curves generated by these functions can be recognized by studying families of curves from which they are derived.

Figure 5-4 shows transformations for three simple but important functions. The family of curves for $y = x^n$ all pass through the point (1, 1). Special cases of this family include a straight line of unit slope ($n = 1$) and an equilateral hyperbola ($n = -1$). Under the transformation $Y = \log_{10} y$ and $X = \log_{10} x$, the curves are transformed to a family of straight lines of slope n ($Y = nX$). The transformed coordinates are shown in Fig. 5-5. Figure 5-5 is so-called log-log paper upon which lines are ruled for the antilogarithm of the rectangular coordinates. We have added scales on the right and top

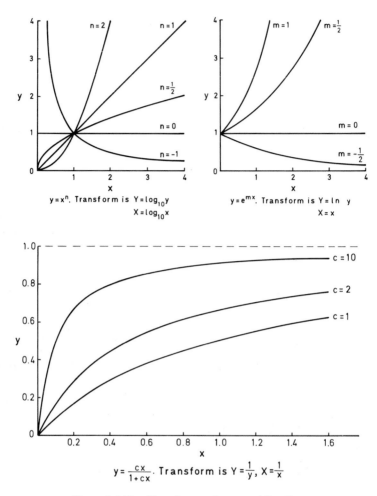

Figure 5-4 Families of curves for several functions.

of the graph for the value of the logarithm; these scales do not appear on commercial log-log paper. The advantage of using log-log paper is that values of x and y may be plotted directly without calculating values of the logarithm. Notice that values of the slope (n) in Fig. 5-5 must be calculated using the $\log_{10} y$ and $\log_{10} x$ scales.

The second function in Fig. 5-4 is $y = e^{mx}$. All the curves intersect the ordinate at $(0, 1)$. If m is negative, y goes to zero asymptotically as x increases; if m is positive, y tends toward infinity as x increases. The transformation $Y = \ln y$ and $X = x$ yields a family of straight lines of slope m ($Y = mX$), as shown in Fig. 5-6. A graph with the ruling shown in Fig. 5-6 is so-called semilog paper. Lines are ruled for the antilogarithm of the rec-

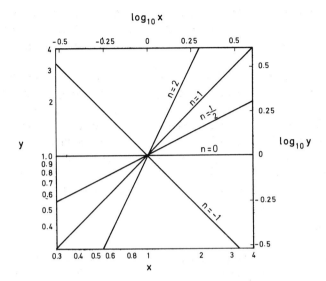

Figure 5-5 Function $y = x^n$ plotted on log-log coordinates.

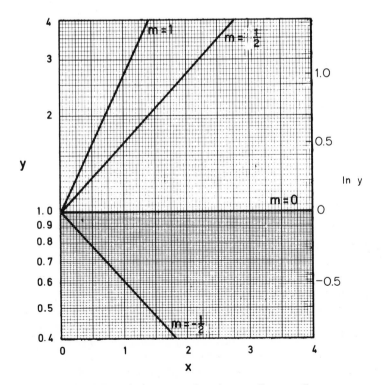

Figure 5-6 Function $y = e^{mx}$ plotted on semilog coordinates.

tangular coordinates of the ordinate, and the abscissa is ruled in the usual way. We have added a scale on the right-hand side of the graph for the value of the natural logarithm; this scale does not appear on commercial semilog paper.

The last function in Fig. 5-4, $y = cx/(1 + cx)$, is not so important as the first two functions. It is characterized by an asymptotic approach of the dependent variable (y) to unity for increasing values of x. All the curves pass through the origin. The transformation $Y = 1/y$ and $X = 1/x$ yields a family of straight lines $[Y = 1 + (X/c)]$. Is there another simple transformation of $y = cx/(1 + cx)$ which generates a family of straight lines?

A few examples of transformations of coordinates that are useful for interpolation of data on properties of substances are given next.

Example 5.1

Table 5.3 shows data for the vapor pressure of benzene which are plotted in Fig. 5-7(a). Transform the coordinates to get a linear plot and derive a formula for the function.

TABLE 5.3
VAPOR PRESSURE OF BENZENE*

Temperature (°C)	Pressure (mm Hg)
−36.7	1
−19.6	5
−11.5	10
−2.6	20
+7.6	40
15.4	60
26.1	100
42.2	200
60.6	400
80.1	760

*Chemical Engineers' Handbook, edited by R. H. Perry and C. H. Chilton, 5th ed., McGraw-Hill, New York, (1973).

Solution:

The transformation $X = 1/T$ and $Y = \log_{10} P^s$ is selected upon the basis of the integrated Clapeyron equation [Eqn. (4.7)]. Figure 5-7(b) shows a plot of the transformed coordinates on semilog paper. Since the data fall almost on a straight line, we can use the formula

$$Y = AX + B$$

where
$$A = \text{slope} = \frac{Y_2 - Y_1}{X_2 - X_1} = \frac{\log_{10}(1) - \log_{10}(4400)}{(4.32 - 2.5) \times 10^{-3}} = -2000°K$$

$$B = Y_2 - AX_2 = (\log_{10} 1) - (-2000)(4.32 \times 10^{-3}) = 8.64$$

Therefore, an approximate formula for the vapor pressure of liquid benzene below its normal boiling point is

$$\log_{10} P^s \text{ (mm Hg)} = -\frac{2000}{T(°K)} + 8.64$$

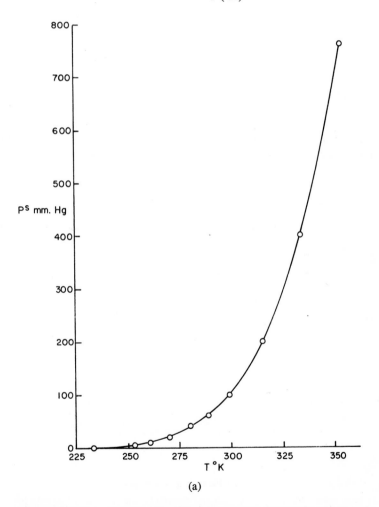

(a)

Figure 5-7 Vapor pressure of liquid benzene as a function of temperature: (a) rectangular coordinates (P^s vs. T); (b) transformed coordinates ($\log_{10} P^s$ vs. $1/T$). [*Chemical Engineers' Handbook*, edited by R. H. Perry and C. H. Chilton, 5th ed., McGraw-Hill, New York (1973).]

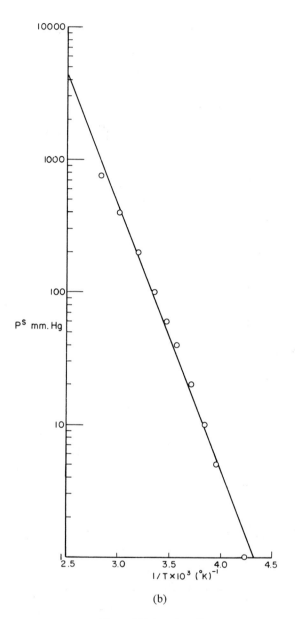

(b)

Figure 5-7 (continued)

Example 5.2

Table 5.4 shows data for the latent heat of vaporization (λ) of liquid methanol; these points are plotted in Fig. 5-8. Transform the coordinates to get a linear plot and derive a formula for the function.

TABLE 5.4
LATENT HEAT OF VAPORIZATION
OF METHANOL*

λ (cal/mole)	T (°K)
8420	337.85
7731	373.15
6200	433.15
4746	473.15
3521	493.15
0	513.15

Chemical Engineers' Handbook, edited by R. H. Perry and C. H. Chilton, 5th ed., McGraw-Hill, New York, (1973).

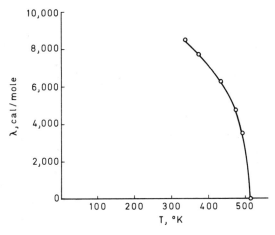

Figure 5-8 Latent heat of vaporization of methanol plotted versus temperature. [*Chemical Engineers' Handbook*, edited by R. H. Perry and C. H. Chilton, 5th ed., McGraw-Hill, New York (1973).]

Solution:

The curve in Fig. 5-8, which intersects the abscissa at the critical temperature of methanol (513°K), does not resemble any of the functions in Fig. 5-4. However, the critical point may be translated to the origin by plotting λ versus $T_c - T$ as shown in Fig. 5-9. The transformed curve in Fig. 5-9 resembles the function $y = x^n$ for $0 < n < 1$ (see Fig. 5-4). Therefore, the transformation $Y = \log_{10} \lambda$ and $X = \log_{10} (T_c - T)$ is plotted in Fig. 5-10; calculation of logarithms is avoided by using log-log paper. Since the plot in transformed coordinates is a straight line, its formula is of the form $Y = mX + b$. The slope

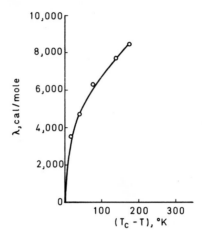

Figure 5-9 Latent heat of vaporization of methanol plotted versus $T_c - T$.

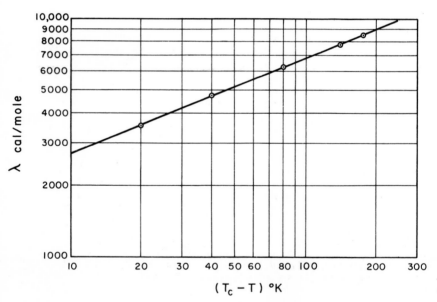

Figure 5-10 Latent heat of vaporization of methanol plotted on log-log paper.

is taken from Fig. 5-10:

$$m = \text{slope} = \frac{Y_2 - Y_1}{X_2 - X_1} = \frac{\log_{10}(9000) - \log_{10}(2750)}{\log_{10}(200) - \log_{10}(10)} = 0.396$$

Let $b = \log_{10} C$. Then

$$Y = mX + b$$

$$\log_{10}\lambda = (0.396)\log_{10}(T_c - T) + \log_{10}C$$

$$\lambda = C(T_c - T)^{0.396}$$

$$C = \frac{\lambda}{(T_c - T)^{0.396}} = \frac{9000}{(200)^{0.396}} = 1100$$

Therefore, the formula for heat of vaporization of methanol from 337°K to the critical point is

$$\lambda \text{ (cal/mole)} = 1100[513.15 - T(^\circ K)]^{0.396}$$

Example 5.3

Experimental measurements of the density of benzene vapor at 563.15°K are given in Table 5.5 and plotted in Fig. 5-11. Notice that the function $P = P\{v\}$ is nonlinear and has a point of inflection (the second derivative changes sign).

TABLE 5.5
MOLAR VOLUME OF BENZENE
VAPOR AT 563.15°K

P (atm)	v (cm³/mole)
30.64	1114
31.60	1067
32.60	1013
33.89	956
35.17	900
36.63	842
38.39	771
40.04	707
41.79	646
43.59	591
45.48	506
47.07	443
48.07	386

Transform coordinates to get a linear plot. Assume that the data obey the virial equation of state, Eqn. (4.17), terminated after the third virial coefficient:

$$\frac{Pv}{RT} = 1 + \frac{B}{v} + \frac{C}{v^2}$$

Solution:

The virial equation may be rearranged to the form

$$v\left[\frac{Pv}{RT} - 1\right] = B + C\left[\frac{1}{v}\right]$$

Therefore, a plot of $Y = v[(Pv/RT) - 1]$ versus $X = [1/v]$ should be a straight line with slope equal to C and Y-intercept equal to B. The transformed set of ordered pairs is obtained from Table 5.5:

$X = \dfrac{1}{v} \times 10^3$	$Y = v\left[\dfrac{Pv}{RT} - 1\right]$
(mole/cm³)	(cm³/mole)
0.898	−291.1
0.937	−288.4
0.987	−289.1
1.046	−285.7
1.111	−283.5
1.188	−280.0
1.297	−277.2
1.414	−273.9
1.548	−268.6
1.692	−261.5
1.976	−254.0
2.257	−243.1
2.591	−231.0

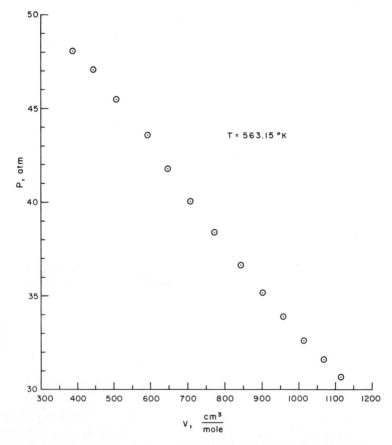

Figure 5-11 Pressure versus molar volume for benzene vapor at 563.15°K.

As shown in Fig. 5-12, the plot of the transformed function is linear. However, these points show some *scatter* due to random experimental errors, and as a result the exact location of the straight line by visual inspection is uncertain. In the next section we shall show how to find the "best" straight line through the points by the method of least squares.

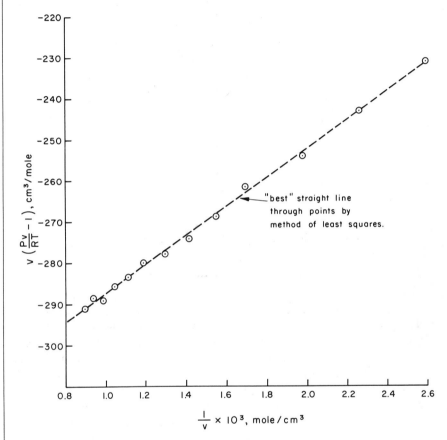

Figure 5-12 Transformed coordinates for molar volume of benzene vapor at 563.15°K.

5.3 Method of Least Squares

Experimental data always contain errors due to imperfect instruments. If experimental points are plotted on a graph (see Fig. 5-13), instrumental error causes the points to *scatter* about the true function (the solid line in Fig. 5-13).

Data in handbooks usually contain almost no discernible scatter. Scatter

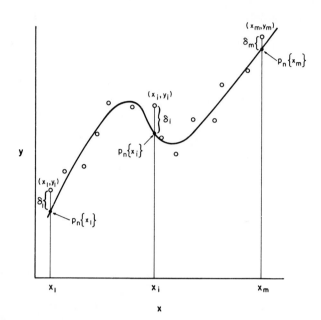

Figure 5-13 Finding the equation (solid line) for experimental points containing *scatter* or random errors.

is removed by data-smoothing techniques in which the raw experimental points are replaced by a *best fit* (i.e., the solid line in Fig. 5-13).

In the previous section methods of graphical correlation were examined. The function was located by drawing a "best" line through the experimental points plotted in a transformed system of coordinates. This is easy to do when scatter is negligible. When scatter is appreciable, as in Fig. 5-13, drawing the function by hand is too crude.

In this section we shall examine the method of least squares, which is a numerical method of evaluating the constants of a formula from experimental points. The method of least squares is as follows: Given a set of m ordered pairs (x_i, y_i), such as the set plotted in Fig. 5-13, find constants for the formula (solid line in Fig. 5-13) so that the sum of squares of the deviations

$$s = \sum_{i=1}^{m} \delta_i^2 \qquad (5.4)$$

is a minimum. The deviation (δ) illustrated in Fig. 5-13 is the difference between the experimental value and the value given by the formula. The deviations are squared to emphasize the larger deviations when computing the constants of the formula.

To be specific, suppose that the formula is for the best straight line through the experimental points

$$y = p_1\{x\} = a_0 + a_1 x \tag{5.5}$$

If there were no scatter, one could solve for a_0 and a_1 using any pair of experimental points and ignoring the rest. The method of least squares takes into account *all* of the experimental points by selecting a_0 and a_1 so as to minimize the sum of squares of the deviations:

$$s = \sum_{i=1}^{m} \delta_i^2 = \sum_{i=1}^{m} [y_i - a_0 - a_1 x_i]^2 \tag{5.6}$$

For a given set of m ordered pairs (x_i, y_i), $i = 1, 2, \ldots, m$, s is a function of a_0 and a_1 only. For s to be a minimum it is necessary that

$$\left(\frac{\partial s}{\partial a_0}\right)_{a_1} = \left(\frac{\partial s}{\partial a_1}\right)_{a_0} = 0$$

Partial differentiation of Eqn. (5.6) yields

$$\left(\frac{\partial s}{\partial a_0}\right)_{a_1} = \sum_{i=1}^{m} -2(y_i - a_0 - a_1 x_i) = 0$$
$$\left(\frac{\partial s}{\partial a_1}\right)_{a_0} = \sum_{i=1}^{m} -2(x_i y_i - a_0 x_i - a_1 x_i^2) = 0 \tag{5.7}$$

This pair of equations is linear in the unknowns $(a_0$ and $a_1)$; the solution is

$$a_1 = \frac{m[\sum x_i y_i] - [\sum x_i][\sum y_i]}{m[\sum x_i^2] - [\sum x_i]^2}$$
$$a_0 = \frac{[\sum y_i] - a_1[\sum x_i]}{m} \tag{5.8}$$

In each case the summation is over the set of m experimental points $i = 1, 2, \ldots, m$.

The next example is an application of Eqns. (5.8) to find the "best" straight line according to the method of least squares.

Example 5.4

Find the equation for the best straight line $(Y = a_0 + a_1 X)$ through the points in Fig. 5-12 using the method of least squares.

Solution:

Let $X = [1/v] \times 10^3$ and $Y = v[(Pv/RT) - 1]$. From the table in Example 5.3,

i	X (mole/cm^3)	Y (cm^3/mole)
1	0.898	-291.1
2	0.937	-288.4
3	0.987	-289.1
4	1.046	-285.7
5	1.111	-283.5
6	1.188	-280.0
7	1.297	-277.2
8	1.414	-273.9
9	1.548	-268.6
10	1.692	-261.5
11	1.976	-254.0
12	2.257	-243.1
13	2.591	-231.0

The summations are

$$[\sum X_i] = 18.942 \text{ mole/cm}^3$$

$$[\sum X_i^2] = 31.051 \text{ (mole/cm}^3)^2$$

$$[\sum X_i Y_i] = -5.0176 \times 10^3$$

$$[\sum Y_i] = -3527.1 \text{ cm}^3/\text{mole}$$

and therefore, from Eqns. (5.8),

$$a_1 = \frac{13(-5.0176 \times 10^3) - (18.942)(-3527.1)}{13(31.051) - (18.942)^2} = 35.25 \text{ (cm}^3/\text{mole})^2$$

$$a_0 = \frac{(-3527.1) - (35.25)(18.942)}{13} = -323 \text{ cm}^3/\text{mole}$$

These values of a_0 and a_1 were used to draw the straight line ($Y = a_0 + a_1 X$) in Fig. 5-12. Substitution for X and Y gives

$$Y = a_0 + a_1 X$$

$$v\left[\frac{Pv}{RT} - 1\right] = a_0 + \frac{a_1 \times 10^3}{v}$$

$$\frac{Pv}{RT} = 1 + \frac{a_0}{v} + \frac{a_1 \times 10^3}{v^2}$$

Comparison of this equation with the virial equation in Example 5.3 gives the following values for the virial coefficients of benzene at 290 °C:

$$B = \text{second virial coefficient} = a_0 = -323 \text{ cm}^3/\text{mole}$$

$$C = \text{third virial coefficient} = a_1 \times 10^3 = 35,250 \text{ (cm}^3/\text{mole})^2$$

Fitting a straight line to a set of experimental points by the method of least squares is obviously a tedious calculation. A computer program for the method of least squares is shown in the next example.

Example 5.5

Prepare a WATFIV* program to compute the coefficients of the best straight line through a set of m ordered pairs (x_i, y_i), $i = 1, 2, \ldots, m$, using the method of least squares.

Use this program to solve the problem worked in Example 5.4.

Solution:

For the set of m ordered pairs, (x_i, y_i), $i = 1, 2, \ldots, m$, the coefficients of the straight line,

$$y = a_0 + a_1 x$$

that minimize

$$\sum_{i=1}^{m} \delta_i^2 = \sum_{i=1}^{m} [y_i - a_0 - a_1 x_i]^2$$

are given by Eqns. (5.8):

$$a_1 = \frac{m \left[\sum_{i=1}^{m} x_i y_i \right] - \left[\sum_{i=1}^{m} x_i \right] \left[\sum_{i=1}^{m} y_i \right]}{m \left[\sum_{i=1}^{m} x_i^2 \right] - \left[\sum_{i=1}^{m} x_i \right]^2}$$

and

$$a_0 = \frac{\left[\sum_{i=1}^{m} y_i \right] - a_1 \left[\sum_{i=1}^{m} x_i \right]}{m}.$$

The WATFIV program reads each ordered pair (x_i, y_i) from a separate card, computes the summations, and finally computes a_1 and a_0 and prints their values. The flow sheet (see Fig. 5-14) illustrates this algorithm.

Flow Diagram

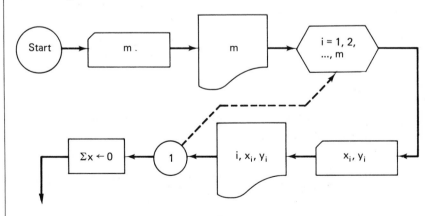

Figure 5-14

*Differences between WATFIV and FORTRAN IV are discussed in Appendix III.

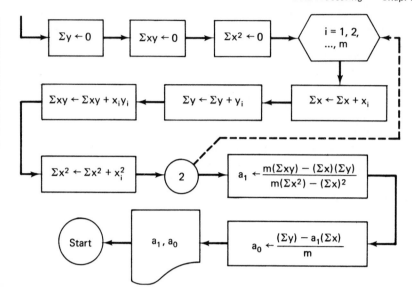

Figure 5-14 (continued)

Table of Symbols

Problem symbol	Program symbol	Definition
a_0	AO	Intercept of straight line
a_1	A1	Slope of straight line
m	M	Number of data points (x_i, y_i)
x_i	X(I)	First coordinate for each data point
y_i	Y(I)	Second coordinate for each data point
$\sum x$	SUMX	Accumulated sum of x_i
$\sum xy$	SUMXY	Accumulated sum of $x_i y_i$
$\sum x^2$	SUMX2	Accumulated sum of x_i^2
$\sum y$	SUMY	Accumulated sum of y_i

Program Listing

```
C**    PROGRAM TO COMPUTE THE COEFFICIENTS OF THE BEST STRAIGHT LINE
C      THAT PASSES AMONG A SET OF M DATA POINTS, (X(I),Y(I)), USING THE
C      METHOD OF LEAST SQUARES.
C
       DIMENSION X(100), Y(100)
C
C**    THE COORDINATES OF EACH DATA POINT, (X(I),Y(I)), ARE READ FROM A
C      SEPARATE CARD; ONE CARD FOR EACH DATA POINT.
C
     3 READ, M
       WRITE (6,101)
       WRITE (6,102) M
       WRITE (6,103)
       DO 1 I = 1,M
       READ, X(I), Y(I)
     1 WRITE (6,104) I, X(I), Y(I)
```

```
C
C**     THE SUMMATIONS IN THE EXPRESSIONS FOR A0 AND A1 ARE COMPUTED.
C
        SUMX = 0
        SUMY = 0
        SUMXY = 0
        SUMX2 = 0
        DO 2 I = 1,M
        SUMX = SUMX + X(I)
        SUMY = SUMY + Y(I)
        SUMXY = SUMXY + X(I)*Y(I)
     2  SUMX2 = SUMX2 + X(I)*X(I)
C
C**     THE COEFFICIENTS A0 AND A1 ARE COMPUTED AND PRINTED.
C
        A1 = (M*SUMXY - SUMX*SUMY)/(M*SUMX2 - SUMX*SUMX)
        A0 = (SUMY - A1*SUMX)/M
        WRITE (6,105)
        WRITE (6,106) A1, A0
        GO TO 3
C
C**     INPUT AND OUTPUT FORMATS.
C
  101   FORMAT ('1THE NUMBER OF DATA POINTS, M =',/)
  102   FORMAT (I10,//)
  103   FORMAT (' I, X(I), Y(I) =',/)
  104   FORMAT (I10,2F15.6)
  105   FORMAT (//,' THE SLOPE, A1, AND INTERCEPT, A0, OF THE BEST STRAIGH
     1T LINE = ',/)
  106   FORMAT (2F15.4)
        END
```

Data

```
                              13
                              0.898, -291.1
                              0.937, -288.4
                              0.987, -289.1
                              1.046, -285.7
                              1.111, -283.5
                              1.188, -280.0
                              1.297, -277.2
                              1.414, -273.9
                              1.548, -268.6
                              1.692, -261.5
                              1.976, -254.0
                              2.257, -243.1
                              2.591, -231.0
```

Computer Output

```
                    THE NUMBER OF DATA POINTS, M =

                         13


                 I, X(I), Y(I) =

                         1        0.898000        -291.100000
                         2        0.937000        -288.399900
                         3        0.987000        -289.100000
                         4        1.046000        -285.699900
                         5        1.111000        -283.500000
                         6        1.188000        -280.000000
                         7        1.297000        -277.199900
                         8        1.414000        -273.899900
                         9        1.548000        -268.600000
                        10        1.692000        -261.500000
                        11        1.976000        -254.000000
                        12        2.257000        -243.100000
                        13        2.591000        -231.000000
```

THE SLOPE, A1, AND INTERCEPT, A0, OF THE BEST STRAIGHT LINE =

    35.2498   -322.6768

In summary, it has been shown that raw experimental points may be processed by graphical correlation or, more accurately, by the method of least squares. In many cases one can find a transformation for which the coordinates are linearly related. If a transformation to linear coordinates cannot be found, the method of least squares may be extended to nonlinear functions (see R. W. Hamming, *Introduction to Applied Numerical Analysis*, McGraw-Hill, New York, 1971, p. 256).

The method of least squares is not the only criterion for finding the "best" coefficients of a formula. One could find coefficients that minimize the sum of the absolute values, instead of the squares, of the deviations (see Fig. 5-13). The result of using the squares of the deviations is that points far off the line are given more weight than points close to the line.

Another interesting criterion for finding the best coefficients is the method of Chebyshev, in which the strategy is to select coefficients that make the largest deviation as small as possible (see B. Carnahan, H.A. Luther, and J.O. Wilkes, *Applied Numerical Methods*, Wiley, New York, 1969).

5.4 Numerical Interpolation

Methods of correlating experimental data were studied in the previous sections. Sometimes, instead of a correlation of all the experimental points, all that is needed is the value of the function at a single point. This value may be found by *interpolation*.

Suppose that it is desired to determine the value of the function $f\{x\}$ at x. The strategy is to derive coefficients for an equation that represents $f\{x\}$ only in the *neighborhood* of x. Points far away from x are not considered.

The equation most often used to represent $f\{x\}$ in the neighborhood of x is an nth degree polynomial $p_n\{x\}$:

$$f\{x\} \simeq p_n\{x\} = \sum_{j=0}^{n} a_j x^j = a_0 + a_1 x + a_2 x^2 + \cdots + a_n x^n \qquad (5.9)$$

The $\simeq$ sign is a reminder that $p_n\{x\}$ is only an approximation to $f\{x\}$. The coefficients are calculated by substituting $n + 1$ data points in the neighborhood of x into Eqn. (5.9), which gives $n + 1$ linear equations for the $n + 1$ coefficients $a_0, a_1, a_2, \ldots, a_n$.

For example, the first-degree polynomial ($n = 1$) is

$$f\{x\} \simeq p_1\{x\} = a_0 + a_1 x \qquad (5.10)$$

Two data points are needed to compute values for the coefficients a_0 and a_1. For example, suppose that (x_i, y_i) and (x_{i+1}, y_{i+1}) are two points close to x, usually $x_i < x < x_{i+1}$. Substitution of these data points into Eqn. (5.10) gives two equations:

$$y_i = a_0 + a_1 x_i$$
$$y_{i+1} = a_0 + a_1 x_{i+1}$$

These two equations are solved for a_0 and a_1 in terms of x_i, x_{i+1}, y_i, and y_{i+1}, and the result is substituted into Eqn. (5.10) to yield

$$y \simeq p_1\{x\} = y_i + (x - x_i)\frac{(y_{i+1} - y_i)}{(x_{i+1} - x_i)} \tag{5.11}$$

Use of Eqn. (5.11) is called *linear* interpolation.

If the function is nonlinear and if the points (x_i, y_i) and (x_{i+1}, y_{i+1}) are not close together, Eqn. (5.11) is a poor approximation. For example, the vapor pressure of benzene versus temperature is a nonlinear function, as shown in Fig. 5-7(a). Moreover, the data points are widely spaced so that a straight line passed through two of them deviates considerably from the actual vapor pressure curve between the same two points. Therefore, linear interpolation using Eqn. (5.11) gives large errors, as illustrated in Example 5.6.

If errors due to linear interpolation are too large, higher-order polynomials may improve the accuracy of the interpolation. The second-degree polynomial is

$$y \simeq p_2\{x\} = a_0 + a_1 x + a_2 x^2 \tag{5.12}$$

Three data points in the neighborhood of x are needed to determine the coefficients a_0, a_1, and a_2. If the points are (x_i, y_i), (x_{i+1}, y_{i+1}), and (x_{i+2}, y_{i+2}), substitution in Eqn. (5.12) gives

$$y_i = a_0 + a_1 x_i + a_2 x_i^2$$
$$y_{i+1} = a_0 + a_1 x_{i+1} + a_2 x_{i+1}^2$$
$$y_{i+2} = a_0 + a_1 x_{i+2} + a_2 x_{i+2}^2$$

These equations are solved for a_0, a_1, and a_2, and the result is substituted in Eqn. (5.12):

$$y \simeq p_2\{x\} = \frac{(x - x_{i+1})(x - x_{i+2})}{(x_i - x_{i+1})(x_i - x_{i+2})}y_i + \frac{(x - x_i)(x - x_{i+2})}{(x_{i+1} - x_i)(x_{i+1} - x_{i+2})}y_{i+1}$$
$$+ \frac{(x - x_i)(x - x_{i+1})}{(x_{i+2} - x_i)(x_{i+2} - x_{i+1})}y_{i+2} \tag{5.13}$$

This second-degree polynomial is the equation of a parabola that passes through three points in the neighborhood of x. Its use is illustrated in the next example.

Example 5.6

The vapor pressure of liquid acetonitrile (CH_3CN) at three temperatures* is

i	T_i (°K)	P_i^s (mm Hg)
1	268.15	20
2	289.05	60
3	300.15	100

Estimate the vapor pressure at 280.85°K using

1. Linear interpolation.
2. Quadratic interpolation.
3. Equation (4.7).

Compare these estimates with the experimental value of 40 mm Hg.

Solution:

    1. *Linear interpolation.* Let $x_i = T_i$ and $y_i = P_i^s$. For $i = 1$, Eqn. (5.11) is

$$y \simeq y_1 + (x - x_1)\frac{(y_2 - y_1)}{(x_2 - x_1)}$$

$$P^s = y \simeq 20 + (280.85 - 268.15)\frac{(60 - 20)}{(289.05 - 268.15)}$$

$$\simeq 44.3 \text{ mm Hg}$$

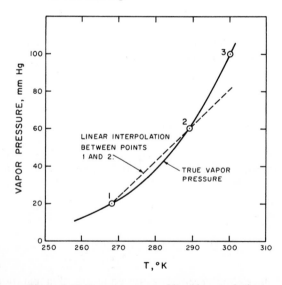

Figure 5-15 Vapor pressure of liquid acetonitrile.

Chemical Engineers' Handbook, edited by R. H. Perry and C. H. Chilton, 5th ed., McGraw-Hill, N. Y. (1973).

at 280.85°K. This linear interpolation is shown by the dashed line in Fig. 5-15.

2. *Quadratic interpolation.* Again let $x_i = T_i$ and $y_i = P_i^s$. For $i = 1$, Eqn. (5.13) is

$$y \simeq \frac{(x - x_2)(x - x_3)}{(x_1 - x_2)(x_1 - x_3)} y_1$$

$$+ \frac{(x - x_1)(x - x_3)}{(x_2 - x_1)(x_2 - x_3)} y_2$$

$$+ \frac{(x - x_1)(x - x_2)}{(x_3 - x_1)(x_3 - x_2)} y_3$$

$$P^s = y \simeq \frac{(280.85 - 289.05)(280.85 - 300.15)}{(268.15 - 289.05)(268.15 - 300.15)} (20)$$

$$+ \frac{(280.85 - 268.15)(280.85 - 300.15)}{(289.05 - 268.15)(289.05 - 300.15)} (60)$$

$$+ \frac{(280.85 - 268.15)(280.85 - 289.05)}{(300.15 - 268.15)(300.15 - 289.05)} (100)$$

$$= 4.73 + 63.39 - 29.32 = 38.8 \text{ mm Hg}$$

3. *Equation (4.7).* We could solve Eqn. (4.7) for the values of A and B using the first pair of data points and then use the same equation to calculate the vapor pressure at the intermediate temperature. An alternative and equivalent procedure is to transform coordinates to $Y = \log_{10} P^s$ and $X = 1/T$ and then interpolate linearly. Thus,

i	$Y = \log_{10} P^s$	$X = 1/T \, (°K)^{-1}$
1	1.3010	0.003729
2	1.7782	0.003460

Letting $Y = \log_{10} P^s$ and $X = 1/T$, Eqn. (5.11) is

$$Y \simeq Y_1 + (X - X_1) \frac{(Y_2 - Y_1)}{(X_2 - X_1)}$$

$$\log_{10} P^s = 1.3010 + (0.003561 - 0.003729) \frac{(1.7782 - 1.3010)}{(0.003460 - 0.003729)}$$

$$= 1.5990$$

$$P^s = 39.72 \text{ mm Hg}$$

Summarizing these results,

	P^s (mm Hg)	Error (%)
Linear interpolation	44.3	10.7
Quadratic interpolation	38.8	3.0
Equation (4.7) for interpolation	39.7	0.7
Experimental value	40.0	

Linear interpolation worked poorly in the previous example because the function is highly nonlinear and the experimental points are too far apart. Quadratic interpolation using three data points is more accurate. The superiority in this example of quadratic interpolation over linear interpolation suggests that the highest-degree polynomial possible should be used for interpolation. At first glance, the only limiting consideration seems to be the added computation needed to evaluate higher-order polynomials. Actually the accuracy of interpolation does not always increase with the degree of the polynomial. Thus, a polynomial of degree 2 may interpolate more accurately than a polynomial of degree 4 under certain conditions when random errors (scatter) in the experimental data are large.

5.5 Property Information Systems

Optimum design of a chemical process depends on the properties of materials. For example, the design of a crystallizer is dictated by the freezing point of the mother liquor, the heat of crystallization, and the rate of growth of the crystals. The design of a gas absorber depends on the solubility of the gas in the liquid and its rate of transfer from the gas phase to the liquid phase. Methods of storing and retrieving properties and data such as these are called property information systems.

Complete property information is seldom available, particularly if the process is a new one. It is usually advisable to get more information about a proposed process by experimentation, which may include the construction of a small prototype or a pilot plant (a scaled-down version of the actual plant). However, there is inevitably some ignorance about the properties of the system, and the art of engineering lies in making shrewd estimates or predictions based upon incomplete information.

Engineers have developed systematic methods for estimating properties of materials, particularly mixtures (see Ch. 4). These estimates are based upon properties of the pure substances. In computer-based information systems, data are stored on disks. The property information system stores data in the data base and returns it upon request. Estimation programs, also stored on the disk, use the data base to calculate the properties that are requested.

A computer-based information system is an automated library in which information is stored on disks instead of books, journals, and reports. Services of the index file and librarian in an ordinary library are performed by an automated retrieval system. The flow of information in a property information system is shown in Fig. 5-16. Computer-based information systems are designed for cryogenic materials, for metals and their alloys, for hydrocarbons, etc. Although kinds of information differ, methods of storing, maintaining, retrieving, and processing the information are similar.

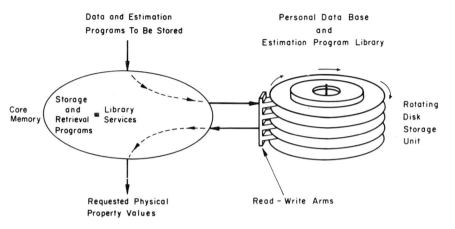

Figure 5-16 Flow of information in a property information system.

In this section we shall describe our property information system at the University of Pennsylvania. Other systems are similar in principle but different in the details of their operation. In this section we shall discuss data storage and retrieval. Examples 10.7–10.9 use the property information system to make process calculations.

Data storage

Information retrieval systems are based upon index terms or *key words* under which the data are stored. Selection of the proper key word is a difficult problem. For example, the normal melting point of benzene could be filed under "melting point," "freezing point," or "benzene." Therefore, the user of a property information system must be familiar with the indexing system. Here we shall consider the *filing* of data under key words.

A sample data record is shown in Fig. 5-17. This particular record contains data for the specific heat of 1-butene as a function of temperature, calculated by a third-degree polynomial, Eqn. (4.32). Values of constants were taken from Table 4.14. In addition to the coefficients of the polynomial, the record includes the source of the information, the estimated maximum error, and the ranges of validity.

Information on a data record is stored in the data base as illustrated schematically in Fig. 5-18. The key words on the data record are typed at a computer terminal in response to queries by the information system. For example, Fig. 5-19 shows the man-computer dialogue for filing the data record in Fig. 5-17. Questions asked by the information system are in capital letters; the response of the person filing the data is in lowercase and follows an asterisk that is typed by the computer.

Name or property	Specific heat
Contributor	K. A. Kobe
Range of validity for temperature, °K	273–1500
Range of validity for pressure, atm	0–2
Maximum expected error, percent	0.25
Estimation program	Third-degree polynomial (POLY3D)
Name of chemical	1-Butene
Data	

Data type	Equation coefficients
a	-0.240
b	0.0865
c	-5.11×10^{-5}
d	1.207×10^{-8}

Figure 5-17 Data record in the University of Pennsylvania Property Information System.

The storage program places the key words in directories that are maintained in high-speed core memory. The directory contains the storage address of the data, which are stored on disks. The disk serves as a secondary memory unit that is less accessible than data in core memory, but its cost per bit of information is less, and its capacity is larger.

Data retrieval

Data retrieval is accomplished by a program that searches the directory (in the core memory of the computer) for data records whose key words match the key words of the retrieval request. The operation is shown schematically in Fig. 5-20. After finding a data record whose key words match those of the retrieval request, the retrieval program transports the data from disk to core memory. If an estimation program is needed, it is placed in core memory too. The property information system then calls upon the estimation program to compute the property values.

We use three retrieval options:

1. *Simple.* Values of the function are given at specified points.
2. *Table.* Values of the function are tabulated. If there are several independent variables, all but one is held constant.
3. *Graph.* Values of the function are plotted for a specified range of one of the independent variables.

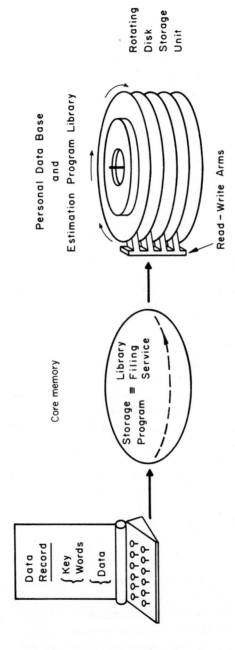

Figure 5-18 Data storage.

```
*store
 PLEASE SUPPLY THE FOLLOWING:
 NAME OF PROPERTY:
*specific heat
 CONTRIBUTOR:
*k.a.kobe
 RANGE OF VALIDITY FOR TEMPERATURE (DEG.K):
*273.,  1500.
 RANGE OF VALIDITY FOR PRESSURE (ATM):
*  0.,   2.
 MAXIMUM EXPECTED ERROR (%):
*0.25
 HOW MANY CHEMICALS?
*1
 TYPE IN NAME(S) OF CHEMICAL(S):
*1-butene
 DATA TYPE: (CONSTANT, COEFFICIENT, TABULAR)
*coefficient
 ESTIMATION ROUTINE:
*third degree polynomial
 HOW MANY COEFFICIENTS?
*4
 TYPE COEFFICIENTS (ONE PER LINE):
*-0.24
*8.65e-2
*-5.11e-5
*1.207e-8
```

Figure 5-19 Storing a data record in the University of Pennsylvania Property Information System using a typewriter computer terminal. (Computer requests information in capital letters; response follows * in lowercase letters.)

For example, let us consider the retrieval of the specific heat of 1-butene using the University of Pennsylvania Property Information System. The key words of the retrieval request are supplied at the computer terminal. The man-computer dialogue for the *simple*, *table*, and *graph* retrieval options are shown in Figs. 5-21, 5-22, and 5-23, respectively. (These figures have been simplified by omitting the portion of the dialogue about contributor, maximum error, and estimation program.)

A list of some of the properties for which data are stored and retrieved in the University of Pennsylvania Property Information System is shown in Table 5.6.

Mixtures

Methods of calculating thermodynamic properties of mixtures were described in Sec. 4.5. The basic concept is that properties of mixtures may be estimated from the properties of pure chemicals (precise calculations require specific information about interactions of molecules in pairs). Sometimes a simple molal average of the pure-component properties [Eqn. (4.34)] will do; usually the relationship is more complicated (see the discussion in Sec. 4.5).

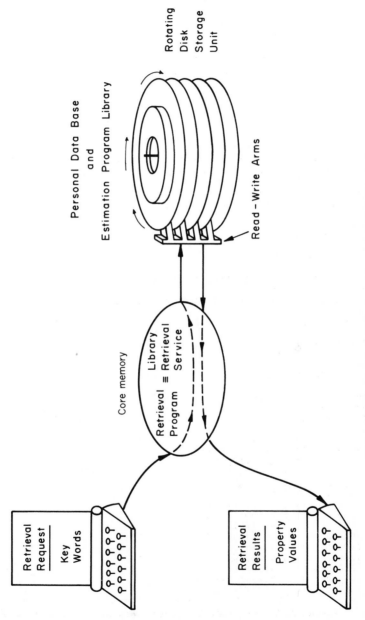

Figure 5-20 Retrieval of data using a property information system.

```
*retrieve
 PLEASE SUPPLY THE FOLLOWING:
 NAME OF PROPERTY:
*specific heat
 HOW MANY CHEMICALS?
*1
 NAME OF CHEMICAL(S):
*1-butene
 RETRIEVAL OPTION: (SIMPLE, TABLE, GRAPH)
*simple
 TEMPERATURE (DEG.K):
*400.
 PRESSURE (ATM):
*1.
 RESULT=    20.950 CAL/MOLE-DEG.K
```

Figure 5-21 Sample request for property information using a typewriter computer terminal. (The questions asked by the computer are in capital letters; the engineer's response follows the * in lowercase letters.)

```
*retrieve
 PLEASE SUPPLY THE FOLLOWING:
 NAME OF PROPERTY:
*specific heat
 HOW MANY CHEMICALS?
*1
 NAME OF CHEMICAL(S):
*1-butene
 RETRIEVAL OPTION: (SIMPLE, TABLE, GRAPH)
*table
 ENTER TEMPERATURE (DEG.K) RANGE AND NO. OF INTERVALS:
*300., 1500., 12
 ENTER PRESSURE (ATM) RANGE AND NO. OF INTERVALS:
*0., 0., 0
 THE TABLE IS READY. DO YOU WANT IT PRINTED
 AT THE TERMINAL?
*yes
 TABULATED RESULTS

 INDEPENDENT VARIABLE                PROPERTY                          SYMBOL
 --------------------                --------                          ------
 TEMPERATURE (DEG.K)   VERSUS   SPECIFIC HEAT (CAL/MOLE-DEG.K)       *

             ||        *        |
 ---------||---------------|
   300.0   ||  0.2143686E 02  |
   400.0   ||  0.2695645E 02  |
   500.0   ||  0.3174371E 02  |
   600.0   ||  0.3587109E 02  |
   700.0   ||  0.3941100E 02  |
   800.0   ||  0.4243581E 02  |
   900.0   ||  0.4501801E 02  |
  1000.0   ||  0.4722998E 02  |
  1100.0   ||  0.4914413E 02  |
  1200.0   ||  0.5083293E 02  |
  1300.0   ||  0.5236876E 02  |
  1400.0   ||  0.5382405E 02  |
  1500.0   ||  0.5527121E 02  |
```

Figure 5-22 Sample request for a table of property values using a typewriter computer terminal.

```
*retrieve
 PLEASE SUPPLY THE FOLLOWING:
 NAME OF PROPERTY:
*specific heat
 HOW MANY CHEMICALS?
*1
 NAME OF CHEMICAL(S):
*1-butene
 RETRIEVAL OPTION: (SIMPLE, TABLE, GRAPH)
*graph
 ENTER TEMPERATURE (DEG.K) RANGE AND NO. OF INTERVALS:
*300., 1500., 12
 ENTER PRESSURE (ATM) RANGE AND NO. OF INTERVALS:
*0., 0., 0
 THE GRAPH IS READY. DO YOU WANT IT PRINTED
 AT THE TERMINAL?
*yes
 GRAPHED RESULTS
```

```
INDEPENDENT VARIABLE            PROPERTY                        SYMBOL
--------------------            --------                        ------
TEMPERATURE (DEG.K)  VERSUS  SPECIFIC HEAT (CAL/MOLE-DEG.K)       *
```

```
 ----------||+-----------------------------+-----------------------------+
    300.0   ||  *
    400.0   ||         *
    500.0   ||               *
    600.0   ||                    *
    700.0   ||                         *
    800.0   ||                              *
    900.0   ||                                 *
   1000.0   ||                                    *
   1100.0   ||                                       *
   1200.0   ||                                          *
   1300.0   ||                                             *
   1400.0   ||                                                *
   1500.0   ||                                                   *
 ----------||+-----------------------------+-----------------------------+
            |                             |                             |
       0.2000 E 02                   0.4000 E 02                   0.6000 E 02
```

Figure 5-23 Sample request for a graph of property values using a type-writer computer terminal.

In any case, a computer-based information system can be programmed to perform calculations of mixture properties using the best method available.

Consider, as an example, the density of a gaseous mixture of n-butane and carbon dioxide at high pressure (about 100 atm). The Benedict-Webb-Rubin equation of state predicts densities of the pure gases with errors not exceeding a few percent; for mixtures of the same gases errors are smaller than 10% and sometimes only a few percent. One of the property estimation programs in the University of Pennsylvania Property Information System calculates the molar volume of a mixture using the Benedict-Webb-Rubin equation of state. First, the estimation program asks the property informa-

TABLE 5.6
SELECTED PROPERTIES FOR WHICH DATA ARE STORED IN THE UNIVERSITY
OF PENNSYLVANIA PROPERTY INFORMATION SYSTEM

Properties	Independent Variables	Index (IP)
Normal melting point		1007
Normal boiling point		1008
Specific heat at zero pressure	T, y	436
Specific heat		
Vapor	T, P, y	431
Liquid	T, P, x	432
Latent heat of vaporization (at N.B.P.)		1102
Heat of formation (1 atm, 25°C)		1101
Enthalpy at zero pressure	T, y	406
Enthalpy		
Vapor	T, P, y	401
Liquid	T, P, x	402
Critical temperature		1001
Critical pressure		1002
Critical volume		1003
Density		
Vapor	T, P, y	101
Liquid	T, P, x	102
Vapor pressure of liquid	T	216
Saturation temperature of vapor	P	217
Vapor-liquid equilibrium constants	T, P, z^*	305

*Overall composition of two-phase mixture.

TABLE 5.7
MOLAR VOLUME (ft^3/lb-mole) OF MIXTURES OF n-BUTANE AND CARBON DIOXIDE AT
2500 psia USING THE BENEDICT-WEBB-RUBIN EQUATION OF STATE AND THE
ESTIMATION PROGRAM BWRVD OF THE UNIVERSITY OF PENNSYLVANIA
PROPERTY INFORMATION SYSTEM

Temperature (°F)	Mole fraction of n-butane					
	0	0.2	0.4	0.6	0.8	1.0
300	2.513	2.126	1.854	1.806	1.899	2.041
320	2.669	2.299	1.999	1.898	1.962	2.092
340	2.816	2.468	2.153	2.003	2.032	2.148
360	2.959	2.633	2.312	2.121	2.112	2.209
380	3.096	2.792	2.473	2.252	2.201	2.275
400	3.230	2.946	2.634	2.391	2.301	2.348

tion system to locate critical constants (T_c, P_c) of each pure substance, from which eight constants for each pure substance are calculated by Eqn. (4.20). The estimation program computes mixture coefficients using empirical mixing rules* and then calculates the molar volume by solving Eqn. (4.19).

The man-computer dialogue for calculating the density of a mixture is shown in Fig. 5-24. The request was repeated for several values of composition (0, 0.2, 0.4, 0.6, 0.8, 1.0) and results in English units are in Table 5.7. The presence of four significant figures in Table 5.7 should not be allowed to obscure the fact that calculated results are in error by several percent. Precise experimental results for this particular mixture have been reported by Olds et al.†

```
*retrieve
 HOW MANY CHEMICALS?
*2
 NAME OF CHEMICAL(S):
*carbon dioxide
*n-butane
 INPUT THE MOLE FRACTIONS. (ON ONE LINE.)
*0.2, 0.8
 CHOOSE A RETRIEVAL OPTION: SIMPLE, TABLE, GRAPH, NONE.
*table
 NAME OF PROPERTY:
*v.density
 ENTER TEMPERATURE DEGK      RANGE AND NO. OF INTERVALS.
*422.04, 477.59, 5
 ENTER PRESSURE ATM          RANGE AND NO. OF INTERVALS.
*170.068, 170.068, 0
 THE TABLE IS READY. DO YOU WANT IT PRINTED
 AT THE TERMINAL?
*yes
 TABULATED RESULTS

 INDEPENDENT VARIABLE          PROPERTY                  SYMBOL
 --------------------          --------                  ------
 TEMPERATURE (DEGK)   VERSUS   V.DENSITY (GMOLE/CC)         *

           ||       *        |
----------||---------------|
   422.04 ||    0.008435    |
   433.15 ||    0.008164    |
   444.26 ||    0.007880    |
   455.37 ||    0.007583    |
   466.48 ||    0.007276    |
   477.59 ||    0.006960    |
```

Figure 5-24 Sample request for a table of values of density for a mixture of 20% carbon dioxide and 80% n-butane.

*R. C. Reid and T. K. Sherwood, *The Properties of Gases and Liquids*, 2nd ed., McGraw-Hill, New York, 1966, Appendix E.

†R. H. Olds, H. H. Reamer, B. H. Sage, and W. N. Lacey, "Phase Equilibria in Hydrocarbon Systems," *Ind. Eng. Chem.*, *41*, 475 (1949).

Requests for properties from FORTRAN Programs

Properties such as density can be retrieved directly from a property information system, as shown in Fig. 5-24. Alternatively, requests for properties can be built into computer programs that use the property data to make process calculations. Values of properties needed during the execution of the program are retrieved simply by naming their independent variables. The accessibility of almost unlimited amounts of property data to the computer program is a powerful tool that permits an engineer to make complex process calculations using comparatively simple programs.

On the one hand, availability of a property information system simplifies writing programs for process calculations. On the other hand, time needed by the computer to retrieve information from disk storage increases the total time needed to execute the program. If a program is to be run over and over again, computer time can be saved by writing property estimation subroutines directly into the program.

Each property information system has its own terminology and details of operation, but methods of requesting data are similar in concept to the system used at the University of Pennsylvania. Suppose that a program written for a certain process calculation needs the value of a property of a pure substance (**PROP**). The property is retrieved by the following statement:

$$PROP = PURE(IP, V1, \ V2, \ NUMBER)$$

PURE is a function that requests properties of pure substances. Its first argument (**IP**) is an integer index for the properties listed in Table 5.6. **IP** names the property (enthalpy, density, etc.). The next two variables (**V1, V2**) contain values for the independent variables (temperature and pressure, usually). The fourth argument of **PURE** is the name of a FORTRAN integer variable for the number of the chemical. Chemicals are numbered in data at the end of the program, not in the main program, so that the program is not affected by changing the chemicals. These data are called a current list of chemicals, e.g.,

Number	Chemical
1	Hexane
2	Cyclohexane
3	Benzene
4	Ethylbenzene

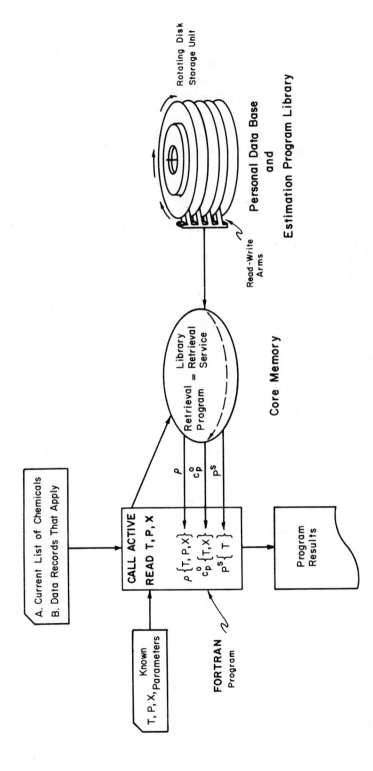

Figure 5-25 Flow of information between property information system and FORTRAN program.

193

Mixture properties (PROP) are retrieved from the property information system for use in the program by the statement

PROP = PPCF(IP, V1, V2, X)

PROP might be, for example, the specific heat of a gaseous mixture (IP = 431). The fourth argument of PPCF is the name of a FORTRAN singly subscripted, real variable that contains mole fractions for each chemical in the current list of chemicals.

When data are needed for each component of a mixture, the statement is

CALL PPCS (IP, V1, V2, X, RES)

For example, PPCS might retrieve values for the vapor pressure of each component contained in the current list of chemicals. For computations of vapor pressure, PPCS does not need the composition of the mixture (X), but there are other properties such as liquid-phase activity coefficients to be considered later for which the mole fraction must be specified. The fifth argument of PPCS, called RES, is the name of the FORTRAN singly subscripted variable in which the property information system places the computed values of the properties.

These three retrieval requests (PURE, PPCF, PPCS) enable FORTRAN programs to obtain property values from the information system. This capability not only simplifies the program but increases its generality as well: New data, new equations for calculating properties, and even new chemicals can be introduced without altering the program.

Figure 5-25 shows the flow of information between the property information system and the FORTRAN program. CALL ACTIVE, the first executable statement in the FORTRAN program, activates the property information system. Subroutine ACTIVE reads the current list of chemicals and key words that identify the data records (e.g., contributor, maximum error, and estimation program). The property information system services requests for property values made during the execution of the program.

These requests for properties are built into computer programs for process calculations in Examples 10.7–10.9.

PROBLEMS

5.1. Given the data

x	y
1	4.00
2	5.66
3	6.93
4	8.00
5	8.94
6	9.80

transform coordinates to obtain a straight line. What is the formula of the function?

5.2. Transform coordinates and get a linear plot of vapor pressure data for methyl ethyl ketone:

$T(°C)$	P^s (mm Hg)
−48.3	1
−28.0	5
−17.7	10
−6.5	20
+6.0	40
14.0	60
25.0	100
41.6	200
60.0	400
79.6	760

Derive a formula for vapor pressure as a function of temperature.

5.3. The viscosity of liquid diethyl ether decreases rapidly with increasing temperature:

$T(°C)$	Viscosity (centipoise)
−80	0.958
−60	0.637
−40	0.461
−20	0.362
0	0.284
20	0.233
40	0.197
60	0.166
80	0.140

For comparison, the viscosity of water at 20°C is 1.00 cP. Find a transformation of coordinates that yields a straight line. Use the straight line as a basis for extrapolation and estimate the viscosity of ether at −100°C.

5.4. The properties of pure bromobenzene are

$$\text{normal boiling point} = 155°C$$

$$\text{critical temperature} = 397°C$$

$$\text{critical pressure} = 44.6 \text{ atm}$$

Using these data, interpolate for the vapor pressure of bromobenzene at 327°C.

5.5. Din* reports the latent heat of vaporization of liquid propane:

T (°K)	Δh (cal/mole)	Vapor Pressure (atm)
341.71	2443	25
351.23	2069	30
359.61	1615	35
367.18	912	40
370.0	0	42.1

Interpolate to find the temperature and latent heat of vaporization corresponding to a vapor pressure of 37.5 atm. (*Hint:* See Examples 5.1 and 5.2.)

5.6. Volumetric properties of ethylene gas at 25°C are reported in Din*:

Pressure (bars)	Volume (cm³/g)	Pressure (bars)	Volume (cm³/g)
1	878.71	14	57.84
2	436.83	16	49.91
3	289.52	18	43.72
4	215.86	20	38.76
5	171.65	25	29.79
10	83.18	30	23.75
12	68.41	35	19.37

(a) Calculate the second and third virial coefficients for ethylene at 25°C. (*Hint:* See Example 5.3.) Notice that experimental points at the lower pressures are less reliable for calculating virial coefficients. Why?

(b) Estimate the second virial coefficient of ethylene at 25°C using Eqn. (4.29). The normal boiling point of ethylene is -103.78°C.

5.7. Freezing points of aqueous solutions of sodium chloride are

Concentration of NaCl (wt. %)	Freezing point (°C)
0	0
10	-6.54
20	-16.45

Estimate the freezing point of a 16% solution. Linear interpolation is unsatisfactory (why?). Interpolate using a second-degree polynomial.

5.8. The following data for the vapor pressure of liquid ammonia were measured in a laboratory:

*F. Din, *Thermodynamic Functions of Gases*, Vol. 2, Butterworths, London, 1962.

T (°K)	Vapor pressure (atm)
250	1.65
260	2.7
270	3.6
280	5.6
290	7.7
300	10.0
310	15.0
320	19.0
330	23.0
340	30.0
350	40.0

These data contain a certain amount of scatter due to experimental errors and must be smoothed. Transform coordinates (logarithm of vapor pressure versus reciprocal absolute temperature) and use the method of least squares to determine a formula for the vapor pressure.

5.9. A mercury manometer can be converted to an electrical pressure transducer by running a fine resistance wire through it. The resistance of the wire is proportional to the difference in mercury levels, Δh (see Fig. 5-26). Since voltage drop is proportional to resistance (Ohm's law), a voltmeter can be used to measure Δh. The following data were recorded:

Voltage drop (mV)	Δh (cm)	Voltage drop (mV)	Δh (cm)
1	0	125	19
5	0	156	22.5
11	1.1	174	25
22	2.4	176	28.1
43	4.1	207	31.6
53	6.6	228	34.8
65	9.4	260	37.8
99	13.9	277	43.6
115	16.7	307	46.3

Find a formula for the calibration curve using the method of least squares.

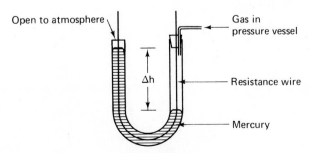

Figure 5-26

5.10. Use the University of Pennsylvania Physical Property Information System to estimate the following properties:

(a) Specific heat. There are two data records for each of the following substances: nitrogen, oxygen, hydrogen, and carbon monoxide. The first contains data for low temperatures and the second contains data for high temperatures (see Table 4.14).

    1. Retrieve (estimate) values of specific heat using both data records. Compare results at 500° and 1200°K.

    2. Retrieve (estimate) the specific heat of a mixture containing 79% nitrogen and 21% oxygen (mole percent) at 500° and 1200°K.

    3. Try to use a data record outside of its permissible temperature or pressure range. Show the result of a retrieval request.

(b) Vapor pressure. Retrieve (estimate) the vapor pressure of ethane and propane as a function of temperature. Compare results with values reported in Perry's handbook or the *Handbook of Chemistry and Physics*.

(c) Boiling point. Retrieve normal boiling points and critical temperatures for ethane, propane, *n*-butane, *n*-pentane, and *n*-hexane. Compare results with values reported in the *Handbook of Chemistry and Physics*.

(d) Density. Retrieve (estimate) the density of steam as a function of temperature and pressure. Compare with the values in Table 4.12.

Material Balances 6
for Process Units

An engineer seeks to understand how a chemical process unit works by constructing a mathematical model. The model is a set of algebraic and differential equations that takes into account principles of conservation (conservation of mass, conservation of energy, conservation of momentum, etc.), equations of motion (the Navier-Stokes equation, Poiseuille's equation, and other generalizations of Newton's second law for fluids in motion), equations describing flow of heat (Fourier's law of heat conduction, the Stefan-Boltzmann law of radiation, etc.), and many other basic equations of physics and chemistry. Often the process is so complicated that it cannot be analyzed in terms of first principles; in this case many of the equations are empirical relationships derived from experience with other similar processes.

In this chapter, let us direct our attention to just one of these laws, the principle of conservation of mass for processes that occur without chemical reaction (e.g., distillation, filtration, absorption, drying). In chemical engineering, applications of the principle of conservation of mass are called *material balances.*

Material balances on continuous processes require the solution of algebraic equations. Numerical methods of solving algebraic equations using digital computers are described in Chs. 11–13 so that details of calculations may be passed over or studied carefully depending on the needs of the student.

6.1 The Principle of Conservation of Mass

A material balance on a process means an application of the principle of conservation of mass: Mass can be neither created nor destroyed. Actually mass is not conserved if its energy changes because mass and energy are related by the famous Einstein equation

$$\Delta E = \Delta m \cdot c^2$$

where c is the speed of light. Chemical reactions are accompanied by large energy changes, and therefore one might expect the change in mass to be large too. For example, during the combustion of a hydrocarbon the energy released is of the order 10^4 cal/g of hydrocarbon. However, because of division by the factor c^2, the change in mass associated with the combustion of 1 g of hydrocarbon is only

$$\Delta m = \frac{\Delta E}{c^2} = \frac{-10^4 \text{ cal}}{(2.9979 \times 10^{10})^2 (\text{cm/sec})^2} \left[\frac{4.184 \times 10^7 \text{ dyne-cm}}{\text{cal}}\right]\left[\frac{\text{g-cm}}{\text{dyne-sec}^2}\right]$$
$$= -0.5 \times 10^{-9} \text{ g}$$

This decrease in mass is less than 1 part per billion. Therefore, for practical purposes, the principle of conservation of mass can be applied to chemical reactions. The conclusion is the same for other processes such as drying or distillation, for which energy changes are even smaller than for chemical reactions. Of course the principle of conservation of mass does not apply to nuclear reactions, for which energy changes are several orders of magnitude greater than those for chemical reactions.

6.2 Types of Processes: Batch and Continuous

Most processes can be classified as either batch or continuous. A batch process is characterized by intermittent addition of reactants and removal of products. Domestic cooking, for example, is a batch process. Many important industrial products are or used to be made by the batch; a good example is the old kettle process for the manufacture of soap. Tallow, coconut oil, and alkali are charged into a kettle several stories high and boiled for days until the saponification reaction is complete:

$$(C_{17}H_{33}COO)_3C_3H_5 + 3KOH = 3C_{17}H_{33}COOK + C_3H_5(OH)_3$$

glyceryl oleate (fat)	caustic potash (alkali)	potassium oleate (soap)	glycerine

Tallow and oils used to make soap are a mixture of fats such as glyceryl oleate. After saponification, the soap is separated from the valuable glycerine by-product, dried, and pressed into cakes. Finally the kettle is washed in preparation for the next batch. Figure 6-1 is a schematic of the batch process for the manufacture of soap.

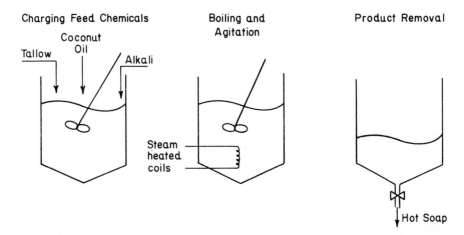

Figure 6-1 Batch soapmaking process.

Most modern, large-scale processes are continuous. Reactants are fed continuously and products are withdrawn continuously, 24 hours a day, with no interruption of flow. The continuous soapmaking process is shown in Fig. 6-2. Feed streams (tallow, coconut oil, water, caustic potash) enter the process continuously, and saponification is achieved continuously in two steps, hydrolysis and neutralization:

Hydrolysis: $(C_{17}H_{33}COO)_3C_3H_5 + 3H_2O = 3C_{17}H_{33}COOH + C_3H_5(OH)_3$
     fat   water   fatty acid   glycerine

Neutralization: $C_{17}H_{33}COOH + KOH = C_{17}H_{33}COOK + H_2O$
        fatty acid   caustic   soap   water
                        potash

The process delivers a steady flow of wet soap, 24 hours a day. Plants automated for continuous saponification produce in 2 hr the same amount of soap that was made in several days by traditional batch methods.*

A general rule is that the batch process is more economical when products are made only in small quantities, either because of limited demand or because of a highly diversified line of products. Thus, the batch process is commonly used in the cosmetic and pharmaceutical industries, and indus-

---

*R. N. Shreve, *Chemical Process Industries*, 3rd ed., McGraw-Hill, New York, 1967.

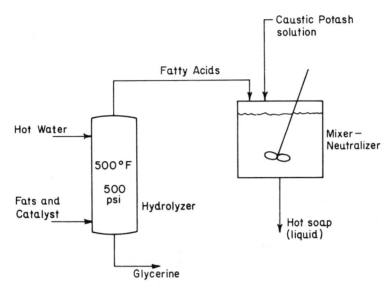

Figure 6-2 Simplified schematic of continuous soapmaking process.

trial chemicals such as sulfuric acid are manufactured by continuous processes.

6.3 Material Balance Equations

Consider a continuous process such as soapmaking (Fig. 6-2). Suppose that we make a material balance upon the mixer-neutralizer. Its boundary and the streams crossing it are clearly identified in Fig. 6-2. There are two feed streams (caustic potash solution and fatty acids) and one product stream (hot soap). The principle of conservation of mass requires that

mass flow rate in — mass flow rate out
$$= \text{rate of accumulation of mass inside boundary} \qquad (6.1)$$

The mass flow rate may be expressed in pounds per hour. Equation (6.1) is for transient or unsteady-state processes in which material is accumulated or depleted within the boundaries of the unit. Such accumulations or depletions occur during start-up or shutdown of a process or, unexpectedly, when there is an accident such as a leak or equipment failure.

In continuous processing, after completion of the start-up, the inlet and outlet valves remain open and chemicals flow continuously in and out of the unit, 24 hours a day. Sometimes it is necessary to adjust inlet and outlet valves to compensate for fluctuations occurring upstream or downstream of the process unit.

Steady state

A continuous process operated so that the accumulation term [right-hand side of Eqn. (6.1)] is zero or negligibly small is called a *steady-state* process:

$$\text{mass flow rate in} = \text{mass flow rate out} \qquad (6.2)$$

At steady state all flow rates are constant (i.e., invariant with time). If we refer again to the mixer-neutralizer in Fig. 6-2, the sum of the mass flow rates of the two feed streams must be equal to the mass flow rate of the product stream according to Eqn. (6.2). Summarizing, at steady state,

1. The rate of accumulation of mass within the boundaries of a process unit is zero.
2. Mass flow rates of all streams are constant.

The concept of a process operated at steady state is an idealization. The rate of accumulation of mass in any real process may be small but is never precisely zero. Flow rates are not exactly constant but fluctuate about a mean value. Nevertheless, the concept of a steady-state process is extremely useful in describing the average production rates of chemical processes. In the rest of this book, no statement to the contrary implies that the process is operated at steady state.

6.4 Multicomponent Streams

Most process streams contain several chemical species or components. If no chemical reactions occur within the boundaries of the process, Eqn. (6.2) may be written for each component that passes through:

$$\text{mass flow rate in} = \text{mass flow rate out} \quad \textit{for each component} \qquad (6.3)$$

Equation (6.3) cannot be applied to the soapmaking process because saponification is a chemical change. Equation (6.3) applies to the subsequent soap-drying process, which does not involve chemical change. In Fig. 6-3, wet soap chips and hot, nearly dry air are fed continuously to a dryer. The hot soap is chilled on a large roller (not shown) and scraped continuously from the roller onto a moving conveyor belt which carries the soap chips into the dryer. Hot, nearly dry air contacts the soap chips as they pass through the dryer. Moist air leaves the dryer continuously. Notice that soap and air flow in different directions. What is the advantage of this countercurrent flow pattern?

If there are no chemical reactions, it makes no difference if Eqn. (6.3) is written in molal units:

$$\text{molal flow rate in} = \text{molal flow rate out} \quad \textit{for each component} \qquad (6.4)$$

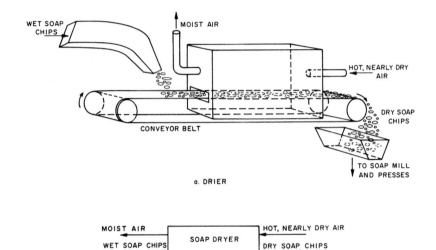

Figure 6-3 Continuous soap drier.

In the next section we shall consider an application of Eqn. (6.4) to a particular problem.

6.5 An Illustrative Problem

Equation (6.4), the material balance equation for steady state in the absence of chemical reactions, seems simple enough. However, for processes containing a large number of multicomponent streams, it is difficult to sort out the number of equations and number of unknowns unless a systematic procedure is followed:

1. Construct the process diagram; number each stream.
2. Identify the quantities which are known (known flow rates and compositions).
3. Check whether the number of equations is equal to the number of unknowns.
4. Solve the equations for the unknown quantities.

Example 6.1

A pilot plant distillation column is used to strip ethyl alcohol from a feed stream of ethyl alcohol and water containing 1.5% ethyl alcohol (mole percent). The feed rate is 16 lb-moles/hr. The distillate stream contains 87% alcohol, and the bottoms stream contains 0.05% alcohol (mole percent). Calculate all flow rates and compositions not specified.

Solution:

1. The process diagram is given in Fig. 6-4.

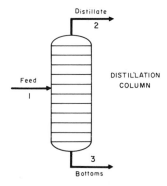

Figure 6-4

2. The quantities that are known are summarized in a table:

		Mole Fraction	
Stream No.	Total lb-moles/hr	Alcohol	Water
1	16	0.015	
2		0.87	
3		0.0005	

There are five unknowns. Since the sum of the mole fractions in any stream is unity, the mole fraction of water in each stream may be calculated:

		Mole Fraction	
Stream No.	Total lb-moles/hr	Alcohol	Water
1	16	0.015	0.985
2	x	0.87	0.13
3	y	0.0005	0.9995

3. There are now two unknowns: the total molar flow rate in streams 2 and 3, called x and y, respectively. Since there are two components, alcohol and water, there are two independent material balance equations. Therefore, there are two unknowns and two independent equations:

alcohol material balance: $0.015(16) = 0.87x + 0.0005y$

water material balance: $0.985(16) = 0.13x + 0.9995y$

4. Solution of these two equations yields

$$x = 0.267 \text{ lb-mole/hr}$$
$$y = 15.733 \text{ lb-moles/hr}$$

Summarizing,

| Stream No. | Total lb-moles/hr | Mole Fraction | |
		Alcohol	Water
1	16.00	0.015	0.985
2	0.267	0.87	0.13
3	15.733	0.0005	0.9995

6.6 General Analysis of Material Balances

The previous example contains all the elements of more difficult material balance problems and therefore leads naturally into the following analysis of the number of independent variables. Given flow rates and compositions of some but not all of the process streams, the problem is to solve for unknown flow rates and compositions by making a material balance. It is assumed that the process unit is operated at steady state and that there are no chemical reactions.

Equations and constraints

Types of equations are classified as

1. Material balance equations.
2. Mole fraction constraints.
3. Equipment constraints.

For a process unit there are a total of N_c material balance equations, one for each of the N_c components that passes through the unit [see Eqn. (6.4)].

The mole fraction constraint is that the sum of mole fractions is unity for each stream. There is one mole fraction constraint for each stream.

Equipment constraints are different for each process unit. For example, two product streams may have the same composition, or the ratio of flow rates of two streams may be a constant. Equipment constraints depend on the nature of the processing equipment; examples will be given later.

Variables

A simple formula for the total number of variables in all the equations (N_v) can be derived if all the components are present in each stream. Suppose that there are N_c chemical species, or components, that cross the boundaries of the process unit. For each stream, the variables are the flow rate and N_c mole fractions or weight fractions, a total of $N_c + 1$ variables. Let there be N_p equipment parameters; these are the constants in equations of type 3 above. If the process unit has N_s streams of matter crossing its boundaries,

$$N_v = N_s(N_c + 1) + N_p \tag{6.5}$$

When one or more components is missing from one or more streams, Eqn. (6.5) does not apply, and the total number of variables in the equations (N_v) must be counted.

Design variables

Suppose that there are N_e independent equations containing a total of N_v variables (see Ch. 12 for a definition of independent equations). The number of design or decision variables (N_d) is

$$N_d = N_v - N_e \tag{6.6}$$

Equation (6.6) is a result of the requirement that the number of equations (N_e) be equal to the number of unknowns $(N_v - N_d)$. Values for each of the design variables must be assigned before the material balance can be solved.

The concept of design variables is illustrated by reworking Example 6.1.

Example 6.2

Set up the equations and determine the number of design variables for the distillation column described in Example 6.1. Do not introduce numerical values until the last step, which is solution of the equations.

Solution:

A general notation scheme is shown in Fig. 6-5. F_i is the (steady) molal flow rate of stream i. x_{ij} is the mole fraction in stream i of component j.

The components are assigned numbers:

Component	No.
Alcohol	1
Water	2

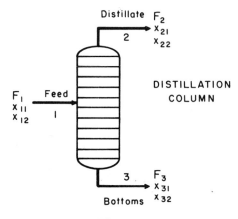

Figure 6-5

1. Equations and constraints.
    a. Material balance equations [Eqn. (6.4)]:

$$F_1 x_{11} = F_2 x_{21} + F_3 x_{31} \tag{1}$$

$$F_1 x_{12} = F_2 x_{22} + F_3 x_{32} \tag{2}$$

    b. Mole-fraction constraints (one for each stream):

$$x_{11} + x_{12} = 1 \tag{3}$$

$$x_{21} + x_{22} = 1 \tag{4}$$

$$x_{31} + x_{32} = 1 \tag{5}$$

    c. Equipment constraints: None.
2. Number of variables: $N_v = (N_s)(N_c + 1) + N_p = (3)(2 + 1) + 0 = 9$.
3. Design or decision variables: $N_d = N_v - N_e = 9 - 5 = 4$. The analysis shows that four of the nine variables are design variables. The other five are the unknowns, values for which may be obtained from the five independent equations. The four design variables chosen in this particular case are F_1, x_{11}, x_{21}, and x_{31}. The set of five unknowns (F_2, F_3, x_{12}, x_{22}, and x_{32}) are then evaluated by simultaneous solution of the five equations (1)–(5).
4. Solution of the equations: Equations (3)–(5) may be solved directly for x_{12}, x_{22}, and x_{32}. We adopt the convention of circling the known variables so that unknowns are not circled:

$$\boxed{F_1}\boxed{x_{11}} = F_2\boxed{x_{21}} + F_3\boxed{x_{31}} \tag{6}$$

$$\boxed{F_1}\boxed{x_{12}} = F_2 x_{22} + F_3 x_{32} \tag{7}$$

Equations (6) and (7) are linear in the variables F_2 and F_3. The solution is

$$F_2 = \frac{F_1(x_{11}x_{32} - x_{12}x_{31})}{\Delta}$$

$$F_3 = \frac{F_1(x_{12}x_{21} - x_{11}x_{22})}{\Delta}$$

where

$$\Delta = (x_{21}x_{32} - x_{31}x_{22})$$

For the values of the design variables prescribed in Example (6.1),

$$F_1 = 16 \text{ lb-moles/hr}$$
$$x_{11} = 0.015$$
$$x_{21} = 0.87$$
$$x_{31} = 0.0005$$

the solution is

$$F_2 = \frac{(16)(0.0145)}{(0.8695)} = 0.267 \text{ lb-moles/hr}$$

$$F_3 = \frac{(16)(0.855)}{(0.8695)} = 15.733 \text{ lb-moles/hr}$$

Another material balance problem is presented to illustrate the procedure for setting up equations and determining the number of design variables.

Example 6.3

An oxygen plant (see Fig. 6-6), operating on the modified Linde-Frankl process, produces low-purity oxygen for industrial use from air containing oxygen, nitrogen, and argon. Hydrocarbons, water, and carbon dioxide are removed from the air feed in previous processing. Practically all the argon goes into the oxygen stream. Analyze the material balance problem, select a set of design variables, and solve the equations using typical values of design variables.

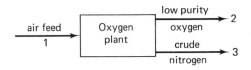

Figure 6-6

Solution:

The components are numbered:

Component	No.
Oxygen	1
Nitrogen	2
Argon	3

1. Equations and constraints.
   a. Material balance equations (one for each component):

$$F_1 x_{11} = F_2 x_{21} + F_3 x_{31} \tag{1}$$

$$F_1 x_{12} = F_2 x_{22} + F_3 x_{32} \tag{2}$$

$$F_1 x_{13} = F_2 x_{23} \tag{3}$$

b. Mole-fraction constraints (one for each stream):

$$x_{11} + x_{12} + x_{13} = 1 \tag{4}$$

$$x_{21} + x_{22} + x_{23} = 1 \tag{5}$$

$$x_{31} + x_{32} \quad\;\; = 1 \tag{6}$$

c. Equipment constraints: None.
2. Number of variables (by actual count): $N_v = 11$ (notice that x_{33} is not counted as a variable).
3. Design variables: $N_d = N_v - N_e = 11 - 6 = 5$. Suppose that we select as design variables the set F_2, x_{21}, x_{32}, x_{11}, and x_{12}, with values

$$\begin{aligned}
F_2 &= 100 \text{ lb-moles/hr} && (O_2 \text{ stream flow rate}) \\
x_{21} &= 0.90 && (O_2 \text{ stream purity}) \\
x_{32} &= 0.953 && (N_2 \text{ stream purity}) \\
x_{11} &= 0.2098 \Big\} \\
x_{12} &= 0.7808 \Big\} && (\text{air composition})
\end{aligned}$$

The composition of the feed stream (x_{11}, x_{12}, x_{13}) is determined by the composition of air. After assigning values to x_{11} and x_{12}, x_{13} is not a design variable because its value is given by Eqn. (4). This awkwardness can be avoided, if desired, by specifying x_{13} as a design variable and crossing out Eqn. (4).
4. Solution of the equations: After circling known variables, it is found that x_{13} and x_{31} are given by

$$x_{31} = 1 - \boxed{x_{32}}$$

$$x_{13} = 1 - \boxed{x_{11}} - \boxed{x_{12}}$$

so that the equations reduce to

$$F_1\boxed{x_{11}} = \boxed{F_2}\boxed{x_{21}} + F_3\boxed{x_{31}}$$

$$F_1\boxed{x_{12}} = \boxed{F_2}x_{22} + F_3\boxed{x_{32}}$$

$$F_1\boxed{x_{13}} = \boxed{F_2}x_{23}$$

$$\boxed{x_{21}} + x_{22} + x_{23} = 1$$

There are four unknowns $(F_1, F_3, x_{22},$ and $x_{23})$ and four linear equations. The solution (see Ch. 12) is

$$F_1 = 524 \text{ lb-moles/hr}$$

$$F_3 = 424 \text{ lb-moles/hr}$$

$$x_{22} = 0.0507$$

$$x_{23} = 0.0493$$

Summarizing, all process flow rates and compositions are given in tabular form:

		Mole Fraction		
Stream No.	Total lb-moles/hr	O_2	N_2	Ar
1	524	0.2098	0.7808	0.0094
2	100	0.90	0.0507	0.0493
3	424	0.047	0.953	0

Molal and weight basis

Compositions of liquid and solid mixtures are often expressed as weight fractions, while compositions of gaseous mixtures are usually expressed as mole fractions. When performing material balance calculations, it is necessary to convert compositions expressed in mole fractions (x_{ij}) to compositions expressed in weight fractions (x'_{ij}) and vice versa.

Conversion formulas, which should be verified by the student, are

$$x'_{ij} = \frac{x_{ij}M_j}{\sum\limits_{j=1}^{N_c} x_{ij}M_j} \qquad (6.7)$$

$$x_{ij} = \frac{x'_{ij}/M_j}{\sum\limits_{j=1}^{N_c} x'_{ij}/M_j} \qquad (6.8)$$

where i is the stream number, j is the component number, and M_j is the molecular weight of the jth component. All flow rates and compositions must be expressed on the same basis. If there are chemical reactions, the molal basis is preferred. Either the molal or weight basis, whichever is more convenient, may be used in the absence of chemical reactions.

Example 6.4

1. A stream of nitrogen gas (call it stream 1) contains 0.5 mole % water vapor. Determine the weight fraction of water.
2. A stream of nitrogen gas contains 0.2 wt. % water vapor. Determine the mole fraction of water.

Solution:

The components are

Component	No.	Molecular Weight
Nitrogen	1	28.01
Water	2	18.02

1. Equation (6.7) is used to convert from mole fractions to weight fractions:

$$x'_{ij} = \frac{x_{ij}M_j}{\sum\limits_{j=1}^{2} x_{ij}M_j} = \frac{x_{ij}M_j}{x_{i1}M_1 + x_{i2}M_2}$$

For stream 1, the weight fraction of water is

$$x'_{12} = \frac{x_{12}M_2}{x_{11}M_1 + x_{12}M_2} = \frac{(0.005)(18.02)}{(0.995)(28.01) + (0.005)(18.02)} = 0.00322$$

2. Equation (6.8) is used to convert from weight fractions to mole fractions:

$$x_{ij} = \frac{x'_{ij}/M_j}{\sum\limits_{j=1}^{2} x'_{ij}/M_j}$$

For stream 1 ($i = 1$), the mole fraction of water is

$$x_{12} = \frac{x'_{12}/M_2}{x'_{11}/M_1 + x'_{12}/M_2} = \frac{0.002/18.02}{0.998/28.01 + 0.002/18.02} = 0.00310$$

Conversion from molal to mass flow rates, and vice versa, depends on the average molecular weight of stream i ($\bar{M}_i$) defined by

$$\bar{M}_i = \sum_{j=1}^{N_c} x_{ij}M_j \tag{6.9}$$

The student should verify that the equations relating mass (F') and molar (F) flow rates are

$$F'_i = F_i \cdot \bar{M}_i \tag{6.10}$$

and

$$F_i = \frac{F'_i}{\bar{M}_i} \tag{6.11}$$

Equipment parameters

Equipment parameters are process variables other than stream parameters (flow rates and compositions) that describe the operation of a particular process unit. For example, the ratio of flow rates of two streams (α) might be defined as

$$\alpha = \frac{F_3}{F_4} \tag{6.12}$$

α is an equipment parameter, and Eqn. (6.12) is an equipment constraint.

Example 6.5 illustrates a material balance problem containing an equipment parameter.

Example 6.5

Hot soap is chilled on a roller and scraped continuously from the roller onto a moving conveyor belt (stream 1) which carries the soap into a dryer (see Fig. 6-7). The entering soap contains 25% water by weight. It is desired to reduce the

Figure 6-7

water content to 15% water by weight (stream 3) and to produce 1200 lb/hr of dried soap chips. The entering air (stream 2) contains 0.3 mole % water vapor. Experiment indicates that the dryer operates efficiently when the dry air/wet chip flow-rate ratio is 3.0.

Calculate the unknown flow rates and compositions. Air may be assumed to be 21 mole % oxygen and 79 mole % nitrogen (molecular weight = 28.97).

Solution:

The components are

Component	No.
Water	1
Air	2
Soap	3

Note that air is treated as if it were a pure substance.

1. Equations and constraints. A weight basis is adopted because most of the flow rates and compositions are given on a weight basis.

    a. Equipment constraints:

    $$F_2' = \alpha F_1' \tag{1}$$

    b. Material balance equations:

    $$F_1'x_{11}' + F_2'x_{21}' = F_3'x_{31}' + F_4'x_{41}' \tag{2}$$

    $$F_2'x_{22}' = F_4'x_{42}' \tag{3}$$

    $$F_1'x_{13}' = F_3'x_{33}' \tag{4}$$

    c. Mass-fraction constraints:

    $$x_{11}' + x_{13}' = 1 \tag{5}$$

    $$x_{21}' + x_{22}' = 1 \tag{6}$$

    $$x_{31}' + x_{33}' = 1 \tag{7}$$

    $$x_{41}' + x_{42}' = 1 \tag{8}$$

Equation (1) is the equipment constraint that defines the dry air/wet chip ratio, α.

2. Number of variables: $N_v = 13$ [flow rates (4), compositions (8), equipment parameter (1)].
3. Design or decision variables: $N_d = N_v - N_e = 13 - 8 = 5$. The design

variables F_3', α, x_{11}', x_{31}', and x_{21}' are selected to coincide with the design variables in the problem statement:

$$F_3' = 1200 \text{ lb/hr}$$

$$\alpha = 3$$

$$x_{11}' = 0.25$$

$$x_{31}' = 0.15$$

$$x_{21}' = 0.00187$$

Equation (6.7) is used to convert the mole fraction of water in the entering air stream to weight fraction:

$$x_{21}' = \frac{x_{21}M_1}{x_{21}M_1 + x_{22}M_2} = \frac{(0.003)(18.02)}{(0.003)(18.02) + (0.997)(28.97)} = 0.00187$$

4. Solution of the equations: The unknown variables x_{13}', x_{22}', and x_{33}' are calculated directly using Eqns. (5)–(7). Then, F_1' and F_2' are calculated using Eqns. (4) and (1), respectively. If Eqns. (2), (3), and (4) are added, it is found that

$$\boxed{F_1'} + \boxed{F_2'} = \boxed{F_3'} + F_4'$$

This equation, called the overall material balance, gives F_4'. Finally, Eqns. (3) and (8) are used to calculate x_{41}' and x_{42}'.

Summarizing the results,

		Weight Fraction		
Stream No.	Total lb/hr	Water	Air	Soap
1	1360	0.25	0	0.75
2	4080	0.00187	0.9981	0
3	1200	0.15	0	0.85
4	4240	0.0395	0.9605	0

The mole fraction of water vapor in the exit air stream is given by Eqn. (6.8):

$$x_{41} = \frac{x_{41}'/M_1}{x_{41}'/M_1 + x_{42}'/M_2} = \frac{0.0395/18.02}{(0.0395/18.02) + (0.9605/28.97)} = 0.062$$

6.7 Common Errors in Specifying Design Variables

Textbook problems such as Example 6.1 are intentionally prepared so that the problem statement contains the exact amount of information needed to solve the problem. In practice, mistakes in specifying design variables sometimes generate solutions which are inconsistent or physically impossible; sometimes a solution does not exist.

1. *No solution.* When an insufficient number of design variables is given, there is no solution to the problem. For Example 6.2, the set of design variables,

$$F_1 = 100 \text{ lb-moles/hr}$$

$$x_{11} = 0.015$$

$$x_{21} = 0.87$$

would be incomplete because the number of equations would be one less than the number of unknowns. Therefore, no solution is possible. Redundant specification can also lead to no solution. Referring again to Example 6.2, the set of design variables,

$$F_1 = 100 \text{ lb-moles/hr}$$

$$F_2 = 1.67 \text{ lb-moles/hr}$$

$$F_3 = 98.33 \text{ lb-moles/hr}$$

$$x_{11} = 0.015$$

contains one redundant specification (F_3 could have been calculated by an overall material balance), and there is no solution.

2. *Inconsistent solution.* When too many design variables are specified, there may be inconsistencies. For example, the set of design variables

$$F_1 = 100 \text{ lb-moles/hr}$$

$$x_{11} = 0.015$$

$$x_{21} = 0.87$$

$$x_{31} = 0.0005$$

$$F_2 = 3.0 \text{ lb-moles/hr}$$

contains more information than necessary to solve the problem. Specifically, the value of F_2 calculated from the first four variables is 1.67 lb-moles/hr. Therefore, this set of design variables is inconsistent.

3. *Physically impossible solution.* For the set of design variables

$$F_1 = 100 \text{ lb-moles/hr}$$

$$x_{11} = 0.015$$

$$x_{21} = 0.87$$

$$x_{31} = 0.03$$

the calculated result is that the flow rate of the distillate stream, F_2, is negative. This physically impossible result arises from the incorrect specification that both product streams contain larger mole fractions of alcohol than the feed stream.

Most of these difficulties can be avoided by counting the number of design variables to make sure that the number of unknowns is equal to the number of independent equations.

6.8 Common Errors in Writing Material Balance Equations

A set of equations is independent if no equation in the set can be obtained by algebraic operations performed on the other equations (see Ch. 12 for a more complete discussion). In Example 6.5 it was convenient to use the overall material balance

$$F_1' + F_2' = F_3' + F_4'$$

to calculate F_4'. However, this equation is not independent of the other equations in Example 6.5 because it may be derived by substituting Eqns. (5), (6), (7), and (8) into the sum of Eqns. (2), (3), and (4). Suppose that the overall material balance had been incorrectly written in Example 6.5 as another independent material balance equation. This would have given an incorrect count of 13 variables, 9 equations, and 4 design variables, for which there would have been no solution.

An overall material balance should be used whenever it simplifies the solution, but it cannot be counted as an independent equation when Eqn. (6.4) is written for each component.

6.9 Separation Processes

In chemical engineering, separation means the process by which a mixture is converted into its pure or nearly pure constituents. The reaction step of a chemical process is usually followed by a series of separation steps, in which unreacted feed chemicals and by-products are removed and products are purified. Separation is the opposite of mixing. Mixing occurs spontaneously, but separations always require the performance of work.

Desalination of seawater, described in Ch. 2, is a typical separation process. Selection of a particular separation method such as distillation or crystallization depends on the physical and chemical properties of the pure substances and the nature of the molecular interactions in the mixture.

Figure 6-8 is a schematic of a typical separation process in which a feed stream is separated into two product streams of different composition. The separation is caused by the addition of another stream of matter or energy called the *separating agent*.*

*C. J. King, *Separation Processes*, McGraw-Hill, New York, 1971.

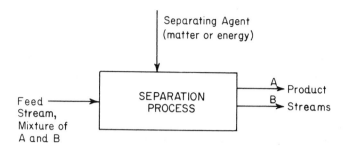

Figure 6-8 Schematic of a separation process.

Sometimes the feed stream consists of two phases and the separation process is the mechanical operation of removing one phase from the other. Examples of *mechanical separation processes* are filters and centrifuges, which separate a slurry into solid and liquid phases, and electrostatic precipitators, which remove small solid or liquid particles from a gas stream.

Most separation processes involve the transfer of mass between two phases followed by mechanical separation. Often the addition of the separating agent causes formation of another phase that is immiscible with the feed. For example, in absorption the feed is a gaseous mixture, and the separating agent is a liquid which dissolves one or more components of the gas. In crystallization the feed is a liquid containing dissolved solute, and the separating agent is the removal of heat, which causes precipitation of the crystals. The products are the crystalline solid and the mother liquor, which are separated mechanically by filtration or by washing, as shown in Fig. 2-11.

The degree of separation depends on the molecular properties of the components of the mixture and the efficiency of the separation. Sometimes only partial separation is possible in a single stage; thus, a feed mixture of 50% A, 50% B might be separated into two mixtures, one 60% A, 40% B and the other 40% A, 60% B. In this case the separation achieved in one stage must be multiplied by connecting several stages in series; these *multistage separation processes* are described in Ch. 10.

In this chapter let us consider the material balance for two important single-stage separation processes:

1. Flash vaporization (or partial condensation).
2. Solvent extraction.

Flash vaporization

A flash vaporization unit is shown in Fig. 2-9. Preheated liquid feed under pressure partially evaporates and cools as it enters the unit. The amount of feed evaporated depends on the condition of the feed (its temperature and pressure), the pressure drop as it flashes into the unit, and the amount of heat removed or added in the vaporizer. In Fig. 2-9 the feed is saltwater, and the vapor is pure water. Since all the salt stays in the liquid, the separation is very effective. In general, vapor flashed from the feed contains several or all of the components of the mixture. Therefore, the solution of the material balance depends on the distribution of each component between liquid and vapor.

If the vaporizer is designed so that there is enough contact time for transfer of mass and heat between liquid and vapor, then a condition of equilibrium is reached, and the distribution of each component is given by its equilibrium constant (k). Using the notation in Fig. 6-9, the equilibrium value of k for the jth component is defined by

$$k_j = \frac{x_{2j}}{x_{3j}} \qquad (6.13)$$

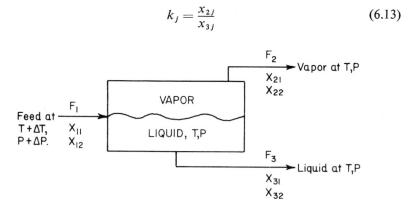

Figure 6-9 Flash vaporization of binary mixture.

Thus, k is the ratio of the mole fraction in the vapor to the mole fraction in the liquid. Conditions of equilibrium are reached when there is no more net transfer of mass between phases. For a binary feed, the component with $k > 1$ is more volatile and is called the light component; the other component has $k < 1$ and is called the heavy component. As a consequence of our assumption of equilibrium, the vapor and liquid products leave the unit at equal values of temperature and pressure.

Thermodynamic calculations of vapor-liquid equilibrium constants (k) are described in Ch. 10. In general the value of k depends on the temperature, pressure, and composition of the products. However, there are several special cases for which the calculation of k is particularly simple:

1. *Insoluble gases.* If one of the components is a gas above its critical temperature and its solubility in the liquid is negligibly small, then for that component $x_{3j} = 0$ and $k_j = \infty$. An example is a two-phase mixture of hydrogen, ethyl alcohol, and water flashed at 30°C, for which the k-value of hydrogen would be very large.

2. *Dissolved solids and nonvolatile liquids.* If one of the components of the feed is a dissolved solid or a nonvolatile liquid with a very low vapor pressure, then for that component $x_{2j} = 0$ and $k_j = 0$. An example is common salt dissolved in water; the k-value of the dissolved salt is zero.

3. *Raoult's law for ideal solutions.* When all the components of the mixture have similar molecular structure, such as adjacent members of a homologous series or isotopes, the equilibrium constant for each component is equal to the vapor pressure of the pure liquid divided by the pressure in the vaporization chamber:

$$k_j = \frac{P_j^s}{P} \qquad (6.14)$$

Equation (6.14) is called Raoult's law for ideal liquid mixtures. For a given pressure, k increases exponentially with temperature in proportion to the vapor pressure [see Fig. 5-7(a)]. The value of k is independent of composition, however. Raoult's law applies with high accuracy to liquid mixtures of benzene + toluene; n-hexane + n-heptane; 1,1-dichloroethane + 1,1,2-trichloroethane; and water + deuterium oxide; for example.

Raoult's law applies to solvents even when the solute-solvent pair is not an ideal mixture, provided that the liquid phase is mostly solvent ($x > 0.95$). For example, solutions of ethyl alcohol and water are not ideal, but for an aqueous solution containing only 5 mole % alcohol the equilibrium constant of water (not the alcohol) is given approximately by Eqn. (6.14).

4. *Henry's law for solutes at low concentration.* If the concentration of any of the components in the liquid phase does not exceed a few mole percent, then the equilibrium constant of that component is given by Henry's law:

$$k_j = \frac{H_j}{P} \qquad (6.15)$$

Henry's constant (H) is different for each solute-solvent pair and is a function of temperature. Henry's constants are tabulated in Perry's handbook* for several gases dissolved in water.

For example, solutions of pyridine (C_5H_5N) and water are highly nonideal. However, if the concentration of pyridine in the liquid does not exceed a few mole percent, one can apply Henry's law, Eqn. (6.15), to the solute (pyridine) and Raoult's law, Eqn. (6.14), to the solvent (water).

Chemical Engineers' Handbook, edited by R. H. Perry and C. H. Chilton, 5th ed., McGraw-Hill, New York (1973).

Example 6.6

Calculate vapor-liquid equilibrium constants for a binary mixture of cyclopentane (C_5H_{10}) and cyclohexane (C_6H_{12}). The vaporization chamber is at atmospheric pressure, and the temperature of liquid and vapor product streams is 60°C.

Solution:

Assume equilibrium and Raoult's law (cyclopentane and cyclohexane molecules differ only by the number of members in the ring). From the *Handbook of Chemistry and Physics*,* the vapor pressures of the pure liquids at 60°C are

Component	No.	Vapor Pressure (atm)
Cyclopentane	1	1.40
Cyclohexane	2	0.512

From Eqn. (6.14),

$$k_1 = \frac{1.40}{1} = 1.40$$

$$k_2 = \frac{0.512}{1} = 0.512$$

Example 6.7

Calculate vapor-liquid equilibrium constants for dilute solutions of pyridine in water at 70°C and 300 mm Hg. Henry's constant for pyridine at 70°C is 3760 mm Hg.†

Solution:

The vapor pressures of liquid pyridine and water at 70°C are

Component	No.	Vapor Pressure, 70°C (mm Hg)
C_5H_5N	1	166
H_2O	2	234

Pyridine and water form nonideal liquid solutions, but for dilute solutions of pyridine one can apply Henry's law to pyridine and Raoult's law to water. From Eqn. (6.15),

$$k_1 = \frac{H_1}{P} = \frac{3760}{300} = 12.53$$

Handbook of Chemistry and Physics, 55th ed., Chemical Rubber Publishing Company, Cleveland, 1974-75.

†R. S. L. Andon, J. D. Cox, and E. F. G. Herington, "The Thermodynamic Properties of Dilute Solutions of Pyridine Bases in Water," *Disc. Faraday Soc., 15*, 168 (1953).

From Eqn. (6.14),

$$k_2 = \frac{P_2^s}{P} = \frac{234}{300} = 0.78$$

Equations (6.14) and (6.15) are both based upon the validity of the perfect gas law ($Pv = RT$) for the vapor and must be modified when the pressure in the flash chamber exceeds a few atmospheres. Effects of nonideality in the liquid phase (failure of Raoult's law) are covered in Ch. 10. In the following material balance problem it is assumed that values of vapor-liquid equilibrium constants are obtained from experimental data or from calculations described in Ch. 10.

Example 6.8

In the process for synthesis of ammonia from nitrogen and hydrogen, the products from the reactor are ammonia, unreacted nitrogen and hydrogen, and small amounts of argon and methane impurities that enter in the feed streams and pass through the reactor. The products from the reactor are cooled and separated in a partial condenser operated at $-28°$F and at 2000 psia. The reactor operates at a high pressure which is maintained in the condenser so that the recycled nitrogen and hydrogen do not have to be compressed. Calculate the flow rates and compositions of the streams leaving the partial condenser for a feed rate of 100 lb-moles/hr. The composition of the feed and the vapor-liquid equilibrium constants are

Component	No.	Mole Fraction in Feed	k, Vapor-Liquid Equilibrium Constant ($-28°$F, 2000 psia)
Nitrogen	1	0.220	66.67
Hydrogen	2	0.660	50
Ammonia	3	0.114	0.015
Argon	4	0.002	100
Methane	5	0.004	33.33

Solution:

The process diagram is the same as Fig. 6-9, but there are five components in each stream.

1. Equations and constraints
   a. Material balance equations:

$$F_1 x_{11} = F_2 x_{21} + F_3 x_{31} \tag{1}$$

$$F_1 x_{12} = F_2 x_{22} + F_3 x_{32} \tag{2}$$

$$F_1 x_{13} = F_2 x_{23} + F_3 x_{33} \tag{3}$$

$$F_1 x_{14} = F_2 x_{24} + F_3 x_{34} \tag{4}$$

$$F_1 x_{15} = F_2 x_{25} + F_3 x_{35} \tag{5}$$

b. Mole-fraction constraints:

$$x_{11} + x_{12} + x_{13} + x_{14} + x_{15} = 1 \tag{6}$$

$$x_{21} + x_{22} + x_{23} + x_{24} + x_{25} = 1 \tag{7}$$

$$x_{31} + x_{32} + x_{33} + x_{34} + x_{35} = 1 \tag{8}$$

c. Equipment constraints:

$$x_{21} = k_1 x_{31} \tag{9}$$

$$x_{22} = k_2 x_{32} \tag{10}$$

$$x_{23} = k_3 x_{33} \tag{11}$$

$$x_{24} = k_4 x_{34} \tag{12}$$

$$x_{25} = k_5 x_{35} \tag{13}$$

2. Number of variables: $N_v = (N_s)(N_c + 1) + N_p = (3)(5 + 1) + 5 = 23$. The equipment parameters are the vapor-liquid equilibrium constants $k_1, k_2, \ldots, k_5$.

3. Design or decision variables: $N_d = N_v - N_e = 23 - 13 = 10$. In accordance with the problem statement, we select as the set of design variables $F_1, x_{11}, x_{12}, x_{14}, x_{15}, k_1, k_2, k_3, k_4,$ and k_5 with the values

$$
\begin{array}{ll}
F_1 = 100 \text{ lb-moles/hr} & k_1 = 66.67 \\
x_{11} = 0.22 & k_2 = 50.0 \\
x_{12} = 0.66 & k_3 = 0.015 \\
x_{14} = 0.002 & k_4 = 100.0 \\
x_{15} = 0.004 & k_5 = 33.33
\end{array}
$$

4. Solution of the equations: Equation (6) is solved directly for x_{13}. Twelve equations remain. Equations (9)–(13) may be conveniently expressed in subscripted notation:

$$x_{2j} = \boxed{k_j} x_{3j}, \quad j = 1, 2, \ldots, 5 \tag{14}$$

or

$$x_{3j} = \frac{x_{2j}}{\boxed{k_j}}, \quad j = 1, 2, \ldots, 5 \tag{15}$$

Equations (1)–(5) may be rearranged:

$$x_{2j} = \frac{\boxed{F_1}\boxed{x_{1j}} - F_3 x_{3j}}{F_2}, \quad j = 1, 2, \ldots, 5 \tag{16}$$

or

$$x_{3j} = \frac{\boxed{F_1}\boxed{x_{1j}} - F_2 x_{2j}}{F_3}, \quad j = 1, 2, \ldots, 5 \tag{17}$$

Substituting Eqn. (14) into Eqn. (17) and solving for x_{3j},

$$x_{3j} = \frac{\boxed{F_1}}{F_2} \frac{\boxed{x_{1j}}}{\left[(F_3/F_2) + \boxed{k_j}\right]}, \quad j = 1, 2, \ldots, 5 \tag{18}$$

Writing Eqn. (8) in summation notation and substituting Eqns. (18),

$$1 = \sum_{j=1}^{5} x_{3j} = \sum_{j=1}^{5} \frac{F_1}{F_2} \frac{x_{1j}}{\left[(F_3/F_2) + k_j \right]} \tag{19}$$

Observe that Eqn. (19) contains two unknowns, F_2 and F_3. An additional equation with these two unknowns is obtained in a similar way: Equation (15) is substituted into Eqn. (16), and the result is solved for x_{2j}:

$$x_{2j} = \frac{F_1}{F_2} \left[\frac{k_j x_{1j}}{k_j + (F_3/F_2)} \right], \quad j = 1, 2, \ldots, 5 \tag{20}$$

Writing Eqn. (7) in summation notation and substituting Eqns. (20),

$$1 = \sum_{j=1}^{5} x_{2j} = \sum_{j=1}^{5} \frac{F_1}{F_2} \left[\frac{k_j x_{1j}}{k_j + (F_3/F_2)} \right] \tag{21}$$

Equation (21) also contains the two unknowns F_2 and F_3. Subtracting Eqn. (21) from Eqn. (19) term by term, it is found that

$$\sum_{j=1}^{5} \frac{x_{1j}(1 - k_j)}{\left[(F_3/F_2) + k_j \right]} = 0 \tag{22}$$

If the liquid/vapor ratio of flow rates is defined by

$$\alpha = \frac{F_3}{F_2} \tag{23}$$

Eqn. (22) is

$$\sum_{j=1}^{5} \frac{x_{1j}(1 - k_j)}{(\alpha + k_j)} = 0 \tag{24}$$

so that α is the only unknown. An algorithm for solving Eqn. (24) for α is given in Example 6.12. Once α is known, F_2 and F_3 are calculated by combining Eqn. (23) with the overall material balance ($F_1 = F_2 + F_3$); thus,

$$F_2 = \frac{F_1}{1 + \alpha} \tag{25}$$

$$F_3 = F_1 - F_2 \tag{26}$$

Then Eqns. (18) and (20) yield all the unknown compositions of the liquid and vapor streams.

The student may verify that for this example the solution of Eqn. (24) is $\alpha = 0.1144$. Summarizing, the complete solution is

Stream No.	lb-moles/hr	N_2	H_2	NH_3	Ar	CH_4
1	100	0.22	0.66	0.1140	0.0020	0.0040
2	89.73	0.2448	0.7339	0.0147	0.0022	0.0044
3	10.27	0.0037	0.0147	0.9815	0.0000	0.0001

Although Example 6.8 was for five components, the equations are in summation notation and apply to an arbitrary number of components. Solution of Eqn. (24) of Example 6.8 gives the ratio of flow rates of liquid and vapor: Eqn. (24) is called the flash equation.

Liquid-liquid extraction

Liquid-liquid extraction, also called solvent extraction, is a separation process based upon differences in solubility of a substance in two immiscible solvents. There are many pairs of liquids which are immiscible; a typical example is benzene and water. The object of extraction is to remove solute (A) from a solution of (A + B) by adding a solvent (S) which is immiscible with B, as shown on Fig. 6-10. Vigorous mixing promotes transport of A from solvent B to solvent S. The two-phase mixture is then transferred to a settling tank where it separates by gravity. The immiscible liquids (B and S) must have different densities and a large value of interfacial tension for easy separation in the settler. Extract (A in S) and raffinate (A in B) phases are removed continuously as overflow and underflow from the settling tank. The combination of mixer and settler in Fig. 6-10 is called a single-contact extractor.

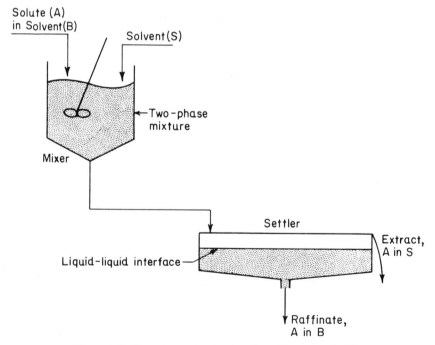

Figure 6-10 Single-contact extraction. B and S are immiscible.

The effect of extraction is to transfer most of the solute (A) from B to S. Motivation for extraction occurs when A and B are difficult to separate but A and S are easy to separate, as by distillation or crystallization.

Extract and raffinate phases removed from the settling tank are practically in equilibrium after the mixing and settling operations so that they are at the same temperature. In addition, distribution of each component between the two liquid phases is given by its equilibrium constant:

$$k_j = \frac{x \text{ (in extract phase)}}{x \text{ (in raffinate phase)}} \tag{6.16}$$

In extraction this equilibrium ratio of mole fractions is called the distribution coefficient. Values of k are fairly complex functions* of temperature and composition. Since the solvents (B and S) are never completely immiscible, some B dissolves in the extract phase and some S dissolves in the raffinate phase (see Fig. 6-10). The extract consists mostly of S, and the raffinate consists mostly of B, so that $k_S > 1$ and $k_B < 1$. In the limit of complete immiscibility, $k_S \rightarrow \infty$ and $k_B \rightarrow 0$. The larger the distribution coefficient of the solute (k_A), the better the recovery. The best measure of the ability of the solvent (S) to extract component A from solution of A + B is the selectivity, defined by

$$s = \frac{k_A}{k_B} \tag{6.17}$$

From Eqn. (6.16),

$$s = \frac{\dfrac{x \text{ (A in extract phase)}}{x \text{ (B in extract phase)}}}{\dfrac{x \text{ (A in raffinate phase)}}{x \text{ (B in raffinate phase)}}} \tag{6.18}$$

If the selectivity is greater than unity, then the ratio of mole fractions of A and B in the extract phase exceeds the same ratio in the raffinate. For easy recovery, the selectivity should be much larger than unity (values of 10 to 100 are typical).

Example 6.9

O
‖
Acetone (CH_3—C—CH_3) is recovered from water by liquid-liquid extraction using methyl isobutyl ketone (MIK),

$$CH_3-\overset{\overset{\displaystyle O}{\|}}{C}-CH_2-CH\overset{\displaystyle CH_3}{\underset{\displaystyle CH_3}{<}}$$

Chemical Engineers' Handbook, edited by R. H. Perry and C. H. Chilton, 5th ed., McGraw-Hill, New York (1973).

which forms an immiscible liquid layer on top of the aqueous layer. Acetone (solute) is more soluble in MIK (solvent) than in water (diluent).

Ninety pounds per hour of a 50% (by weight) solution of acetone and water is extracted with 110 lb/hr of pure MIK solvent. Experimental values of equilibrium constants (weight fractions) are

Component	No.	k_j
Acetone	1	1.67
Water	2	0.06
MIK	3	23

Calculate the percentage recovery of acetone and the composition of the extract and raffinate phases for a single-contact extractor.

Solution:

The process schematic is shown in Fig. 6-11.

Figure 6-11

1. Equations and constraints. In this particular case the solvent is pure and the feed contains no solvent. However, the equations will be written for the more general case when all three components appear in each stream.
   a. Material balance equations:

$$F_1 x_{11} + F_2 x_{21} = F_3 x_{31} + F_4 x_{41} \tag{1}$$

$$F_1 x_{12} + F_2 x_{22} = F_3 x_{32} + F_4 x_{42} \tag{2}$$

$$F_1 x_{13} + F_2 x_{23} = F_3 x_{33} + F_4 x_{43} \tag{3}$$

   b. Mole-fraction constraints:

$$x_{11} + x_{12} + x_{13} = 1 \tag{4}$$

$$x_{21} + x_{22} + x_{23} = 1 \tag{5}$$

$$x_{31} + x_{32} + x_{33} = 1 \tag{6}$$

$$x_{41} + x_{42} + x_{43} = 1 \tag{7}$$

   c. Equipment constraints (equilibrium constants):

$$x_{31} = k_1 x_{41} \tag{8}$$

$$x_{32} = k_2 x_{42} \tag{9}$$

$$x_{33} = k_3 x_{43} \tag{10}$$

2. Number of variables: $N_v = N_s(N_c + 1) + N_p = 4(3 + 1) + 3 = 19$.

3. Design variables: $N_d = N_v - N_e = 19 - 10 = 9$. In accordance with the problem statement, values of design variables are

$$
\begin{array}{lll}
F_1 = 90 \text{ lb/hr} & x_{21} = 0 & k_1 = 1.67 \\
F_2 = 110 \text{ lb/hr} & x_{22} = 0 & k_2 = 0.06 \\
 & x_{13} = 0 & k_3 = 23 \\
 & x_{11} = 0.5 &
\end{array}
$$

In this example all flow rates are in units of mass per unit time, and all compositions (x) are mass fractions. The usual prime symbol to indicate mass units instead of molar units is not used. The value of the selectivity for this system (based upon mass fractions) is

$$ s = \frac{k_1}{k_2} = \frac{1.67}{0.06} = 27.8 $$

4. Solution of equations: This set of equations is very similar to the set of equations written for the vapor-liquid equilibrium problem in Example 6.8. The main difference is that there is only one feed stream in Example 6.8, and in this example there are two feed streams. Since the flow rates and compositions of both feed streams are given, this problem may be solved using the equations in Example 6.8 if streams 1 and 2 are combined and treated as a single feed stream (1):

$$ F_1 = 90 + 110 = 200 \text{ lb/hr} $$

$$ x_{11} = \frac{(90)(0.5)}{200} = 0.225 $$

$$ x_{12} = \frac{(90)(0.5)}{200} = 0.225 $$

$$ x_{13} = \frac{110}{200} = 0.550 $$

Streams 2 and 3 in Example 6.8 correspond to streams 3 and 4, respectively, in this example so that α becomes the ratio of raffinate/extract:

$$ \alpha = \frac{F_4}{F_3} $$

From Eqn. (24) of Example 6.8,

$$ \frac{x_{11}(1 - k_1)}{\alpha + k_1} + \frac{x_{12}(1 - k_2)}{\alpha + k_2} + \frac{x_{13}(1 - k_3)}{\alpha + k_3} = 0 $$

$$ \frac{0.225(1 - 1.67)}{\alpha + 1.67} + \frac{0.225(1 - 0.06)}{\alpha + 0.06} + \frac{0.550(1 - 23)}{\alpha + 23} = 0 $$

The solution, using any of the methods of Ch. 11, is

$$ \alpha = 0.295 = \frac{F_4}{F_3} $$

Therefore,

$$ F_3 = \frac{F_3 + F_4}{1 + (F_4/F_3)} = \frac{200}{1 + 0.295} = 155 \text{ lb/hr} $$

$$ F_4 = 200 - 155 = 45 \text{ lb/hr} $$

The composition of the raffinate is given by Eqn. (18) of Example 6.8 (modified for differences in notation):

$$x_{4j} = \frac{F_1 x_{1j}}{F_3(\alpha + k_j)}$$

$$x_{41} = \frac{200(0.225)}{155(0.295 + 1.67)} = 0.15$$

$$x_{42} = \frac{200(0.225)}{155(0.295 + 0.06)} = 0.82$$

$$x_{43} = \frac{200(0.55)}{155(0.295 + 23)} = 0.03$$

Finally the composition of the extract is calculated from Eqns. (8)–(10):

$$x_{31} = k_1 x_{41} = 1.67(0.15) = 0.25$$
$$x_{32} = k_2 x_{42} = 0.06(0.82) = 0.05$$
$$x_{33} = k_3 x_{43} = 23(0.03) \quad = 0.70$$

Summarizing,

Stream	No.	F_i (lb/hr)	Weight fraction		
			Acetone	Water	MIK
Feed	1	90	0.5	0.5	0
Solvent	2	110	0	0	1.0
Extract	3	155	0.25	0.05	0.70
Raffinate	4	45	0.15	0.82	0.03

The percentage recovery of acetone is

$$\frac{155(0.25)}{90(0.5)} \times 100 = 86\%$$

In practice the remainder of the acetone would be recovered by adding more stages.

Distribution coefficients (k) provided in the previous example for the system acetone + water + methyl isobutyl ketone are for 25°C and the particular composition of extract and raffinate given in the table. Different values of distribution coefficients are observed at other compositions. The previous problem was artificial because the distribution coefficients are not usually known until the compositions of extract and raffinate phases are calculated.

The problem of calculating the compositions of extract and raffinate phases when distribution coefficients are unknown can be worked graphically. The graphical solution in Example 6.11 below is preceded by a brief discussion of graphical methods for ternary systems.

The composition of a ternary mixture has three coordinates (x_1, x_2, x_3) which are not independently variable because their sum must be unity. This constraint on the sum allows the domain of compositions of a ternary mixture to be plotted in two dimensions. The simplest two-dimensional figure for this purpose is an equilateral triangle, shown in Fig. 6-12. Each point within the triangle represents a different composition of a ternary mixture. The vertices represent pure components (A, B, C), and binary mixtures are located at points on the sides of the triangle. The altitude of the triangle is set equal to unity. The mole fraction of each component at point P is equal to the length of the perpendicular line dropped from P to the side opposite the vertex for that component. It is a theorem of geometry that the sum of the lengths of three perpendicular lines dropped from a point inside an equilateral triangle to each of its three sides is equal to its altitude. Therefore, the mole fraction constraint is automatically obeyed, as shown in Fig. 6-12.

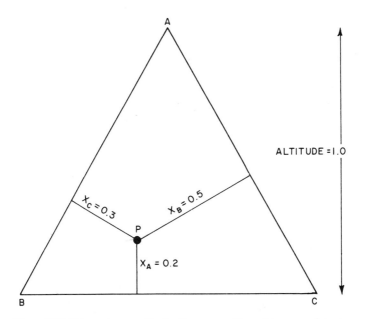

Figure 6-12 Triangular coordinates for composition of ternary mixture.

In practice, construction of perpendicular lines is eliminated by using specially ruled graph paper, shown in Fig. 6-13. Compositions are read directly by projecting the altitude onto a scale constructed on the side of the triangle. For example, the composition at point P is $x_A = 0.2$, $x_B = 0.5$, and $x_C = 0.3$.

The *lever rule*, illustrated in Fig. 6-14, is the most important property of triangular diagrams. Suppose that a ternary mixture is separated into two

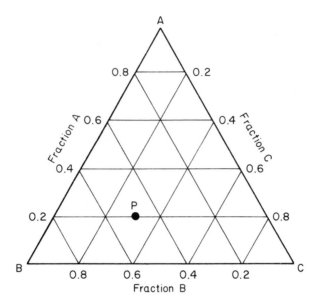

Figure 6-13 Graph paper for triangular coordinates of composition of ternary mixtures.

streams of different composition. Material balance equations and mole-fraction constraints are

$$F_1 x_{11} = F_2 x_{21} + F_3 x_{31} \qquad (6.19)$$

$$F_1 x_{12} = F_2 x_{22} + F_3 x_{32} \qquad (6.20)$$

$$F_1 x_{13} = F_2 x_{23} + F_3 x_{33} \qquad (6.21)$$

$$x_{11} + x_{12} + x_{13} = 1 \qquad (6.22)$$

$$x_{21} + x_{22} + x_{23} = 1 \qquad (6.23)$$

$$x_{31} + x_{32} + x_{33} = 1 \qquad (6.24)$$

Let the compositions of streams 2 and 3 be plotted on a triangular diagram as shown in Fig. 6-14 by points P_2 and P_3, respectively. The lever rule is that the composition of stream 1, represented by point P_1, lies on a straight line connecting P_2 and P_3 and located so that

$$\frac{F_2}{F_3} = \frac{\text{length of line segment } P_1 P_3}{\text{length of line segment } P_1 P_2} \qquad (6.25)$$

Proof that the lever rule is a graphical solution of the material balance equations is shown in Fig. 6-15. The fraction of component 1 is measured as shown by the dashed line drawn perpendicular to the side of the triangle

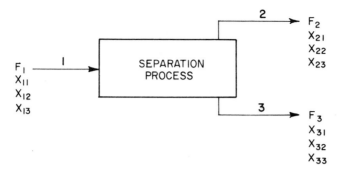

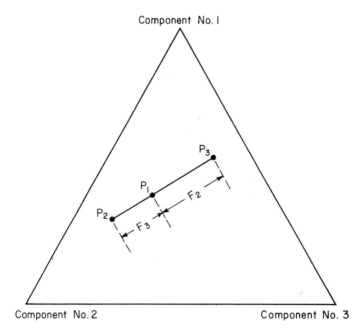

Figure 6-14 Lever rule for mixing or separation of ternary mixtures.

opposite the vertex for component 1. From similar triangles,

$$\frac{x_{31} - x_{11}}{x_{11} - x_{21}} = \frac{\text{length of line segment } P_1 P_3}{\text{length of line segment } P_1 P_2} \qquad (6.26)$$

Therefore, according to the lever rule,

$$\frac{x_{31} - x_{11}}{x_{11} - x_{21}} = \frac{F_2}{F_3} \qquad (6.27)$$

with similar equations for components 2 and 3. If the overall material balance

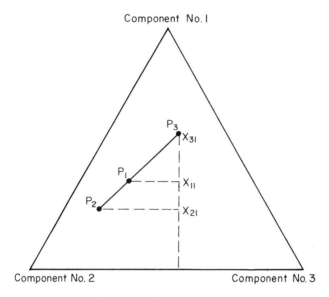

Figure 6-15 Proof of lever rule.

$(F_1 = F_2 + F_3)$ is substituted into Eqn. (6.19), then the latter is identical to Eqn. (6.27). Therefore, the lever rule satisfies the material balance equations. Mole fraction constraints are automatically satisfied by the properties of the triangular diagram. It can be shown that if points P_1, P_2, and P_3 do not lie on a straight line, then the material balance equations are not obeyed.

The lever rule also applies to the reverse of separation (Fig. 6-14) when two streams of different composition are mixed to form a single stream. If mass fractions are used, then flow rates must have units of mass per unit time; for mole fractions, flow rates are in moles per unit time.

Example 6.10

Ten pounds of pure C is added to a 40-lb mixture of 40% A and 60% B (by weight) to form a homogeneous ternary mixture of A, B, and C. Find the composition of the product using the lever rule.

Solution:

The composition of the binary mixture (A + B) is located at point R in Fig. 6-16. Composition of pure C is located at the vertex, point C. Compositions are mass fractions. Here the lever rule is applied to mass instead of mass flow rate:

$$\frac{\text{mass of C}}{\text{mass of A + B}} = \frac{RS}{SC} = \frac{10}{40} = \frac{1}{4}$$

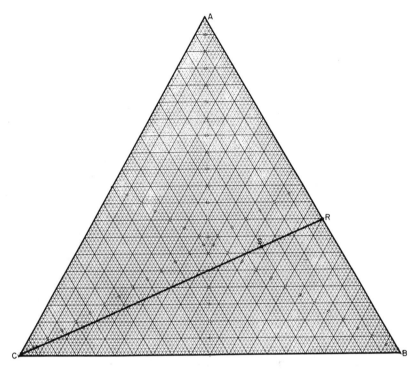

Figure 6-16 Composition of ternary mixture (S) using lever rule.

This locates point S on straight line RC. Reading directly from the triangular diagram,

Component	Mass Fraction
A	0.32
B	0.48
C	0.20

Triangular diagrams are particularly useful for plotting phase diagrams of ternary mixtures which exhibit limited miscibility. For example, Fig. 6-17 is the ternary phase diagram for the system acetone + methyl isobutyl ketone (MIK) + water at 25°C and atmospheric pressure. The dome-shaped line separates the region of two liquid phases (underneath the dome) from the region of complete miscibility (above the dome). A mixture of overall composition M separates into two liquid layers with compositions indicated by points A and B and relative amounts given by the lever rule. Compositions

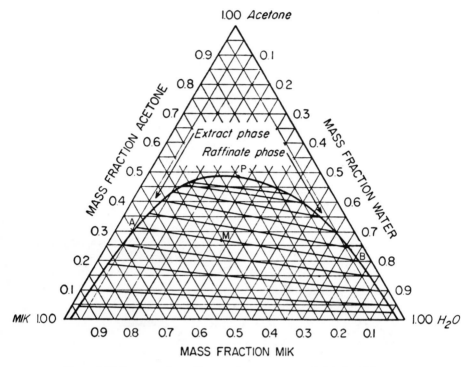

Figure 6-17 Ternary phase diagram for acetone, methyl isobutyl ketone
(MIK), and water at 25°C and 1 atm.
[D. F. Othmer, R. E. White, and E. Trueger, "Extraction in Spray and
Packed Columns," *Ind. Eng. Chem.*, *31*, 1144 (1939).]

of equilibrium phases are given by *tie lines* connecting points on opposite
sides of the dome.

Compositions of equilibrium phases may be measured systematically
by adding incremental amounts of acetone to two-phase mixtures of MIK
and water. As the acetone content of each layer increases, the compositions
of equilibrium layers approach each other and become equal at point P,
called the *plait point*. If the starting mixture is 90% MIK and 10% water
(overall composition), then continued addition of acetone will cause the
water-rich phase (raffinate) to decrease in size and finally disappear. If the
starting mixture has an overall composition of 90% water and 10% MIK,
continued addition of acetone will cause the MIK-rich layer (extract) to
diminish in size and eventually disappear. However, if the starting mixture
has an overall composition of about 48% MIK and 52% water, both layers
will persist in approximately equal amounts as acetone is added until the
plait point (P) is reached. At the plait point, further addition of acetone
will cause the two liquid layers to merge into a homogeneous solution.

Let us turn next to the graphical solution of material balances in liquid-liquid extraction problems.

Example 6.11

Rework Example 6.9 using the ternary phase diagram for the system acetone + methyl isobutyl ketone (MIK) + water.

Solution:

The notation is the same as in Example 6.9.

To apply the lever rule, the combination of streams 1 and 2 is treated as a single feed (F_1) with the following values of flow rate and overall composition:

$$F_1 = 200 \text{ lb/hr}$$

$$x_{11} = 0.225$$

$$x_{12} = 0.225$$

$$x_{13} = 0.550$$

This composition is indicated by point T in Fig. 6-18. The tie line identifies the compositions of extract and raffinate phases at points Y and Z:

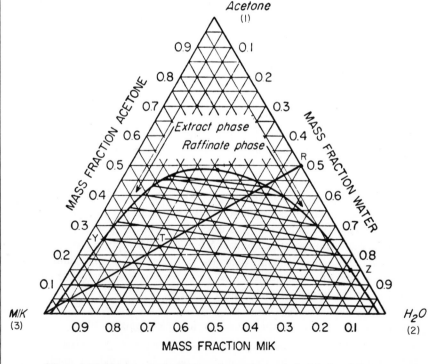

Figure 6-18 Ternary phase diagram for acetone, methyl isobutyl ketone (MIK), and water at 25°C and 1 atm.

| | | Mass Fraction | |
Component	No.	Extract	Raffinate
Acetone	1	0.25	0.15
Water	2	0.05	0.82
MIK	3	0.70	0.03

The lever rule is

$$\frac{\text{extract}}{\text{raffinate}} = \frac{F_3}{F_4} = \frac{TZ}{TY} = \frac{0.82 - 0.225}{0.225 - 0.05} = 3.4$$

Therefore,

$$F_3 = \frac{F_3 + F_4}{1 + (F_4/F_3)} = \frac{200}{1 + (1/3.4)} = 155 \text{ lb/hr}$$

$$F_4 = 200 - 155 = 45 \text{ lb/hr}$$

This graphical solution should be compared with the equations in Example 6.9. The lever rule satisfies Eqns. (1)–(3), the properties of the equilateral triangle satisfy Eqns. (4)–(7), and the tie lines give the composition of the extract phase as a function of the composition of the raffinate phase, thus replacing Eqns. (8)–(10).

What are the values of the equilibrium constants (k) at the plait point?

6.10 Solution of Material Balances
Using Computers

The advantages of computers for solving complex problems are well known. For simple problems, however, the preparation of a new computer program may take longer than a direct manual calculation. Therefore, the decision of whether or not to use a computer is based upon the estimated time it will take to prepare the program, unless one is already available in the computer library.

Computer programs are often prepared when it is necessary to change values of design variables frequently in the course of engineering calculations and feasibility studies for new processes. Programs for process units are also required when the modular approach (see Ch. 8) is applied to material and energy balances of chemical processes. In the modular approach, values of design variables for individual process units are systematically varied to converge upon the solution for the entire process.

A computer program for a material balance on a process unit is for a specific set of design variables and has the following structure:

1. Values of design variables are read from cards and printed.
2. Guess values (if any) of unknown variables needed for iterative solutions of nonlinear equations are read from cards and printed.

3. Equations are solved. Subroutines such as SIMUL (see Ch. 12) are often used.
4. The set of solution values is printed.

Programs in this text have been written in the WATFIV* language, a dialect of FORTRAN IV. The WATFIV variable F(I) is the flow rate of stream I and the variable X(I, J) is mole fraction of component J in stream I. The variables F and X must be dimensioned within each program to provide sufficient storage for each stream and each component. Equipment parameters and other parameters are assigned descriptive WATFIV variable names. A table of symbols is provided with each program to equate problem symbols and program names.

Use of a doubly subscripted mole-fraction variable, X(I, J), is an inefficient method of storage when only a few components are present in each stream; all other values of mole fractions are zero. However, more efficient methods add to programming complexity and are not used in this textbook.

In the remainder of this section, a material balance program for a process unit is presented in detail. The program implements the algorithm discussed in Example 6.8. This computer program is used in Ch.8 to solve a problem involving a system of process units.

Example 6.12

Prepare a computer program that performs the material balance on a five-component flash vaporizer (or partial condenser) as described in Example 6.8. The design variables are the flow rate and composition of the feed.

Solution:

The analysis of the problem is given in steps 1–3 of Example 6.8. The algorithm is illustrated in Fig. 6.19. Values of design variables are read from cards, the equations are solved, and the results are printed.

Equation (24),

$$f\{\alpha\} = \sum_{j=1}^{5} \frac{(x_{1j})(1 - (k_j))}{(\alpha + (k_j))} = 0$$

where $\alpha = F_3/F_2$, is a single equation with one unknown (α) and can be solved using Newton's method,

$$\alpha \longleftarrow \alpha^* - \frac{f\{\alpha^*\}}{f'\{\alpha^*\}}$$

where α^* represents the guess solution value (see Sec. 11.4 for details of Newton's method). By differentiation of $f\{\alpha^*\}$,

$$f'\{\alpha^*\} = \frac{df}{d\alpha}\bigg|_* = -\sum_{j=1}^{5} \frac{(x_{1j})(1 - (k_j))}{(\alpha^* + (k_j))^2}$$

*The differences between WATFIV and FORTRAN IV are discussed in Appendix III.

The program applies Newton's method iteratively until a solution is obtained satisfying

$$\left| \frac{\alpha - \alpha^*}{\alpha^*} \right| \leq \epsilon$$

or until the maximum number of iterations, k_{max}, is exceeded and indicates failure to converge to a solution. The initial guess value, α^*, is estimated by assuming that the liquid product is pure ammonia; this is not a bad assumption because ammonia is much heavier (small k-value) than the other components.

Flow Diagram

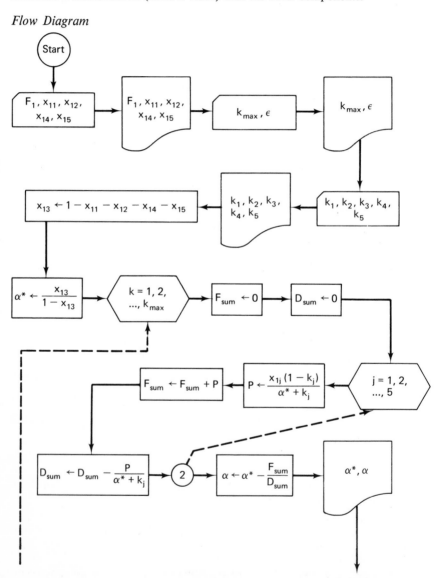

Figure 6-19

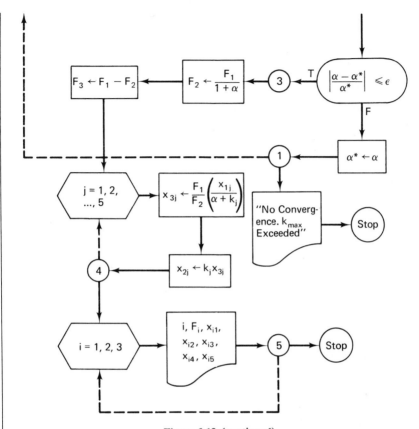

Figure 6-19 (continued)

Table of Symbols

Problem Symbol	Program Symbol	Definition	Units
f	FSUM	$f\{\alpha\} = \sum\limits_{j=1}^{5} \dfrac{x_{1j}(1 - k_j)}{(\alpha + k_j)}$	
f'	DSUM	$f'\{\alpha\} = -\sum\limits_{j=1}^{5} \dfrac{x_{1j}(1 - k_j)}{(\alpha + k_j)^2}$	
F_i	F(I)	Molar flow rate of stream i	lb-moles/hr
k_{max}	KMAX	Maximum no. of Newton's method iterations	
k_j	KEQ(J)	k-value of component j	
x_{ij}	X(I,J)	Mole fraction of component j in stream i	
α	ALPHA	F_3/F_2	
α^*	ALPHAS	Guess value of α	
ϵ	EPS	Fractional convergence tolerance	

Program Listing

```
C**     PROGRAM TO CARRY OUT HIGH PRESSURE SEPARATOR MATERIAL BALANCE FOR
C       THE AMMONIA PROCESS WHERE THE FEED STREAM (1) FLOW RATE AND MOLE
C       FRACTIONS ARE SPECIFIED.
C

        REAL KEQ(5)
        DIMENSION X(3,5), F(3)
        READ, F(1), X(1,1), X(1,2), X(1,4), X(1,5)
        WRITE (6,100)
        WRITE (6,101) F(1), X(1,1), X(1,2), X(1,4), X(1,5)
        READ, KMAX, EPS
        WRITE (6,105)
        WRITE (6,106) KMAX, EPS

C
C**     READ EQUILIBRIUM CONSTANTS
C

        READ, KEQ(1), KEQ(2), KEQ(3), KEQ(4), KEQ(5)
        WRITE (6,107)
        WRITE(6,108) KEQ(1), KEQ(2), KEQ(3), KEQ(4), KEQ(5)

C
C**     SOLVE MOLE FRACTION, MATERIAL BALANCE, AND EQUILIBRIUM CONSTRAINT
C       EQUATIONS
C

        X(1,3) = 1 - X(1,1) - X(1,2) - X(1,4) - X(1,5)
        ALPHAS = X(1,3)/(1.0 - X(1,3))
        WRITE(6,109)
        DO 1 K = 1, KMAX
        FSUM = 0
        DSUM = 0
        DO 2 J = 1,5
        PROD = X(1,J)*(1.0 - KEQ(J))/(ALPHAS + KEQ(J))
        FSUM = FSUM + PROD
    2   DSUM = DSUM - PROD/(ALPHAS + KEQ(J))
        ALPHA = ALPHAS - FSUM/DSUM
        WRITE(6,110) ALPHAS,ALPHA
        IF (ABS((ALPHA - ALPHAS)/ALPHAS) .LE. EPS) GO TO 3
    1   ALPHAS = ALPHA
        WRITE (6,102)
        STOP
    3   F(2) = F(1)/(1.0 + ALPHA)
        F(3) = F(1) - F(2)
        DO 4 J = 1,5
        X(3,J) = (F(1)/F(2)) * X(1,J)/(ALPHA + KEQ(J))
    4   X(2,J) = KEQ(J)*X(3,J)
C
C**     PRINT RESULTS
C
        WRITE (6,103)
        DO 5 I = 1,3
    5   WRITE (6,104) I, F(I), X(I,1), X(I,2), X(I,3), X(I,4), X(I,5)
        STOP

C
C**     INPUT AND OUTPUT FORMATS
C
  100   FORMAT ('1F(1), X(1,1), X(1,2), X(1,4), X(1,5) = '/)
  101   FORMAT ( F10.2, 4F10.4)
  102   FORMAT ( 'NO CONVERGENCE.  KMAX EXCEEDED.')
  103   FORMAT (/,' STREAM I, F(I), X(I,1), X(I,2), X(I,3), X(I,4), X(I,5)
       1 ='/)
  104   FORMAT (I8, F10.2, 5F10.4)
  105   FORMAT (//' KMAX, EPS = '/)
  106   FORMAT (I8, F11.5)
  107   FORMAT (//,' KEQ(1), KEQ(2), KEQ(3), KEQ(4), KEQ(5) ='/)
  108   FORMAT ( 5F10.4,/)
  109   FORMAT(/,' INTERMEDIATE VALUES OF ALPHAS AND ALPHA =',/)
  110   FORMAT(2F12.6)
        END
```

Data

```
100.0, 0.22, 0.66, 0.002, 0.004
25, 0.0001
66.67, 50., 0.015, 100., 33.33
```

Computed Output

```
F(1), X(1,1), X(1,2), X(1,4), X(1,5) =

   100.00      0.2200      0.6600      0.0020      0.0040


KMAX, EPS =

   25      0.00010


KEQ(1), KEQ(2), KEQ(3), KEQ(4), KEQ(5) =

   66.6700     50.0000      0.0150    100.0000     33.3300


INTERMEDIATE VALUES OF ALPHAS AND ALPHA =

   0.128668      0.112873
   0.112873      0.114422
   0.114422      0.114441
   0.114441      0.114441

STREAM I, F(I), X(I,1), X(I,2), X(I,3), X(I,4), X(I,5) =

   1      100.00      0.2200      0.6600      0.1140      0.0020      0.0040
   2       89.73      0.2448      0.7339      0.0147      0.0022      0.0044
   3       10.27      0.0037      0.0147      0.9815      0.0000      0.0001
```

Discussion

Only four iterations are required to calculate α when $\epsilon = 0.0001$. This rapid convergence is a result of the proximity of the solution to the initial guess value.

The computer program can readily be extended to an arbitrary number (N_c) of components by

1. Reading from cards a value for N_c, N_c values of mole fraction in the feed, N_c k-values, and α^*.
2. Replacing two DO statements with

   DO 2 J = 1,NC

   DO 4 J = 1,NC

3. Replacing statements 5 and 104 with

   5 WRITE (6,104) I,F(I), (X(I,J), J = 1,NC)

   104 FORMAT (I8, F10.2, 5F10.4/(18X, 5F10.4)).

PROBLEMS

6.1. Calculate the change in mass of 1 lb of water when it freezes at 32°F. Is the mass of ice larger or smaller than the mass of liquid water?

6.2. Solve the material balance on the distillation column described in Example 6.1 after making the following changes in values of design variables:

1. Double the feed flow rate (new flow rate = 32 lb-moles/hr).
2. Double the concentration of alcohol in the feed stream (new concentration = 3 mole % alcohol).

6.3. A three-component mixture is partially separated in a distillation tower. Component 1 is the most volatile, and component 3 is least volatile. Most but not all of component 2 goes into the distillate. Calculate the steady-flow rates of distillate (F_2) and bottoms (F_3) for the conditions shown in Fig. 6-20.

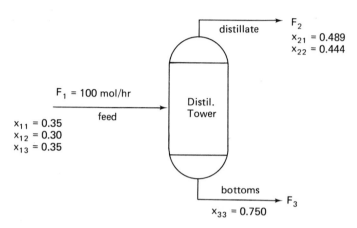

Figure 6-20

6.4. Set up the equations and determine the number of design variables for a mixer with two inlet streams and one product stream. (See Fig. 6-21.) Assume that there are three components. Make a selection of design variables and assign a set of numerical values.

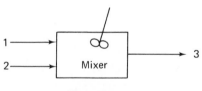

Figure 6-21

6.5. Spent sulfuric acid solution is brought up to strength for a pickling process in a mixer. (See Fig. 6-22.) Spent solution of 3 % sulfuric acid by weight is mixed with a 50 % solution by weight (both solutions aqueous) to obtain the desired product concentration of 40 % acid by weight. Solve for feed flow rates on the basis of 100 lb/hr of product.

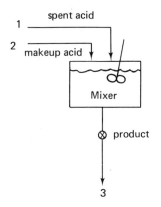

Figure 6-22

6.6. A process stream has the following composition:

	Mole %
Methane	22
Chloromethane	30
Dichloromethane	17
Chloroform	9
Carbon tetrachloride	22

Compute
a. The average molecular weight.
b. The weight percent of chloroform.
c. The molar flow rate if the mass flow rate is 1000 lb/hr.

6.7. A mixture of benzene and carbon tetrachloride is separated by distillation. (See Fig. 6-23.) Carbon tetrachloride is slightly more volatile than benzene. During continuous operation of the tower, the following flow rates and compositions are observed:

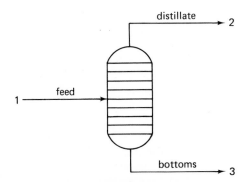

Figure 6-23

Stream Number	Flow Rate (lb-moles/hr)	Mole Fraction of CCl$_4$
1	5.26	0.445
2	2.32	0.932

Calculate the flow rate and composition of the bottoms stream. What is the flow rate of each stream in pounds per hour?

6.8. Compute the volumetric flow rate (cubic feet per minute) of air entering the drier in Example 6.5. The air enters at 93°C and 1 atm.

6.9. Stream 1 (see Fig. 6-24) is a 2N aqueous solution of diethanolamine (amine, diethyl, 2,2'-dihydroxy). Stream 3 is a mixture of carbon dioxide and air at 50°C, 1 atm, containing 26 mole % carbon dioxide; the flow rate is 10 lb-mole/hr. The organic base (diethanolamine) reacts with the acidic gas (carbon dioxide) to produce an ionic equilibrium in solution. Assume that stream 2 is in equilibrium with stream 3 at 50°C and calculate flow rates and compositions of all streams. Check your solution by calculating mass flow rates.

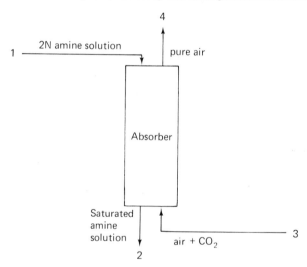

Figure 6-24

EQUILIBRIUM DATA FOR 2N DIETHANOLAMINE SOLUTION AT 50°C*

Partial Pressure of CO$_2$ (mm Hg)	Liquid Concentration (moles of CO$_2$/mole of amine)
668.4	0.680
242.3	0.562
183.8	0.548
71.0	0.489
10.2	0.302

*Data from Perry's handbook, 4th ed., p. 14–9.

6.10. A gas absorber (see Fig. 1-2) is used to remove ammonia from air. Liquid entering the top of the absorber is pure water. Ammonia-air mixture comes into the bottom of the absorber at 10 atm, 30°C, and contains 5.5 mole % ammonia. Assume that all the ammonia is absorbed from the air and that the water leaving the bottom of the absorber is saturated with ammonia at 30°C. If the flow rate of the entering air-ammonia mixture is 6750 ft³ (measured at 25°C, 1 atm) per hour, calculate flow rates and compositions of other streams. Find the flow rate of pure water in gallons per hour.

SOLUBILITY OF AMMONIA IN WATER AT 30°C*

Weight NH_3 per 100 weights H_2O	Partial Pressure of NH_3 (mm Hg)
40	719
30	454
25	352
20	260
15	179
10	110

*Data from Perry's handbook, 4th ed., p. 14–4.

6.11. The feed stream to a distillation column contains N_c components. What is the number of design variables for an overall material balance? Pick a specific set of design variables for $N_c = 5$.

6.12. Some sets of design variables give solutions that have no physical meaning (negative flow rates, for example). Show, for the oxygen plant described in Example 6.3, that the set of design variables,

$$F_1 = 100 \text{ moles/hr}$$
$$x_{11} = 0.2098$$
$$x_{12} = 0.7808$$
$$x_{21} = 0.93$$
$$x_{22} = 0.03$$

is not physically possible.

6.13. A mixture of 40 mole % benzene and 60 mole % ethylbenzene is charged to a still and heated to 50°C at 0.115 atm. Assuming that Raoult's law is valid, show that the k-values for benzene and ethylbenzene are 3.1 and 0.403, respectively. Compute the mole fractions in the vapor and liquid phases at equilibrium.

6.14. The availability of oxygen for marine life near the surface of rivers, lakes, and streams cannot exceed the equilibrium concentration corresponding to a partial pressure of oxygen in air equal to 0.21 atm. What is the equilibrium concentration in grams of oxygen per liter of water? Henry's law constant for oxygen dissolved in water is 43,800 atm at 25°C.

6.15. Water is used to extract sugar from 50 tons/hr of wet, sliced sugar beets. The beets have the following composition:

Component	Weight Fraction
Water	0.48
Pulp	0.40
Sugar	0.12

Liquor leaving the extractor contains 5 wt. % sugar. Forty-five percent of the sugar in the sliced beets is recovered, and the residual beets contain 3 tons of liquor per ton of pulp. Calculate the flow rate of each stream in tons per hour.

6.16. Water is used to leach caustic (NaOH) from calcite ($CaCO_3$) solids containing 10 wt. % caustic. Compute the fraction of caustic recovered in a single-stage leaching unit if the mass ratio of water to solids entering the unit is 2 to 1. The mass of caustic solution adhering to unit mass of inert solid ($CaCO_3$), w, has been measured experimentally as a function of solute concentration, c,

$$w = 6.23c + 1.47$$

where c is pounds of NaOH per pound of aqueous solution.

6.17. Use the precedence-ordering method described in Sec. 13.1 to order the equations for the flash separator in Example 6.8. Adopt the same set of 10 design variables to solve the set of 13 equations.

6.18. One thousand pounds per hour of a solution of 40% acetic acid (CH_3COOH) and 60% isoamyl acetate

$$\left(CH_3-COO-CH_2-CH_2 \begin{array}{c} \diagup CH_3 \\ \diagdown CH_3 \end{array} \right)$$

is mixed with 1000 lb/hr of water in an extraction unit at 24°C. Compute flow rates and compositions for a single-stage extraction unit assuming equilibrium. What percentage of the acetic acid is recovered in the extract phase? The ternary phase diagram for this system is given in Fig. 6-25. All compositions are in weight percent.

6.19. Solubility of carbon dioxide gas in Coca-Cola at 30°C is given approximately by Henry's law,

$$Py = Hx$$

where $H = 2100$ atm at 30°C, y is the mole fraction of CO_2 in the vapor, and x is the mole fraction of CO_2 in the Coca-Cola. If the Coca-Cola is bottled at 1.2 atm and 30°C, how much carbon dioxide (cm³ of gas) is released from the liquid (12 fluid oz) when the cap is removed? Assume that the vapor is pure carbon dioxide ($y = 1$).

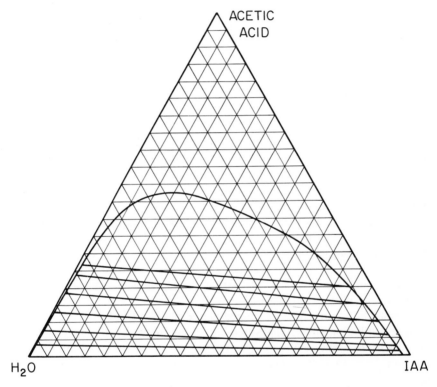

Figure 6-25 Ternary equilibrium diagram for isoamyl acetate—acetic acid—water at 24°C. [D. F. Othmer, R. E. White, and E. Trueger, "Liquid-Liquid Extraction Data," *Ind. and Eng. Chem. 33*, 1240 (1941)]

Material Balances for Chemical Reactors

7

A material balance is an application of the principle of conservation of matter. The Einstein equation (see Ch. 6) predicts that a certain amount of mass is destroyed in an exothermic chemical reaction, but the amount is so infinitesimal that it can be ignored in a material balance. Although matter is effectively conserved, its molecular structure may change in accordance with the principles of chemistry.

Conservation principles developed and applied in Ch. 6 are for processes such as distillation and drying which proceed without chemical reaction. The analysis procedure which forms the heart of Ch. 6 is not altered by chemical reactions, but Eqn. (6.4) must be replaced by an equation for chemically reacting systems.

7.1 Chemical Reactions

Equations of chemical reactions convey a remarkable amount of information in concise form. For example, the equation

$$Fe_3O_4 + 4H_2 \underset{\Delta}{\rightleftharpoons} 3Fe + 4H_2O \tag{7.1}$$

is an abbreviated statement of the following facts:

1. There exist four stable chemical compounds: black iron oxide (Fe_3O_4), hydrogen (H_2), iron (Fe), and water (H_2O).
2. Black iron oxide (magnetite) can be reduced in a hydrogen atmosphere to yield elemental iron.

3. The reaction is reversible: elemental iron, if heated with water vapor, forms black iron oxide instead of the red oxide or rust formed under atmospheric conditions.
4. Since the number of moles of gas (four) is the same on both sides of the equation, pressure will have practically no effect upon the yield of iron.
5. The reaction is endothermic, and, according to the principle of mass action, the yield of pure iron is increased by the addition of heat. The endothermic character of the reaction is emphasized by the triangle, which means that heating is needed to make the reaction "go."
6. One thousand pounds of black iron oxide ore yield 724 lb of pure iron.*
7. Reduction of 1000 lb of black iron oxide ore requires 6200 ft³ of hydrogen (measured at the standard conditions of 32°F and 1 atm).†
8. The reversible nature of the reaction, implied by the double arrows, indicates that complete conversion of magnetite to iron in a single contact is impossible.

Equation (7.1) has still another property: It is a *balanced* equation. That is, the number of atoms of every element is the same on both sides of the equation. For Reaction (7.1) there are three atoms (or gram-atoms) of iron, four atoms of oxygen, and eight atoms of hydrogen before and after chemical reaction. Balancing a chemical reaction is based upon conservation of atoms. Atoms can neither be created nor destroyed in a chemical reaction (nuclear reactions are excluded).

Chemical equations are often simple enough to be balanced by inspection. If the reaction is complicated, it can be balanced using matrices. Let us consider an arbitrary chemical reaction involving an unspecified number of chemical compounds. The stoichiometric coefficient of the jth compound (v_j) is the number, always rational and often an integer, written before the same compound in a balanced chemical reaction. The convention is that the stoichiometric coefficient is positive if the compound is a product and negative if the compound is a reactant. For example, for Eqn. (7.1),

Compound	Stoichiometric coefficient, v
Fe	3
H_2O	4
Fe_3O_4	−1
H_2	−4

*The molecular weights of black iron oxide (231.5) and iron (55.85) provide the ratio

$$\frac{(1000)}{231.5}(3)(55.85) = 724 \text{ lb of iron/1000 lb of ore}$$

†Since the normal volume of a perfect gas at standard conditions (32°F, 1 atm) is 359 ft³/lb-mole,

$$\frac{(1000)}{231.5}(4)(359) = 6200 \text{ ft}^3 \text{ of hydrogen/1000 lb of ore}$$

A chemical reaction may be written in the general form

$$0 = \sum_j v_j C_j \qquad (7.2)$$

where C_j is the jth chemical compound and the summation is over all reactants and products which participate in the reaction. Thus, Eqn. (7.1), written in the form of (7.2), would be

$$0 = 3Fe + 4H_2O - Fe_3O_4 - 4H_2 \qquad (7.3)$$

The equation for the conservation of the kth element in a balanced chemical reaction is

$$\sum_{j=1}^{N_c} v_j m_{jk} = 0 \qquad (k = 1, 2, \ldots, N_e) \qquad (7.4)$$

m_{jk} is the number of atoms in the jth compound of the kth element and the summation is over all reactants and products. Equation (7.4) ensures that the number of atoms of every element present is the same on both sides of the reaction equation. A chemical reaction is balanced by solving the set of equations (7.4) for the stoichiometric coefficients. The algebra is illustrated by the following example.

Example 7.1

Balance the chemical equation for the oxidation of chromite $(FeCr_2O_4)$ with sodium carbonate:

$$Fe(CrO_2)_2 + O_2 + Na_2CO_3 = Fe_2O_3 + Na_2CrO_4 + CO_2$$

Solution:

Equation (7.2) is written with unknown values of stoichiometric coefficients:

$$0 = v_1(FeCr_2O_4) + v_2(O_2) + v_3(Na_2CO_3)$$
$$+ v_4(Fe_2O_3) + v_5(Na_2CrO_4) + v_6(CO_2)$$

Notation is simplified by the code

Compound	No. (j)	Element	No. (k)
$Fe(CrO_2)_2$	1	Fe	1
O_2	2	Cr	2
Na_2CO_3	3	O	3
Fe_2O_3	4	Na	4
Na_2CrO_4	5	C	5
CO_2	6		

The set of equations (7.4), one for each element, is

Element	k	Equation (7.4)
Fe	1	$v_1 + 2v_4 = 0$
Cr	2	$2v_1 + v_5 = 0$
O	3	$4v_1 + 2v_2 + 3v_3 + 3v_4 + 4v_5 + 2v_6 = 0$
Na	4	$2v_3 + 2v_5 = 0$
C	5	$v_3 + v_6 = 0$

There are six unknowns (v_j, $j = 1, 2, \ldots, 6$) and only five equations. The solution of these linear, homogeneous algebraic equations may be expressed in terms of one of the coefficients, say, v_1:

$$v_2 = \tfrac{7}{4}v_1$$
$$v_3 = 2v_1$$
$$v_4 = -\tfrac{1}{2}v_1$$
$$v_5 = -2v_1$$
$$v_6 = -2v_1$$

The value of v_1 is arbitrary. It is customary to pick the smallest value of v_1 (more precisely, the smallest absolute value) which clears all fractions. In this case $v_1 = -4$ (minus because chromite is a reactant) so that

$$v_1 = -4$$
$$v_2 = -7$$
$$v_3 = -8$$
$$v_4 = 2$$
$$v_5 = 8$$
$$v_6 = 8$$

The balanced chemical reaction is

$$4Fe(CrO_2)_2 + 7O_2 + 8Na_2CO_3 = 2Fe_2O_3 + 8Na_2CrO_4 + 8CO_2$$

It is noted that the solution of these equations may be written more compactly in matrix notation. The coefficient matrix for the set of five equations is

$$\begin{bmatrix} 1 & 0 & 0 & 2 & 0 & 0 \\ 2 & 0 & 0 & 0 & 1 & 0 \\ 4 & 2 & 3 & 3 & 4 & 2 \\ 0 & 0 & 2 & 0 & 2 & 0 \\ 0 & 0 & 1 & 0 & 0 & 1 \end{bmatrix}$$

A reduction of this 5×6 matrix by the Gauss-Jordan method (see Ch. 12) yields

$$\begin{bmatrix} 1 & 0 & 0 & 0 & 0 & 1/2 \\ 0 & 1 & 0 & 0 & 0 & 7/8 \\ 0 & 0 & 1 & 0 & 0 & 1 \\ 0 & 0 & 0 & 1 & 0 & -1/4 \\ 0 & 0 & 0 & 0 & 1 & -1 \end{bmatrix} \quad \text{of rank 5}$$

According to the theory of homogeneous, linear equations, it can be shown that:

$$\begin{bmatrix} v_1 \\ v_2 \\ v_3 \\ v_4 \\ v_5 \end{bmatrix} = - \begin{bmatrix} 1/2 \\ 7/8 \\ 1 \\ -1/4 \\ -1 \end{bmatrix}[v_6]$$

The solution written previously is obtained for the value $\nu_6 = 8$ (positive because CO_2 is a product, 8 to clear all fractions).

Example 7.1 shows that chemical reactions are balanced by solving sets of homogeneous linear equations. The example also shows that the stoichiometric coefficients may be multiplied by a constant without upsetting the atom balance. For example, both chemical equations

$$H_2 + \tfrac{1}{2}O_2 = H_2O$$

and

$$2H_2 + O_2 = 2H_2O$$

are balanced, but the stoichiometric coefficients in the second equation are each twice the values of the corresponding coefficients in the first equation.

Overall reaction equations like (7.1) say nothing about the step-by-step mechanism of the reaction. The inference from Eqn. (7.1) that four gaseous hydrogen molecules are involved in a simultaneous collision with the crystalline lattice of the oxide, so that four gaseous water molecules are emitted from the surface as collision products, is incorrect. The first step in the overall reaction (7.1) is a chemisorption of hydrogen molecules on the surface of the oxide, followed by a complicated series of reactions involving intermediate products. Some of these intermediate products are so short-lived that they are difficult to detect. It is the science of chemical kinetics which is devoted to the study of the mechanisms and rates of reactions. Kinetic studies are extremely useful because they provide information about the rates of the individual reactions (and therefore the overall reaction) in terms of variables such as concentration, temperature, and catalyst activity.

7.2 Material Balance Equations for Chemical Reactors

The set of material balance equations for a steady-state, nonreacting process is given by Eqn. (6.4):

$$\sum_{i=1}^{N_s} F_i x_{ij} = 0 \qquad (j = 1, 2, \ldots, N_c) \tag{7.5}$$

F_i is the molar flow rate of the ith stream. Entering streams have F_i positive and streams leaving the process have F_i negative. The left-hand side of Eqn. (7.5) is the rate of accumulation of the jth compound within the boundaries of the process; this rate is zero at steady-state conditions.

If there is only one chemical reaction, its rate is measured by the net rate of production (or consumption) of the jth compound:

$$r = \frac{1}{\nu_j} \frac{dn_j}{dt} \tag{7.6}$$

Conversely, the rate of production of any compound may be written in terms of the reaction rate:

$$\frac{dn_j}{dt} = rv_j \tag{7.7}$$

According to Eqn. (7.7) the rate of production (or disappearance) of the jth compound (dn_j/dt) is proportional to its stoichiometric number (v_j). If the jth compound is a product of the reaction, dn_j/dt and v_j are positive; if the jth compound is a reactant, dn_j/dt and v_j are negative. In either case, the rate of reaction (r) is positive if the reaction proceeds in a forward direction. For the steady-state condition of interest here, r is a positive constant.

Example 7.2

For the balanced reaction

$$CH_4 + H_2O \rightleftharpoons CO + 3H_2$$

the rate of production of H_2 in a reactor operated at steady state is 6 moles/hr. What is the rate of consumption of CH_4?

Solution:

For the component code,

Component	No. (j)
CH_4	1
H_2O	2
CO	3
H_2	4

Eqn. (7.6) is written for H_2,

$$r = \frac{1}{v_4}\frac{dn_4}{dt} = \frac{1}{3}(6 \text{ moles/hr}) = 2 \text{ moles/hr}$$

and Eqn. (7.7) is written for CH_4,

$$\frac{dn_1}{dt} = rv_1 = (2 \text{ moles/hr})(-1) = -2 \text{ moles/hr}$$

i.e., the rate of consumption of methane is 2 moles/hr.

Addition of the rate of production of the jth component by chemical reaction, given by Eqn. (7.7), to the left-hand side of Eqn. (7.5) gives the material balance equation for a single reaction in a steady-state reactor:

$$\begin{array}{l}\text{net rate of production of} \\ \text{compound } j \text{ in reactor}\end{array} = \sum_{i=1}^{N_s} F_i x_{ij} + rv_j = 0 \qquad (j = 1, 2, \ldots, N_c) \tag{7.8}$$

According to this equation, the rate of accumulation within the reactor of the jth compound, which must be zero at steady state, is the sum of two rates:

the net rate of flow into the process ($\sum F_i x_{ij}$) and the rate of production by chemical reaction (rv_j).

Example 7.3

A reformer (see Fig. 7-1) produces carbon monoxide from methane by the reaction of Example 7.2. The feed is 20 moles/hr containing 25 mole % methane. What is the flow rate of unreacted methane out of the reactor for the reaction rate given in Example 7.2?

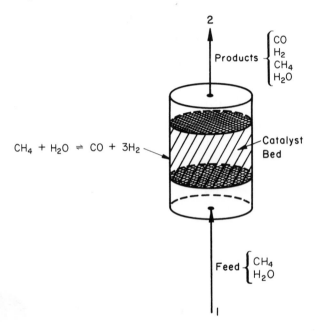

Figure 7-1 Catalytic reactor.

Solution:

For the same notation as in Example 7.2, Equation (7.8) is written for methane ($j = 1$):

$$F_1 x_{11} - F_2 x_{21} + rv_1 = 0$$

Rearranging,

$$\text{moles of unreacted methane} = F_2 x_{21} = F_1 x_{11} + rv_1$$
$$= (20\,\text{moles/hr})(0.25) + (2\,\text{moles/hr})(-1)$$
$$= 3\,\text{moles/hr}$$

A material balance on a chemical reactor is based upon conservation of chemical elements. The net rate of production of the kth element, which must be zero for any chemical reaction, is obtained by multiplying the rate of production of the jth compound [Eqn. (7.8)] by the number of atoms of element k in compound j (m_{jk}) and summing over all compounds:

$$\begin{matrix} \text{net rate of production} \\ \text{of element } k \text{ in reactor} \end{matrix} = \sum_{j=1}^{N_c} \sum_{i=1}^{N_s} F_i x_{ij} m_{jk} + r \sum_{j=1}^{N_c} v_j m_{jk} = 0 \qquad (7.9)$$

According to Eqn. (7.4) the second term in Eqn. (7.9) vanishes so that

$$\sum_{j=1}^{N_c} \sum_{i=1}^{N_s} F_i x_{ij} m_{jk} = 0 \qquad (k = 1, 2, \ldots, N_e) \qquad (7.10)$$

Equations (7.10) form a set of N_e equations, one for each chemical element present. The left-hand side of (7.10) is the net flow rate of element k into the reactor; at steady state this rate must be zero. Often the set of N_e equations generated by (7.10) is not comprised of equations that are all independent.

Equations (7.10) are called stoichiometric equations because the rate of reaction (r) does not appear explicitly. Without rate data, the material balance equations cannot be solved unless there is information on the extent of the reaction. The maximum yield is given by thermodynamics in terms of the equilibrium constant. If the pressure is low enough so that the perfect gas law applies and if all compounds are gaseous, the equilibrium constant (K) is a very simple function of the composition and pressure of the product stream:

$$K = P^{\Sigma v_j} \prod x_j^{v_j} \qquad (P \text{ in atm}) \qquad (7.11)$$

K is a function of temperature (see Appendix IV). If temperature is fixed, K is constant, independent of the pressure and composition of the mixture. x_j is the equilibrium mole fraction of the jth component. For a reactor operated at steady state, the x_js are the mole fractions in the gaseous product stream. The symbol $\prod$ stands for the product of mole fractions, each mole fraction raised to the power v_j, for all *gaseous* species which participate in the reaction. Other expressions can be derived for equilibria involving solid and liquid species.

Example 7.4

For the gas-phase reaction

$$N_2 + 3H_2 \rightleftharpoons 2NH_3$$

the equilibrium constant [assuming that pressure is low enough to use Eqn. (7.11)] is

$$K = (P)^{2-1-3} \frac{x_3^2}{x_1 x_2^3} = P^{-2} \frac{x_3^2}{x_1 x_2^3} \qquad (P \text{ in atm})$$

for the component code

Compound	No.
N_2	1
H_2	2
NH_3	3

Since K is constant at a given temperature, it is apparent that an isothermal increase in pressure (P) must increase the yield (larger x_3, smaller x_1, x_2 subject to the mole fraction constraint equation).

All chemical reactions may be classified according to the value of K:

Value of K	Type of reaction
$K \ll 1$	Reaction not feasible
$K \simeq 1$	Reversible reaction
$K \gg 1$	Irreversible reaction

For reversible reactions, it is impossible to convert all the reactants to products in a single pass through the reactor. Unused reactants in the product stream must be separated and used over again.

For the combustion of methane,

$$CH_4 + 2O_2 \longrightarrow CO_2 + 2H_2O$$

K is of the order of a googol (1 googol $= 10^{100}$), and the reaction is highly irreversible. The reverse reaction,

$$CO_2 + 2H_2O \longrightarrow CH_4 + 2O_2$$

has a value of K smaller than 10^{-100} and is therefore not feasible. "Not feasible" means that the reaction will not occur spontaneously; it may be possible to force the reaction by doing external work, by electrolysis, for example.

The *equilibrium* yield of product may be calculated from the equilibrium constant (K). The *actual* yield of product is always less than the equilibrium yield. Some reactions are very slow. Indeed, in the absence of a suitable catalyst, some reactions are so slow that they are undetectable. Hence, the actual yield obtained in a chemical reactor depends on two factors:

1. Equilibrium constant (K).
2. Rate of reaction.

Table 7.1 summarizes the interaction of these factors and their effect upon the extent of reaction.

TABLE 7.1
INFLUENCE OF EQUILIBRIUM CONSTANT AND REACTION RATE UPON
EXTENT OF REACTION

Value of equilibrium constant	Rate of reaction	% Conversion of reactants to products
$K \gg 1$	Very fast	$\simeq 100$
	Very slow	$\simeq 0$
$K \simeq 1$	Very fast	Equilibrium conversion
	Very slow	$\simeq 0$
$K \ll 1$	Very fast	$\simeq 0$
	Very slow	$\simeq 0$

Table 7.1 shows that reactions which are irreversible $(K \gg 1)$ do not necessarily occur when the reactants are mixed; they may be extremely slow. A reasonably large value of the equilibrium constant (K) is a necessary but not sufficient condition for obtaining a good yield of products.

Example 7.5

A gas furnace burns propane fuel; the balanced chemical reaction for complete combustion is

$$C_3H_8 + 5O_2 \longrightarrow 3CO_2 + 4H_2O$$

This is a fast and irreversible reaction $(K \gg 1)$. The process diagram is given in Fig. 7-2. Solve for the composition and flow rate of stream 3 in terms of feed stream variables. Assume that the fuel is pure propane and that air is 21% oxygen, 79% nitrogen.

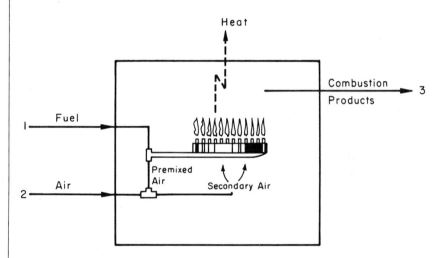

Figure 7-2 Industrial gas burner.

Solution:

The components are

Component	No. (j)
C_3H_8	1
O_2	2
CO_2	3
H_2O	4
N_2	5

1. Equations and constraints.
    a. Equipment constraints. At the flame temperature (2200°K) this reaction is very fast and goes to equilibrium. The equilibrium constant is

$$K = P\frac{x_{33}^3 x_{34}^4}{x_{31} x_{32}^5} \simeq 10^{100} \qquad (P \text{ in atm})$$

(The value of K for this highly irreversible reaction is calculated using thermochemical data and methods described in Appendix IV.) Since oxygen is present in excess of the stoichiometric ratio of 5 molecules of oxygen per molecule of propane, x_{32} cannot be zero and the equilibrium constant is satisfied by $x_{31} = 0$. For convenience, the air-fuel ratio (α) is introduced as a parameter:

$$\alpha = \frac{F_2}{F_1} \qquad (1)$$

b. Material balance equations.

    (1) Reacting species [Eqn. (7.10)]:

$$\text{element C:} \qquad 3F_1 = F_3 x_{33} \qquad (2)$$

$$\text{H:} \qquad 8F_1 = 2F_3 x_{34} \qquad (3)$$

$$\text{O:} \quad 2F_2 x_{22} = 2F_3 x_{32} + 2F_3 x_{33} + F_3 x_{34} \qquad (4)$$

    (2) Inert species:

$$\text{N}_2: \quad F_2 x_{25} = F_3 x_{35} \qquad (5)$$

c. Mole-fraction constraints:

$$x_{32} + x_{33} + x_{34} + x_{35} = 1 \qquad (6)$$

2. Number of variables: $N_v = 10$ (three flow rates, six mole fractions, and one parameter).
3. Design or decision variables: $N_d = N_v - N_e = 10 - 6 = 4$. F_1 and α are convenient design variables. The composition of air $(x_{22} = 0.21, x_{25} = 0.79)$ is fixed by the environment.
4. Solution of the equations. It follows directly from Eqn. (1) that

$$F_2 = \boxed{\alpha}\boxed{F_1}$$

There remain five equations [Eqns. (2)–(6)] and five unknowns $(F_3, x_{32}, x_{33}, x_{34}, x_{35})$. These nonlinear equations may be linearized by a simple substitution,

$$n_{ij} = F_i x_{ij}$$

where n_{ij} is the molar flow rate in stream i of component j. Using this substitution, Eqns. (2)–(5) become

$$n_{33} \qquad\qquad = 3\,\boxed{F_1}$$

$$2n_{34} \qquad\qquad = 8\,\boxed{F_1}$$

$$2n_{32} + 2n_{33} + n_{34} \qquad = 2\,\boxed{\alpha}\boxed{F_1}\boxed{x_{22}}$$

$$n_{35} = \qquad \boxed{\alpha}\boxed{F_1}\boxed{x_{25}}$$

The n_{ij} may be calculated directly. Then, using Eqn. (6),

$$\sum_{j=1}^{N_c} n_{ij} = \sum F_i x_{ij} = F_i \sum x_{ij} = F_i$$

$$F_3 = n_{32} + n_{33} + n_{34} + n_{35} = (2 + \alpha)F_1$$

$$x_{32} = \frac{n_{32}}{F_3} = \frac{\alpha x_{22} - 5}{2 + \alpha}$$

$$x_{33} = \frac{n_{33}}{F_3} = \frac{3}{2 + \alpha}$$

$$x_{34} = \frac{n_{34}}{F_3} = \frac{4}{2 + \alpha}$$

$$x_{35} = \frac{n_{35}}{F_3} = \frac{\alpha x_{25}}{2 + \alpha}$$

Observe that

$$\alpha \geq \frac{5}{x_{22}}$$

because x_{32} cannot be negative. The solution is valid for air/fuel ratios equal to or greater than $5/(0.21) = 23.8$. This minimum value of α for complete burning of propane corresponds to the stoichiometric ratio of five molecules of oxygen to one molecule of propane.

Specifically, the solution for $F_1 = 1$ lb-mole/hr and $\alpha = 28$ is

	lb moles/hr,			Mole Fraction		
Stream No. (i)	F_i	C_3H_8	O_2	CO_2	H_2O	N_2
1	1	1	0	0	0	0
2	28	0	0.21	0	0	0.79
3	30	0	0.0293	0.1000	0.1333	0.7374

This solution may be checked by the equality of the entering and exit mass flow rates. According to Eqns. (6.2) and (6.10),

$$F_1' + F_2' = F_3'$$

$$F_1 \bar{M}_1 + F_2 \bar{M}_2 = F_3 \bar{M}_3$$

$$(1)(44.10) + (28)(28.85) = (30)(28.40)$$

$$852 \text{ lb/hr} = 852 \text{ lb/hr}$$

7.3 Material Balance for Simultaneous Reactions

Equation (7.10), derived for single reactions, applies as well for simultaneous reactions at steady state.

Example 7.5 shows that material balances on reacting systems are straightforward when the reaction is fast and irreversible. Yields of reversible reactions are limited by the value of the chemical equilibrium constant (K), which, as shown in the following example, introduces nonlinearities into the material balance equations.

Example 7.6

In the Ostwald process, ammonia is oxidized to make NO_2 in two reactions:

$$4NH_3 + 5O_2 \longrightarrow 4NO + 6H_2O$$

$$2NO + O_2 \rightleftharpoons 2NO_2$$

The product, NO_2, is later absorbed in water to form nitric acid. Suppose that the oxidation reactions are run at 800°C and a pressure of 150 atm. A gauze of platinum wire is an effective catalyst. The reactions are exothermic, and cooling water is needed to maintain the reaction temperature at 800°C; at this temperature the first reaction is irreversible. The second reaction is reversible; its equilibrium constant at 800°C is given by Eqn. (7.11):

$$K = \frac{1}{P} \frac{(x_{NO_2})^2}{(x_{NO})^2 (x_{O_2})} = 0.005 \qquad (P \text{ in atm})$$

The value of K was calculated from thermochemical data (see Appendix IV). Mole fractions refer to the product stream.

The process diagram is shown in Fig. 7-3. Assume that stream 1 is pure ammonia, that air is 21% oxygen and 79% nitrogen, that nitrogen is inert, and that the oxidation products are at equilibrium at 800°C. Calculate the flow rate and composition of the oxidation products.

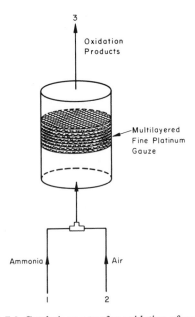

Figure 7-3 Catalytic reactor for oxidation of ammonia.

Solution:

The components are

Component	No. (j)
NH_3	1
O_2	2
NO	3
NO_2	4
H_2O	5
N_2	6

1. Equations and constraints.
   a. Equipment constraints. Since the first reaction is irreversible, all the ammonia will be consumed at equilibrium if the molar ratio of feed oxygen to ammonia exceeds 5/4:

$$x_{31} = 0$$

   The equilibrium constant of the second reaction is

$$K' = KP = \frac{x_{34}^2}{x_{33}^2 x_{32}} \tag{1}$$

   For convenience, the air-to-ammonia ratio is introduced as a parameter:

$$\alpha = \frac{F_2}{F_1} \tag{2}$$

   b. Material balance equations.
      (1) Reacting species [Eqn. (7.10)]:

$$\text{element N:} \qquad F_1 = F_3 x_{33} + F_3 x_{34} \tag{3}$$

$$\text{O:} \quad 2F_2 x_{22} = 2F_3 x_{32} + F_3 x_{33} + 2F_3 x_{34} + F_3 x_{35} \tag{4}$$

$$\text{H:} \qquad 3F_1 = 2F_3 x_{35} \tag{5}$$

      (2) Inert species:

$$N_2: \quad F_2 x_{26} = F_3 x_{36} \tag{6}$$

   c. Mole-fraction constraints:

$$x_{32} + x_{33} + x_{34} + x_{35} + x_{36} = 1 \tag{7}$$

2. Number of variables: $N_v = 12$ (three flow rates, seven mole fractions, and two parameters).
3. Design or decision variables: $N_d = N_v - N_e = 12 - 7 = 5$. F_1, α, and K' are chosen as design variables. $x_{22} = 0.21$ and $x_{26} = 0.79$ are fixed by the environment.
4. Solution of the equations. After calculation of F_2 by

$$F_2 = \textcircled{\alpha}\,\textcircled{F_1}$$

there are six equations containing six unknowns ($F_3, x_{32}, x_{33}, x_{34}, x_{35}$,

x_{36}). Equation (1) is nonlinear, and the equations cannot be linearized using the substitutions of Example 7.5. The equations are simplified by substituting x_{35} from Eqn. (5) and x_{36} from Eqn. (6) into the remaining equations:

$$\boxed{K'} = \frac{x_{34}^2}{x_{33}^2 x_{32}} \qquad (8)$$

$$\boxed{F_1} = F_3(x_{33} + x_{34}) \qquad (9)$$

$$\boxed{c_1} = F_3(2x_{32} + x_{33} + 2x_{34}) \qquad (10)$$

$$x_{32} + x_{33} + x_{34} + \frac{\boxed{c_2}}{F_3} = 1 \qquad (11)$$

where

$$c_1 = 2F_2 x_{22} - \frac{3F_1}{2}$$

$$c_2 = \frac{3F_1}{2} + F_2 x_{26}$$

These four equations are reduced to an equation cubic in x_{33} (using the precedence-ordering techniques in Sec. 13.1),

$$\boxed{K'} = \frac{\left(\boxed{c_3} x_{33} + \boxed{c_4} \right)^2}{x_{33}^2 \left(\boxed{c_5} + \boxed{c_6} x_{33} \right)} \qquad (12)$$

where

$$c_3 = -\frac{5F_1 + 4F_2}{3F_1 + 4F_2}$$

$$c_4 = \frac{4F_1}{3F_1 + 4F_2}$$

$$c_5 = \frac{-7F_1 + 4F_2 x_{22}}{3F_1 + 4F_2}$$

$$c_6 = \frac{5F_1 + 2F_2 x_{26}}{3F_1 + 4F_2}$$

The remaining unknowns are computed in order:

$$x_{34} = c_3 x_{33} + c_4 \qquad (13)$$

$$x_{32} = c_6 x_{33} + c_5 \qquad (14)$$

$$F_3 = \frac{F_1}{x_{33} + x_{34}} \qquad (15)$$

$$x_{35} = \frac{3F_1}{2F_3} \qquad (16)$$

$$x_{36} = \frac{F_2 x_{26}}{F_3} \qquad (17)$$

Specifically for the values of design variables,

$$F_1 = 10 \text{ lb-mole/hr}$$

$$\alpha = 10$$

$$K' = 0.75$$

the complete solution is

Stream No. (i)	lb-moles/hr, F_i	Mole fraction					
		NH_3	O_2	NO	NO_2	H_2O	N_2
1	10	1	0	0	0	0	0
2	100	0	0.21	0	0	0	0.79
3	111.6	0	0.0680	0.0731	0.0165	0.1344	0.7080

In practice the ammonia is not entirely used up, even in the presence of excess O_2. Although the reaction for oxidation of NH_3 is irreversible, chemical reactors convert only about 95% of the ammonia entering the reactor. The actual yield of NO_2 from NO according to the second reaction is less than the value calculated using the equilibrium constant, Eqn. (1). These differences between theoretical and actual yield can always, in principle, be reduced by improvements in the design of the chemical reactor. The calculation shows that even at equilibrium the amount of NO oxidized to NO_2 is small. For this reaction K increases with decreasing temperature. According to Eqn. (1), increased pressure as well as reduced temperature favors the formation of NO_2. NO oxidation can be accomplished after the ammonia oxidation at a lower temperature.

7.4 Degree of Conversion of Nonequilibrium Reactions

In the previous development the chemical equilibrium constant was introduced as a constraint equation, one for each reversible chemical reaction. An irreversible reaction is a special case for which the equilibrium constant is so large $(K \gg 1)$ that one of the reactants, whichever is present in an amount smaller than the stoichiometric proportion, is entirely consumed.

If the time needed for the reaction is short compared with the residence time in the reactor, the equilibrium constant provides an upper limit for the yield of the reaction which is not much higher than the actual yield.

If the rate of the reaction is slow (i.e., if the time needed for the reaction is long compared to the residence time in the reactor), the yield is determined by the reaction rate. For rate-limited reactions, the yield of product is considerably less than the equilibrium yield calculated using the equilibrium constant (K). It is useful to introduce as a parameter the degree of conversion (γ) of the reaction, defined as the fractional conversion of one of the reactants. Let the reactant be compound j. Compound j enters the reactor in stream 1 at the rate

$$F_1 x_{1j} = \text{molar flow rate of compound } j \text{ into reactor}$$

Compound j leaves the reactor in stream 2 at the rate

$$F_2 x_{2j} = \text{molar flow rate of compound } j \text{ out of reactor}$$

Therefore, the fractional conversion of compound j, a reactant, into other products is

$$\text{fractional conversion} = \gamma_j = \frac{F_1 x_{1j} - F_2 x_{2j}}{F_1 x_{1j}} \qquad (7.12)$$

If $\gamma_j = 0$, compound j does not react; if $\gamma_j = 1$, all of compound j is consumed in the chemical reaction. When the molar ratio of two reactants in the feed stream is equal to the ratio of their stoichiometric coefficients (ν), the fractional conversion of the two reactants is the same. If the reactants are not present in stoichiometric proportion, the fractional conversion (γ) will be different for each reactant.

The equilibrium yield and the actual degree of conversion are compared in the following example.

Example 7.7

The feed to an ammonia reactor, shown in Fig. 7-4, contains nitrogen, hydrogen, recycled ammonia, and inert impurities (methane and argon). The

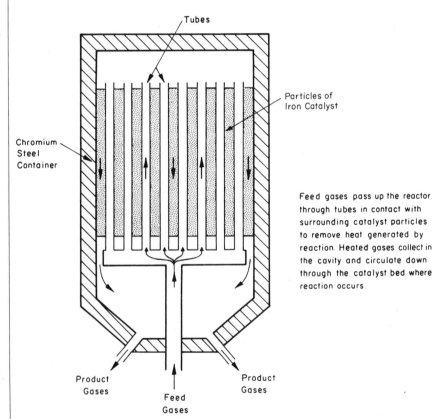

Figure 7-4 Cross section of tubular ammonia reactor. (R. F. Baddour, P. L. Brian, B. A. Logeais, and J. P. Eymery, "Steady-State Simulation of an Ammonia Synthesis Converter," *Chem. Eng. Sci.*, *20* (1965), p. 281.)

reaction is

$$N_2 + 3H_2 \rightleftharpoons 2NH_3$$

Nitrogen and hydrogen in the feed are in the stoichiometric proportion $1:3$. Determine the flow rate and composition of the product stream in terms of the feed stream variables.

The flow diagram is shown in Fig. 7-5.

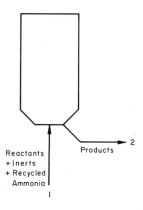

Reactants
+ Inerts
+ Recycled
Ammonia

Products

Figure 7-5 Flow diagram for ammonia reactor.

The components are

Compound	No.
N_2	1
H_2	2
NH_3	3
Ar	4
CH_4	5

Solution A (Equilibrium Yield of Ammonia)

1. Equations and constraints.
   a. Equipment constraints. The equilibrium constant, assuming that the pressure is not too high, is given by Eqn. (7.11):

$$K = P^{-2}\frac{x_{23}^2}{x_{21}x_{22}^3} \qquad (P \text{ in atm})$$

For fixed pressure,

$$\frac{K}{P^{-2}} = K' = \frac{x_{23}^2}{x_{21}x_{22}^3} \tag{1}$$

The constraint of stoichiometric proportions of reactants is

$$\frac{x_{12}}{x_{11}} = 3 \tag{2}$$

   b. Mole-fraction constraints:

$$x_{11} + x_{12} + x_{13} + x_{14} + x_{15} = 1 \tag{3}$$

$$x_{21} + x_{22} + x_{23} + x_{24} + x_{25} = 1 \tag{4}$$

c. Material balance equations.
   (1) Reacting species:

$$\text{element N:} \quad 2F_1x_{11} + F_1x_{13} = 2F_2x_{21} + F_2x_{23} \tag{5}$$

$$\text{H:} \quad 2F_1x_{12} + 3F_1x_{13} = 2F_2x_{22} + 3F_2x_{23} \tag{6}$$

   (2) Inert species:

$$\text{Ar:} \quad F_1x_{14} = F_2x_{24} \tag{7}$$

$$\text{CH}_4: \quad F_1x_{15} = F_2x_{25} \tag{8}$$

2. Number of variables: $N_v = N_s(N_c + 1) + N_p = 2(5 + 1) + 1 = 13$. The parameter is K'.
3. Design or decision variables: $N_d = N_v - N_e = 13 - 8 = 5$. The set $\{F_1, x_{11}, x_{14}, x_{15}, K'\}$ is selected.
4. Solution of the equations. From Eqns. (2), (5), and (6) it follows that

$$x_{22} = 3x_{21} \tag{9}$$

a result which might have been anticipated: If the reactants are present in stoichiometric proportion, then the unused reactants in the product stream are also in stoichiometric proportion. x_{12} is obtained directly from Eqn. (2), and x_{13} is obtained from Eqn. (3). This leaves six equations $\{(1), (4), (5), (7), (8), \text{ and } (9)\}$; note that Eqn. (9) replaces Eqn. (6). Combination of Eqns. (1) and (9) gives

$$x_{23} = x_{21}^2 \sqrt{27 \boxed{K'}} \tag{10}$$

Combination of Eqns. (5) and (7) gives

$$x_{24} = \boxed{x_{14}} \frac{(2x_{21} + x_{23})}{[2\boxed{x_{11}} + \boxed{x_{13}}]} \tag{11}$$

Combination of Eqns. (5) and (8) gives

$$x_{25} = \boxed{x_{15}} \frac{(2x_{21} + x_{23})}{[2\boxed{x_{11}} + \boxed{x_{13}}]} \tag{12}$$

Substitution of Eqns. (9), (11), and (12) into (4) yields

$$4x_{21} + x_{23} + \frac{[\boxed{x_{14}} + \boxed{x_{15}}]}{[2\boxed{x_{11}} + \boxed{x_{13}}]}(2x_{21} + x_{23}) = 1 \tag{13}$$

After substitution of x_{23} from Eqn. (10) into Eqn. (13), Eqn. (13) is quadratic in x_{21}. For example, if:

$$F_1 = 100 \text{ lb-moles/hr}$$

$$x_{11} = 0.230$$

$$x_{14} = 0.008$$

$$x_{15} = 0.018$$

$$K' = 0.25$$

the complete solution is

Stream No. (i)	lb-moles/hr, F_i	Mole fraction				
		N_2	H_2	NH_3	Ar	CH_4
1	100	0.230	0.690	0.054	0.008	0.018
2	94.24	0.2135	0.6405	0.1184	0.0085	0.0191

The flow rate of nitrogen into the reactor is $(100)(0.23) = 23$ lb-moles/hr. The flow rate out of the reactor is $(94.24)(0.2135) = 20.12$ lb-moles/hr. Therefore, the equilibrium degree of conversion of the nitrogen is

$$\text{equilibrium degree of conversion} = \frac{\text{amount reacted}}{\text{amount into reactor}} = \frac{23 - 20.12}{23}$$

$$= 0.125$$

Since the nitrogen and hydrogen are present in stoichiometric proportion, the degree of conversion of the hydrogen is also 12.5%.

Solution B (Actual Conversion)

Steps 1, 2, and 3 are the same as for Solution A except for Eqn. (1), which is replaced by a new equation for the actual degree of conversion (γ) of feed nitrogen to ammonia,

$$\gamma = \frac{F_1 x_{11} - F_2 x_{21}}{F_1 x_{11}} \tag{1}$$

or

$$F_2 x_{21} = (1 - \gamma) F_1 x_{11}$$

Therefore, the equipment parameter K' is replaced by γ. Equations (2)–(8) of Solution A are unchanged.

As before, Eqn. (6) is replaced by

$$x_{22} = 3x_{21} \tag{9}$$

x_{12} is obtained directly from Eqn. (2), and then x_{13} is given by Eqn. (3). The equations reduce to the set

$$F_2 x_{21} = (1 - \gamma)(F_1)(x_{11})$$

$$2F_2 x_{21} + F_2 x_{23} = 2(F_1)(x_{11}) + (F_1)(x_{13})$$

$$F_2 x_{24} = (F_1)(x_{14})$$

$$F_2 x_{25} = (F_1)(x_{15})$$

$$x_{21} + x_{22} + x_{23} + x_{24} + x_{25} = 1$$

$$x_{22} = 3x_{21}$$

There are six equations and six unknowns: $F_2, x_{21}, x_{22}, x_{23}, x_{24}, x_{25}$. The same transformation which linearizes the nonlinear equations in Example 7.5 works here. We replace $F_i x_{ij}$ with n_{ij}, the molar flow rate of component j in stream i:

$$n_{21} = (1 - \gamma)(F_1)(x_{11})$$

$$2n_{21} + n_{23} = (F_1)(2(x_{11}) + (x_{13}))$$

$$n_{24} = (F_1)(x_{14})$$

$$n_{25} = (F_1)(x_{15})$$

This set of linear equations can be solved directly for the n_{ij}. Then

$$n_{22} = 3n_{21}$$

$$F_2 = n_{21} + n_{22} + n_{23} + n_{24} + n_{25}$$

$$x_{21} = \frac{n_{21}}{F_2}, \qquad x_{22} = \frac{n_{22}}{F_2}, \quad \text{etc.}$$

For the set of design variables,

$$F_1 = 100 \text{ lb-moles/hr}$$

$$x_{11} = 0.23$$

$$x_{14} = 0.008$$

$$x_{15} = 0.018$$

$$\gamma = 0.10$$

the complete solution is

	lb-moles/hr,	Mole fraction				
Stream No. (i)	F_i	N_2	H_2	NH_3	Ar	CH_4
1	100	0.230	0.690	0.054	0.008	0.018
2	95.4	0.2170	0.6509	0.1048	0.0084	0.0189

Since the actual conversion of nitrogen (10%) is less than the equilibrium value (12.5%), the mole fraction of ammonia in the product (0.1048) is less than the equilibrium value (0.1184).

Several principles illustrated in the previous examples are summarized as follows:

1. Separate material balance equations are written for inert and chemically active compounds.
2. If the mole fractions of a pair of reactants are in the stoichiometric ratio, then leftover reactants in the product stream are present in the same stoichiometric ratio. The principle fails when there are simultaneous reactions.
3. Transformation of the material balance equations from mole fractions (x_{ij}) to molar flow rates (n_{ij}) sometimes linearizes the equations—see Examples 7.5 and 7.7.

4. Some measure of the yield of each chemical reaction is needed for the solution of the material balance problem. The appropriate parameter for reactions which do not approach equilibrium is the degree of conversion. The parameter for reactions which reach, or nearly reach, equilibrium is the chemical equilibrium constant.

7.5 Material Balances by Inspection

When fractional conversion is known, material balance calculations may be made by inspection; a systematic analysis is unnecessary. The balanced chemical reaction contains sufficient information to solve the material balance. The following example is typical.

Example 7.8

Petroleum refineries convert butane to more valuable gasoline. One reaction path involves dehydrogenation of n-butane to 1-butene:

$$n\text{-}C_4H_{10} \xrightarrow[\substack{Cr_2O_3/Al_2O_3 \\ \text{catalyst}}]{1000°F} C_4H_8 + H_2 \qquad \text{(dehydrogenation)}$$

$$n\text{-butane} \longrightarrow \text{1-butene} + \text{hydrogen}$$

Approximately 30% of the n-butane is converted to butene on each pass through the reactor, and the remainder is separated and recycled.

Gasoline is synthesized at low temperature in the presence of HF catalyst:

$$i\text{-}C_4H_{10} + C_4H_8 \xrightarrow[\text{HF catalyst}]{} C_8H_{18} \qquad \text{(alkylation)}$$

$$\text{isobutane} + \text{1-butene} \longrightarrow \text{"isooctane"}$$

Isooctane means 2, 2, 4-trimethylpentane (other isomers are also obtained). The molar ratio of isobutane/butene is set at 10 to 1 to avoid polymerization of butene, which is entirely consumed in the alkylation reaction.

1. Ten thousand pounds per hour of n-butane (including recycle) is fed to the dehydrogenation reactor. What is the mass flow rate of butene and hydrogen?
2. All the butene formed in the dehydrogenation reactor is recovered from the product and fed to the alkylation reactor. What is the production rate of gasoline?

Solution:

Molecular weights are

Compound	Molecular weight
H_2	2.02
C_4H_{10}	58.12
C_4H_8	56.10
C_8H_{18}	114.22

1.

$$\text{moles of } n\text{-butane/hr} = \frac{10,000}{58.12} = 172 \text{ lb-moles/hr}$$

Since 30% of the n-butane is dehydrogenated,

$$\text{moles of butene/hr} = \text{moles of } H_2/\text{hr} = (0.3)(172)$$
$$= 51.6 \text{ lb-moles/hr}$$
$$\text{production rate of } H_2 = (51.6)(2.02) = 104 \text{ lb/hr}$$
$$\text{production rate of butene} = (51.6)(56.10) = 2896 \text{ lb/hr}$$

2. Since all the butene is converted to isooctane,

$$\text{production rate of gasoline} = (51.6)(114.22) = 5894 \text{ lb/hr}$$

Excess isobutane used in the alkylation reaction is separated from iso-octane and recycled.

7.6 Simplified Model of a Chemical Reactor: The CSTR (Continuous Stirred-Tank Reactor)

The rate of a chemical reaction depends on the activity of the catalyst, the velocity of the reactants through the reactor, the size and design of the reactor, temperature, pressure, and other variables. Equations are complex for tubular reactors (Fig. 7-4) because even at steady state there is a spatial variation in properties (concentration, temperature) as the reactants pass through the catalyst bed.

The continuous stirred-tank reactor (CSTR) shown in Fig. 7-6 is simpler to describe than a tubular reactor because there is no spatial variation in temperature or concentration. According to the CSTR model, the contents of the reactor are stirred vigorously so that concentration (and all other prop-

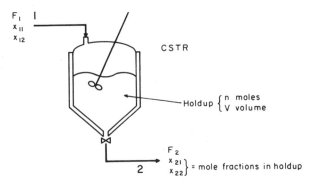

Figure 7-6 Schematic of CSTR (continuous stirred-tank reactor).

erties) within the reactor is uniform. Therefore, the concentration of the product stream (2) is the same as the concentration of the holdup liquid inside the CSTR.

Suppose that the chemical reaction is an isomerization:

$$C_2 \underset{k_r'}{\overset{k_r}{\rightleftharpoons}} C_1 \tag{7.13}$$

Compounds C_1 and C_2 have the same number of atoms of the same elements, but their molecular structure is different. For example, isomerization of n-butane to isobutane is

$$n\text{-}C_4H_{10} \rightleftharpoons i\text{-}C_4H_{10}$$

Structurally,

There are two reactions occurring in the CSTR: the forward reaction, which produces C_1, and the unwanted reverse reaction, which produces C_2. The rate (per unit volume) of this unimolecular reaction should be directly proportional to the concentration of reactant, n_2/V. For the forward reaction,

$$r'_{\text{for}} = k_r \left[\frac{n_2}{V} \right] \tag{7.14}$$

where n_2 is the number of moles of compound C_2 in a CSTR of volume V. r' is the rate of reaction per unit volume of holdup liquid in the CSTR (units of moles per unit time per unit volume). k_r, the rate constant of the forward reaction, is a strong function of temperature but independent of concentration. Similarly, for the reverse reaction,

$$r'_{\text{rev}} = k_r' \left[\frac{n_1}{V} \right] \tag{7.15}$$

where n_1 is the number of moles of product (C_1) in the CSTR. The net rate of formation of C_1 is the difference between the forward and the reverse reactions:

$$r'_{\text{net}} = r'_{\text{for}} - r'_{\text{rev}} = k_r \left(\frac{n_2}{V} \right) - k_r' \left(\frac{n_1}{V} \right) \tag{7.16}$$

Since the concentration inside the CSTR is equal to the concentration in the product stream (2),

$$r'_{\text{net}} = \frac{n}{V} [k_r x_{22} - k_r' x_{21}] \tag{7.17}$$

where n is the total number of moles of holdup liquid in the CSTR. (See Fig. 7-6.)

The reactor does not operate at equilibrium. At equilibrium, the net rate of production would be zero because the forward reaction would be perfectly balanced by the reverse reaction:

$$r'_{net} = 0 \qquad \text{(at equilibrium)} \tag{7.18}$$

Substitution of Eqn. (7.17) into (7.18) gives

$$\frac{k_r}{k'_r} = \frac{x_{21}}{x_{22}} \qquad \text{(at equilibrium)} \tag{7.19}$$

Assuming that isomers form an ideal liquid solution (a very good assumption), the chemical equilibrium constant (K) for Reaction (7.13) is

$$K = \frac{x_{21}}{x_{22}} \qquad \text{(at equilibrium)} \tag{7.20}$$

Comparison of Eqns. (7.19) and (7.20) shows that

$$K = \frac{k_r}{k'_r} \tag{7.21}$$

In spite of the fact that Eqns. (7.18)–(7.21) refer to equilibrium, the quantities k_r, k'_r, and K are constants so that (7.21) is a general relationship between equilibrium and rate constants. Equation (7.21) is valid whether or not the CSTR produces the equilibrium yield. Substituting the value for k'_r from (7.21) into (7.17) and using the mole fraction constraint $x_{22} = 1 - x_{21}$,

$$r'_{net} = \left(\frac{nk_r}{V}\right)\left[1 - \left(1 + \frac{1}{K}\right)x_{21}\right] \tag{7.22}$$

According to Eqn. (7.8) the rate of production of C_1 is given by

$$r = F_2 x_{21} - F_1 x_{11} \tag{7.23}$$

Since

$$r' = \frac{r}{V} \tag{7.24}$$

combination of Eqns. (7.22)–(7.24) gives

$$nk_r\left[1 - \left(1 + \frac{1}{K}\right)x_{21}\right] = F_2 x_{21} - F_1 x_{11} \tag{7.25}$$

Since the reaction is an isomerization, the molecular weights of the inlet and outlet streams are identical, and

$$F_1 = F_2 \tag{7.26}$$

Substituting (7.26) into (7.25) and solving for x_{21},

$$x_{21} = \frac{1 + (F_1 x_{11}/nk_r)}{1 + (1/K) + (F_1/nk_r)} \tag{7.27}$$

Equation (7.27) for an isomerization reaction in a CSTR contains the parameters K and nk_r. n, the number of moles of liquid holdup inside the CSTR, is directly proportional to the size of the CSTR.

If the equilibrium constant is very small ($K \ll 1$), there will be no product ($x_{21} = 0$). If the reaction is irreversible, K is very large, and in the limit ($K \to \infty$)

$$x_{21} = \frac{x_{11} + (nk_r/F_1)}{1 + (nk_r/F_1)} \tag{7.28}$$

If there is no product in the feed, $x_{11} = 0$,

$$x_{21} = \frac{1}{1 + (F_1/nk_r)} \tag{7.29}$$

Hence, for irreversible reactions, the mole fraction of product decreases with increasing feed rate (F_1) and increases with increasing values of the rate constant (k_r).

If the reaction is reversible ($K \simeq 1$), the mole fraction of product (x_{21}) cannot exceed the equilibrium value. Figure 7-7 shows the relationship between the mole fraction of product and the feed rate for a reactor with $nk_r = 1$ mole/hr, $K = 1$, and $x_{11} = 0$. The equilibrium conversion ($x_{21} = 0.5$) is obtained only in the limit of infinitesimally slow feed rates.

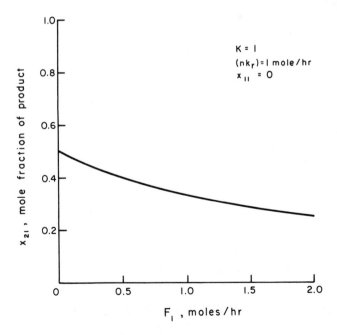

Figure 7-7 Mole fraction of product as a function of feed rate for reversible reaction.

There are several limiting cases for the CSTR model which illustrate the limits in Table 7.1. Let the product in the feed stream (x_{11}) be zero so that

$$x_{21} = \frac{1}{1 + (1/K) + (F_1/nk_r)} \tag{7.30}$$

1. Irreversible reaction ($K \gg 1$):

$$x_{21} = \frac{1}{1 + (F_1/nk_r)} \tag{7.31}$$

The reaction is rate-limited.
2. Fast reaction ($k_r \gg F_1/n$):

$$x_{21} = \frac{1}{1 + (1/K)} = \frac{K}{K + 1} \tag{7.32}$$

The amount of product is fixed by the equilibrium constant.
3. Fast, irreversible reaction ($k_r \gg F_1/n$, $K \gg 1$):

$$x_{21} = 1 \tag{7.33}$$

All the reactant is converted to product.

The CSTR model will be used in the next chapter to illustrate the principle of recycling. The behavior of a CSTR operated without recycling is shown in Example 7.9.

Example 7.9

Isomerization of n-butane to isobutane is accomplished with the aid of a catalyst at 250°F and 50 atm. Under these conditions n-butane and isobutane are liquids. Using the CSTR model and assuming a feed of pure n-butane, calculate the rate of production of isobutane as a function of feed rate.

Solution:

The schematic of the process is given in Fig. 7-6. The components are

Component	No. (j)
i-C_4H_{10}	1
n-C_4H_{10}	2

1. Equations and constraints.
   a. Equipment constraints. The rate of the reaction is given by Eqn. (7.8):

   $$r = F_2 x_{21} - F_1 x_{11}$$

   The reaction kinetics of this unimolecular reaction give [see Eqn. (7.17)]

   $$r = n[k_r x_{22} - k'_r x_{21}]$$

These two equations, combined, describe the operation of the reactor:

$$F_2 x_{21} - F_1 x_{11} = n[k_r x_{22} - k_r' x_{21}] \tag{1}$$

In addition, the rate constants of forward and reverse reactions are related to the equilibrium constant by

$$\frac{k_r}{k_r'} = K \tag{2}$$

b. Mole-fraction constraints:

$$x_{11} + x_{12} = 1 \tag{3}$$

$$x_{21} + x_{22} = 1 \tag{4}$$

c. Material balance equations. There is only one independent material balance equation; we choose the C atom balance:

$$4F_1 x_{11} + 4F_1 x_{12} = 4F_2 x_{21} + 4F_2 x_{22} \tag{5}$$

2. Number of variables: $N_v = N_s(N_c + 1) + N_p = 2(2 + 1) + 4 = 10$. The equipment parameters are k_r, k_r', n, and K.
3. Design or decision variables: $N_d = N_v - N_e = 10 - 5 = 5$. The set F_1, x_{11}, k_r, n, K is selected.
4. Solution of the equations. From Eqns. (3)–(5), it follows that [see Eqn. (7.26)]

$$F_1 = F_2 \tag{6}$$

Combination of Eqns. (1), (2), (4), and (6) yields [see Eqn. (7.27)]

$$x_{21} = \frac{1 + (F_1 x_{11}/nk_r)}{1 + (1/K) + (F_1/nk_r)} \tag{7}$$

Equation (7) was derived somewhat less systematically in the previous development.

The following values of design variables are adopted:

$x_{11} = 0$

$K = 1.17 =$ equilibrium constant

$k_r = 7.2 \times 10^{-4}$ sec^{-1} = rate constant of forward reaction

$n = 19.5$ lb-moles = holdup in CSTR

$0 < F_1 < \infty$ (see problem statement)

The flow rate of product, for $x_{11} = 0$, is

$$n_{21} = F_2 x_{21} = F_1 x_{21} = \frac{F_1}{1 + (1/K) + (F_1/nk_r)} \tag{8}$$

Values of x_{21} and $F_2 x_{21}$, calculated using Eqns. (7) and (8), are plotted on Fig. 7-8 as a function of the feed rate (F_1). The figure shows that the maximum mole fraction of product is obtained at the limit of zero feed rate. This limiting value of x_{21} is the equilibrium value given by Eqn. (7.32). As the flow rate (F_1) increases, the flow rate of product increases but at the expense of a progressively more dilute concentration of product (x_{21}). In the limit of infinite feed rate $(F_1$

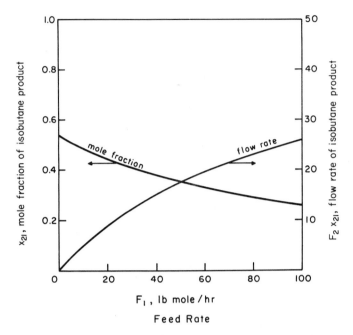

Figure 7-8 CSTR reactor for isomerization of *n*-butane to isobutane.

very large), the mole fraction of product (x_{21}) goes to zero but F_2x_{21} is finite in the limit

$$\lim_{F_1 \to \infty} (F_2 x_{21}) = \lim_{F_1 \to \infty} \left[\frac{F_1}{1 + (1/K) + (F_1/nk_r)} \right] = nk_r$$

In this case, the maximum product flow rate (F_2x_{21}) for the design variables specified is

$$nk_r = 19.5 \text{ lb-moles} \times (7.2 \times 10^{-4} \text{ sec}^{-1}) \times \left[\frac{3600 \text{ sec}}{\text{hr}} \right] = 50.5 \text{ lb-moles/hr}$$

7.7 Solution of Material Balances on Reactors Using Computers

Material balances on chemical reactors generally include nonlinear equations such as chemical equilibrium constraints. Iterative solutions of sets of nonlinear algebraic equations are usually obtained with the aid of a digital computer. In the following example, a typical material balance problem is solved using the precedence-ordering methods described in Sec. 13.1.

Example 7.10

Prepare a computer program for a material balance of the ammonia reactor operating at equilibrium in Example 7.7. The program is to determine product flow rate and mole fractions, given feed composition.

Solution:

Let us consider the more general case when the ratio of hydrogen to nitrogen in the feed is *not* constrained to the stoichiometric ratio of 3 so that Eqn. (2) in Example 7.7 no longer applies.

For the reactor (see Fig. 7-9), the components are

Compound	No.
Nitrogen	1
Hydrogen	2
Ammonia	3
Argon	4
Methane	5

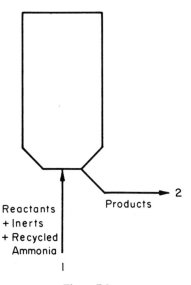

Reactants
+ Inerts
+ Recycled
Ammonia

Products

2

Figure 7-9

The material balance problem is analyzed as follows:

1. Equations and constraints.
   a. Equipment constraints. For a reactor operating at equilibrium and at a fixed pressure,

$$K' = \frac{x_{23}^2}{x_{21}x_{22}^3} \tag{1}$$

   b. Mole-fraction constraints:

$$x_{21} + x_{22} + x_{23} + x_{24} + x_{25} = 1 \tag{2}$$

   c. Material balance equations.
      (1) Reacting species:

$$\text{element N:} \quad 2F_1x_{11} + F_1x_{13} = 2F_2x_{21} + F_2x_{23} \tag{3}$$

$$\text{H:} \quad 2F_1x_{12} + 3F_1x_{13} = 2F_2x_{22} + 3F_2x_{23} \tag{4}$$

(2) Inert species:

$$\text{Ar:} \quad F_1 x_{14} = F_2 x_{24} \tag{5}$$

$$\text{CH}_4: \quad F_1 x_{15} = F_2 x_{25} \tag{6}$$

2. Number of variables: $N_v = N_s(N_c + 1) + N_p = 2(5 + 1) + 1 = 13$. The equipment parameter is K'.
3. Design or decision variables: $N_d = N_v - N_e = 13 - 6 = 7$. In accordance with the problem statement, we select as the set of design variables $F_1, x_{11}, x_{12}, x_{13}, x_{14}, x_{15}$, and K'.
4. Solution of the equations. Methods for precedence-ordering a set of nonlinear equations are described in Sec. 13.1. The result of applying these methods is presented in Table 7.2, which contains the ordered equations. Details for this set of equations are given in Appendix I.

Newton's method is applied to solve the equation

$$f\{F_2\} = \boxed{K'}\boxed{\gamma_2} + F_2)\boxed{\gamma_3} + 3F_2)^3 - 16F_2^2\boxed{\gamma_1} - F_2)^2 = 0 \tag{7}$$

for F_2. The Newton's method formula (see Sec. 11.4) is

$$F_2 \longleftarrow F_2^* - \frac{f\{F_2^*\}}{f'\{F_2^*\}} \tag{8}$$

where F_2^* is the guess value for F_2. Convergence to a solution value is achieved when

$$\left| \frac{F_2 - F_2^*}{F_2^*} \right| \leq \epsilon$$

where ϵ is specified as the convergence tolerance. The derivative of the

TABLE 7.2
ORDERED EQUATIONS

Solution order	Equation No.	Output variable	Equation
1	1	F_2	$16F_2^2(\gamma_1 - F_2)^2 = K'(\gamma_2 + F_2)(\gamma_3 + 3F_2)^3$
2	2	x_{23}	$x_{23} = \dfrac{\beta}{2F_2} - 1$
3	3	x_{21}	$x_{21} = \dfrac{\alpha_1 - F_2 x_{23}}{2F_2}$
4	4	x_{22}	$x_{22} = \dfrac{\alpha_2 - 3F_2 x_{23}}{2F_2}$
5	5	x_{24}	$x_{24} = \dfrac{\alpha_3}{F_2}$
6	6	x_{25}	$x_{25} = \dfrac{\alpha_4}{F_2}$

where

$$\alpha_1 = F_1(2x_{11} + x_{13}) \qquad \beta = \alpha_1 + \alpha_2 + 2(\alpha_3 + \alpha_4)$$

$$\alpha_2 = F_1(2x_{12} + 3x_{13}) \qquad \gamma_1 = \frac{\beta}{2}$$

$$\alpha_3 = F_1 x_{14} \qquad \gamma_2 = \alpha_1 - \frac{\beta}{2}$$

$$\alpha_4 = F_1 x_{15} \qquad \gamma_3 = \alpha_2 - \frac{3\beta}{2}$$

function, $f'\{F_2^*\}$, is obtained by numerical approximation,

$$f'\{F_2^*\} \simeq \frac{f\{F_2^* + \delta\} - f\{F_2^*\}}{\delta}$$

where δ is specified such that $\delta \ll F_2^*$.

The WATFIV program, below, reads design variable values from cards, computes x_{13} and the constant terms in the ordered equations, solves Eqn. (7) using Newton's method, computes the product stream mole fractions directly, and prints the results. See Fig. 7-10 for flow diagram.

Flow Diagram

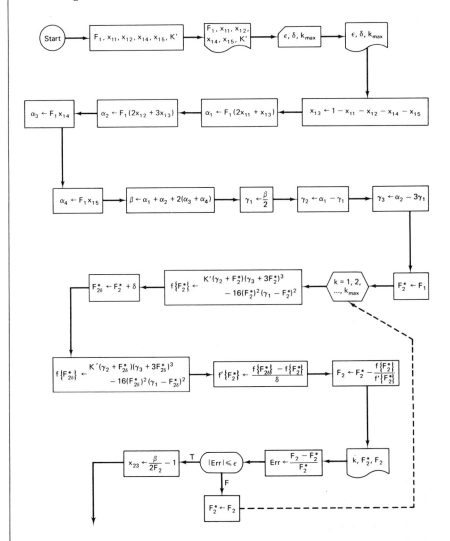

Figure 7-10

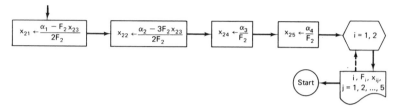

Figure 7-10 (continued)

Table of Symbols

Problem symbol	Program symbol	Definition	Units
	ERR	$(F_2 - F_2^*)/F_2^*$	
f	FUNC	Function evaluated at F_2^*, $f\{F_2^*\}$	(lb-moles/hr)^4
	FUNCD	Function evaluated at $F_2^* + \delta$, $f\{F_2^* + \delta\}$	(lb-moles/hr)^4
f'	DERIV	Derivative of function evaluated at F_2^*	(lb-moles/hr)^3
F_i	F(I)	Flow rate of stream i	lb-moles/hr
F_2^*	F2S	Guess value for F_2	lb-moles/hr
	F2SDEL	$F_2^* + \delta$	lb-moles/hr
k	K	Newton's method iteration counter	
k_{max}	KMAX	Maximum number of Newton's method iterations	
K'	KEQ	Reaction equilibrium constant	
x_{ij}	X(I,J)	Mole fraction in stream i of component j	
α_i	ALPHAI	Constant in ordered equations	lb-moles/hr
β	BETA	Constant in ordered equations	lb-moles/hr
γ_i	GAMI	Constant in ordered equations	lb-moles/hr
δ	DELTA	Numerical derivative increment	lb-moles/hr
ϵ	EPSI	Convergence tolerance	

Program Listing

```
C***   PROGRAM TO SOLVE THE AMMONIA REACTOR MATERIAL BALANCE EQUATIONS
C      AND CONSTRAINTS.  NEWTON'S METHOD SOLVES A SINGLE EQUATION IN A
C      SINGLE UNKNOWN, THE PRODUCT FLOW RATE, F(2).  ALL PRODUCT STREAM
C      COMPOSITIONS ARE COMPUTED DIRECTLY.  THE INITIAL GUESS VALUE FOR
C      F(2), F2S = F(1).
C
       DIMENSION X(2,5), F(2)
       REAL KEQ
C
C***   READS AND PRINTS DATA.
C
```

```
      3  READ, F(1), X(1,1), X(1,2), X(1,4), X(1,5), KEQ
         WRITE (6,100)
         WRITE (6,101) F(1), X(1,1), X(1,2), X(1,4), X(1,5), KEQ
         READ, EPSI, DELTA, KMAX
         WRITE (6,110)
         WRITE (6,111) EPSI, DELTA, KMAX
C
C***  COMPUTES X(1,3) AND CONSTANTS USED THROUGHOUT PROGRAM.
C
         X(1,3) = 1.0 - X(1,1) - X(1,2) - X(1,4) - X(1,5)
         ALPHA1 = F(1)*(2.0*X(1,1) + X(1,3))
         ALPHA2 = F(1)*(2.0*X(1,2) + 3.0*X(1,3))
         ALPHA3 = F(1)*X(1,4)
         ALPHA4 = F(1)*X(1,5)
         BETA = ALPHA1 + ALPHA2 + 2.0*(ALPHA3 + ALPHA4)
         GAM1 = BETA/2.0
         GAM2 = ALPHA1 - GAM1
         GAM3 = ALPHA2 - 3.0*GAM1
         WRITE (6,120)
C
C***  APPLIES NEWTON'S METHOD TO SOLVE FOR F(2).
C
         F2S = F(1)
         DO 1 K = 1,KMAX
         FUNC = KEQ*(GAM2 + F2S)*(GAM3 + 3.0*F2S)**3 - 16.0*F2S*F2S*
        1(GAM1 - F2S)**2
         F2SDEL = F2S + DELTA
         FUNCD = KEQ*(GAM2 + F2SDEL)*(GAM3 + 3.0*F2SDEL)**3 - 16.0*F2SDEL*
        1F2SDEL*(GAM1 - F2SDEL)**2
         F2S = F2SDEL - DELTA
         DERIV = (FUNCD - FUNC)/DELTA
         F(2) = F2S - FUNC/DERIV
         WRITE (6,121) K, F2S, F(2)
         ERR = (F(2) - F2S)/F2S
         IF (ABS(ERR) .LE. EPSI)  GO TO 2
      1  F2S = F(2)
         WRITE (6,130)
         GO TO 3
C
C***  COMPUTES PRODUCT COMPOSITIONS DIRECTLY.
C
      2  X(2,3) = 0.5*BETA/F(2) - 1.0
         X(2,1) = (ALPHA1 - F(2)*X(2,3))/(2.0*F(2))
         X(2,2) = (ALPHA2 - 3.0*F(2)*X(2,3))/(2.0*F(2))
         X(2,4) = ALPHA3/F(2)
         X(2,5) = ALPHA4/F(2)
C
C***  PRINTS RESULTS.
C
         WRITE (6,140)
         DO 4 I = 1,2
      4  WRITE (6,121) I, F(I), (X(I,J), J = 1,5)
         GO TO 3
C
C***  INPUT AND OUTPUT FORMAT STATEMENTS.
C
    100  FORMAT ( '1F(1), X(1,1), X(1,2), X(1,4), X(1,5), KEQ = '/)
    101  FORMAT (' ', 8F10.4)
    110  FORMAT (//, ' EPSI, DELTA, KMAX = '/)
    111  FORMAT (' ', 2F10.4, I12)
    120  FORMAT (//, ' K, F2S, F(2) = '/)
    121  FORMAT (' ', I12, 7F10.4)
    130  FORMAT (//, ' KMAX EXCEEDED'//)
    140  FORMAT (//, ' STREAM I, F(I), X(I,1), X(I,2),..., X(I,5) ='/)
         END
```

Data

```
              100.0, 0.22, 0.685, 0.012, 0.02, 0.2
              0.0001, 0.0001, 25
```

Computed Output

```
F(1), X(1,1), X(1,2), X(1,4), X(1,5), KEQ =
   100.0000    0.2200    0.6850    0.0120    0.0200    0.2000


EPSI, DELTA, KMAX =
    0.0001     0.0001         25


K, F2S, F(2) =
            1   100.0000   95.3359
            2    95.3358   96.0600
            3    96.0600   95.9986
            4    95.9986   96.0051


STREAM I, F(I), X(I,1), X(I,2),..., X(I,5) =
            1   100.0000   0.2200   0.6850   0.0630   0.0120   0.0200
            2    96.0051   0.2083   0.6511   0.1072   0.0125   0.0208
```

PROBLEMS

7.1. Balance the following chemical reactions:

(a) $As_2S_5 + HNO_3 \longrightarrow H_3AsO_4 + H_2SO_4 + H_2O + NO_2$.

(b) $HNO_3 + CuS \longrightarrow Cu(NO_3)_2 + S + H_2O + NO$.

(c) $K_2Cr_2O_7 + HCl \longrightarrow KCl + CrCl_3 + H_2O + Cl_2$.

7.2. Synthesis gas for ammonia is produced by reforming natural gas. The principal reaction is

$$CH_4 + H_2O \longrightarrow CO + 3H_2$$

What volume of methane at 25°C and 10 atm is required to produce 1 ton of hydrogen gas?

7.3. The overall reaction for coal gasification (2.7) is

$$2CH + \tfrac{1}{2}O_2 + H_2O \longrightarrow CH_4 + CO_2$$

CH is an approximate formula for coal. How many cubic feet per hour of O_2 at STP (0°C and 1 atm) are required to gasify 2 tons/hr of coal?

7.4. One means of providing oxygen for space flights of short duration is to store oxygen in water and electrolyze as needed. Consider a three-man flight of 20 days' duration. How many pounds of water are required for oxygen generation, if the daily requirement is 20 ft³ (measured at 0°C and 1 atm) per man?

7.5. The overall reaction for the Solvay process is

$$CaCO_3 + 2NaCl \longrightarrow Na_2CO_3 + CaCl_2$$

How many pounds of limestone ($CaCO_3$) and salt are needed to produce 5000 lb of soda ash (Na_2CO_3)?

7.6. Fluorocarbons for refrigeration are made from chlorinated hydrocarbons by reaction with anhydrous hydrogen fluoride, using antimony pentachloride

catalyst. One hundred pounds per hour of difluorodichloromethane are made
by the reaction

$$CCl_4 + 2HF \xrightarrow{\text{SbCl}_5} CCl_2F_2 + 2HCl$$

Calculate the rate of reaction in pound-moles per hour. What is the rate of
production of hydrogen chloride in pound-moles per hour?

7.7. A furnace provides heat for generating process steam in a refinery. Analysis
of the fuel gas entering the burner gives

	Mole %
CH_4	52
H_2	24
N_2	15
CO	6
CO_2	3
	100

Let r be the molal air/fuel ratio. Assume that air is

	Mole %
O_2	21
N_2	79

Assume that the CH_4, H_2, and CO in the fuel gas are completely oxidized so
that combustion products consist of H_2O, CO_2, O_2, and N_2.

a. Write the material balance equations for the burner shown in Fig. 7-11 in
terms of flow rates and compositions and determine the number of design
variables. Use the following component code,

	Component No.
CH_4	1
H_2	2
N_2	3
CO	4
CO_2	5
O_2	6
H_2O	7

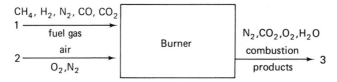

Figure 7-11

and the following stream specification,

	Stream No.
Fuel gas	1
Air	2
Products	3

b. Solve the problem for the following specification of design variables:

$$F_1 = 100 \text{ moles/hr}$$
$$r = 6.5$$
$$x_{11} = 0.52$$
$$x_{12} = 0.24$$
$$x_{13} = 0.15$$
$$x_{14} = 0.06$$
$$x_{26} = 0.21$$

7.8. The industrial gas burner shown in Fig. 7-12 uses propane fuel. The operator suspects that the air-to-fuel ratio is running too low. He measures the flow rate of the flue gases ($F_3 = 1000$ liters/hr measured at 260°C, 1 atm). An analysis of the flue gases shows a CO_2 content of 8.6 mole %. Show the operator how he can calculate the air-to-fuel ratio.

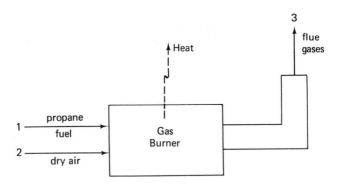

Figure 7-12

7.9. Figure 7-13 is the Ostwald ammonia oxidation process. Assume that the reaction is irreversible. Neglect possible formation of NO_2. Solve for the following conditions:

$$F_1 = 10 \text{ moles/hr}$$
$$\alpha = \frac{F_2}{F_1} = 10 \quad \text{(air-to-ammonia ratio)}$$

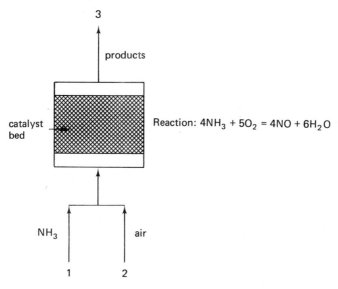

Figure 7-13

7.10. The chlorination of methane is carried out in a steady flow reactor. In Fig.7-14, feed stream 1 is pure methane; feed stream 2 is pure chlorine. If the flow rate of chlorine relative to the flow rate of methane is properly adjusted, the more expensive chlorine is almost completely reacted. The product stream (3) contains

Compound	No.
CH_4	1
CH_3Cl	2
CH_2Cl_2	3
$CHCl_3$	4
CCl_4	5
Cl_2	6
HCl	7

Figure 7-14

During a recent test, the meters measuring the feed methane and chlorine appeared to be in error. It was decided to calculate the input flow rates from accurately measured output quantities. At a product flow rate of $F_3 = 100$ moles/hr, a chemical analysis of the product stream yielded the following data:

$$x_{32} = 0.082$$
$$x_{33} = 0.059$$
$$x_{34} = 0.051$$
$$x_{35} = 0.033$$
$$x_{36} = 0.005$$

Mole fractions of methane and hydrogen chloride in the product stream were not measured. Calculate all unknown flow rates and compositions. What is the *mass* flow rate of the product stream?

7.11. Exchange of mass with surroundings by the human body is an unsteady-state operation. However, for an adult not gaining or losing weight, the *average* daily exchange of mass with the surroundings may be approximated as a steady-state operation. Flow of mass to and from the human body is simplified as shown in Fig. 7-15. Drink, stream 2, is assumed to be pure water.

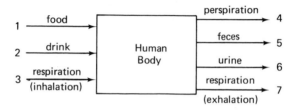

Figure 7-15

The respiration process is the inhalation of oxygen in stream 3 and the exhalation of water and carbon dioxide in stream 7. Perspiration is assumed to be pure water. Urine is assumed to be a solution of urea (NH_2CONH_2) in water. Food consists of

$$\begin{aligned} \text{Carbohydrates:} \quad & C_{12}H_{22}O_{11} \\ \text{Fat:} \quad & (C_{17}H_{35}COO)_3\text{—}C_3H_5 \\ \text{Protein:} \quad & C_{5.2}H_{8.5}O_{1.4}N \\ \text{Water:} \quad & H_2O \\ \text{Inert solids.} \quad & \end{aligned}$$

Feces consist of inert solids and water.

(a) What is the number of independent material balance equations (excluding inerts)?

(b) Assume that the following information is known:

$$F_1 = 1800 \text{ g/day} \quad \text{(excluding 600 g/day of inerts)}$$
$$F_2 = 1000 \text{ g/day}$$
$$F_4 = 500 \text{ g/day}$$
$$F_5 = 200 \text{ g/day} \quad \text{(excluding 600 g/day of inerts)}$$
$$F_6 = 1500 \text{ g/day}$$

Weight percents (on an inert-free basis) of carbohydrate, fat, protein, and water in the food are 16.7, 5.6, 5.6, and 72.1, respectively. Write the material balance equations and show that the number of equations is equal to the number of unknowns.

(c) Solve the material balance equations for unknown flow rates and compositions.

7.12. For the ammonia reactor described in Example 7.7, solve for the unknown flow rate and compositions using the following set of design variables:

$$F_2 = 100 \text{ moles/hr}$$

$$x_{13} = 0.06$$

$$x_{14} = 0$$

$$x_{15} = 0$$

$$K' = 0.25$$

Feed nitrogen and hydrogen are in stoichiometric proportion.

7.13. Prepare a FORTRAN program for a material balance of the NH_3 reactor in Example 7.10. Your program should contain $F_2, x_{15}, x_{22}, x_{23}, x_{24},$ and K' as design variables and solve for the unknown variables. Run your program for

$$F_2 = 93 \text{ moles/hr}$$

$$x_{15} = 0.004$$

$$x_{22} = 0.6606$$

$$x_{23} = 0.1127$$

$$x_{24} = 0.0022$$

$$K' = 0.2$$

7.14. In the Claus process, sulfur dioxide and hydrogen sulfide react to form elemental sulfur and water:

$$SO_2(g) + 2H_2S(g) \xrightarrow{Fe_2O_3} 3S(l) + 2H_2O(l)$$

One hundred moles per hour of sulfur dioxide are mixed with the stoichiometric amount of hydrogen sulfide. Eighty-five percent of the feed gases is converted to product. What is the production rate of sulfur in pounds per hour?

7.15. The chamber sulfuric acid process makes sulfuric acid from sulfur dioxide. The overall process is given by the flow diagram in Fig. 7-16.

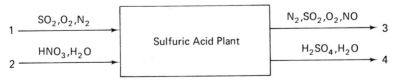

Figure 7-16

Component	No.
SO_2	1
HNO_3	2
H_2O	3
O_2	4
N_2	5
NO	6
H_2SO_4	7

The overall reaction is $2SO_2 + O_2 + 2H_2O = 2H_2SO_4$. Assume that the fractional conversion of SO_2 according to this reaction is 0.98 ($\gamma = 0.98$). The overall reaction for nitric acid, which functions as a catalyst for this process, is

$$4HNO_3 = 2H_2O + 3O_2 + 4NO$$

Assume that there is no nitric acid in the product streams.

(a) Write the equations for this process.

(b) Solve the equations for the flow rate and composition of stream 4 under the following conditions:

$$F_1 = 66 \text{ moles/hr}$$
$$F_2 = 24.41 \text{ moles/hr}$$
$$x_{11} = 0.1515$$
$$x_{14} = 0.1782$$
$$x_{22} = 0.0022$$
$$\gamma = 0.98$$

7.16. Sulfur dioxide gas is oxidized continuously in a chemical reactor:

$$2SO_2 + O_2 = 2SO_3$$

The gases are fed in stoichiometric ratio and permitted to achieve equilibrium ($K = 72.3$) at 610°C.

(a) How is the equilibrium yield of SO_3 affected by the use of air instead of pure oxygen, assuming that the stoichiometric ratio of oxygen is maintained?

(b) How does a pressure increase affect the yield of SO_3?

7.17. Production of synthetic natural gas by steam reforming of naphtha was described in Ch. 2:

$$4C_7H_{16} + 14H_2O = 21CH_4 + 7CO_2 + 4H_2$$

The product gas leaving the reformer, after drying, has the composition

	Mole fraction
CH_4	0.656
CO_2	0.219
H_2	0.125

This mixture is subjected to the water-gas shift reaction at 675°F, 30 atm:

$$CO_2 + H_2 = CO + H_2O \qquad\qquad (1)$$

Then the dried products (CH_4, CO_2, H_2, CO) undergo a methanation reaction at 600°F, 30 atm:

$$CO + 3H_2 = CH_4 + H_2O \tag{2}$$

Assume that both Reactions (1) and (2) go to equilibrium. The equilibrium constants are

$$K_1 = 0.0538 \quad (675°F)$$
$$K_2 = 10^6 \quad (600°F)$$

Calculate the composition after each reaction and compare to the values given in Table 2.1.

7.18. How many independent chemical reactions are there for the following compounds: S_2, S_4, S_6, SO_2, SO_3, O_2, O_3?

7.19. A chemically reacting mixture consists of the following compounds:

$$SCl_2$$
$$O_2$$
$$S_2Cl_2$$
$$SCl_4$$
$$SO_2$$
$$SO_3$$

Find the independent chemical reactions and the number of independent material balance equations.

7.20. If a power plant uses fuel oil containing too much sulfur, then sulfur dioxide must be removed from the stack gases to prevent pollution of the atmosphere. One way of doing this is to use carbon monoxide to reduce the sulfur dioxide to elemental sulfur. The reduction produces some by-products listed in Fig. 7-17. Assuming that all reactions proceed to equilibrium, write the equations and determine the number of design variables for the reactor.

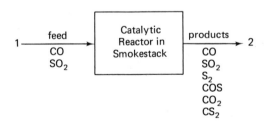

Figure 7-17

7.21. Hydrogen can be made by steam reforming of methane [$CH_4 + H_2O \rightarrow H_2$ + by-products]. The by-products are carbon monoxide and carbon dioxide. For the compounds CH_4, H_2O, H_2, CO, and CO_2, determine the number of independent material balance equations and the number of independent chemical reactions. What are these reactions?

7.22. The chemical reaction

$$A(liquid) \rightleftharpoons B(liquid)$$

is made in a steady-flow reactor (see Fig. 7-18) holding 2.6 moles of liquid.

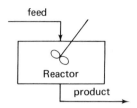

Figure 7-18

Feed is pure A and product is a mixture of B and unreacted A. Densities of liquid A and liquid B are equal. Data were taken on conversion at different flow rates:

Feed rate (moles/hr)	Mole fraction B in product stream
2.65	0.640
4.60	0.590
8.55	0.513
17.32	0.392

Estimate the rate constant for the forward and reverse reaction.

7.23. Analysis of feed and product streams in a blast furnace yields the following compositions:

Feed

Ore	%	Limestone	%	Coke	%	Air	%
Fe_2O_3	96	$CaCO_3$	100	C	100	N_2	79
SiO_2	4					O_2	21

Product

Pig iron	%	Slag	%	Gas	%
Fe	92	FeO	44	CO_2	10
Si	3	CaO	56	CO	25
C	5			N_2	65

All streams were analyzed but no flow rates were measured. Air and gas compositions are in *mole* percent; the rest are *weight* percentages.
(a) How many independent material balances can be written?
(b) How many chemical reactions are occurring? Write them down.
(c) Set up the material balance equations on the basis of 100 pounds of pig iron.
(d) Solve the equations for the flow rates at steady state.

Material Balances
for Systems
of Process Units

8

Transistors, capacitors, and transformers are electrical components needed for design of electronic equipment. Basic units of architectural design are bricks, steel beams, panels, and concrete slabs. Chemical processes are also composed of basic units: reactors, absorbers, distillation towers, crystallizers, electrolytic cells, and many other devices. Operations performed by process units, such as chemical reaction and absorption, are called unit operations. Skill in modifying, integrating, and even designing new unit operations for the performance of a desired chemical transformation is one of the special talents of a chemical engineer.

Chapters 6 and 7 were devoted to material balances for single units. A chemical process consists of many of these units suitably connected (see Chs. 1–3). These connections allow exchange of mass and energy. Fluctuations in streams connecting the units affect the overall operation of the chemical plant. Therefore, a chemical process must be studied not only in terms of its process units but also in terms of its overall behavior.

Synthesis of a process flow sheet (Ch. 3) is intimately connected with its *analysis*. A flow sheet is analyzed by assembling equations for each unit into a single set of equations governing the entire process. Then, performance characteristics predicted by analysis suggest modifications which lead to new and better process designs.

8.1 Recycle Streams

The flow pattern for a chemical process is seldom a once-through path from feed to products. Byproducts and leftover reactants are recycled to the feed stream or to intermediate process streams. Recycle streams in chemical processes introduce feedback. As a result of feedback, the behavior of the last process unit influences the behavior of preceding units.

It is essential to understand the reason for recycling. Suppose that a chemical process were operated without recycling. There would be, inevitably, leftover reactants or secondary products. These materials are almost always too valuable to throw away. Even if the material is not valuable, it is probably impossible to get rid of it without contaminating the environment. The point is best illustrated by an example involving the butane isomerization process, illustrated in Fig. 8-1 and discussed in Example 8.1. Observe that the analysis of a process containing many units is similar to that for single process units.

Example 8.1   *Isobutane from n-Butane without Recycling*

The process shown in the flow diagram (Fig. 8-1) converts a feed stream (1) of *n*-butane to isobutane in a catalytic reactor. The conversion to isobutane is incomplete, and the products from the reactor (stream 2) are separated by distillation into isobutane (stream 3) and unreacted *n*-butane (stream 4). The isobutane is more volatile than the *n*-butane and is obtained from the distillation tower as the distillate.

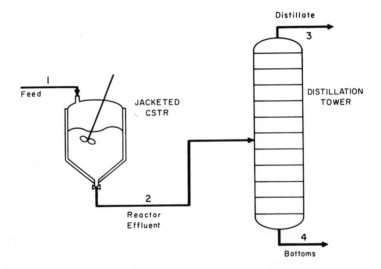

Figure 8-1 Butane isomerization process.

Use the continuous stirred-tank reactor (CSTR) model, discussed in Sec. 7.6, for the butane isomerization

$$n\text{-}C_4H_{10} \rightleftharpoons i\text{-}C_4H_{10}$$

Determine all process flow rates and mole fractions.

Solution:

The components are

Component	No. (j)
i-C_4H_{10}	1
n-C_4H_{10}	2

1. Equations and constraints.
   a. Material balance equations and equipment constraints. All independent material balance equations and equipment constraints are assembled for the collection of process units (only two in this case).
      (1) Reactor:

$$x_{21} = \frac{1 + (F_1 x_{11}/nk_r)}{1 + (1/K) + (F_1/nk_r)} \tag{1}$$

$$4F_1(x_{11} + x_{12}) = 4F_2(x_{21} + x_{22}) \tag{2}$$

Equation (1) is the CSTR equation [see Eqn. (7.27)] and Eqn. (2) is the carbon atom balance.
      (2) Distillation tower:

$$F_2 x_{21} = F_3 x_{31} + F_4 x_{41} \tag{3}$$

$$F_2 x_{22} = F_3 x_{32} + F_4 x_{42} \tag{4}$$

   b. Mole-fraction constraints:

$$x_{11} + x_{12} = 1 \tag{5}$$

$$x_{21} + x_{22} = 1 \tag{6}$$

$$x_{31} + x_{32} = 1 \tag{7}$$

$$x_{41} + x_{42} = 1 \tag{8}$$

2. Number of variables: $N_v = (N_s)(N_c + 1) + N_p = 4(2 + 1) + 2 = 14$. The total number of variables for the process as a whole is given by the same expression used for single process units. The two equipment parameters are the quantity nk_r, which has units of pound-moles per hour and is proportional to the size of the CSTR, and the chemical equilibrium constant K.

3. Design or decision variables: $N_d = N_v - N_e = 14 - 8 = 6$. A convenient set of design variables is (nk_r), K, F_1, x_{11}, x_{31}, x_{41}.

4. Solution of the equations. x_{21} is calculated from Eqn. (1). The overall material balance equation for the reactor,

$$F_2 = \boxed{F_1}$$

is the result of combining Eqns. (2), (5), and (6). Molar flow rates of feed and product are equal for this unimolecular reaction. x_{12}, x_{22}, x_{32}, and x_{42} are obtained directly from Eqns. (5)–(8). There remain two linear equations in two unknowns:

$$\boxed{F_2}\,\boxed{x_{21}} = F_3\,\boxed{x_{31}} + F_4\,\boxed{x_{41}}$$
$$\boxed{F_2}\,\boxed{x_{22}} = F_3\,\boxed{x_{32}} + F_4\,\boxed{x_{42}}$$

The following set of design variable values is selected for comparison with the recycle process to be described in the next example. The feed stream is pure n-butane, and the distillation tower separates the reactor effluent into pure i-butane and pure n-butane.

$$F_1 = 100 \text{ lb-moles/hr}$$
$$(nk_r) = 38 \text{ lb-moles/hr}$$
$$K = 0.728$$
$$x_{11} = 0$$
$$x_{31} = 1$$
$$x_{41} = 0$$

The solution is summarized below:

Stream No.	Flow Rate (lb-moles/hr)	Mole Fraction	
		i-C$_4$H$_{10}$	n-C$_4$H$_{10}$
1	100	0	1
2	100	0.2	0.8
3	20	1	0
4	80	0	1

Example 8.1 was based upon a feed rate of 100 lb-moles/hr of n-butane. The rate of production of isobutane was 20 lb-moles/hr, representing a 20% conversion of n-butane to isobutane. Eighty pound-moles per hour of n-butane are left over. What happens to the unreacted n-butane?

One possibility for using up the n-butane is to construct a series of processes so that unreacted n-butane from one process provides feed for the next process. The processes in series are shown in Fig. 8-2. Each process is a replica of the process described in Example 8.1 and converts 20% of its n-butane feed into isobutane. Therefore, the flow rate of the unreacted n-butane leaving the third process is $F_1(0.8)(0.8)(0.8) = 0.512F_1$. This value should be compared to $0.8F_1$ unreacted n-butane for a single process. The

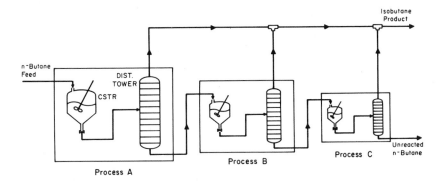

Figure 8-2 Butane processes in series.

series approach substantially reduces the amount of unreacted *n*-butane but at the expense of building several identical though smaller processes. The series approach is usually impractical.

Another idea is to recycle the unreacted *n*-butane back to the feed stream, as illustrated in Fig. 8-3. The following example is instructive.

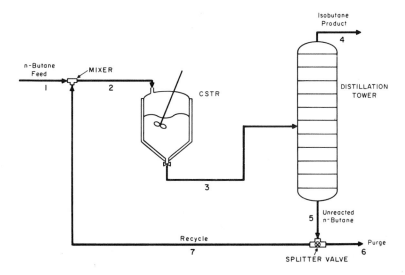

Figure 8-3 Butane process with recycle.

Example 8.2   Isobutane from n-Butane with Recycling

A feed of *n*-butane, stream 1, is mixed with recycle, stream 7. See Fig. 8-3. The mixture is fed to a catalytic reactor, and the products, isobutane and un-reacted *n*-butane, are separated in a distillation tower. A fraction α of the bottoms stream is recycled back to the feed stream. Isobutane product is obtained as distillate in stream 4. The reactor obeys the CSTR model described in Sec. 7.6.

Determine the effects of variations in fraction recycled (α) and feed rate (F_1) upon the yield of isobutane.

Solution:

The components are

Component	No.
Isobutane	1
n-Butane	2

1. Equations and constraints.
    a. Material balance equations and equipment constraints.
        (1) Reactor:

$$x_{31} = \frac{1 + (F_2 x_{21}/nk_r)}{1 + (1/K) + (F_2/nk_r)} \tag{1}$$

$$4F_3(x_{31} + x_{32}) = 4F_2(x_{21} + x_{22}) \quad \text{(or simply } F_2 = F_3) \tag{2}$$

(2) Distillation tower:

$$F_3 x_{31} = F_4 x_{41} + F_5 x_{51} \tag{3}$$

$$F_3 x_{32} = F_4 x_{42} + F_5 x_{52} \quad \text{(or } F_3 = F_4 + F_5) \tag{4}$$

(3) Splitter:

$$\alpha = \frac{F_7}{F_5} \tag{5}$$

$$x_{71} = x_{51} \tag{6}$$

$$x_{61} = x_{51} \tag{7}$$

$$F_5 = F_6 + F_7 \tag{8}$$

(4) Mixer:

$$F_1 x_{11} + F_7 x_{71} = F_2 x_{21} \tag{9}$$

$$F_1 x_{12} + F_7 x_{72} = F_2 x_{22} \quad \text{(or } F_1 + F_7 = F_2) \tag{10}$$

b. Mole-fraction constraints:

$$x_{11} + x_{12} = 1 \tag{11}$$

$$x_{21} + x_{22} = 1 \tag{12}$$

$$x_{31} + x_{32} = 1 \tag{13}$$

$$x_{41} + x_{42} = 1 \tag{14}$$

$$x_{51} + x_{52} = 1 \tag{15}$$

$$x_{61} + x_{62} = 1 \tag{16}$$

$$x_{71} + x_{72} = 1 \tag{17}$$

2. Number of variables: $N_v = N_s(N_c + 1) + N_p = 7(2 + 1) + 3 = 24$. The equipment parameters are α for the splitter and (nk_r) and K for the reactor.

3. Design or decision variables: $N_d = N_v - N_e = 24 - 17 = 7$. We choose the set F_1, x_{11}, x_{41}, x_{51}, α, (nk_r), K.

4. Solution of the equations. Equations (2), (4), and (10) are replaced by overall material balance equations for the reactor, distillation tower, and mixer, respectively:

$$F_2 = F_3 \tag{2}$$

$$F_3 = F_4 + F_5 \tag{4}$$

$$F_1 + F_7 = F_2 \tag{10}$$

The equations may be solved using the precedence-ordering methods of Ch. 13. For the purpose of illustrating the effect of recycling, consider the following special case:

$$x_{11} = x_{51} = 0$$

$$x_{41} = 1$$

Thus, the feed and bottoms streams are pure n-butane and the distillate stream is pure i-butane and

$$x_{12} = x_{41} = x_{52} = x_{62} = x_{72} = x_{22} = 1$$

and

$$x_{21} = 0$$

The remaining equations simplify to

$$x_{31} = \frac{1}{1 + (1/K) + (F_2/(nk_r))}$$

$$F_2 = F_1 + F_7$$

$$F_4 = F_2 x_{31}$$

$$F_5 = F_2 - F_4$$

$$F_7 = \alpha F_5$$

$$F_6 = F_5 - F_7$$

This is a set of six equations in six unknowns: F_2, F_4, F_5, F_6, F_7, and x_{31}. The equations may be combined to yield

$$x_{31} = \frac{1}{1 + (1/K) + \{[F_1/(nk_r)]/(1 - \alpha + \alpha x_{31})\}}$$

This is a single equation in a single unknown. It is easier to solve for x_{31} after rearrangement in the quadratic form:

$$\alpha\left(1 + \frac{1}{K}\right)x_{31}^2 + \left[\left(1 + \frac{1}{K}\right)(1 - \alpha) + \frac{F_1}{nk_r} - \alpha\right]x_{31} - (1 - \alpha) = 0$$

The solution is provided by the formula for quadratic equations of the form $ax_{31}^2 + bx_{31} + c = 0$:

$$x_{31} = \frac{-b \pm \sqrt{b^2 - 4ac}}{2a}$$

Once x_{31} is known, F_2 is given by

$$F_2 = \frac{F_1}{(1 - \alpha + \alpha x_{31})}$$

Finally, the other flow rates (F_4, F_5, F_6, and F_7) follow directly from the equations written previously.

Discussion:

It is interesting that recycling introduces nonlinearities into the material balance equations. It follows from the quadratic equation that there are certain limitations on admissible values of F_1, α, K, and (nk_r). Specifically it is required that

$$b^2 - 4ac \geq 0$$

for physically real solutions. The case of total recycle ($\alpha = 1$) is a special case for which the quadratic equation reduces to a linear equation,

$$\left(1 + \frac{1}{K}\right)x_{31}^2 + \left(\frac{F_1}{nk_r} - 1\right)x_{31} = 0$$

and solving for x_{31},

$$x_{31} = \frac{1 - (F_1/nk_r)}{1 + (1/K)}$$

This equation shows that the feed rate (F_1) cannot exceed (nk_r) for *total recycle* [when $F_1 > (nk_r)$, x_{31} is negative].

Consider the following set of design variable values:

$$(nk_r) = 38 \text{ lb-moles/hr}$$
$$K = 0.728$$
$$\alpha = 1.0 \quad \text{(total recycle)}$$
$$F_1 = \text{variable} \quad [0 \leq F_1 \leq (nk_r)]$$

It is assumed, unrealistically, that the distillation achieves perfect separation regardless of flow rate. Results, calculated using the equations above, are plotted in Fig. 8-4. The flow rate through the reactor ($F_2 = F_3$) and the mole fraction of isobutane in the reactor product (x_{31}) are plotted as a function of the feed flow rate (F_1).

At total recycle, the feed rate is equal to the product rate ($F_1 = F_4$). As the feed rate increases toward the maximum value for the specified equipment size, the product rate increases at the same rate but at the expense of larger and larger internal flow rates. High internal flow rates (F_2) mean high operating costs for mechanical and thermal energy requirements. Since operating costs are roughly proportional to F_2, the rapid increase of operating cost with production rate is

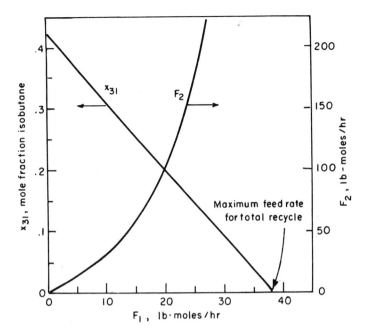

Figure 8-4 Mole fraction isobutane in product (x_{31}) and molar flow rate through reactor ($F_3 = F_2$) versus feed rate (F_1). For total recycle.

apparent by the plot of F_2 in Fig. 8-4. The optimum flow rate is a problem in economics. For a given piece of equipment, the penalty for doubling the rate of production may be a quadrupling of operating costs.

The previous example illustrates the principle of recycling. Recycling solves the problem of what to do with unreacted material. Unreacted material in the product stream is separated and returned to the reactor where it is mixed with the feed stream.

The severe but unavoidable penalty for recycling is increased operating cost.

The recycle principle is also applied to physical (nonreacting) processes such as absorption and distillation.

8.2 Purging

The problem of what to do with unreacted material in the product streams is solved by recycling. Recycling solves one problem but creates another. The new problem is that recycling can produce unexpectedly high concentrations of contaminants and intermediate products in internal process streams. Contaminants sometimes form potentially explosive mixtures with primary components. Accumulations of contaminants are relieved by continuous purging of a small portion of the recycle stream.

Before widespread recognition of the dangers of pollution, purge streams were sometimes released to the environment. Recently, environmental engineers have developed special units (fixed-bed adsorbers, electrostatic precipitators) for concentration and removal of undesirable chemicals in purge streams and for treatment of gases from combustion processes such as power plants and automobiles. In spite of these efforts, environmental control has not kept pace with the increased volume of pollution, which has become a significant problem of this generation.

The necessity of cleaning purge streams is obvious. The need for purging in the first place is illustrated by an example.

Example 8.3

The process is the same as in Example 8.2, the catalytic conversion of n-butane to isobutane, with one change: The n-butane feed stream contains ethyl mercaptan (C_2H_5SH), an impurity at low concentration. Several simplifications are made in order to focus upon the impurity problem: no isobutane in the feed stream, no n-butane in the distillate, and no isobutane in the bottoms. We shall study the worst possible case, which occurs when all the impurity concentrates in the bottoms (stream 5).

The process flow diagram shown in Fig. 8-5 is the same as in Fig. 8-3 and is repeated here for convenience.

What is the effect of the fraction purged, $\beta = F_6/F_5$, on the concentration of ethyl mercaptan in the reactor?

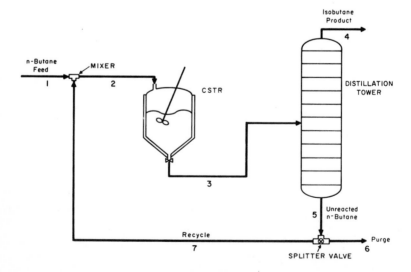

Figure 8-5

Solution:

The component code selected is

Component	No. (j)
Isobutane	1
n-Butane	2
Ethyl mercaptan	3

1. Equations and constraints.
   a. Material balance equations and equipment constraints.
      (1) Reactor. The equation for conversion of n-butane to isobutane in a CSTR (Sec. 7.6) is modified to account for the presence of ethyl mercaptan:

$$x_{31} = \frac{1 - x_{23}}{1 + (1/K) + [F_2/(nk_r)]} \tag{1}$$

Equation (1) assumes that there is no isobutane in the feed. The material balance equations for the reactor are

$$4F_3(x_{31} + x_{32}) = 4F_2x_{22} \quad \text{(or } F_2 = F_3) \tag{2}$$

$$F_2x_{23} = F_3x_{33} \tag{3}$$

   (2) Distillation tower:

$$F_3x_{31} = F_4x_{41} \tag{4}$$

$$F_3x_{32} = F_5x_{52} \tag{5}$$

$$F_3x_{33} = F_5x_{53} \tag{6}$$

   (3) Splitter:

$$\beta = \frac{F_6}{F_5} \tag{7}$$

$$x_{72} = x_{52} \tag{8}$$

$$x_{62} = x_{52} \tag{9}$$

$$F_5 = F_6 + F_7 \tag{10}$$

   (4) Mixer:

$$F_1x_{12} + F_7x_{72} = F_2x_{22} \tag{11}$$

$$F_1x_{13} + F_7x_{73} = F_2x_{23} \quad \text{(or } F_2 = F_1 + F_7) \tag{12}$$

   b. Mole-fraction constraints:

$$x_{12} + x_{13} = 1 \tag{13}$$

$$x_{22} + x_{23} = 1 \tag{14}$$

$$x_{31} + x_{32} + x_{33} = 1 \tag{15}$$

$$x_{52} + x_{53} = 1 \tag{16}$$

$$x_{62} + x_{63} = 1 \tag{17}$$

$$x_{72} + x_{73} = 1 \tag{18}$$

2. Number of variables: $N_v = 23$ (13 mole fractions, 7 flow rates, and 3 parameters). Equipment parameters are (nk_r) and K for the reactor and fraction purged (β) for the splitter.
3. Design or decision variables: $N_d = N_v - N_e = 23 - 18 = 5$. The set $F_1, x_{13}, (nk_r), K, \beta$ is selected.
4. Solution of the equations. The ordered equations are given in Table 8.1. The reader should consult Ch. 13 for details of the precedence-ordering procedure. Values of design variables are

$$F_1 = 20 \text{ lb-moles/hr}$$
$$K = 0.728$$
$$(nk_r) = 38 \text{ lb-moles/hr}$$
$$x_{13} = 0.005$$
$$\beta = \text{variable} \qquad (0 \le \beta \le 0.02)$$

The most interesting result is the relationship between the concentration of ethyl mercaptan in the reactor and the fraction purged, shown in Fig. 8-6. The graph shows that the amount of ethyl mercaptan in the internal

TABLE 8.1
ORDERED EQUATIONS

Solution Order	Equation No.	Output Variable	Equation
1	13	x_{12}	$x_{12} = 1 - x_{13}$
2	5	x_{33}	$(1 - x_{33})\left[1 - \dfrac{1}{1 + (1/K) + (F_1 x_{13}/\beta nk_r x_{33})} - \dfrac{1}{(1 - \beta)}\right] + \left(\dfrac{\beta}{1 - \beta}\right)\left(\dfrac{x_{12}x_{33}}{x_{13}}\right) = 0$
3	11	x_{52}	$x_{52} = \dfrac{x_{13} - (x_{13} + x_{12}\beta)x_{33}}{x_{13} - \beta x_{33}}$
4	12	F_2	$F_2 = \left(\dfrac{F_1 x_{13}}{\beta}\right)\dfrac{1}{x_{33}}$
5	6	F_5	$F_5 = \dfrac{F_2 x_{33}}{(1 - x_{52})}$
6	2	x_{23}	$x_{23} = x_{33}$
7	3	F_3	$F_3 = F_2$
8	1	x_{31}	$x_{31} = \dfrac{1 - x_{23}}{1 + (1/K) + (F_2/nk_r)}$
9	15	x_{32}	$x_{32} = 1 - x_{31} - x_{33}$
10	10	F_7	$F_7 = (1 - \beta)F_5$
11	18	x_{73}	$x_{73} = 1 - x_{52}$
12	8	x_{72}	$x_{72} = x_{52}$
13	16	x_{53}	$x_{53} = 1 - x_{52}$
14	14	x_{22}	$x_{22} = 1 - x_{23}$
15	7	F_6	$F_6 = \beta F_5$
16	9	x_{62}	$x_{62} = x_{52}$
17	17	x_{63}	$x_{63} = 1 - x_{52}$
18	4	F_4	$F_4 = F_3 x_{31}$

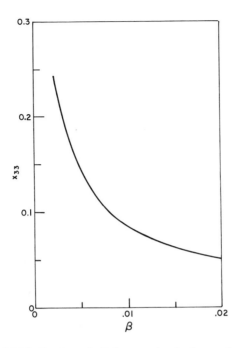

Figure 8-6 Mole fraction of ethyl mercaptan in the reactor (x_{33}) versus fraction purged (β). For feed impurity $x_{13} = 0.005$.

recycle loop rises very rapidly as the amount purged decreases. Also, the concentration of ethyl mercaptan in the reactor is an order of magnitude higher than the concentration in the feed stream.

The previous example shows the use of purging to counteract accumulation of impurities in recycle loops of chemical processes.

Purging is not necessary if the impurity passes out freely in the product stream. Difficulties arise when the impurity tends to concentrate in the recycle loop. Under these circumstances, the concentration of the impurity may be several orders of magnitude higher than the value in the feed stream. An unexpected accumulation of a reactive impurity may cause a fire or an explosion.

8.3 Material Balance on a Chemical Process

The previous examples serve as patterns for solution of material balance problems. Several logical steps in the analysis of a process are apparent:

1. *Preparation of flow diagram.* Process streams appear in the flow diagram as lines (directional). Process units appear as nodes. Process streams and process units are catalogued for identification.

Example 8.4

The flow diagram for the isobutane isomerization process of Example 8.3 is shown in Fig. 8-7.

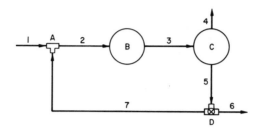

Figure 8-7

Process Streams	Process Units
1 Fresh feed	A Mixer
2 Combined feed	B Reactor
3 Reactor effluent	C Distillation tower
4 Distillate (product)	D Splitter
5 Bottoms	
6 Purge	
7 Recycle	

2. *Specification of component code.* Assignment of a number to each chemical species simplifies notation.
3. *Determination of equations and constraints.* Appropriate material balance and equipment-constraint equations are written for each process unit. There are N_s mole fraction constraint equations, one for each process stream.
4. *Determination of variables.* If each component is present in each stream, there are N_c mole-fraction variables and one flow rate variable for each stream. The total number of variables is given by

$$N_v = N_s(N_c + 1) + N_p$$

where N_s is the total number of streams, N_p is the total number of equipment parameters, and N_c is the number of chemicals present. (If several components are missing in several streams, it is easier to count the variables directly.)
5. *Specification of design variables.* The number of design variables which must be specified in order to solve the set of N_e equations is

$$N_d = N_v - N_e$$

Selection of design variables is dictated by the problem. Usually the flow rate and composition of the feed are known and the problem is to solve for the flow rate and composition of the product. Sometimes the product flow rate or composition is fixed by production requirements, and the problem is to calculate feed flow rates and compositions.

There is no solution to the material balance for some choices of design variables. Sometimes physically impossible solutions, such as negative flow rates or mole fractions larger than unity, are obtained. Difficulties of this type may be avoided, but not eliminated, by specifying feed stream variables and all the equipment parameters.

6. *Solution of equations.* Once equations have been written and values of design variables have been specified, solution of the equations is a problem in mathematics. The mathematical part of the problem may be the most difficult, especially if the material balance consists of a large number of nonlinear equations. Two ways of solving sets of nonlinear algebraic equations are

   a. Precedence-ordering by methods described in Sec. 13.1 and illustrated in Example 8.3.
   b. An iterative procedure based upon material balance equations for the individual units. This is called the modular approach.

The second of these techniques will be illustrated in the remaining sections of this chapter.

8.4 The Modular Approach

Chemical processes are complex combinations of process units. Since process units are the building blocks with which chemical processes are constructed, it is only natural that we should study their individual behavior before attempting to analyze their interactions within a chemical process. The modular approach is based upon this reasoning.

Chemical processes are analyzed in order to determine the effect of performance of process units upon overall process yield, product purity, and cost. The analysis often reveals weaknesses or defects, which, in turn, suggest further improvements in the design of critical unit operations.

Examples of models of processing units have been presented in Chs. 6 and 7. In the modular approach, each unit or module is analyzed individually. Finally the modules are assembled in accordance with the design of the process, and the complete set of equations for all the modules is solved for the unknown variables.

In practice, a digital computer is always used to implement the modular approach. Although the need for a computer is apparent, the modular approach is first discussed in general terms. The role of the computer is studied in Sec. 8.5.

A unit module is an algorithm that solves material balance equations and constraints for a process unit, given certain values of design variables. The module may be regarded as a *transfer function* for conversion of data on design variables into information about the unknowns. When design variables are feed-stream parameters, it is said that information flow through the module is parallel to material flow through the process unit. On the other hand, when design variables are product-stream parameters, the direction of information transfer is said to be counter to material transfer.

The modular approach for solving equations and constraints associated with a system of process units is applied after analysis of the process as a whole, that is, after all equations and variables have been identified and design variables have been selected. The modular approach may be thought of as an equation-solving procedure that uses unit modules to solve subsets of equations.

Consider the butane isomerization process of Example 8.1 as summarized in Fig. 8-8. Six design variables were selected for the process as a whole: F_1, x_{11}, x_{31}, x_{41}, (nk_r), and K. These are called overall design variables. The distillation column has associated with it nine variables and five equations; hence, there are four local design variables (for example, F_2, x_{21}, x_{31}, and x_{41}). Since only two of these local design variables have been specified for the process as a whole, a material balance of the distillation unit cannot be carried out separately. The reactor is described by eight variables and has four equations associated with it; hence, there are four local design variables. The list of local design variables [F_1, x_{11}, (nk_r), and K] is contained in the list of overall design variables. Therefore, the material balance for the reactor can be made separately, and the solution yields values for the missing local design variables of the distillation column (F_2, x_{21}) so that its material balance equations can be solved.

The calculation order is determined by the selection of local and overall design variables, as summarized in Fig. 8-8. If the list of local design variables for one unit is a subset of the list of overall design variables, as it is for the reactor in Fig. 8-8, then equations for that unit can be solved separately. In more complex problems, particularly those involving recycling, none of the material balances on process units can be performed individually, and a strategy for determining the best calculation order must be devised.

Consider the butane isomerization process with recycle in Example 8.2. The overall process and its modules are summarized in Fig. 8-9. Examination of Fig. 8-9 shows that none of the material balances on modules can be solved separately because one or more local design variables are unknown.

In this situation it is convenient to locate the module containing the least number of unspecified local design variables and to provide guess values. These unknown local design variables are called *tear variables* (see Sec. 13.2). In Fig. 8-9 the stream splitter has only one unspecified local design variable,

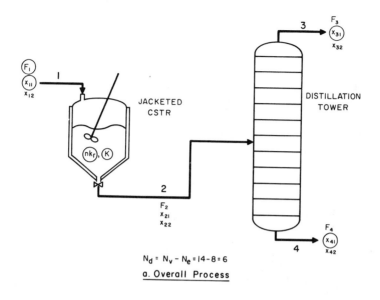

$N_d = N_v - N_e = 14 - 8 = 6$

a. Overall Process

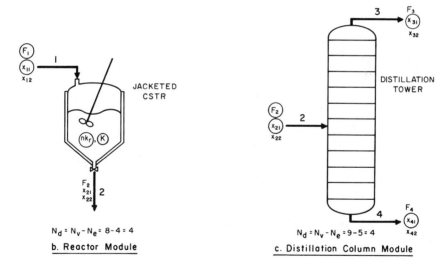

$N_d = N_v - N_e = 8 - 4 = 4$

b. Reactor Module

$N_d = N_v - N_e = 9 - 5 = 4$

c. Distillation Column Module

Figure 8-8 Modules for butane isomerization process (without recycle).

F_5. A guess value is selected for F_5, and the material balance on the splitter is solved first. Then material balances for the mixer, reactor, and distillation column are calculated, in order, based upon the guess value for F_5. Finally, based upon the material balance for the distillation column, the newly calculated value of F_5 is compared with the original guess value. If the two

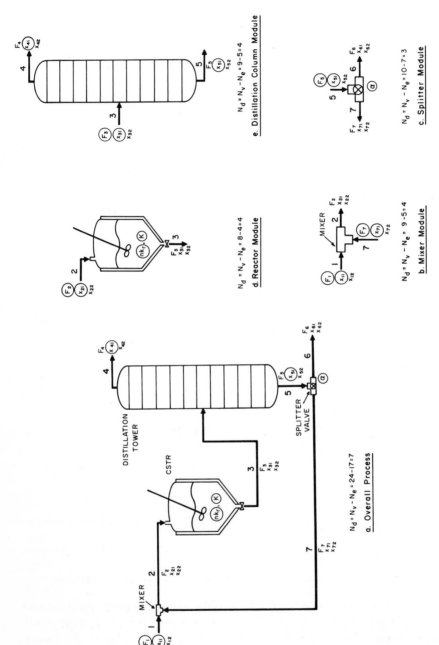

Figure 8-9 Process modules for butane isomerization process (with recycle).

308

values do not agree, the guess value is improved using the method of successive substitutions or some other iterative method (several numerical methods are suitable and some of them are preferred for specific situations—see Chs. 11 and 13). Material balances on modules are repeated using the same order of calculation until convergence is achieved; that is, until

$$\left| \frac{F_s - F_s^*}{F_s^*} \right| \leq \epsilon$$

where the asterisk refers to the guess value. Since 100 or more repetitions may be required, the modular approach is executed with the aid of a computer.

The modular approach summarized in Fig. 8-9 should be compared to the solution procedure in Example 8.2. Clearly, for this simple example, it is more convenient to solve the entire set of equations than to use the iterative modular approach. (We have used this process as an example only to illustrate how the modular approach works.) However, when the equations and constraints associated with a system of process units are so complex that they cannot be solved by simple reduction or substitution methods, the modular approach may be the best.

Example 8.5

The Haber process (see Sec. 2.1) for direct union of the elements to make ammonia is one of the great triumphs of chemical engineering. A flow diagram of the ammonia process is shown in Fig. 8-10. Feed consists of dried hydrogen and nitrogen gas containing argon and methane impurities. The feed is at 10 atm and is compressed to 200 atm after mixing with a low-pressure recycle stream. Compressed gas is mixed with a high-pressure recycle stream and enters a catalytic reactor (see Sec. 1.2) where it is preheated to reaction temperature (about 500°C) and reacts:

$$N_2 + 3H_2 \rightleftharpoons 2NH_3$$

High pressure shifts the reaction, which would otherwise have a low yield at 500°C, to the right according to the principle of Le Chatelier. Even at 500°C the uncatalyzed reaction is very slow, and an iron catalyst is needed to speed up the reaction. The catalyzed reaction approaches the equilibrium yield, about 10% ammonia, which is removed from unreacted synthesis gas by cooling and condensation. A purge stream relieves accumulation of impurities in the unreacted gases, which are recycled to the reactor. Liquefied ammonia from the high-pressure separator contains dissolved gases, which are removed by flashing to 10 atm in a flash drum; gas is recycled, and liquid ammonia is withdrawn as product.

The process diagram in Fig. 8-10 omits details of heat exchange to heat and cool process streams which are important in an energy balance but irrelevant to a material balance.

Make a material balance on the ammonia process and solve the equations using the modular approach. Determine the effect of purging upon recycle and production rates.

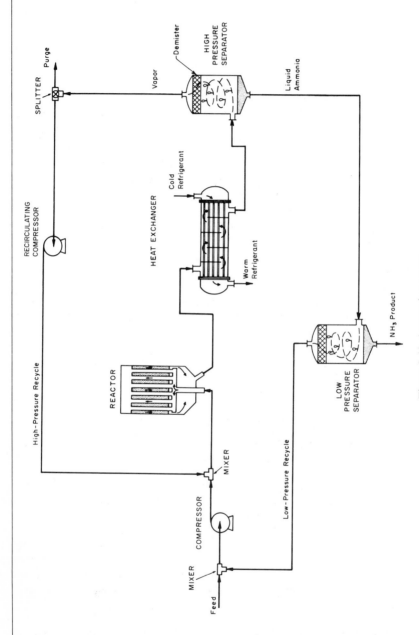

Figure 8-10 Ammonia process.

310

Solution:

Compressor and heat exchanger units alter temperature and pressure of process streams but not their composition and flow rates; therefore, these units are omitted from the flow diagram in Fig. 8-11 for a material balance:

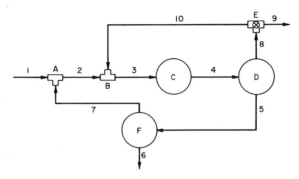

Figure 8-11

Process Units		Process Streams	
A	Low-pressure mixer	1	Feed
B	High-pressure mixer	2	Low-pressure feed plus recycle
C	Reactor	3	High-pressure feed plus recycle
D	High-pressure separator	4	Products from reactor
E	Stream splitter	5	High-pressure liquid
F	Low-pressure separator	6	Product
		7	Low-pressure recycle
		8	High-pressure recycle
		9	Purge
		10	High-pressure recycle

The component code is

Component	No. (j)
Nitrogen	1
Hydrogen	2
Ammonia	3
Argon	4
Methane	5

The first step is to write the material balance and equipment-constraint equations for each process unit.

1. Equations and constraints.
   a. Material balance equations and equipment constraints.

(1) Low-pressure mixer:

$$F_1 x_{11} + F_7 x_{71} = F_2 x_{21} \tag{1}$$

$$F_1 x_{12} + F_7 x_{72} = F_2 x_{22} \tag{2}$$

$$F_1 x_{13} + F_7 x_{73} = F_2 x_{23} \tag{3}$$

$$F_1 x_{14} + F_7 x_{74} = F_2 x_{24} \tag{4}$$

$$F_1 x_{15} + F_7 x_{75} = F_2 x_{25} \tag{5}$$

(2) High-pressure mixer:

$$F_2 x_{21} + F_{10} x_{10\text{-}1} = F_3 x_{31} \tag{6}$$

$$F_2 x_{22} + F_{10} x_{10\text{-}2} = F_3 x_{32} \tag{7}$$

$$F_2 x_{23} + F_{10} x_{10\text{-}3} = F_3 x_{33} \tag{8}$$

$$F_2 x_{24} + F_{10} x_{10\text{-}4} = F_3 x_{34} \tag{9}$$

$$F_2 x_{25} + F_{10} x_{10\text{-}5} = F_3 x_{35} \tag{10}$$

(3) Reactor. There are three reacting compounds (N_2, H_2, and NH_3). There are two material balance equations, one for nitrogen atoms and one for hydrogen atoms. In addition, there are two material balance equations for the inert components (Ar and CH_4).

$$\text{N:} \quad 2F_3 x_{31} + F_3 x_{33} = 2F_4 x_{41} + F_4 x_{43} \tag{11}$$

$$\text{H:} \quad 2F_3 x_{32} + 3F_3 x_{33} = 2F_4 x_{42} + 3F_4 x_{43} \tag{12}$$

$$\text{Ar:} \quad F_3 x_{34} = F_4 x_{44} \tag{13}$$

$$\text{CH}_4\text{:} \quad F_3 x_{35} = F_4 x_{45} \tag{14}$$

Chemical equilibrium is specified by Eqn. (7.11):

$$K = P^{-2} \frac{x_{43}^2}{x_{41} x_{42}^3} \quad (P \text{ in atm})$$

Actually pressure is high, and Eqn. (7.11) should be modified to account for gas-phase imperfections, but we omit this refinement for simplicity of calculation. For a fixed pressure, it is convenient to define a new chemical equilibrium constant $K' = K/P^{-2} = KP^2$.

$$x_{43}^2 = K' x_{41} x_{42}^3 \tag{15}$$

(4) High-pressure separator (see Example 6.8):

$$F_4 x_{41} = F_5 x_{51} + F_8 x_{81} \tag{16}$$

$$F_4 x_{42} = F_5 x_{52} + F_8 x_{82} \tag{17}$$

$$F_4 x_{43} = F_5 x_{53} + F_8 x_{83} \tag{18}$$

$$F_4 x_{44} = F_5 x_{54} + F_8 x_{84} \tag{19}$$

$$F_4 x_{45} = F_5 x_{55} + F_8 x_{85} \tag{20}$$

$$\frac{x_{81}}{x_{51}} = k_1 \tag{21}$$

$$\frac{x_{82}}{x_{52}} = k_2 \tag{22}$$

$$\frac{x_{83}}{x_{53}} = k_3 \tag{23}$$

$$\frac{x_{84}}{x_{54}} = k_4 \tag{24}$$

$$\frac{x_{85}}{x_{55}} = k_5 \tag{25}$$

(5) Splitter:

$$F_8 = F_9 + F_{10} \tag{26}$$

$$x_{10-1} = x_{81} \tag{27}$$

$$x_{10-2} = x_{82} \tag{28}$$

$$x_{10-3} = x_{83} \tag{29}$$

$$x_{10-4} = x_{84} \tag{30}$$

$$x_{91} = x_{81} \tag{31}$$

$$x_{92} = x_{82} \tag{32}$$

$$x_{93} = x_{83} \tag{33}$$

$$x_{94} = x_{84} \tag{34}$$

$$F_9 = \alpha F_8 \tag{35}$$

(6) Low-pressure separator (see Example 6.8):

$$F_5 x_{51} = F_6 x_{61} + F_7 x_{71} \tag{36}$$

$$F_5 x_{52} = F_6 x_{62} + F_7 x_{72} \tag{37}$$

$$F_5 x_{53} = F_6 x_{63} + F_7 x_{73} \tag{38}$$

$$F_5 x_{54} = F_6 x_{64} + F_7 x_{74} \tag{39}$$

$$F_5 x_{55} = F_6 x_{65} + F_7 x_{75} \tag{40}$$

$$\frac{x_{71}}{x_{61}} = k_1' \tag{41}$$

$$\frac{x_{72}}{x_{62}} = k_2' \tag{42}$$

$$\frac{x_{73}}{x_{63}} = k_3' \tag{43}$$

$$\frac{x_{74}}{x_{64}} = k_4' \tag{44}$$

$$\frac{x_{75}}{x_{65}} = k_5' \tag{45}$$

b. Mole-fraction constraints (one for each stream):

$$x_{11} + x_{12} + x_{13} + x_{14} + x_{15} = 1 \tag{46}$$

$$x_{21} + x_{22} + x_{23} + x_{24} + x_{25} = 1 \tag{47}$$

$$x_{31} + x_{32} + x_{33} + x_{34} + x_{35} = 1 \tag{48}$$

$$x_{41} + x_{42} + x_{43} + x_{44} + x_{45} = 1 \tag{49}$$

$$x_{51} + x_{52} + x_{53} + x_{54} + x_{55} = 1 \tag{50}$$

$$x_{61} + x_{62} + x_{63} + x_{64} + x_{65} = 1 \tag{51}$$

$$x_{71} + x_{72} + x_{73} + x_{74} + x_{75} = 1 \tag{52}$$

$$x_{81} + x_{82} + x_{83} + x_{84} + x_{85} = 1 \tag{53}$$

$$x_{91} + x_{92} + x_{93} + x_{94} + x_{95} = 1 \tag{54}$$

$$x_{10\text{-}1} + x_{10\text{-}2} + x_{10\text{-}3} + x_{10\text{-}4} + x_{10\text{-}5} = 1 \tag{55}$$

2. Number of variables: $N_v = N_s(N_c + 1) + N_p = 10(5 + 1) + 12 = 72$. The equipment parameters are

Symbol

K'	Chemical equilibrium constant for ammonia reaction
α	Fraction purged $= F_9/F_8$
k_1, k_2, k_3, k_4, k_5	Five vapor-liquid equilibrium constants for high-pressure separator
$k'_1, k'_2, k'_3, k'_4, k'_5$	Five vapor-liquid equilibrium constants for low-pressure separator

3. Design or decision variables: $N_d = N_v - N_e = 72 - 55 = 17$. We select as design variables the equipment parameters and the variables of the feed stream: $F_1, x_{11}, x_{12}, x_{14}, x_{15}, K', \alpha, k_1, k_2, k_3, k_4, k_5, k'_1, k'_2, k'_3, k'_4, k'_5$.
4. Solution of the equations. The set of 55 material balance equations can be set up for solution using precedence-ordering methods described in Sec. 13.1. With 55 equations, the precedence-ordering task is difficult but not impossible. In this example, the modular approach is selected to study how it works.

Computer programs for the reactor (Example 7.10) and the separators (Example 6.12) have already been prepared. Local design variables selected for these modules, as well as modules for the mixer and splitter, are shown in Fig. 8-12. Numbering of streams in the modules [Fig. 8-12(b), (c), (d), (e)] is revised when the module is inserted in the process [Fig. 8-12(a)].

Because of recycling, each process unit has one or more local design variables that are unknown (i.e., not contained in the list of design variables for the process as a whole). Since feed-stream variables are specified, mixer A is the place to begin the computations. A guess is made for values of the flow rate and composition of stream 7. Since the material balance on mixer A yields the flow rate and composition of stream 2, the next unit is mixer B. Another guess is needed for the flow rate and composition of stream 10, but then material balances can be carried out consecutively for mixer B, reactor C, high-pressure separator D, splitter E, and low-pressure separator F. Material balances on the last two units yield new values for flow rates and compositions of streams 7 and 10. If calculated values for streams 7 and 10 do not agree with guess values, then guess values are improved using numerical methods (for example, successive substitutions) until convergence is achieved.

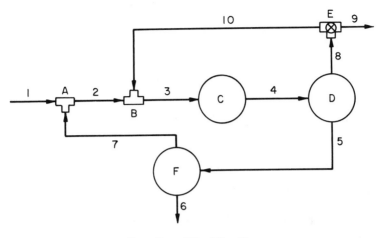

$$N_d = N_v - N_e = 72 - 55 = 17$$
$$= F_1, x_{11}, x_{12}, x_{14}, x_{15}, \alpha, K', k_1, k_2, k_3, k_4, k_5,$$
$$k_1', k_2', k_3', k_4', k_5'.$$

a. Overall Process

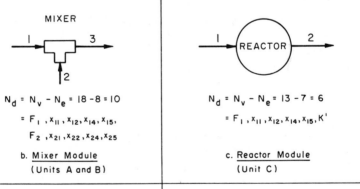

MIXER

$$N_d = N_v - N_e = 18 - 8 = 10$$
$$= F_1, x_{11}, x_{12}, x_{14}, x_{15},$$
$$F_2, x_{21}, x_{22}, x_{24}, x_{25}$$

b. Mixer Module
(Units A and B)

REACTOR

$$N_d = N_v - N_e = 13 - 7 = 6$$
$$= F_1, x_{11}, x_{12}, x_{14}, x_{15}, K'$$

c. Reactor Module
(Unit C)

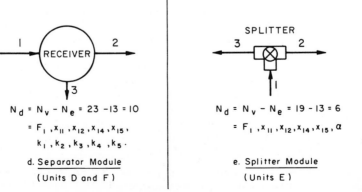

RECEIVER

$$N_d = N_v - N_e = 23 - 13 = 10$$
$$= F_1, x_{11}, x_{12}, x_{14}, x_{15},$$
$$k_1, k_2, k_3, k_4, k_5.$$

d. Separator Module
(Units D and F)

SPLITTER

$$N_d = N_v - N_e = 19 - 13 = 6$$
$$= F_1, x_{11}, x_{12}, x_{14}, x_{15}, \alpha$$

e. Splitter Module
(Units E)

Figure 8-12 Modules for ammonia process.

Of course an educated guess for the flow rates and compositions of the recycle streams (7, 10) speeds up convergence. The convergence criterion is the relative difference ε in successive guess values defined by Eqn. (11.4).

At this point the solution is interrupted for a brief discussion of computer executive systems.

8.5 The Modular Approach Using a Digital Computer

A digital computer is needed to perform repetitive calculations that arise when the modular approach is applied to material balance problems. The computer program is a calling program that specifies calculation order for the modules. It is possible to go a step farther and prepare a computer executive program that automatically writes the calling program for the modules and performs the calculations given the flow diagram of the process.

Computer executive programs designed to perform material and energy balances on chemical processes include PACER (1), U.P. PACER (2), CHESS (3), GEMCS (4), SPEED-UP (5), FLOWTRAN (6), GPFS (7), and others.* These programs have the same basic features. Modules for process units (reactors, condensers, etc.) are stored in a computer library (magnetic disks) to be called as needed by the executive program. Provision is made for inserting new modules into the computer library. The user of the executive program selects modules for each process unit and enters the flow diagram of the process (topology), values of design variables, and convergence criteria.

Modules in computer library

Most executive programs contain a library of frequently used modules. Typical modules are illustrated in Fig. 8-13. The mixer has an arbitrary number of feed streams and one product stream. The splitter has a single feed stream and an arbitrary number of product streams of the same composition. The equilibrium-flash module separates a liquid (or two-phase mixture

*(1) C. M. Crowe et al., *Chemical Plant Simulation*, Prentice-Hall, Englewood Cliffs, N.J., 1971.

(2) R. Whittall and W. D. Seider, *User's Manual—University of Pennsylvania PACER*, The University of Pennsylvania, Philadelphia, Pennsylvania (1970).

(3) R. L. Motard et al., *CHESS, Chemical Engineering Simulation System*, Technical Publishing Co., Houston, 1968.

(4) A. I. Johnson and T. Toong, *GEMCS, Information Handling Program*, McMaster University, Hamilton, Ontario, Canada, 1968.

(5) R. W. H. Sargent and A. W. Westerberg, "SPEED-UP in Chemical Engineering Design," *Trans. Inst. Chem. Engrs.*, *42*, T-190–T-197 (1964).

(6) J. D. Seader, W. D. Seider, and A. C. Pauls, *FLOWTRAN Simulation—An Introduction*, Ulrich's Bookstore, Ann Arbor, Michigan, 1974.

(7) *GPFS, General Purpose Flowsheet Simulator*, Sun Oil Company, Philadelphia, 1968.

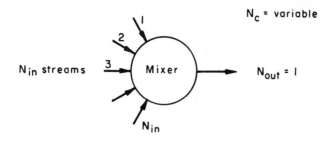

N_c = variable

N_{in} streams

Mixer

N_{out} = 1

N_{in}

Design variables : Feed stream variables
Unknown variables : Product " "

a. MIXER

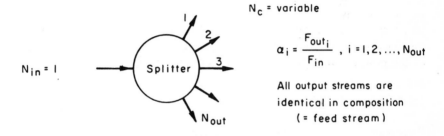

N_c = variable

N_{in} = 1

Splitter

N_{out}

$$\alpha_i = \frac{F_{out_i}}{F_{in}} \quad , \quad i = 1, 2, \ldots, N_{out}$$

All output streams are
identical in composition
(= feed stream)

Design variables : Feed stream variables,
α_i, $i = 1$, N_{out}
Unknown variables : Product stream variables

b. SPLIT

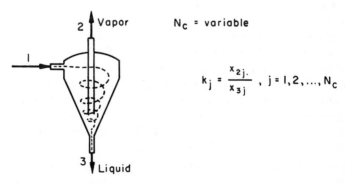

2 ↑ Vapor N_c = variable

1

3 ↓ Liquid

$$k_j = \frac{x_{2j}}{x_{3j}} \quad , \quad j = 1, 2, \ldots, N_c$$

Design variables : Feed stream variables,
k_j , $j = 1, 2, \ldots, N_c$
Unknown variables : Product stream variables

c. Vapor - Liquid Equilibrium Flash - SEPRAT

Figure 8-13 General unit modules.

of liquid and vapor) into a liquid and vapor stream. In each of these modules, design variables are the equipment parameters and the state and flow rate of the feed.

Most modules solve the energy balance (see Chs. 9-10) as well as the material balance. If a process contains an operation for which there is no module in the computer library, a new module for that operation is prepared and entered into the library.

Process topology

A *topology matrix* identifies streams flowing into and out of each process unit. Process units and process streams are numbered in separate lists. Rows of the topology matrix contain the number of the process unit, the name of its program module, and the numbers of its feed and product streams. This information is entered into the topology matrix from cards. The flow diagram of the process can be reconstructed from the topology matrix.

Stream and equipment parameters

Stream parameters are flow rate, temperature, pressure, composition, enthalpy, and entropy. These variables are stored in a matrix, one row for each stream and one column for each variable. Values of design variables and guesses for unknowns are entered into the matrix from cards. During calculations, values of stream parameters are transferred back and forth between the matrix and the modules.

The executive system maintains a list of equipment parameters for each process unit. Values are read from cards and transferred to the appropriate module for calculations.

Interaction between the program module, the matrix of stream parameters, and the list of equipment parameters is shown in Fig. 8-14. The program module obtains values of feed-stream variables from the matrix of stream parameters and values of equipment parameters from the list of equipment parameters. After solving the material balance, the module inserts calculated values of product-stream variables in the matrix of stream parameters. For processes with recycle, calculated values of stream parameters are checked for convergence before they replace old values in the matrix of stream parameters.

Calculation order

Process units are listed in the order of execution that minimizes the amount of iterative calculations. The calculation order and convergence criteria are entered as data to the executive program.

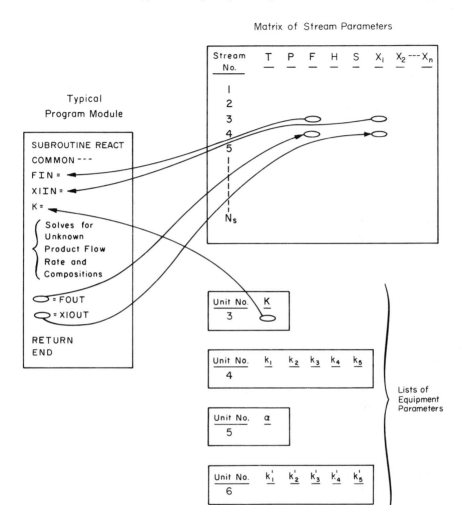

Figure 8-14 Interaction of module with matrix of stream parameters and lists of equipment parameters.

Execution sequence

The sequence of operations is

1. The topology matrix, matrix of stream parameters, list of equipment parameters, calculation order, and convergence criteria are read from cards by the executive program.
2. The executive program identifies the first and succeeding process units from the calculation order and obtains the name of the module and its stream numbers from the topology matrix.

3. The executive system transfers control to the program module and regains control after the calculation is finished by a **RETURN** statement. If the process unit lies in a recycle loop, convergence criteria are examined.
4. Steps 2 and 3 are repeated for successive process units until the calculation order listing has been exhausted and all convergence criteria have been satisfied.
5. The solution, which is the contents of the matrix of stream parameters, is printed.

Example of modular approach

Next we return to the material balance problem set up in Example 8.5 and solve it using the U.P. PACER executive program.

Example 8.5 (Continued from Sec. 8.4)

Solution (continued):

The following values of design variables are chosen:

Feed

$F_1 = 100$ lb-moles/hr (basis)
$x_{11} = 0.240$ (N_2)
$x_{12} = 0.743$ (H_2)
$x_{13} = 0.000$ (NH_3)
$x_{14} = 0.006$ (Ar)
$x_{15} = 0.011$ (CH_4)

Notice that the ratio of hydrogen to nitrogen is close but not exactly equal to the stoichiometric ratio of 3 to 1.

Chemical equilibrium constant:

$$K' = 0.35$$

Fraction purged:

$$\alpha = 0.02$$

Vapor-liquid equilibrium constants:

Component No.	High-Pressure Separator, k_i	Low-Pressure Separator, k'_i
1	105	2400
2	90	1750
3	0.06	0.28
4	100	1400
5	33	500

U.P. PACER Data.   A summary of data printed by the executive program after reading the data cards is as follows:

1. Topology matrix:

```
TOPOLOGY MATRIX
-------- ------

    NUMBER    NAME    |      MATERIAL STREAMS
    ------    ----    |      --------  -------
      1       MIXER   |   1     7    -2
      2       MIXER   |   2    10    -3
      3       REACT   |   3    -4
      4       SEPRAT  |   4    -8    -5
      5       SPLIT   |   8    -9   -10
      6       SEPRAT  |   5    -7    -6
```

A minus sign is used to distinguish product streams from feed streams.

2. Equipment parameters:

```
EQUIPMENT PARAMETERS
--------- ----------

    EQUIPMENT NO. --    3
    NAME          --  REACT

        REACTION EQUIL. CONST.       =        0.35000


    EQUIPMENT NO. --    4
    NAME          --  SEPRAT

        NITROGEN EQUIL. CONST.       =      105.00000
        HYDROGEN EQUIL. CONST.       =       90.00000
        AMMONIA EQUIL. CONST.        =        0.06000
        ARGON EQUIL. CONST.          =      100.00000
        METHANE EQUIL. CONST.        =       33.00000


    EQUIPMENT NO. --    5
    NAME          --  SPLIT

        FRAC. OF RECYCLE PURGED      =        0.02000


    EQUIPMENT NO. --    6
    NAME          --  SEPRAT

        NITROGEN EQUIL. CONST.       =     2400.00000
        HYDROGEN EQUIL. CONST.       =     1750.00000
        AMMONIA EQUIL. CONST.        =        0.28000
        ARGON EQUIL. CONST.          =     1400.00000
        METHANE EQUIL. CONST.        =      500.00000
```

Equipment parameters are identified by a character string, which is given in the data to U.P. PACER.

3. Matrix of stream parameters:

	1	2	3	4
FLOW RATE-LB MOLE/HR	100.0000	0.0	0.0	0.0
NITROGEN	0.2400	0.0	0.0	0.0
HYDROGEN	0.7430	0.0	0.0	0.0
AMMONIA	0.0	0.0	0.0	0.0
ARGON	0.0060	0.0	0.0	0.0
METHANE	0.0110	0.0	0.0	0.0

	5	6	7	8
FLOW RATE-LB MOLE/HR	0.0	0.0	0.0	0.0
NITROGEN	0.0	0.0	0.0	0.0
HYDROGEN	0.0	0.0	0.0	0.0
AMMONIA	0.0	0.0	0.0	0.0
ARGON	0.0	0.0	0.0	0.0
METHANE	0.0	0.0	0.0	0.0

	9	10
FLOW RATE-LB MOLE/HR	0.0	0.0
NITROGEN	0.0	0.0
HYDROGEN	0.0	0.0
AMMONIA	0.0	0.0
ARGON	0.0	0.0
METHANE	0.0	0.0

An experienced engineer would enter a better first guess of the unknowns in order to speed up the convergence.

4. Calculation order and convergence criteria:

```
CALCULATION ORDER
----------- -----

    NUMBER        NAME        MODE
    ------        ----        ----

       1         MIXER          2
       2         MIXER          2
       3         REACT          2
       4         SEPRAT         2
       5         SPLIT          2
       6         SEPRAT         3


CONVERGENCE CRITERIA
----------- --------

        FLOW RATE-LB MOLE/HR        .100000E-03
        NITROGEN                    .100000E-03
        HYDROGEN                    .100000E-03
        AMMONIA                     .100000E-03
        ARGON                       .100000E-03
        METHANE                     .100000E-03
        MAXIMUM NO. OF LOOPS        600
```

The modes in the calculation order listing are for process units that do not lie in a recycle loop (mode = 1), process units that do lie in a recycle loop (mode = 2), and the last process unit in a recycle loop (mode = 3). If, upon completion of the last process unit in a recycle loop (mode = 3), any stream parameter in that loop has not satisfied its convergence criterion, all computations for that loop are repeated using the method of successive substitutions. The method of successive substitutions converges very slowly, and convergence is accelerated by using Wegstein's method to get new guess values for the variables of one stream in the loop:

```
CONVERGENCE ACCELERATION
----------- ------------

        MATERIAL STREAM NO.                     PARAMETER
        -------- ------ ---                     ---------

                3                       FLOW RATE-LB MOLE/HR
                3                       NITROGEN
                3                       HYDROGEN
                3                       AMMONIA
                3                       ARGON
                3                       METHANE
```

This iterative cycle is repeated until convergence criteria are satisfied or until the maximum number of iterations has been exceeded (no convergence). The convergence criterion is the relative difference ϵ in successive guess values [Eqn. (11.4)].

Modules. The separator and reactor programs in Examples 6.12 and 7.10 are converted to modules that exchange information with the matrix of stream parameters and the lists of equipment parameters. These modules are named SEPRAT and REACT, respectively.

U.P. PACER Results. Convergence was obtained after 102 iterations from the first guess of zero for unknown flow rates and compositions. A more realistic guess would have accelerated the convergence. The solution printed by U.P. PACER executive program is

```
                                        STREAM NUMBER
                                        ------ ------

                                   1          2          3          4
                                  ----       ----       ----       ----
FLOW RATE-LB MOLE/HR          100.0000   100.6632   787.5764   744.1895
NITROGEN                        0.2400     0.2391     0.1742     0.1552
HYDROGEN                        0.7430     0.7411     0.6668     0.6182
AMMONIA                         0.0        0.0018     0.0520     0.1133
ARGON                           0.0060     0.0061     0.0380     0.0402
METHANE                         0.0110     0.0118     0.0691     0.0731


                                   5          6          7          8
                                  ----       ----       ----       ----
FLOW RATE-LB MOLE/HR           43.2412    42.5780     0.6633   700.9482
NITROGEN                        0.0016     0.0000     0.0996     0.1646
HYDROGEN                        0.0073     0.0003     0.4583     0.6559
AMMONIA                         0.9884     0.9994     0.2798     0.0593
ARGON                           0.0004     0.0000     0.0266     0.0426
METHANE                         0.0023     0.0003     0.1357     0.0775


                                   9         10
                                  ----       ----
FLOW RATE-LB MOLE/HR           14.0190   686.9292
NITROGEN                        0.1646     0.1646
HYDROGEN                        0.6559     0.6559
AMMONIA                         0.0593     0.0593
ARGON                           0.0426     0.0426
METHANE                         0.0775     0.0775
```

This solution satisfies the 55 equations of the material balance for one set of design variables. The overall mass balance provides an additional check on the calculations,

$$F_1 = F_6 + F_9$$

$$F_1 \bar{M}_1 = F_6 \bar{M}_6 + F_9 \bar{M}_9$$

$$(100)(8.637) = (42.58)(17.025) + (14.02)(9.888)$$

$$863.7 = 863.5$$

where $\bar{M}$ means average molecular weight [Eqn. (6.9)].

The flow rate of stream 7 (low-pressure recycle) is small compared to other flow rates and could be neglected in rough calculations.

After the program has been tested for one set of design variables, operating characteristics of the process are studied by systematically varying values of key variables. For example, the production rate of ammonia (F_6) increases with decreasing fraction purged, approaching 48 lb-moles/hr in the limit as $\alpha \longrightarrow 0$. (See Fig. 8-15). The recycle rate (F_{10}) also increases with decreasing fraction purged, approaching infinity as $\alpha \longrightarrow 0$ and impurities accumulate in the recycle loop. In practice, one strikes an economic balance between higher production revenues and added costs of recirculation.

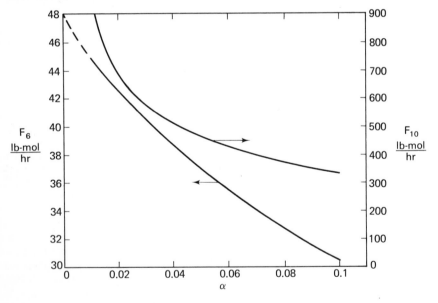

Figure 8-15

PROBLEMS

8.1. A butane isomerization process produces 40 mole/hr of pure isobutane. A purge stream, removed continuously, contains 83.1% n-butane and 16.9% impurity. The feed stream is n-butane containing 0.5% impurity. Determine the flow rate of the purge stream. (*Hint:* Make an overall material balance.)

8.2. One hundred moles per hour of feed gases (nitrogen and hydrogen in stoichiometric proportion) are partially converted to ammonia in a catalytic reactor. See Fig. 8-16. Unreacted gases are recycled; the product stream contains 95% ammonia. Calculate the flow rate of the product stream. (*Hint:* Make an overall material balance.)

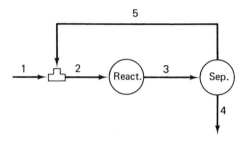

Figure 8-16

8.3. Solve the isobutane recycle problem of Example 8.2 for the following set of design variables:

$$F_4 = 20 \text{ moles/hr} \qquad \text{(product flow rate)}$$

$$F_5 = 150 \text{ moles/hr} \qquad \text{(recycle flow rate)}$$

$$x_{41} = 0.96 \qquad \text{(mole fraction of isobutane in product)}$$

$$x_{11} = 0.10 \qquad \text{(mole fraction of isobutane in feed)}$$

$$\alpha = 1.0$$

The constants for the reactor are $(nk_r) = 38.1 \text{ moles/hr}$ and $K = 0.728$. (*Hint:* Make use of the overall material balance equation.)

8.4. In the vinyl chloride process, Sec. 3.4, suppose that 50% of the feed to the pyrolysis unit is converted to vinyl chloride and hydrogen chloride. Revise the material balance in Fig. 3-4. What is the new recycle rate?

8.5. Solve the material balance equations for the process of catalytic conversion of *n*-butane to isobutane, Example 8.3, using the modular approach. In this case we know the explicit solution. The modular approach is used as a last resort when the explicit solution cannot be derived. Here, however, the object is to see how the modular approach works. Assume the same values of design variables as in Example 8.3. Let $\beta = 0.005$. Make a reasonable first guess for the recycle flow rate and carry out about five iterations using the method of successive substitutions. Plot F_2 as a function of iteration parameter k. What is the solution for F_2? Is the convergence fast or slow? Use Wegstein's method for the first few iterations and compare the speed of convergence for the value of F_2 with that of successive substitutions.

8.6. A simplified flow diagram for the production of butadiene from butane is shown in Fig. 8-17. The feed stream (1) is pure *n*-butane. The reactor converts *n*-butane to 1,3-butadiene and 2-butene. The distillation produces pure

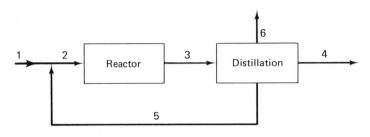

Figure 8-17

hydrogen in stream 6 and pure butadiene in stream 4. The recycle stream (5) is free of hydrogen and butadiene.

Substance	Formula	Code
n-Butane	$CH_3CH_2CH_2CH_3$	1
1,3-Butadiene	$CH_2=CHCH=CH_2$	2
2-Butene	$CH_3CH=CHCH_3$	3
Hydrogen	H_2	4

The reactor yields the following compositions (mole fraction):

$$x_{32} = 0.18$$
$$x_{33} = 0.31$$

The feed rate, F_1, is 100 moles/hr.
a. How many independent chemical reactions can be written?
b. Determine the total number of variables for the butadiene process.
c. Write down all the equations describing the process.
d. Make a list of the unknowns and show that the number of unknowns is equal to the number of equations.
e. Solve (obtain numerical results) for all the unknowns. (*Hint:* Use the *overall* material balance for the butadiene plant.)
f. What is the total mass flow rate of the product streams (4 plus 6)?
g. In the problem statement F_1 was chosen as a design variable. Show that F_1 and F_5 could be chosen as design variables but that F_4 and F_6 may not be chosen as design variables.

8.7. Propane is catalytically dehydrogenated to produce propylene by being heated quickly to a temperature of 550° to 650°C and passed over a granular solid catalyst.* As the reaction proceeds, carbon is deposited on the catalyst, neces-

---

*O. A. Hougen, K. M. Watson, and R. A. Ragatz, *Chemical Process Principles, Part I, Material and Energy Balances,* 2nd Ed., John Wiley & Sons, N. Y. (1956), p. 213.

sitating its periodic reactivation by burning off the carbon with oxygen-bearing gases. In a laboratory experiment in which pure propane is fed to the reactor, the product analysis per mole of propane feed is

Gas	No. of moles
Propane	0.613
Propylene	0.294
Hydrogen	0.350
Ethylene	0.0041
Ethane	0.073
Methane	0.0441

Based upon these data it is desired to design a plant to produce 50 tons/day of propylene in a mixture of 98.8% purity. The flow diagram of the proposed process is shown in Fig. 8-18. Fresh propane feed, mixed with propane recycle

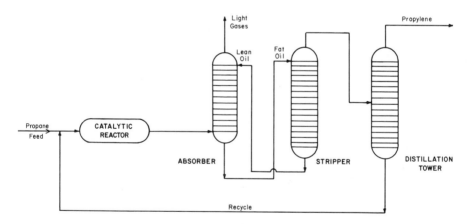

Figure 8-18

stock, is fed to a heater from which it is discharged to a catalytic reactor, operating under such conditions as to produce the same conversion of propane as was obtained in the laboratory experiment. The reactor effluent gases are cooled and compressed to a suitable pressure for separation of the light gases. This separation is accomplished by absorption of the propane and propylene, together with small amounts of the lighter gases, in a cooled absorption oil which is circulated through an absorption tower. The "fat oil" from the bottom of the absorber is pumped to a stripping tower where, by application of heat at the bottom of the tower, the dissolved gases are distilled away from the oil, which is then cooled and recirculated to the absorber. The gases from the stripping tower are passed to a high-pressure fractionating tower which separates them into propane recycle stock as a bottoms product and propylene and lighter gases as overhead. The following compositions are established as preliminary design bases estimated from the vaporization characteristics of the gases:

1. The light gases from the absorber are to contain 1.1% propane and 0.7% propylene by volume. Substantially all hydrogen, ethylene, and methane leaving the reactor will appear in the light gases. The ethane, however, will appear in both the light gases and the product.
2. The propane recycle stock is to contain 98% propane and 2% propylene by weight.
3. The propylene product is to contain 98.8% propylene, 0.7% ethane, and 0.5% propane by weight.

It may be assumed that the small amount of propylene in the feed to the reactor passes through unchanged.

a. Calculate the amount of carbon formed on the catalyst, expressed as weight percent of the propane fed to the catalyst chamber.
b. Calculate the process period in minutes required to build a carbon deposit equal to 2% by weight of the catalyst (the total feed is passed over the catalyst at the rate of 66 moles/liter of catalyst per hour; the density of the catalyst is 865 g/liter).
c. Make an overall material balance.
d. Make a once-through material balance.
e. Calculate the ultimate yield of recovered propylene expressed as a mole percentage of propane in fresh feed.
f. Calculate the yield per pass of propylene made in the reactor expressed as a mole percentage of total propane entering the reactor.

(*Hint:* For the material balance, treat the absorber, stripper, and fractionating tower as a single unit.)

8.8. Let's solve a simplified version of the material balance for a propane dehydrogenation plant. The process schematic is shown in Fig. 8-19. Assume that the only reaction is the dehydrogenation of propane to propylene; there are no

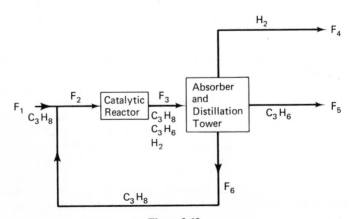

Figure 8-19

side reactions. The yield of propylene per pass is 30% (i.e., 30% of the propane entering the reactor is converted to propylene). Assume that the amount of carbon formed on the catalyst is negligible. The product flow rate is $F_5 = 50$ moles/hr. Calculate the flow rates of all the other streams. Notice that all streams except stream 3 are pure.

8.9. Use an executive program (e.g., U.P. PACER) to perform a material balance on the butane isomerization process in Example 8.3 for the following design variable values:

$$F_1 = 20 \text{ moles/hr}$$
$$x_{13} = 0.005$$
$$K = 0.728$$
$$nk_r = 38 \text{ moles/hr}$$
$$\beta = 0.01$$

Note: For the U.P. PACER program, use the modules BUTMIX, BUTRCT, BUTFRC, and SPLITN; these modules are illustrated in Fig. 8-20 with local design variables circled. The stream numbers and component numbers correspond to those in Example 8.3.

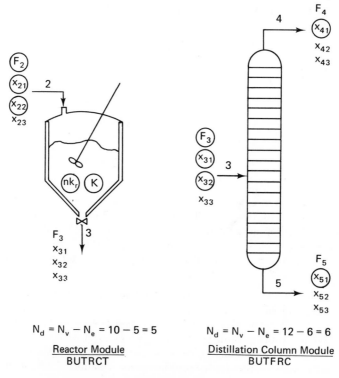

$$N_d = N_v - N_e = 10 - 5 = 5$$

Reactor Module
BUTRCT

$$N_d = N_v - N_e = 12 - 6 = 6$$

Distillation Column Module
BUTFRC

Figure 8-20

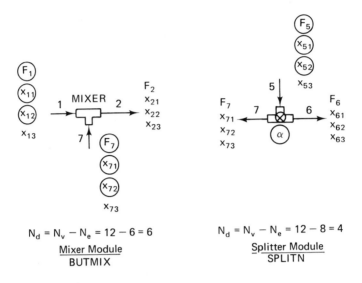

$$N_d = N_v - N_e = 12 - 6 = 6$$

Mixer Module
BUTMIX

$$N_d = N_v - N_e = 12 - 8 = 4$$

Splitter Module
SPLITN

Figure 8-20 (continued)

8.10. Use an executive program (U.P. PACER, etc.) to perform a material balance on the ammonia process in Example 8.5 for the following set of design variable values:

$$F_1 = 100 \text{ lb-moles/hr} \qquad k_4 = 100$$
$$x_{11} = 0.24 \qquad k_5 = 33$$
$$x_{12} = 0.743 \qquad k'_1 = 2400$$
$$x_{14} = 0.006 \qquad k'_2 = 1750$$
$$x_{15} = 0.011 \qquad k'_3 = 0.28$$
$$k_1 = 105 \qquad k'_4 = 1400$$
$$k_2 = 90 \qquad k'_5 = 500$$
$$k_3 = 0.06$$

and K' and α as specified. For $K' = 0.175$, 0.35, and 0.70, compute F_6 and F_{10} at $\alpha = 0.01, 0.02, 0.05, 0.1, 0.5$, and 1.0. Prepare graphs of F_6 and F_{10} versus α with K' as the parameter. *Note:* For U.P. PACER, use the RANGE and CHANGE data sections to eliminate having to rerun the program for each case. These sections reduce the number of iterations to obtain results when values of K' and α decrease.

8.11. a. Consider the ammonia process in Example 8.5 and the following set of design variables: $F_4, x_{42}, x_{43}, x_{44}, x_{35}, K', k_1, k_2, k_3, k_4, k_5, \alpha, k'_1, k'_2, k'_3, k'_4, k'_5$. Compare this set of design variables with the set in Example 8.5. What are the advantages and disadvantages of each set? Carry out the first step of the modular approach; that is, select a set of unit modules and a calculation order for the solution of the equations. Unit modules should be identified in a figure similar to Fig. 8-12.

b. Use an executive program (U.P. PACER, etc.) to perform a material balance on the ammonia process for the following set of design variable values:

$$F_4 = 1604 \qquad x_{35} = 0.0656$$
$$x_{42} = 0.7675 \qquad K' = 0.35$$
$$x_{43} = 0.0838 \qquad \alpha = 0.01$$
$$x_{44} = 0.0370$$

and $k_1, \ldots, k_5$ and $k'_1, \ldots, k'_5$ as in Example 8.5. Use the reactor program in Problem 7.13 and a new mixer program. Install these programs in the library of the executive program (for U.P. PACER, use the U.P. PACER translator).

8.12. Saturated hydrocarbons (propane, *n*-butane) are converted to olefins (propylene, *cis*-2-butene) in preparation for alkylation and polymerization reactions.* As shown in the flow chart (Fig. 8-21a), a mixture of 10 wt. % C_2H_6, 20 wt. % C_3H_8, and 70 wt. % C_4H_{10} are charged as liquid from storage to a dehydrogenation furnace at the rate of 5000 lb/hr. In the furnace the C_2H_6 goes through unchanged; 10% of the C_3H_8 passing through the furnace is dehydrogenated ($C_3H_8 \longrightarrow C_3H_6 + H_2$); and 70% of the *n*-butane is dehydrogenated ($C_4H_{10} \longrightarrow C_4H_8 + H_2$); *cis*-2-butene is formed. The flash separator removes H_2 and C_2H_6 as gases; the liquid, in equilibrium with the gases, is passed to the first distillation column where C_3H_6 is removed overhead. A second distillation tower removes C_3H_8 overhead, C_4H_{10} from a side-draw (which is condensed and split for reflux and recycle), and product C_4H_8 from the bottoms. All C_3H_8 and C_4H_{10} streams are recycled. The distillation columns operate at a 15/1 reflux ratio ($R/D = 15$). Use an executive program (U.P. PACER, etc.) to perform a material balance on the process. To simplify the solution, the modules illustrated in the detailed flow diagram (Fig. 8-21b) may be used. Modules such as these are included in the module libraries of most executive programs; those provided in the U.P. PACER library are

1. **MIXSPT.** This subroutine models a mixing-splitting unit containing any number of input material streams and any number of output material streams as follows. Mass flows in all input streams are mixed. The fraction of the total mass flow assigned to the first output stream, the second output stream, the third output stream, etc., is specified in the first, second, third, etc., equipment parameter for the process unit. *Restrictions:* There must be at least one input stream and at least one output stream. There may be no more than five input streams and five output streams. Fractions must sum to 1.

2. **FRAC.** This subroutine models a simple fractionation device containing any number of input streams and exactly two output streams as follows. Mass flows of all input streams are mixed. The fractions of components 1, 2, 3, . . . in the mixed input to be assigned to the first output stream are

*D. M. Himmelblau, *Basic Principles and Calculations in Chemical Engineering*, 3rd Ed., Prentice-Hall, Inc., (1974), p. 429.

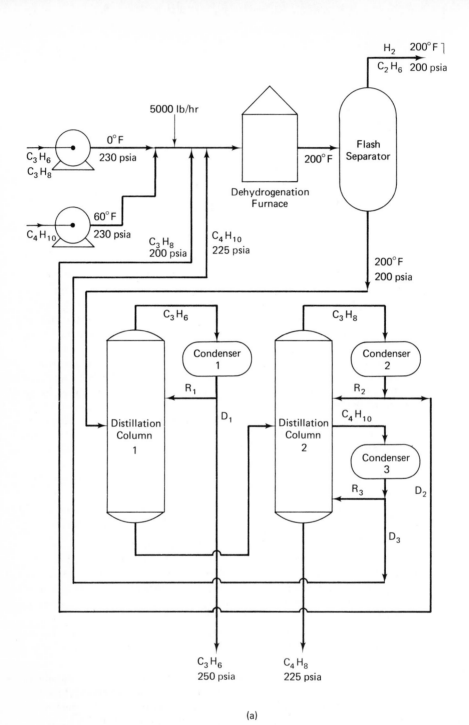

(a)

Figure 8-21

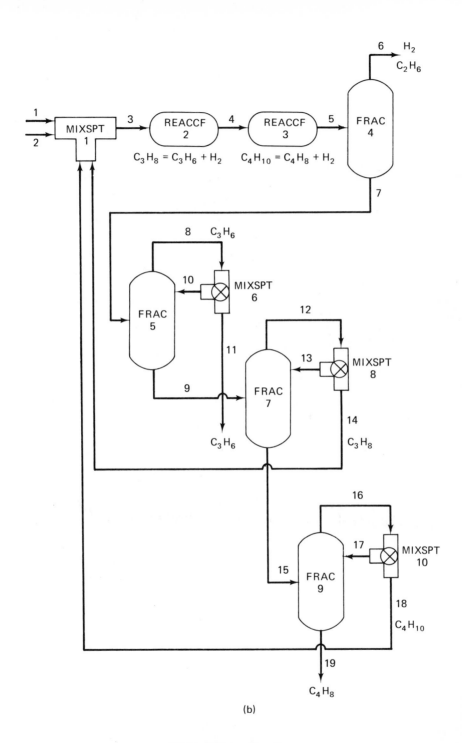

(b)

Figure 8-21 (continued)

specified in the first, second, third, etc., equipment parameter for the process unit. *Restrictions:* There must be at least one and no more than five input streams.

3. **REACCF.** This subroutine models a simple chemical reaction device with any number of input streams and exactly one output stream as follows. Mass flows of all input streams are mixed. The conversion fraction, key component index (first, second, third component, etc.), and stoichiometric coefficients are specified by equipment parameters for the unit:

   Parameter 1:   Conversion fraction of the key component.

   Parameter 2:   Key component index.

   Parameters 3, 4, . . .:   Stoichiometric coefficient for the components, in order (positive for reactants and negative for products) by component (parameter 3 for the first component, parameter 4 for the second component, etc.).

Restrictions: Should the specified reaction, key component, and conversion fraction be unattainable because of depletion of another reactant, the maximum possible conversion will be assigned and a message written to indicate the situation.

Assume that all separations are complete; that is, stream 6 contains all the H_2 and C_2H_6 that enters the first fractionator, stream 8 is pure C_3H_6, stream 12 is pure C_3H_8, stream 16 is pure C_4H_{10}, and stream 19 is pure C_4H_8. This assumption is unnecessary when modules that model the performance of a distillation column are available.

Introduction to Energy Balances **9**

9.1 First Law of Thermodynamics

The first law of thermodynamics is that energy can be neither created nor destroyed. The idea of conservation of energy was established by James Prescott Joule and Julius Robert von Mayer in the middle of the nineteenth century. Although it was shown by Einstein* that mass and energy are different forms of the same thing, the older laws of conservation of mass and conservation of energy are obeyed separately within the precision of experimental observations for nonnuclear processes.

The principle of conservation of energy, or first law, may be applied to a small machine, a chemical processing unit, or a whole chemical process. Engineers call this kind of calculation an *energy balance* because it is basically an accounting procedure. The first law of thermodynamics has its simplest form for a control mass (i.e., any specified mass of material):

$$\Delta U + \Delta(\text{K.E.}) + \Delta(\text{P.E.}) = Q + W \qquad \text{(control mass)} \qquad (9.1)$$

First let us consider the meaning of the terms individually. The symbol Δ means the increase in the value of the quantity following it during a specified time interval; thus,

$$\Delta U = U_{\text{final}} - U_{\text{initial}}$$

Internal energy (U) means all the energy possessed by a mass (m) of substance other than its macroscopic kinetic energy (K.E.) and its gravitational

*A. Einstein, *Ann. Physik.*, *18*, 639 (1905).

335

potential energy (P.E.). Internal energy includes kinetic energy of electrons orbiting atomic nuclei, electrostatic potential energy due to interactions of electrons with nuclei and with each other, vibrational energy of atoms in molecules, rotational kinetic energies of polyatomic molecules, potential energy of intermolecular forces, and kinetic energy of individual molecules. Internal energy of a substance is a function of its state (its temperature, pressure, and composition) but is independent of the macroscopic velocity of its center of gravity and its height in a gravitational field; otherwise macroscopic kinetic energy and gravitational potential energy could not be isolated from internal energy.

Macroscopic kinetic energy is a property of the motion of the center of gravity of a body and does not include kinetic energies of motion of individual molecules in random directions. If the center of gravity of a nonrotating body of mass m moves at velocity v, then

$$\text{K.E.} = \tfrac{1}{2}mv^2 \qquad (9.2)$$

relative to the same body at rest. Potential energy of mass m at height z in a gravitational field where the local acceleration of gravity is constant and equal to $\mathbf{g}$ is

$$\text{P.E.} = mgz \qquad (9.3)$$

relative to $z = 0$.

Example 9.1

One pound of mass moving at a velocity of 22.4 ft/sec has a macroscopic kinetic energy equal to

$$\text{K.E.} = \frac{1}{2}\,mv^2 = \frac{1}{2}\,(1)(22.4)^2 \left[\frac{\text{lb-ft}^2}{\text{sec}^2}\right]\left[\frac{\text{lb}_f\text{-sec}^2}{32.174\ \text{ft-lb}}\right]\left[\frac{\text{Btu}}{778\ \text{ft-lb}_f}\right] = 0.01\ \text{Btu}$$

One pound of mass at a height of 7.8 ft (relative to the datum plane) where $\mathbf{g} = 32.2$ ft/sec² has a gravitational potential energy equal to

$$\text{P.E.} = mgz = (1)(32.2)(7.8)\left[\frac{1}{(32.174)(778)}\right] = 0.01\ \text{Btu}$$

Since 10 Btu of heat energy are needed to heat 1 lb of water 10°F, it is apparent that changes in kinetic and potential energy are often negligible in comparison with thermal effects. For processes involving phase changes or chemical reactions, ΔU may be hundreds or thousands of Btu per pound of mass.

Energy is always measured relative to some datum level: macroscopic kinetic energy relative to the body at rest, gravitational potential energy relative to an arbitrary height above sea level ($z = 0$), internal energy of a substance relative to some reference state such as 25°C and 1 atm. Often, for convenience, it is assumed that $U = 0$ at the reference state.

Heat (Q) is the amount of energy transported from a region of higher temperature to a region of lower temperature by the mechanism of thermal conduction or radiation.

Work (W) is the product of force ($\mathbf{F}$) times displacement (x). The most important kinds of work performed in chemical processing are compression work, mechanical shaft work, and electrical work.

It is important to recognize that both heat and work are transfers of energy across a boundary from one body to another.

Equation (9.1) is written so that positive heat ($+Q$) and positive work ($+W$) correspond to an increase in energy. Therefore, heat absorbed by the control mass from the surroundings and work done on the control mass by the surroundings are both positive quantities. If the control mass is hotter than its surroundings and releases heat, then Q is negative. If the control mass expands and does work on the surroundings, then W is negative. (Many engineers define work in the sense opposite to ours by writing the first law as $\Delta U = Q - W$, but this is only a matter of convention.)

Compression work

The differential amount of work (dW) performed when a force ($\mathbf{F}$) displaces an object a differential distance (dx) is

$$dW = \mathbf{F}\, dx \tag{9.4}$$

where $\mathbf{F}$ is the component of the force in the direction of the displacement. Compression work is performed by the piston shown in Fig. 9-1 as it compresses the gas in the cylinder. If the piston has cross-sectional area A and if the pressure beneath the piston is P, then the force exerted on the gas is

$$\mathbf{F} = PA$$

so that

$$dW = PA\, dx \tag{9.5}$$

But $A\, dx$ is the differential change in volume (dV) of the gas due to motion of the piston, so

$$dW = -P\, dV \tag{9.6}$$

The negative sign was inserted to conform to our convention that a decrease in volume of the gas (dV negative) corresponds to work done on the control mass (dW positive). Total work done on the gas during a finite displacement of the piston is calculated by the integral

$$W = \int_{V_1}^{V_2} -P\, dV \tag{9.7}$$

Evaluation of this integral requires data on the execution of the compression: P as a function of V from the initial volume (V_1) to the final volume (V_2).

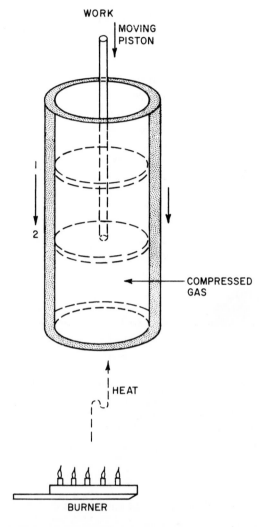

Figure 9-1 Increase of internal energy of gas due to absorption of heat and due to performance of work on gas.

Example 9.2

One mole of air is compressed isothermally by a piston from 20 liters to 10 liters at 25°C. (See Fig. 9-2.) Compute the work done on the gas by the piston. Assume that air is a perfect gas.

Solution:

$$W = -\int_{V_1}^{V_2} P\,dV$$

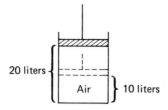

Figure 9-2

For a perfect gas under isothermal conditions,

$$W = -\int_{V_1}^{V_2} \frac{nRT}{V}\, dV = -nRT \int_{V_1}^{V_2} \frac{dV}{V} = nRT \ln \frac{V_1}{V_2}$$

$$= (1 \text{ mole}) \left(\frac{0.08206 \text{ liter-atm}}{\text{mole-}^\circ\text{K}} \right) (298.15^\circ\text{K}) \ln\left(\frac{20}{10}\right)$$

$$= 16.96 \text{ liter-atm} \left(\frac{24.22 \text{ cal}}{\text{liter-atm}} \right)$$

$$= 411 \text{ cal}$$

Mechanical work by rotating shaft

Mechanical shaft work is performed, for example, by electrical motors driving pumps, compressors, and mixers. Equation (9.4) still applies, but displacement is measured in terms of angular displacement at the point of application of force, as shown in Fig. 9-3,

$$dx = R\, d\theta \qquad (9.8)$$

where R is the radius of the shaft at the point of application of the force and θ is angular displacement in radians. From Eqns. (9.4) and (9.8),

$$dW = \mathbf{F}\, dx = \mathbf{F}R\, d\theta = \tau\, d\theta \qquad (9.9)$$

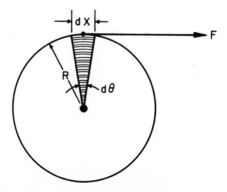

Figure 9-3 Shaft work.

where τ is the torque applied to the shaft. The rate of transfer of energy as work through the rotating shaft is

$$\frac{dW}{dt} = \tau\frac{d\theta}{dt} = \tau\,\omega \qquad (9.10)$$

where ω is angular velocity in radians per unit time (one revolution = 2π rad).

Example 9.3

An internal combustion engine consists of four cylinders, one of which is illustrated in Fig. 9-4. Each cycle consists of four steps:

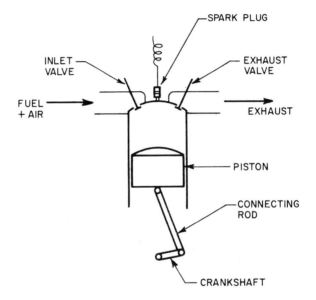

Figure 9-4

1. On the *intake* stroke, the piston moves downward with the intake valve open and the exhaust valve closed as a mixture of air and vaporized fuel enters from the carburetor.
2. During the *compression* stroke (CDA in Fig. 9-5), air and fuel are compressed with inlet and exhaust valves closed.
3. As the piston reaches the top dead center (TDC) position, a spark ignites the mixture, and the *expansion* or power stroke (ABC in Fig. 9-5) occurs with both valves closed.
4. During the *exhaust* stroke, the piston moves upward with the exhaust valve open.

Intake and exhaust strokes, which occur at atmospheric pressure, are not shown in Fig. 9-5. The maximum volume of the cylinder at C is 24.4 in.^{3} (400 cm^3) and the minimum volume is 2.03 in.^{3}, so the compression ratio is 24.4/2.03 = 12 to 1.

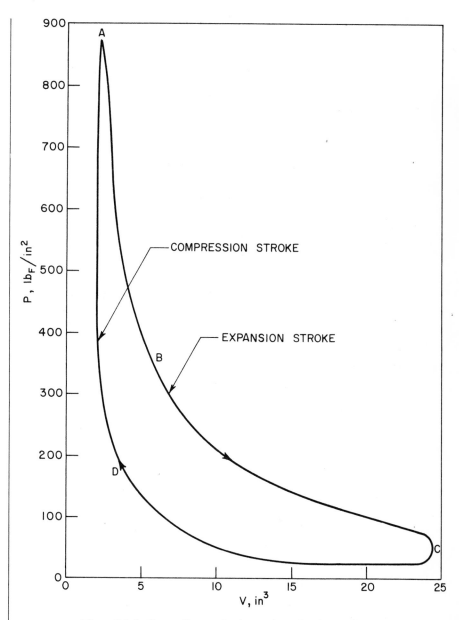

Figure 9-5 Indicator diagram for internal combustion engine.

Compute the net work delivered by the piston during one cycle. Assume that the work done by the piston during the exhaust stroke cancels the work done on the piston during the intake stroke, so that intake and exhaust strokes can be ignored. If the mechanical efficiency of the engine is 98%, determine the torque delivered by four cylinders at 2800 rpm.

Solution:

Instantaneous pressure in the cylinder as a function of its volume in Fig. 9-5 is called an indicator diagram. Work done by the ignited gas mixture during expansion is the area under the curve ABC; work done on the gas during compression is the area under curve CDA. Therefore, net work delivered to the crankshaft (neglecting work done during intake and exhaust strokes) is the area enclosed by the curve ABCD:

$$W_{net} = \oint P \, dV = \text{area ABCD}$$

There are several ways to measure this area. A planimeter measures the area of any plane figure by passing a tracer around the boundary line. Another method is to draw a fine grid and count the squares that lie within the curve; squares with more than half of their area outside the curve are not counted. A third method is to cut out the curve ABCD and weigh it; its area is equal to its mass (g) divided by its area density (g/cm^2). The result is

$$W_{net} = 3{,}650 \text{ in.-lb}_f = 304 \text{ ft-lb}_f/\text{cylinder}$$

As the crankshaft makes one revolution, two cylinders are in the intake-exhaust half of their cycle, and the other two cylinders complete the compression-expansion strokes. For each crankshaft revolution, net work performed by two cylinders is

$$W = 2(304) = 608 \text{ ft-lb}_f/\text{crankshaft revolution}$$

At 98% efficiency, work delivered is

$$W = (0.98)(608) = 596 \text{ ft-lb}_f/\text{crankshaft revolution}$$

Power delivered to the crankshaft is

$$\text{power} = \frac{W}{t} = \frac{\text{work/rev}}{\text{time/rev}} = (\text{work/rev})(\text{rev/time})$$

$$= 596 \left(\frac{\text{ft-lb}_f}{\text{rev}}\right) 2800 \left(\frac{\text{rev}}{\text{min}}\right)\left(\frac{\text{hp-sec}}{550 \text{ ft-lb}_f}\right)\left(\frac{\text{min}}{60 \text{ sec}}\right) = 50.6 \text{ hp}$$

Angular velocity of the crankshaft is

$$\omega = 2800\left(\frac{\text{rev}}{\text{min}}\right)\left(\frac{2\pi \text{ rad}}{\text{rev}}\right)\left(\frac{\text{min}}{60 \text{ sec}}\right) = 293.2 \text{ rad/sec}$$

Torque at 2800 rpm is [Eqn. (9.10)]

$$\tau = \frac{dW/dt}{\omega} = \left(\frac{50.6 \text{ hp}}{293.2 \text{ sec}^{-1}}\right)\left(\frac{550 \text{ ft-lb}_f}{\text{hp-sec}}\right) = 94.9 \text{ ft-lb}_f$$

Electrical work

Electromotive force ($\mathcal{E}$) is work per unit of electrical charge transported through the control mass (1 V = 1 Joule per coulomb),

$$dW = \mathcal{E} \, dZ \qquad\qquad (9.11)$$

where Z is amount of electrical charge. Electrical work is performed on the control mass during electrolysis (W is positive); fuel cells or voltaic cells perform electrical work on the surroundings (W is negative). The rate of performing electrical work is

$$\frac{dW}{dt} = \varepsilon\frac{dZ}{dt} = \varepsilon I \tag{9.12}$$

where I is electrical current. For steady, direct current (dc) and constant voltage (ε), Eqn. (9.12) may be integrated:

$$W = \varepsilon It \tag{9.13}$$

W is given in joules for ε in volts, I in amperes, and t in seconds.

Example 9.4

Water is electrolyzed in a cell consisting of two platinum electrodes in a dilute aqueous solution of sulfuric acid (see Fig. 9-6). Hydrogen is collected at the cathode, and oxygen is evolved at the anode according to the reactions

$$\text{cathode:} \quad 2H^+ + 2e^- = H_2$$
$$\underline{\text{anode:} \qquad\quad H_2O = 2H^+ + 2e^- + \tfrac{1}{2}O_2}$$
$$\text{overall:} \qquad\quad H_2O = H_2 + \tfrac{1}{2}O_2$$

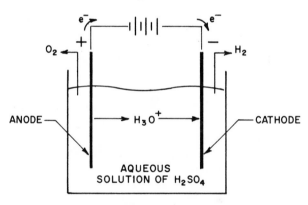

Figure 9-6

Calculate electrical work in kilowatt-hours per pound of hydrogen if the potential difference between the electrodes is 1.7 V.

Solution:

The equations show that production of 1 mole of hydrogen requires 2 moles of electrons. The quantity of electrical charge per mole of electrons is called Faraday's constant, which is 96,487 C/mole. Therefore,

$$Z = \frac{96,487 \text{ C}}{\text{mole of electrons}}\left(\frac{2 \text{ moles of electrons}}{\text{mole of } H_2}\right)\left(\frac{\text{mole}}{2.016 \text{ g}}\right)\left(\frac{453.6 \text{ g}}{\text{lb}}\right)$$
$$= 4.342 \times 10^7 \ C/\text{lb of } H_2$$

Work at constant voltage is calculated from Eqn. (9.11):

$$W = \int \mathcal{E}\, dZ = \mathcal{E}Z = 1.7 \left(\frac{J}{C}\right) 4.342 \times 10^7 \left(\frac{C}{\text{lb of } H_2}\right)\left(\frac{\text{kw-hr}}{3.6 \times 10^6\, J}\right)$$

$$= 20.5 \text{ kw-hr/lb of hydrogen}$$

First law for control mass

Having considered separately each of the terms in Eqn. (9.1), let us consider the simple experiment shown in Fig. 9-1. A gas is confined in a cylinder by a leakproof piston which is at position 1 at the beginning of the experiment. The gas is compressed by pushing the piston downward to position 2 and heated during the compression by a source of heat outside the cylinder. The first step is to choose a control mass; let it be the gas inside the cylinder. If the apparatus is stationary, there is no change in macroscopic kinetic energy of the gas and a negligible change in its gravitational potential energy. According to Eqn. (9.1), the increase in internal energy of the gas (ΔU) is equal to the heat it absorbs from the flame (Q) plus the work done on the gas by the piston (W).

It is extremely important to define the control mass before trying to apply Eqn. (9.1). If the gas enclosed by the piston and cylinder is the control mass, then calculation of ΔU for the gas requires knowledge of the heat absorbed by the gas alone. If the entire piston-cylinder apparatus (including the gas inside) is selected as control mass, then Q is the total heat absorbed by the apparatus, and ΔU has two terms, one for the piston-cylinder apparatus and one for the gas.

If the compression is done quickly so that there is no time for transfer of heat, then the compression is called adiabatic $(Q = 0)$ and $\Delta U = W$.

The significance of Eqn. (9.1) is that in order to increase the energy of a control mass, heat must be supplied or work must be done by the surroundings (environment). Therefore, increase in energy of the control mass is exactly matched by decrease in energy of the environment so that, overall, energy is conserved.

First law for control volume—steady-state operation

Actually the concept of control mass is not convenient for the study of chemical processes in which fluids are moved continuously from one location to another, mixed with other substances, and made to undergo chemical and physical transformations. Instead of trying to set up a control mass and follow its progress through the chemical process, it is easier to set up a *control volume* as shown by the example in Fig. 9-7. The boundary of the control volume, shown by the dashed line, is carefully selected so that its interaction with the

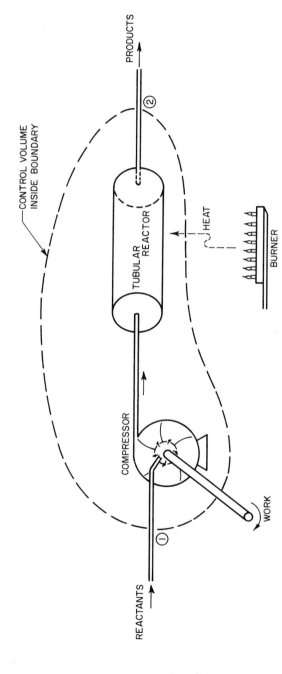

Figure 9-7 Energy balance for a control volume containing a chemical process operated at steady state.

345

surroundings is unambiguous. In this case there are four interactions: work done by the rotating shaft that operates the pump, heat from the burner, reactants entering, and products leaving.

Steady state means that reactants flow into the control volume and products flow out at equal mass flow rates. Energy, in the form of heat and work, crosses the boundary at a steady rate. Within the boundary of the control volume there is no increase or decrease in the amount of mass and energy. All instruments (thermometers, pressure gauges, liquid-level indicators, etc.) within the control volume have steady readings.

A schematic of the same control volume, distorted to keep track of a control mass, is shown in Fig. 9-8. Mass flow rates of reactants entering and products leaving the control volume are equal. Suppose that reactants and products enter and leave the control volume as fluids in pipes with cross-sectional areas A_1 and A_2, respectively. At time zero we select the entire contents of the control volume plus unit mass of feed as the control mass, which is shown shaded in Fig. 9-8(a). If the specific volume of the feed is v'_1, then

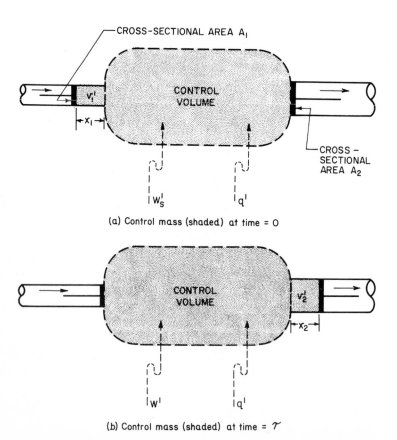

(a) Control mass (shaded) at time = 0

(b) Control mass (shaded) at time = τ

Figure 9-8 Steady flow of mass across the boundary of a control volume.

the distance x_1 is equal to

$$x_1 = \frac{v_1'}{A_1} \tag{9.14}$$

Later, at time τ, the feed has entered the control volume, and an equal mass of product of specific volume v_2' has been pushed out of the control volume a distance

$$x_2 = \frac{v_2'}{A_2} \tag{9.15}$$

At time τ the control mass occupies a new spatial location, which is shown shaded in Fig. 9-8(b). Let q' be the heat entering the control volume per unit mass of reactant, and let w' be shaft work or electrical work per unit mass of reactant. Besides w', there is work associated with pushing the reactants into the control volume (w_1') and work associated with the products leaving the control volume (w_2'). From Eqn. (9.1),

$$\Delta u' + \Delta(\text{k.e.}) + \Delta(\text{p.e.}) = q' + w' + w_1' + w_2' \tag{9.16}$$

All the quantities in Eqn. (9.16) are written in lowercase as a reminder that they refer to unit mass of material passing through the control volume. From Eqns. (9.2) and (9.3), k.e. $= \frac{1}{2}v^2$ and p.e. $= gz$.

Because of our assumption of steady state, nothing has changed within the control volume during time τ, and therefore $\Delta u'$ must refer to the change in internal energy of the reactants as they undergo compression and chemical transformation:

$$\Delta u' = u_2' - u_1' \tag{9.17}$$

u_1' and u_2' are internal energy per unit mass of reactants and products, respectively.

Flow-work terms w_1' and w_2' in Eqn. (9.16) are related to properties of the fluid. Referring to Fig. 9-8, entering reactants are forced into the control volume by upstream fluid, which is represented as a piston to emphasize the point that it does work equal to force $(\mathbf{F}_1)$ times displacement (x_1):

$$w_1' = \mathbf{F}_1 x_1 \tag{9.18}$$

The force exerted by the piston (upstream fluid) is equal to the pressure at the point where reactants enter the control volume (P_1) multiplied by the cross-sectional area:

$$\mathbf{F}_1 = P_1 A_1 \tag{9.19}$$

Combining Eqns. (9.14), (9.18), and (9.19),

$$w_1' = P_1 v_1' \tag{9.20}$$

w_1' is positive because upstream fluid, which is part of the surroundings, does work on the control mass (shown shaded in Fig. 9-8). Similarly,

$$w_2' = -P_2 v_2' \tag{9.21}$$

w_2' is negative because the control mass does work on the surroundings (the downstream fluid, which is represented as a piston in Fig. 9-8).

Substitution of Eqns. (9.20) and (9.21) into (9.16) gives

$$\Delta u' + \Delta(\text{k.e.}) + \Delta(\text{p.e.}) = q' + w' + P_1 v'_1 - P_2 v'_2 \qquad (9.22)$$

or

$$[u'_2 + P_2 v'_2 + (\text{k.e.})_2 + (\text{p.e.})_2] - [u'_1 + P_1 v'_1 + (\text{k.e.})_1 + (\text{p.e.})_1]$$
$$= q' + w' \qquad (9.23)$$

The group $U + PV$ is called enthalpy (H),

$$H = U + PV \qquad (9.24)$$

or, for H, U, and V in units of energy or volume per unit mass,

$$h' = u' + Pv' \qquad (9.25)$$

Therefore, Eqn. (9.23) can be written simply as

$$\Delta h' + \Delta(\text{p.e.}) + \Delta(\text{k.e.}) = q' + w' \qquad \text{(control volume,} \atop \text{steady state)} \qquad (9.26)$$

where

$$\Delta h' = h'_2 - h'_1 = h'_{\text{product}} - h'_{\text{feed}}$$

Referring back to Fig. 9-7, Eqn. (9.26) says that the sum of increases in enthalpy and kinetic and potential energy of unit mass of a substance as it passes through a control volume at steady state is equal to the heat absorbed by the control volume plus the work done on the control volume by the surroundings. Equation (9.26) does not apply to conditions of unsteady state when energy or mass accumulates in the control volume.

The $P \times V$ product in Eqn. (9.24) has units of energy, and it is useful to think of enthalpy as convected energy (internal energy plus flow energy) associated with mass as it crosses the boundary of a control volume. Under this convention, work (w) on the right-hand side of Eqn. (9.26) means all kinds of work except flow work ($P_1 v'_1$ and $P_2 v'_2$).

In many chemical processes such as distillation and chemical reaction, changes of kinetic and potential energy of process streams are negligible in comparison with other terms (see Example 9.1) so that

$$\Delta h' = q' + w' \qquad \left(\begin{array}{l} \text{control volume} \\ \text{steady state} \\ \text{macroscopic potential and kinetic} \\ \quad \text{energy negligible} \end{array} \right) \qquad (9.27)$$

Equation (9.27) is written in terms of unit mass. The equation can also be written in terms of rates. If there are several feed, product, work, and heat streams, then

$$\sum_i F_i h_i + \sum_i \frac{dQ_i}{dt} + \sum_i \frac{dW_i}{dt} = 0 \qquad \left(\begin{array}{l} \text{control volume} \\ \text{steady state} \\ \text{macroscopic potential and kinetic} \\ \quad \text{energy negligible} \end{array} \right)$$

$$(9.28)$$

The sign convention is that F is positive for reactants and negative for products; dQ_i/dt is positive if heat enters the control volume; dW_i/dt, which is positive if work is done on the control volume by the surroundings, refers to all kinds of work except flow work. F has units of moles per unit time, and h has units of energy per mole (e.g., calories per mole). Alternatively, the flow rate may be in mass units (F') if enthalpy has units of energy per unit mass (h'). In either case dQ_i/dt, dW_i/dt, and the product $F \times h$ all have units of energy per unit time, or power.

Equation (9.28) is not the most basic but it is the most important form of the first law of thermodynamics for the majority of applications in chemical engineering. Calculations of heat or work using Eqn. (9.28) require values of enthalpy, which must be calculated from bits of data such as heat capacity, latent heat, and heats of formation. Methods of calculating enthalpy are considered later in this chapter.

9.2 Enthalpy and Heat

Increase in enthalpy (ΔH) is equal to heat absorbed (Q) for

1. Nonflow systems maintained at constant pressure provided the only work performed is compression or expansion.
2. Steady-flow systems if no work is done on the substance as it passes through the control volume.

Enthalpy used to be called heat content because its increase is equal to heat absorbed under these special conditions. Later the name heat content was dropped because it fostered the incorrect concept that the amount of heat in a body is a physical property.

The equality of ΔH and Q for these two types of processes can be proved by the first law of thermodynamics. If a stationary control mass of substance is heated at constant pressure, then from Eqn. (9.1)

$$\Delta U = Q + W \qquad (9.29)$$

If the only work is compression work at constant pressure (P_0), then from Eqn. (9.7)

$$W = -P_0 \, \Delta V \qquad (9.30)$$

ΔV is increase in volume of the substance. Combination of the last two equations gives

$$Q = \Delta U + P_0 \, \Delta V \qquad (9.31)$$

But, according to Eqn. (9.24) at constant pressure,

$$\Delta H = \Delta U + P_0 \, \Delta V \qquad (9.32)$$

so that

$$\Delta H = Q \quad \left(\begin{array}{l} \text{control mass} \\ \text{nonflow system} \\ \text{constant pressure} \\ \text{no work other than compression work} \end{array} \right) \qquad (9.33)$$

If heat is evolved by the control mass at constant pressure as by cooling, condensation of a vapor, or an exothermic chemical reaction, then both Q and ΔH have negative values.

Equation (9.33) is for a control mass or batch operation. For a steady-flow system, it follows from Eqn. (9.27) that

$$\Delta h' = q' \qquad \left(\begin{array}{l}\text{steady flow} \\ \text{control volume} \\ \text{no work performed} \\ \text{macroscopic K.E. and P.E. negligible}\end{array}\right) \qquad (9.34)$$

provided no work (other than flow work) is done on the substance as it passes through the control volume. Typical applications of Eqn. (9.34) are to heat exchangers and chemical reactors operated at steady state. Unlike Eqn. (9.33), there is no limitation of constant pressure for Eqn. (9.34).

9.3 Calculation of Enthalpy of Nonreacting Substances

Enthalpies measured in calorimetric experiments are reported in tables for selected substances. For example, enthalpy of steam as a function of its temperature and pressure is given in Table 4.12. Complete tables are given in *Thermodynamic Properties of Steam* by J. H. Keenan and F. G. Keyes, Wiley, New York, 1936.

Although enthalpies are tabulated for important substances such as water, the usual source of data on enthalpy is its first derivative with respect to temperature, called the heat capacity at constant pressure:

$$C_p = \left(\frac{\partial H}{\partial T}\right)_P \qquad (9.35)$$

If enthalpy is measured in calories and temperature in $°K$, then heat capacity has units of calories per $°K$. C_p is directly proportional to the amount of substance. Therefore, the molar heat capacity defined by

$$c_p = \left(\frac{\partial h}{\partial T}\right)_P \qquad (9.36)$$

is usually reported in handbooks in units of cal/mole-$°K$. Alternatively, if h is measured in cal/g, then c_p has units of cal/g-$°K$.

Experimental values of heat capacity at atmospheric pressure for benzene are plotted in Fig. 9-9. Notice that heat capacity is a discontinuous function of temperature at the melting point and boiling point of benzene, where its state changes from solid to liquid and from liquid to vapor, respectively. As for most substances, the heat capacity of the liquid is considerably higher than that of the solid or gas at the same temperature.

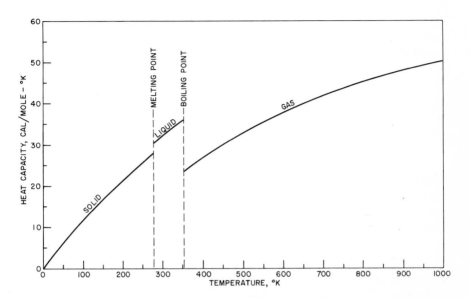

Figure 9-9 Heat capacity of benzene at atmospheric pressure.

Since heat capacity is the first derivative of enthalpy with respect to temperature, differences in enthalpy are calculated by integrating the heat capacity:

$$\Delta h = \int_{T_1}^{T_2} c_p \, dT \quad \text{(constant pressure)} \tag{9.37}$$

The integration is at constant pressure, usually atmospheric pressure. If c_p is constant over the interval from T_1 to T_2, which is a good approximation when the interval is small, then

$$\Delta h = c_p \, \Delta T = c_p (T_2 - T_1) \tag{9.38}$$

If the heat capacity is not constant but varies linearly with temperature,

$$\Delta h = \bar{c}_p \, \Delta T = \bar{c}_p (T_2 - T_1) \tag{9.39}$$

where $\bar{c}_p$ is the value of the heat capacity at the midpoint of the temperature interval.

Example 9.5

Calculate the change in enthalpy for heating benzene gas from 100° to 500°C at atmospheric pressure.

Solution:

The heat capacity of benzene gas (c_p^0) is given by Eqn. (4.32), and values of constants are in Table 4.14. Strictly, c_p^0 is for very low pressure, but the value at atmospheric pressure is almost the same.

$$c_p^0 = a + bT + cT^2 + dT^3$$

From Eqn. (9.37),

$$\Delta h = \int_{T_1}^{T_2} c_p \, dT = aT + \frac{b}{2}T^2 + \frac{c}{3}T^3 + \frac{d}{4}T^4 \Big|_{T_1}^{T_2}$$

$$= a(T_2 - T_1) + \frac{b}{2}(T_2^2 - T_1^2) + \frac{c}{3}(T_2^3 - T_1^3) + \frac{d}{4}(T_2^4 - T_1^4)$$

Inserting numerical values for the constants from Table 4.14 (temperature must be converted from °C to °K),

$$\Delta h = -8.65(773.15 - 373.15) + \tfrac{1}{2}(0.11578)(773.15^2 - 373.15^2)$$
$$+ \tfrac{1}{3}(-7.54 \times 10^{-5})(773.15^3 - 373.15^3)$$
$$+ \tfrac{1}{4}(18.54 \times 10^{-9})(773.15^4 - 373.15^4)$$
$$= -3460 + 26,544 - 10,310 + 1566$$
$$= 14,340 \text{ cal/mole}$$

As shown in Fig. 9-9, the heat capacity of benzene gas increases from 25 to 44 cal/mole-K° as temperature goes from 100° to 500°C. Although the variation of c_p with temperature is not linear, Eqn. (9.39) can be used to make a rough calculation. The value of c_p at the midpoint of the temperature interval (300°C) is 36.4 cal/mole-°K:

$$\Delta h = c_p \, \Delta T \simeq 36.4(400) = 14,560 \text{ cal/mole}$$

The error is less than 2%.

Example 9.6

Calculate the enthalpy change for heating benzene liquid from its melting point (5.5°C) to its normal boiling point (80.1°C) at atmospheric pressure.

Solution:

The heat capacity is not constant (see Fig. 9-9), but the increase with temperature is nearly linear. Therefore, from Eqn. (9.39),

$$\Delta h = \bar{c}_p \, \Delta T$$

The temperature of the midpoint of the interval (from 5.5° to 80.1°C) is 42.8°C = 316.0°K at which $\bar{c}_p = 33.3$ cal/mole-°K, so

$$\Delta h = (33.3)(74.6) = 2484 \text{ cal/mole}$$

Latent heat

Heat absorbed by a substance at constant pressure is equal to its increase in enthalpy under the conditions prescribed by Eqn. (9.33). It is convenient to distinguish *sensible* heat, which raises the temperature of a substance without changing its phase (solid, liquid, or gas), and *latent* heat, which changes its phase at constant temperature. For example, the amount of heat required to melt solid benzene at its normal melting point (5.5°C) is called its latent heat of fusion, and the amount of heat needed to vaporize liquid benzene at its normal boiling point (80.1°C) is called its latent heat of vaporization. Selected values of latent heats are reported in Table 4.10. Latent heats for hundreds of elements and compounds, both organic and inorganic, are reported in handbooks.*

Chemical processes often combine changes in both the temperature and the state of substances in a single operation, so that heat requirements contain sensible and latent contributions. A typical calculation is shown in the next example.

Example 9.7

Calculate the change in enthalpy when solid benzene at 5.5°C is transformed to gaseous benzene at 500°C.

Solution:

The process is divided into four steps for which the enthalpy change is known:

1. Melting at the normal melting point (5.5°C) and atmospheric pressure. The heat of fusion, which is tabulated in Perry's handbook, is equal to the change in enthalpy [Eqn. (9.33)]:
$$\Delta h = q = 2350 \text{ cal/mole}$$

2. Heating of liquid from 5.5° to 80.1°C at atmospheric pressure. From Example 9.6,
$$\Delta h = 2484 \text{ cal/mole}$$

3. Vaporization of liquid at normal boiling point (80.1°C) and atmospheric pressure. The heat of vaporization, from Perry's handbook, is
$$\Delta h = q = 7140 \text{ cal/mole}$$

4. Heating of gas from 80.1 to 500°C. The calculation is similar to Example 9.5:
$$\Delta h = -8.65(773.15 - 353.25) + \tfrac{1}{2}(0.11578)(773.15^2 - 353.25^2)$$
$$+ \tfrac{1}{3}(-7.54 \times 10^{-5})(773.15^3 - 353.25^3)$$
$$+ \tfrac{1}{4}(18.54 \times 10^{-9})(773.15^4 - 353.25^4)$$
$$= -3632 + 27,380 - 10,507 + 1584$$
$$= 14,825 \text{ cal/mole}$$

The total enthalpy change is
$$\Delta h = 2350 + 2484 + 7140 + 14,825 = 26,799 \text{ cal/mole}$$

Conservation of energy means that changes of internal energy (and enthalpy) depend only on the initial and final state (defined by temperature, pressure, and phase) and are independent of the particular succession of states

*R. H. Perry and C. H. Chilton, *Chemical Engineers' Handbook*, 5th Ed., McGraw-Hill, New York (1973).

or path. Therefore, changes of internal energy and enthalpy are calculated by selecting a path for which thermodynamic properties such as specific heat and latent heat are known or can be measured easily. This path may be direct or circuitous, as illustrated in Example 9.8.

Example 9.8

Calculate the latent heat of sublimation of ice under vacuum (0.00602 atm) at 0°C. The following data are available:

1. Latent heat of fusion of ice at 0°C is 79.7 cal/g (ice $\longrightarrow$ liquid).
2. Latent heat of vaporization of liquid water at 100°C is 539.5 cal/g (liquid $\longrightarrow$ gas).

Solution:

Heat of sublimation of ice at 0°C (solid $\longrightarrow$ gas) is not equal to the sum $79.7 + 539.5 = 619$ cal/g because the latent heat of vaporization is measured at 100°C. However a multistep process that sublimes ice at 0°C can be imagined as follows:

1. Compress ice from 0.00602 atm to atmospheric pressure. Enthalpy of liquids and solids is practically independent of pressure at pressures close to atmospheric, so $\Delta h \simeq 0$.
2. Melt ice at 0°C and atmospheric pressure, for which $\Delta h = 79.7$ cal/g (ice $\longrightarrow$ liquid).
3. Heat liquid water from 0° to 100°C at atmospheric pressure. Specific heat of liquid water over this interval is almost constant and equal to 1.000 cal/g-°C. From Eqn. (9.38),

$$\Delta h = c_p\, \Delta T = (1.000)(100) = 100 \text{ cal/g}$$

4. Vaporize liquid water at 100°C and atmospheric pressure, for which $\Delta h = 539.5$ cal/g.
5. Expand steam from atmospheric pressure to 0.00602 atm at 100°C. The theory of perfect gases predicts that the enthalpy change accompanying isothermal compression or expansion is zero. For real gases, enthalpy is almost independent of pressure up to several atmospheres. The small enthalpy change for expansion of steam is taken from the steam tables*: $\Delta h = 5.5$ cal/g.
6. Cool steam from 100° to 0°C at constant pressure (0.00602 atm). Using the equation from Example 9.5 and constants for water vapor from Table 4.14,

$$\Delta h = a(T_2 - T_1) + \frac{b}{2}(T_2^2 - T_1^2) + \frac{c}{3}(T_2^3 - T_1^3) + \frac{d}{4}(T_2^4 - T_1^4)$$

$$= 7.700(273 - 373) + \tfrac{1}{2}(4.594 \times 10^{-4})(273^2 - 373^2)$$
$$+ \tfrac{1}{3}(2.521 \times 10^{-6})(273^3 - 373^3) + \tfrac{1}{4}(-8.587 \times 10^{-10})(273^4 - 373^4)$$

$$= -770 - 14.8 - 26.5 + 3.0 = -808.3 \text{ cal/mole}$$

$$= \frac{-808.3}{18.016} = -44.9 \text{ cal/g}$$

*J. H. Keenan and F. G. Keyes, *Thermodynamic Properties of Steam*, Wiley, New York, 1936.

The enthalpy change for sublimation of ice at 0°C is the sum of these six steps:

$$\Delta h = 0 + 79.7 + 100 + 539.5 + 5.5 - 44.9 = 679.8 \text{ cal/g}$$

Since enthalpy is a state function, the enthalpy change is the same for direct sublimation at 0°C and the roundabout path because both paths have the same initial state (ice at 0°C, 0.00602 atm) and the same final state (water vapor at 0°C, 0.00602 atm).

Reference state for enthalpy

Absolute enthalpy of a substance has no meaning; enthalpy is always measured relative to a reference state. Absolute enthalpy would have meaning if the enthalpy of every substance were zero in the limit as absolute temperature goes to zero, but this is not what is observed. Even at very low temperature there are large changes of enthalpy (and internal energy) accompanying chemical reactions.

The procedure is to specify for each substance a reference state (pressure, temperature, phase) at which its enthalpy is set equal to zero. Enthalpy in Eqn. (9.28) means enthalpy (h) relative to the value at the reference state (h^0) and

$$h = h - h^0$$

because $h^0 \equiv 0$.

Changes in enthalpy are independent of the reference state because it cancels out in Δh. For example, Table 9.1 shows selected values of enthalpy of water for two reference states: saturated liquid at 0°C and saturated liquid at 50°C. Observe that values of Δh ($h_D - h_C$, $h_D - h_B$, etc.) are independent of the reference state.

TABLE 9.1
ENTHALPY OF WATER FOR DIFFERENT REFERENCE STATES

State	Phase	T (°C)	P (atm)	Enthalpy (cal/g)	
				Ref. State A	Ref. State B
A	Sat'd liquid	0	0.006	0	−50.0
B	Sat'd liquid	50	0.122	50.0	0
C	Sat'd vapor	100	1	639.1	589.1
D	Vapor	200	10	675.1	625.1

Example 9.9

An evaporator vaporizes 1500 kg of carbon tetrachloride per hour at atmospheric pressure (see Fig. 9-10). There are two feed streams: 1000 kg/hr of liquid at 30°C and 500 kg/hr of liquid at 70°C. The product is superheated vapor at 200°C. Calculate the heat load for the evaporator.

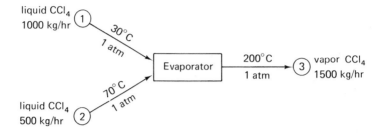

Figure 9-10

Solution:

Since there is no work other than flow work, Eqn. (9.28) is

$$F_1h_1 + F_2h_2 - F_3h_3 + \frac{dQ}{dt} = 0$$

Stream 1 A convenient reference state for CCl_4 is the liquid at 30°C ($T_0 = 30°C$) so that

$$h_1 = 0 \quad \text{(at reference state)}$$

Stream 2 Heat capacity of liquid CCl_4 increases only a few percent over the interval from 30° to 70°C, so Eqn. (9.39) may be used. At 50°C, the heat capacity of liquid CCl_4 is 0.207 cal/g-°K,* so

$$h_2 = \bar{c}_p(T_2 - T_0) = 0.207(40) = 8.28 \text{ cal/g}$$

Stream 3

Enthalpy of stream 3 is the sum of three enthalpy changes:

1. Heat liquid from reference state (30°C) to its normal boiling point (76.7°C):

$$\Delta h = \bar{c}_p(T_b - T_0) = 0.207(46.7) = 9.67 \text{ cal/g}$$

2. Vaporize liquid at its normal boiling point (76.7°C):

$$\Delta h = 46.42 \text{ cal/g}†$$

3. Heat vapor from 76.7°C to 200°C. As in Example 9.5,

$$\Delta h = \int_{T_b}^{T_3} c_p^{vapor} dT = a(T_3 - T_b) + \frac{b}{2}(T_3^2 - T_b^2) + \frac{c}{3}(T_3^3 - T_b^3)$$

$$+ \frac{d}{4}(T_3^4 - T_b^4)$$

$$= 12.24(473.15 - 349.85) + \frac{0.034}{2}(473.15^2 - 349.85^2)$$

$$- \frac{2.995 \times 10^{-5}}{3}(473.15^3 - 349.85^3)$$

$$+ \frac{8.828 \times 10^{-9}}{4}(473.15^4 - 349.85^4)$$

*J. S. Rowlinson, *Liquids and Liquid Mixtures*, Butterworths, London, 1959.
†Perry's handbook.

$$= 1509.2 + 1725.1 - 630 + 77.5 = 2681.8\left(\frac{cal}{mole}\right)\left(\frac{moles}{153.82\ g}\right)$$

$$= 17.43\left(\frac{cal}{g}\right)$$

$$h_3 = 9.67 + 46.42 + 17.43 = 73.52\ cal/g$$

Therefore,

$$\frac{dQ}{dt} = F_3 h_3 - F_1 h_1 - F_2 h_2$$

$$= 1500(73.52) - 1000(0) - 500(8.28)$$

$$= 106,140\left(\frac{kg}{hr}\right)\left(\frac{cal}{g}\right)\left(\frac{1000\ g}{kg}\right) = 1.061 \times 10^8\ cal/hr = 421,000\ Btu/hr$$

9.4 Calculation of Enthalpy of Reacting Substances

Heat absorbed or liberated by a chemical reaction is equal to ΔH for the reaction, provided the conditions prescribed in Eqns. (9.33) and (9.34) are satisfied. ΔH means enthalpy of products minus enthalpy of reactants so that

Type of Reaction	Sign of ΔH	Direction of Heat Flow
Endothermic	$+$	From surroundings into reactor
Exothermic	$-$	From reactor to surroundings

The enthalpy change of an isothermal chemical reaction (ΔH) is defined as

$$\Delta H = \sum_j v_j h_j \qquad (9.40)$$

where v_j is the stoichiometric coefficient of the jth compound and h_j is its molar enthalpy at the temperature of the reaction. Summation is over all compounds that participate in the reaction.

Example 9.10

What is ΔH at 25°C for the reaction

$$Zn(OH)_2(s) + 2HCl(aq) = 2H_2O(l) + ZnCl_2(aq)$$

Solution:

$$\Delta H = h_{ZnCl_2(aq)} + 2h_{H_2O(l)} - h_{Zn(OH)_2(s)} - 2h_{HCl(aq)}$$

where each value of molar enthalpy (h) is measured at 25°C.

A reference state for enthalpy of an inert compound may be chosen on the basis of convenience, as was shown in Example 9.9. What is to be the reference state for the enthalpy (h) of a compound that participates in a chemical reaction? Whatever reference state is chosen, it must be consistent for all compounds that participate in the reaction. The most popular convention is to choose the elements at 25°C and 1 atm as the reference state. If an element can exist in different phases or different crystalline structures, then the most stable phase or crystal is chosen for the reference or standard state. These states are listed for a few of the elements in Table 9.2; a complete list is given in handbooks.* Enthalpy of each element in its standard state is assigned a value of zero.

TABLE 9.2
STANDARD STATES OF ELEMENTS AT 25°C, 1 ATM

Element	Standard State (enthalpy = 0)
Br_2	Liquid
Ca	Solid
C	Solid (graphite)
Cl_2	Gas
Cu	Solid
F_2	Gas
H_2	Gas
I_2	Solid
Fe	Solid
Mg	Solid
Hg	Liquid
N_2	Gas
O_2	Gas
P	Solid (white)
K	Solid
Na	Solid
S	Solid (rhombic)
Sn	Solid (white)

Under this convention, the enthalpy of any chemical compound at 25°C and 1 atm is equal to the heat of reaction for forming that compound from its elements in their standard state.

Example 9.11

What is the enthalpy of gaseous methane at 25°C relative to its elements?

Solution:

The reaction for forming methane from its elements at 25°C is

$$C(graphite) + 2H_2(g) = CH_4(g)$$

Handbook of Chemistry and Physics, 55th ed., published by Chemical Rubber Publishing Company, Cleveland, 1974-1975.

From Eqn. (9.40),

$$\Delta h^f_{298} = h_{CH_4(g)} - h_{C(graphite)} - 2h_{H_2(g)}$$

By convention,

$$h_{C(graphite)} = 0$$

$$h_{H_2(g)} = 0$$

Therefore,

$$h_{CH_4(g)} = (\Delta h^f_{298})_{CH_4(g)}$$

The previous example shows that the enthalpy of a reacting compound at 25°C and 1 atm is equal to its enthalpy of formation from the elements (Δh^f) at 25°C or 298.15°K. Enthalpies of formation from the elements are reported for a few compounds in Table 9.3. The enthalpy of formation of an element is zero for its most stable state (iodine in solid state, carbon in graphite crystals) but not for other states (iodine in gaseous state, carbon in diamond crystals).

TABLE 9.3
STANDARD ENTHALPIES OF FORMATION (Δh^f) AT 25°C AND 1 ATM

Substance	Reaction	Δh^f (cal/mole)
$CO(g)$	$C(graphite) + \frac{1}{2}O_2 = CO(g)$	$-26,420$
$CO_2(g)$	$C(graphite) + O_2 = CO_2(g)$	$-94,050$
$CH_4(g)$	$C(graphite) + 2H_2(g) = CH_4(g)$	$-17,889$
$H_2O(g)$	$H_2(g) + \frac{1}{2}O_2(g) = H_2O(g)$	$-57,800$
$H_2O(l)$	$H_2(g) + \frac{1}{2}O_2(g) = H_2O(l)$	$-68,320$
$C(diamond)$	$C(graphite) = C(diamond)$	450
$I_2(g)$	$I_2(s) = I_2(g)$	$14,880$
$HCl(g)$	$\frac{1}{2}H_2(g) + \frac{1}{2}Cl_2(g) = HCl(g)$	$-22,060$
$Fe_3O_4(s)$	$3Fe(s) + 2O_2(g) = Fe_3O_4(s)$	$-267,000$
$C_6H_6(l)$	$6C(graphite) + 3H_2(g) = C_6H_6(l)$	$11,720$

Extensive tables of standard enthalpy of formation are available in hand-books* for thousands of chemical compounds. Enthalpy of a reacting compound in a feed or product stream at temperature T is equal to its enthalpy of formation from the elements at 298.15°K plus the enthalpy change for bringing it from 298.15°K to temperature T [see Eqn. (9.37)]:

$$h_j = (\Delta h^f_j)_{298} + \int_{298}^{T} c_{pj}\, dT \qquad (P = 1 \text{ atm}) \qquad (9.41)$$

Both heat of formation (Δh^f) and specific heat at constant pressure (c_p) refer to the same phase (solid, liquid, or gas). Equation (9.41) is for compounds at atmospheric pressure, but the effect of pressure upon enthalpy of liquids and solids is usually negligible. Pressure has no effect upon the enthalpy of a perfect gas. A correction term that accounts for the effect of pressure upon

*Ibid.

enthalpy of real gases is described in thermodynamic textbooks [see for example, *Thermodynamics and Its Applications* by M. Modell and R. C. Reid, Prentice-Hall, Inc., Englewood Cliffs, N. J. (1974)].

Example 9.12

Calculate the enthalpy of methane gas at 200°C and 1 atm relative to the elements at 25°C.

Solution:

The standard heat of formation of methane gas from its elements is $-17,889$ cal/mole (Table 9.3). The specific heat at constant pressure for methane is given by a third-degree polynomial in Table 4.14. Integration is similar to Example 9.5:

$$\int_{298.15}^{473.15} c_p \, dT = 4.750(473.15 - 298.15) + \frac{0.012}{2}(473.15^2 - 298.15^2)$$

$$+ \frac{3.03 \times 10^{-6}}{3}(473.15^3 - 298.15^3)$$

$$- \frac{2.63 \times 10^{-9}}{4}(473.15^4 - 298.15^4)$$

$$= 831.2 + 809.9 + 80.2 - 27.8 = 1693.5 \text{ cal/mole}$$

From Eqn. (9.41),

$$h = -17,899 + 1694 = -16,195 \text{ cal/mole}$$

Heat of reaction

Heat of reaction (ΔH) at temperature T may be found by substituting Eqn. (9.41) into (9.40),

$$\Delta H = \sum v_j (\Delta h_j^f)_{298} + \int_{298}^{T} \Delta c_p \, dT \qquad (9.42)$$

where

$$\Delta c_p = \sum v_j c_{pj} \qquad (9.43)$$

Δc_p is specific heat of products minus specific heat of reactants and, like c_p, is a function of temperature.

The standard heat of reaction (ΔH^0) is the value of ΔH at 298.15°K or, from Eqn. (9.42),

$$\Delta H^0 = \sum v_j (\Delta h_j^f)_{298} \qquad \text{(standard heat of reaction)} \qquad (9.44)$$

because the integral vanishes.

Example 9.13

For the reaction

$$Fe_3O_4(s) + 2CO(g) + 2H_2(g) = 3Fe(s) + 2CO_2(g) + 2H_2O(g)$$

what is the standard heat of reaction at 25°C and 1 atm?

Solution:

From Eqn. (9.44) and Table 9.3,

$\Delta H° = 3 \, \Delta h^f_{Fe(s)} + 2 \, \Delta h^f_{CO_2(g)} + 2 \, \Delta h^f_{H_2O(g)} - \Delta h^f_{Fe_3O_4(s)} - 2\Delta h^f_{CO(g)} - 2 \, \Delta h^f_{H_2(g)}$

$= 3(0) + 2(-94,050) + 2(-57,800) - 1(-267,000) - 2(-26,420) - 2(0)$

$= 16,140 \text{ cal}$

The reaction is endothermic.

Example 9.14

What is the standard heat of reaction at 25°C per pound of methane:

$$CO(g) + 3H_2(g) = CH_4(g) + H_2O(g)$$

Solution:

From Eqn. (9.44) and Table 9.3,

$\Delta H° = \Delta h^f_{CH_4(g)} + \Delta h^f_{H_2O(g)} - \Delta h^f_{CO(g)} - 3 \, \Delta h^f_{H_2(g)}$

$= (-17,889) + (-57,800) - (-26,420) - 3(0)$

$= -49,269 \text{ cal/g-mole of methane}$

The minus sign indicates that the reaction is exothermic.

$$\frac{-(49,269)(1.8)}{16.043} = -5528 \text{ Btu/lb of methane}$$

Standard heat of combustion of hydrocarbon

The standard heat of combustion of a hydrocarbon is the absolute value of the standard heat of reaction at 25°C and 1 atm for

$$(\text{hydrocarbon}) + O_2(g) = CO_2(g) + H_2O(l)$$

Values of the standard heat of combustion for selected hydrocarbons are given in handbooks.*

Example 9.15

Calculate the standard heat of combustion in calories per gram for liquid benzene at 25°C. Products are gaseous carbon dioxide and liquid water.

Solution:

The balanced reaction for combustion of benzene is

$$C_6H_6(l) + 7.5O_2(g) = 6CO_2(g) + 3H_2O(l)$$

From Eqn. (9.44) and Table 9.3,

$$\Delta H° = 6(-94,050) + 3(-68,320) - (11,720) - 7.5(0)$$

$$= -780,980 \text{ cal}$$

*Ibid.

The minus sign indicates that the reaction is exothermic, as expected for combustion of a hydrocarbon.

$$\text{standard heat of combustion} = \frac{780{,}980 \text{ cal}}{\text{mole}} \frac{\text{mole}}{78.11 \text{ g}} = 9998 \text{ cal/g}$$

Additivity of heats of reaction

Since enthalpy is a state function, the overall enthalpy change for a chemical reaction composed of several steps is the sum of the heats of reaction for each step.

Example 9.16

Calculate the standard heat of reaction for

$$Fe_3O_4(s) + 2CO(g) + 2H_2(g) = 3Fe(s) + 2CO_2(g) + 2H_2O(g)$$

by summing the reactions for forming the compounds from their elements.

Solution:

This reaction involving four compounds (Fe_3O_4, CO, CO_2, H_2O) and two elements (H_2, Fe) can be written as the sum of four reactions listed in Table 9.3:

	Heat of Reaction (cal)
$Fe_3O_4(s) = 3Fe(s) + 2O_2(g)$	$-1(-267{,}000)$
$2CO(g) = 2C(\text{graphite}) + O_2(g)$	$-2(-26{,}420)$
$2C(\text{graphite}) + 2O_2(g) = 2CO_2(g)$	$2(-94{,}050)$
$2H_2(g) + O_2(g) = 2H_2O(g)$	$2(-57{,}800)$

$$Fe_3O_4(s) + 2CO(g) + 2H_2(g) = 3Fe(s) + 2CO_2(g) + 2H_2O(g)$$

Since the reaction of interest is the sum of the first four reactions,

$$\Delta H = -1(-267{,}000) - 2(-26{,}420) + 2(-94{,}050) + 2(-57{,}800) = 16{,}140 \text{ cal}$$

Therefore, reduction of iron from magnetite (Fe_3O_4) to elemental iron by this reaction is endothermic and requires 16,140 cal of heat per gram-mole of iron oxide at 25°C. The same result was obtained in Example 9.13.

It should be observed that the heat of reaction depends on the direction of the reaction and the values of the stoichiometric coefficients. Thus, for the reverse reaction,

$$3Fe(s) + 2CO_2(g) + 2H_2O(g) = Fe_3O_4(s) + 2CO(g) + 2H_2(g)$$
$$\Delta H^0 = -16{,}140 \text{ cal}$$

For reactions with different stoichiometric coefficients,

$$Fe_3O_4(s) + 2CO(g) + 2H_2(g) = 3Fe(s) + 2CO_2(g) + 2H_2O(g)$$
$$\Delta H^0 = 16{,}140 \text{ cal}$$

$$2Fe_3O_4(s) + 4CO(g) + 4H_2(g) = 6Fe(s) + 4CO_2(g) + 4H_2O(g)$$

$$\Delta H^0 = 32{,}280 \text{ cal}$$

Therefore, to avoid ambiguity, it is a good idea to write down the reaction for which the heat of reaction is calculated.

Mixtures

The enthalpy of a reacting substance is calculated by Eqn. (9.41). If the substance is inert in the particular problem under study, then its enthalpy of formation is redundant and may be set equal to zero. Furthermore, the reference temperature may be chosen for convenience in the case of inert substances.

The enthalpy of a mixture of substances (h_{mix}) is the sum of enthalpies of its constituents:

$$h_{mix} = \sum_{j=1}^{N_c} h_j x_j \tag{9.45}$$

h_j and x_j are molar enthalpy and mole fraction, respectively, of the jth compound. Summation is over the N_c components of the mixture. Equation (9.45) is for mixtures of perfect gases and mixtures of ideal liquids that exhibit no heat effect when mixed isothermally. A correction term for nonideal liquid mixtures and real gas mixtures is described in textbooks on thermodynamics*.

9.5 Energy Balance Under Nonisothermal Conditions

If a chemical reaction occurs under isothermal conditions, its enthalpy change may be calculated by Eqn. (9.42). This equation is useful in the simple case when reactants are present in stoichiometric proportions, when the reaction proceeds to completion (100% conversion), and when feed and products are at the same temperature. If feed and products are at different temperatures or if the reaction is incomplete, one must make an energy balance by means of Eqn. (9.28).

An energy balance based upon Eqn. (9.28) can be useful in several ways. If the states (temperature, pressure, composition, phase) of feed and product streams are known, then either heat load or power requirement can be calculated. If heat load or power requirement is a design variable, then Eqn. (9.28) can be applied to calculate the enthalpy and therefore the temperature of the products.

Although the principle of an energy balance is straightforward, calculations are difficult and proficiency is acquired by working examples.

*Thermodynamics and Its Applications, op. cit.

Example 9.17

De Beni and Marchetti* proposed a process for thermochemical production of hydrogen from water according to the following set of reactions:

$$CaBr_2 + 2H_2O = Ca(OH)_2 + 2HBr$$
$$HgO = Hg + \tfrac{1}{2}O_2$$
$$2HBr + Hg = HgBr_2 + H_2$$
$$HgBr_2 + Ca(OH)_2 = CaBr_2 + HgO + H_2O$$

The first two reactions are to be run at high temperature (600°–730°C) and the last two reactions are carried out at lower temperature (200°–250°C). The sum of these four reactions is simply the splitting of water:

$$H_2O = H_2 + \tfrac{1}{2}O_2$$

All the other compounds [$CaBr_2$, $Ca(OH)_2$, HBr, $HgBr_2$, HgO, Hg] are separated and recycled so that the overall process is as shown in Fig. 9-11. The purpose of this process is the manufacture of hydrogen to be used as a nonpolluting, multipurpose fuel. According to one design of the process, heat rejected to the environment (Q_2) is 62,200 cal/g-mole of water. What is the heating requirement (Q_1) in kilowatt-hours per pound of hydrogen?

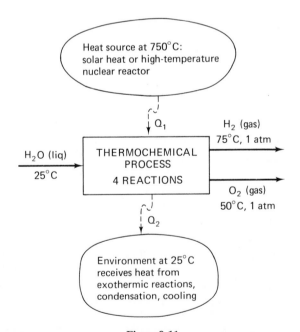

Figure 9-11

*C. Marchetti, "Hydrogen and Energy," *Chem. Economy Eng. Rev.*, 5, 7 (1973).

Solution:

Standard heats of formation at 25°C are (see Table 9.3)

$$\Delta h^f_{298} \text{ (cal)}$$

$H_2O(l)$	$-68,320$
$H_2(g)$	0
$O_2(g)$	0

Specific heats of hydrogen and oxygen are nearly constant over the temperature interval from 25° to 75°C so that Eqn. (9.39) may be used:

Gas	Temperature Interval	$\bar{c}_p$ (cal/mole-°K)
H_2	25°–75°C	6.90
O_2	25°–50°C	7.06

$\bar{c}_p$ is calculated at the midpoint of the interval using Eqn. (4.32) and constants from Table 4.14.

From Eqn. (9.41),

$$h_{H_2O} = -68,320 + \qquad\quad 0 \qquad\quad = -68,320 \text{ cal/mole}$$
$$h_{H_2} = \quad 0 \quad + (6.90)(348 - 298) = 345 \qquad \text{cal/mole}$$
$$h_{O_2} = \quad 0 \quad + (7.06)(323 - 298) = 176 \qquad \text{cal/mole}$$

These are molar enthalpies of feed and product streams, which are assumed to be pure. Let the basis for the calculation be 1 g-mole of feed (H_2O), which yields 1 g-mole of hydrogen and $\frac{1}{2}$ g-mole of oxygen. From Eqn. (9.27),

$$H_{prod} - H_{react} = Q_1 - Q_2$$

Waste heat is $Q_2 = 62,200$ cal and

$$H_{react} = h_{H_2O} = -68,320 \text{ cal}$$
$$H_{prod} = (1)(345) + \tfrac{1}{2}(176) = 433 \text{ cal}$$

Therefore,

$$Q_1 = H_{prod} - H_{react} + Q_2$$
$$= 433 - (-68,320) + 62,200 = 130,953 \text{ cal}$$
$$q'_1 = \frac{130,953 \text{ cal}}{\text{g-mole of } H_2} \left(\frac{\text{g-moles of } H_2}{2.016 \text{ g}} \right) \left(\frac{453.6 \text{ g}}{\text{lb}} \right) \left(\frac{1.162 \times 10^{-6} \text{ kw-hr}}{\text{cal}} \right)$$
$$= 34.2 \text{ kw-hr/lb of } H_2$$

Notice that the change of enthalpy for cooling products to 25°C (433 cal/g-mole of hydrogen) is small compared to the heat of reaction for splitting water at 25°C and could have been neglected without appreciable error:

$$H_2O = H_2 + \tfrac{1}{2}O_2$$
$$\Delta H = 0 + 0 - (-68,320) = 68,320 \text{ cal/g-mole of } H_2$$

Neglecting sensible heat for heating products above 25°C, the heat source must supply heat for the endothermic water-decomposition reaction plus heat loss to the environment or

$$q_1 \simeq 68{,}320 + 62{,}200 = 130{,}520 \text{ cal/g-mole of } H_2$$

Example 9.18

A coal gasifier reacts coal, oxygen, and steam to produce a power gas which may be used directly as a fuel or processed to make methane. In a test run, graphite instead of coal was fed to the gasifier under the conditions shown in Fig. 9-12. Feed rates:

> graphite: 100 lb/hr
>
> oxygen: 1300 ft³/hr   (measured at 25°C, 1 atm)
>
> steam: 490 ft³/hr   (measured at 25°C, 1 atm)

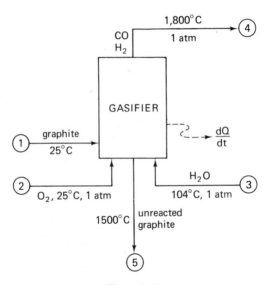

Figure 9-12

Chemical reactions in the gasifier are

$$C + H_2O \longrightarrow CO + H_2$$

$$2C + O_2 \longrightarrow 2CO$$

Small amounts of carbon dioxide formed under these conditions are ignored.

1. Make a material balance and find the flow rate and composition of the product gas.
2. Calculate the rate of generation of heat (dQ/dt) by an energy balance.
3. What is the overall thermal efficiency for gasification of graphite?

$$\eta \equiv \frac{\text{std heat of combustion of product gas}}{\text{std heat of combustion of graphite}}$$

Solution:

1. *Material balance.* Let the compounds be numbered as follows:

Compound	No.
C	1
O_2	2
H_2O	3
CO	4
H_2	5

Equations are

$$\text{C balance:} \quad F_1 = F_5 + F_4 x_{44} \tag{1}$$

$$\text{H balance:} \quad 2F_3 = 2F_4 x_{45} \tag{2}$$

$$\text{O balance:} \quad 2F_2 + F_3 = F_4 x_{44} \tag{3}$$

$$x_{44} + x_{45} = 1 \tag{4}$$

There are four equations and four unknowns (F_4, x_{44}, x_{45}, F_5).
Conversion to molar flow rates:

$$F_1 = \frac{100}{12.011} = 8.326 \text{ lb-moles/hr}$$

At 25°C, 1 atm, the molar volume of a perfect gas is

$$v = \frac{RT}{P} = \frac{0.7302 \text{ ft}^3\text{-atm}}{\text{lb-mole °R}} \frac{536.67°R}{1 \text{ atm}} = 392 \text{ ft}^3/\text{lb-mole}$$

$$F_2 = \frac{1300}{392} = 3.316 \text{ lb-moles/hr}$$

$$F_3 = \frac{490}{392} = 1.25 \text{ lb-moles/hr}$$

Solution of equations:

$$F_4 x_{44} = 2F_2 + F_3 = 2(3.316) + 1.25 = 7.882 \text{ lb-moles/hr}$$

$$F_4 x_{45} = F_3 = 1.25 \text{ lb-moles/hr}$$

$$F_4 = F_4 x_{44} + F_4 x_{45} = 7.882 + 1.25 = 9.132 \text{ lb-moles/hr}$$

$$x_{44} = \frac{F_4 x_{44}}{F_4} = \frac{7.882}{9.132} = 0.863$$

$$x_{45} = 1 - x_{44} = 0.137$$

$$F_5 = F_1 - F_4 x_{44} = 8.326 - 7.882 = 0.444 \text{ lb-mole/hr}$$

2. *Energy balance.* The enthalpy of each compound which participates in chemical reactions is calculated from Eqn. (9.41). In this particular example there are no inert substances. The integral in Eqn. (9.41) must be evaluated for each compound not at 25°C. For steam, the temperature interval is small, so

$$\int_{298}^{377} c_p \, dT \simeq c_p \, \Delta T = (8.109)(377 - 298) = 641 \text{ cal/g-mole}$$

where c_p is calculated at the midpoint of the interval (64.5°C = 337.65°K) using Eqn. (4.32) and constants in Table 4.14.

Heat capacity of graphite over the temperature range from 298° to 2000°K is given by*

$$c_p = a + bT - \frac{c}{T^2}$$

with

$$\left.\begin{array}{l} a = 4.03 \\ b = 0.114 \times 10^{-2} \\ c = 2.04 \times 10^5 \end{array}\right\} \quad \text{for } c_p \text{ in cal/g-mole-°K and } T \text{ in °K}$$

$$\int_{T_1}^{T_2} c_p \, dT = a(T_2 - T_1) + \frac{b}{2}(T_2^2 - T_1^2) + c\left(\frac{1}{T_2} - \frac{1}{T_1}\right)$$

$$= 4.03(1773 - 298) + \frac{0.114 \times 10^{-2}}{2}(1773^2 - 298^2)$$

$$+ 2.04 \times 10^5 \left(\frac{1}{1773} - \frac{1}{298}\right)$$

$$= 7116 \text{ cal/g-mole} \qquad \text{(graphite at 1500°C)}$$

Heat capacities of CO and H_2 are taken from Table 4.14. The integral (see Example 9.5) is

$$\int_{T_1}^{T_2} c_p \, dT = a(T_2 - T_1) + \frac{b}{2}(T_2^2 - T_1^2) + \frac{c}{3}(T_2^3 - T_1^3) + \frac{d}{4}(T_2^4 - T_1^4)$$

For carbon monoxide,

$$\int_{T_1}^{T_2} c_p \, dT = 6.480(2073 - 298) + \frac{0.1566 \times 10^{-2}}{2}(2073^2 - 298^2)$$

$$- \frac{0.02387 \times 10^{-5}}{3}(2073^3 - 298^3) + 0$$

$$= 11,502 + 3296 - 707 = 14,091 \text{ cal/g-mole}$$

For hydrogen,

$$\int_{T_1}^{T_2} c_p \, dT = 6.424(2073 - 298) + \frac{0.1039 \times 10^{-2}}{2}(2073^2 - 298^2)$$

$$- \frac{0.007804 \times 10^{-5}}{3}(2073^3 - 298^3) + 0$$

$$= 11,403 + 2187 - 231 = 13,359 \text{ cal/g-mole}$$

Using Eqn. (9.41),

Substance	T (°K)	Δh_{298}^f	$\int_{298}^{T} c_p \, dT$	Molar Enthalpy at T (cal/g-mole)
C(graphite)	298	0	0	0
C(graphite)	1773	0	7,116	7,116
O_2	298	0	0	0
H_2O	377	−57,800	641	−57,159
CO	2073	−26,420	14,091	−12,329
H_2	2073	0	13,359	13,359

*G. N. Lewis, M. Randall, K. S. Pitzer, and L. Brewer, *Thermodynamics*, 2nd ed., McGraw-Hill, New York, 1961.

Molar enthalpy of the power gas mixture is given by Eqn. (9.45):

$$h_4 = -12,329(0.863) + 13,359(0.137) = -8810 \text{ cal/g-mole}$$

According to the first law of thermodynamics, Eqn. (9.28),

$$F_1h_1 + F_2h_2 + F_3h_3 - F_4h_4 - F_5h_5 - \frac{dQ}{dt} = 0$$

There is no work term, and, according to the direction of the arrow shown on the process diagram, dQ/dt is positive if heat flows from the gasifier to its surroundings.

$$\frac{dQ}{dt} = F_1h_1 + F_2h_2 + F_3h_3 - F_4h_4 - F_5h_5$$

$$= 8.326(0) + 3.316(0) + 1.25(-57,159) - 9.132(-8810)$$

$$- 0.444(7116)$$

$$= 5845 \frac{\text{lb-moles}}{\text{hr}} \frac{\text{cal}}{\text{g-mole}} \frac{453.6 \text{ g}}{\text{lb}} \frac{\text{Btu}}{252 \text{ cal}} = 10,521 \text{ Btu/hr}$$

3. *Thermal Efficiency.* Unreacted graphite is recycled so that the process yields 9.132 lb-moles/hr of power gas per $8.326 - 0.444 = 7.882$ lb-moles/hr of graphite. The power gas consists of 7.882 lb-moles/hr of carbon monoxide and 1.25 lb-moles/hr of hydrogen.

Combustion of carbon monoxide:

$$CO + \tfrac{1}{2}O_2 = CO_2$$

Using standard heats of formation (Table 9.3),

$$\Delta H = (-94,050) - (-26,420) - \tfrac{1}{2}(0) = -67,630 \text{ cal/g-mole of CO}$$

Standard heat of combustion of carbon monoxide at 25°C is 67,630 cal/g-mole of CO.

Combustion of hydrogen:

$$H_2 + \tfrac{1}{2}O_2 = H_2O(l)$$

$$\Delta H = (-68,320) - 0 - \tfrac{1}{2}(0) = -68,320 \text{ cal/g-mole of } H_2$$

Standard heat of combustion of hydrogen at 25°C (assuming that water vapor is condensed) is 68,320 cal/g-mole of H_2.

Combustion of graphite:

$$C + O_2 = CO_2$$

$$\Delta H = (-94,050) - 0 - \tfrac{1}{2}(0) = -94,050 \text{ cal/g-mole of C}$$

Standard heat of combustion of graphite at 25°C is 94,050 cal/g-mole of C.

Overall thermal efficiency of the graphite gasification process is

$$\eta = \frac{\text{std heat of combustion, product gas}}{\text{std heat of combustion, graphite}}$$

$$= \frac{7.882(67,630) + 1.25(68,320)}{7.882(94,050)} \times 100 = 83.4\%$$

Thus, the amount of heat generated by combustion of the power gas is 83% of the heat available from direct combustion of graphite. (Notice that the conversion factor from gram-moles to pound-moles is omitted because it cancels in the numerator and denominator.) The loss (17%) could be reduced by recovering some of the thermal energy of the hot power gas.

Coal contains a considerable amount of hydrogen (see Ch. 2), and therefore coal gasification yields a product gas containing a much larger percentage of hydrogen gas (with small amounts of H_2S, COS, CO_2, and H_2O).

Example 9.19

The freezer unit of a vacuum freezing-vapor compression process for desalination of sea water (see Ch. 2) operates, under conditions at steady state, as shown in Fig. 9-13. Make a material and energy balance on the freezer to calculate unknown flow rates and rate of absorption of heat from the environment.

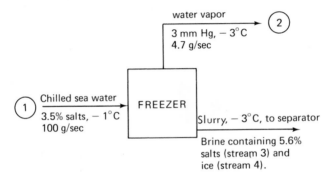

Figure 9-13

Solution:

1. *Material balance:*

Substance	No.
H_2O	1
Salt	2

"Salt" is a complex mixture of dissolved ions (see Ch. 2), but since its composition does not change, it can be treated as a single substance.

Equations (mass units):

$$F_1 x_{12} = F_3 x_{32}$$
$$F_1 = F_2 + F_3 + F_4$$

Solution of equations:

$$F_3 = F_1 \frac{x_{12}}{x_{32}} = (100)\frac{(0.035)}{(0.056)} = 62.5 \text{ g/sec}$$
$$F_4 = F_1 - F_2 - F_3 = 100 - 4.7 - 62.5 = 32.8 \text{ g/sec}$$

Summary:

Stream No.	F (g/sec)	Mass Fraction		State of H_2O	T (°C)
		H_2O	Salt		
1	100	0.965	0.035	Liquid	−1
2	4.7	1	0	Vapor	−3
3	62.5	0.944	0.056	Liquid	−3
4	32.8	1	0	Ice	−3

2. *Energy balance.* The energy balance may be simplified by ignoring the salts, which remain in the dissolved state and constitute only a small fraction of feed and product. The enthalpy change of the salts is small compared to that of water. The energy balance, Eqn. (9.28), is

$$F_1 h_1 - F_2 h_2 - F_3 h_3 - F_4 h_4 + \frac{dQ}{dt} = 0$$

where h, according to the simplification, is the specific enthalpy of water in each stream and F is the mass flow rate of water. Heats of formation are not needed in this problem because there are no chemical reactions. To calculate a consistent value of enthalpy in each stream, a standard state must be chosen for water. Let us choose $h = 0$ for liquid water at 0°C.

Stream 1. For liquid water at −1°C,

$$h_1 = \int_0^{-1°C} c_p\, dT \simeq c_p\, \Delta T = (1.00)(-1 - 0) = -1 \text{ cal/g}$$

Stream 2. For water vapor at −3°C, enthalpy is calculated in two steps:

    a. Vaporize water at 0°C: $h = 597.7$ cal/g.*
    b. Cool water vapor from 0° to −3°C: $\Delta h \simeq c_p\, \Delta T = 0.445(-3 - 0) = -1.3$ cal/g.

Therefore,

$$h_2 = 597.7 - 1.3 = 596.4 \text{ cal/g}$$

Stream 3. For liquid water at −3°C,

$$h_3 \simeq c_p\, \Delta T = 1.00(-3 - 0) = -3 \text{ cal/g}$$

Stream 4. For ice at −3°C, enthalpy is calculated in two steps:

    a. Freeze water at 0°C: $\Delta h = -79.7$ cal/g.†
    b. Cool ice from 0° to −3°C: $\Delta h \simeq c_p\, \Delta T = 0.502(-3 - 0) = -1.5$.

Therefore,

$$h_4 = -79.7 - 1.5 = -81.2 \text{ cal/g}$$

Handbook of Chemistry and Physics, op. cit.
†*Ibid.*

The energy balance on the freezer for the water (excluding salts) is

$$\frac{dQ}{dt} = F_2 h_2 + F_3 h_3 + F_4 h_4 - F_1 h_1$$

$$= 4.7(596.4) + 59(-3) + 32.8(-81.2) - 96.5(-1)$$

$$= 59.2 \text{ cal/sec}$$

This heat leak from the surroundings into the freezer is a result of imperfect insulation. Notice that the ratio of ice to vapor generated in the freezer is

$$\frac{\text{ice}}{\text{water vapor}} = \frac{F_4}{F_2} = \frac{32.8}{4.7} = 7.0$$

This is somewhat less than the theoretical value of 7.5 for isothermal heat exchange of ice and vapor at 0°C (see Ch. 2).

PROBLEMS

9.1. Calculate the specific kinetic energy, in Btu/lb, of a fluid traveling at a velocity of 100 mph.

9.2. Turbines in a hydroelectric plant are fed by water falling from a height of 100 ft. Estimate the number of tons of water per hour needed to keep a 100-W light bulb burning.

9.3. Calculate the increase in potential energy, relative to sea level, of a 175-lb man who climbs to the top of Mount Fujiyama (height 12,395 ft). How much energy in kilocalories must be supplied by metabolic processes?

9.4. Gas is confined in a cylinder by a piston with a cross-sectional area of 10 cm². 0.25 cal of work is required to push the piston downward a distance of 1 mm. What is the pressure of the gas in the cylinder?

9.5. One mole of propane is compressed isothermally by a piston from 30 to 0.5 liters at 400°K. Compute the work done on the gas by the piston. Assume that propane is a van der Waals fluid. How does the work compare with that for a perfect gas? How much heat is liberated to the surroundings?

9.6. One kilogram of neon gas is compressed very slowly, at a constant temperature of 20°C, from 1 to 50 atm. For neon gas,

$$U = \tfrac{3}{2} nRT = \text{internal energy}$$

$$PV = nRT$$

How much heat is evolved by the neon during compression?

9.7. Starting at atmospheric pressure (see point A in Fig. 9-14), gas enclosed in a piston-cylinder apparatus is carried through a clockwise cycle back to point A. Calculate the net heat absorbed by the gas for the cycle.

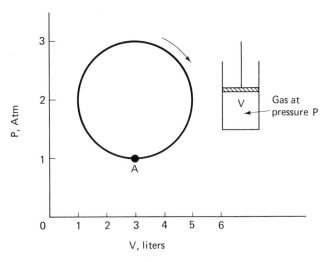

Figure 9-14

9.8. Consider the indicator diagram in Fig. 9-5. How much torque is delivered to the crankshaft of a six-cylinder engine operating at 2000 rpm?

9.9. One mole of air is expanded isothermally against a piston, at 1 atm, from 20 to 40 liters at 10°C. Compute the work done on the piston by the gas. Assume that air is a perfect gas. How much heat enters the cylinder from the surroundings? Compute the change in enthalpy of air in the cylinder.

9.10. Prepare a plot of enthalpy of benzene versus temperature between 100° and 500°K. Let the reference state be solid benzene at 100°K and 1 atm. The latent heats of fusion and vaporization are 30.1 and 103.57 cal/g, respectively. (*Hint:* Use Fig. 9-9.)

9.11. Calculate the enthalpies of the gases CH_4, O_2, N_2, and CO_2 at 500°F and atmospheric pressure relative to
a. The pure gases at 300°F and 1 atm.
b. The elements at 25°C and 1 atm.

9.12. Calculate the enthalpies of benzene, water, and carbon tetrachloride at 1500°C and 1 atm. Let the reference state be the pure liquids at 30°C and 1 atm.

9.13. Calculate the heat of reaction for the following reactions at 25°C and at 750°C (1 atm):

$$2CO(g) \longrightarrow CO_2(g) + C(graphite)$$
$$CH_4(g) \longrightarrow C(graphite) + 2H_2(g)$$
$$C_2H_4(g) + Cl_2(g) \longrightarrow C_2H_4Cl_2(l)$$
$$2SO_2(g) + O_2(g) \longrightarrow 2SO_3(g)$$

Use standard thermochemical data in the *Handbook of Chemistry and Physics*.

9.14. Product gases from a burner have the composition

	Mole %
O_2	2.93
CO_2	10.00
H_2O	13.33
N_2	73.74

Calculate the enthalpy of the combustion products at 2100°C and 1 atm relative to the elements at 25°C.

9.15. In the vinyl chloride process, 15,830 lb/hr of dichloroethane at 90°C and 1.5 atm are mixed with 10,550 lb/hr of recycle at 146°C. Compute the temperature of the mixed stream. (See Fig. 3-3.)

9.16. Liquid dichloroethane enters an evaporator (Fig. 3-6) at 112°C and 26 atm. It is heated to its boiling point (242°C) and vaporized. Calculate the heat required. How many pounds of saturated steam at 5 atm are condensed per pound of dichloroethane? The specific heat of liquid dichloroethane, between 112° and 242°C, is approximately 0.37 cal/g-°C. Estimate the latent heat of vaporization using Pitzer's theory of corresponding states.

9.17. See Fig. 9-15. Stream 1 (pure liquid water) is mixed adiabatically at 1 atm with stream 2 (pure sulfuric acid). Calculate the temperature and composition of the product stream for

$$F_1 = 100 \text{ lb/hr}, \qquad T_1 = 80°F$$
$$F_2 = 25 \text{ lb/hr}, \qquad T_2 = 100°F$$

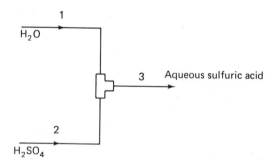

Figure 9-15

An enthalpy-concentration diagram for aqueous sulfuric acid is given in Perry's handbook, 4th ed., p. 3-190.

9.18. Hot sulfur dioxide gas is condensed to the saturated liquid in Fig. 9-16. Calculate the rate of heat transfer, dQ/dt, for

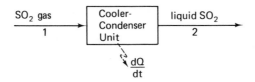

Figure 9-16

$$F_1 = 100 \text{ lb/hr}, \qquad T_1 = 2000°F, P_1 = 150 \text{ psia}$$
$$T_2 = 80°F, \qquad P_2 = 60 \text{ psia}$$

There are data on the enthalpy of sulfur dioxide on p. E-30 of the *Handbook of Chemistry and Physics*, 54th ed. Specific heat of the gas is given in Table 4.14.

9.19. Steam enters a supersonic nozzle with a velocity of 10 ft/sec at a pressure of 500 psia and a temperature of 1000°F. At the nozzle discharge, pressure and temperature are measured and found to be 300°F and atmospheric pressure. What is the discharge velocity from the nozzle? Assume that the nozzle is adiabatic. Thermodynamic properties of steam (Keenan and Keyes) are

500 psia, 1000°F	1 atm, 300°F
$h = 1520$ Btu/lb	$h = 1193$ Btu/lb
$v = 1.700$ ft^3/lb	$v = 30.53$ ft^3/lb

9.20. A gas turboexpander delivers 834 W of mechanical power. (See Fig. 9-17.) The gas is oxygen at the steady mass flow rate of 15 g/sec. Oxygen enters the turbine at 200°K, 60 atm, and leaves at 9 atm. Calculate the exit temperature of the oxygen. Assume that the turbine is adiabatic.

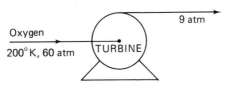

Figure 9-17

9.21. A multistage flash distillation process produces 2.5 million gal of freshwater per day from seawater as shown in Fig. 2-8.
  a. Make an overall material balance to determine flow rates of seawater feed and brine returned to the ocean.
  b. Make an energy balance on the flashing brine as it passes through the multistage evaporator to determine the flow rate of recycle brine.

9.22. The freezer unit of a vacuum freezing-vapor compression process for desalination of sea water (see Ch. 2) operates adiabatically, under conditions at steady state as shown in Fig. 9-18. Make a material and energy balance to calculate unknown flow rates. For simplicity, ignore the salt in the energy balance (but not in the material balance). What is the ratio of ice to vapor generated in the freezer?

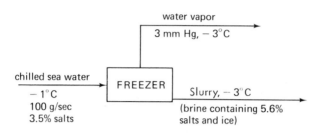

Figure 9-18

9.23. Bioenergetics is an application of material and energy balances to living things. The steady-state material balance on a man is

MATERIAL BALANCE, MAN—1 DAY

	F'				Weight Fraction				
Stream	(g/day)	O_2	CO_2	H_2O	Carbo.	Fat	Prot.	Urea	Inert
In									
Food	2400	—	—	0.5416	0.125	0.0417	0.0417	—	0.250
Drink	1000	—	—	1.0	—	—	—	—	—
Inhalation	809	1.0	—	—	—	—	—	—	—
Out									
Perspiration	869	—	—	1.0	—	—	—	—	—
Feces	800	—	—	0.25	—	—	—	—	0.75
Urine	1500	—	—	0.9813	—	—	—	0.0187	—
Exhalation	1035	—	0.806*	0.194*	—	—	—	—	—

*Mole fraction.

a. Check this material balance (C, H, O, N, total mass, inerts) assuming no accumulation of matter in the body.

Thermochemical and miscellaneous data are

HEAT OF COMBUSTION

Substance	Chemical Comp.	Heat of Combustion (gas CO_2, liq H_2O) (kcal/g)
Carbohydrate	$C_{12}H_{22}O_{11}$	4.0
Fat	$(C_{17}H_{35}COO)_3$-C_3H_5	9.0
Protein	$C_{5.2}H_{8.5}O_{1.4}N$	4.0
Urea	H_2N-CO-NH_2	

MISCELLANEOUS BIOENERGETIC DATA

Energy yield from food combustion $= 5$ cal/cm^3 of O_2
Basal metabolic rate for adult $= 70$ kcal/hr
Energy from food combustion: 2000–4000 kcal/day for adult
                                2500–3000 kcal/day for "normal" adult
                                1000–1500 kcal/day for strict diet

---

b. Calculate the chemical energy obtained from combustion of food in kcal/day using the material balance given.
c. This chemical energy goes to

1. Vaporize water (respiration and perspiration).
2. Heat loss to surroundings by radiation, conduction, and convection.
3. Work done on surroundings.

Assuming that the work done is 200 kcal/day, calculate the heat loss to the surroundings by radiation, conduction, and convection in kcal/day. How much is this in watts?

9.24. The temperature of a sick man rises from 37° to 39.4°C. Assuming that this thermal energy is derived from the combustion of carbohydrates, how much is consumed in grams?

9.25. A 210-lb man consumes 3000 kcal/day and neither gains nor loses weight. He wants to reduce his weight to 190 lb in 3 months. Prescribe his diet in grams of food per day, assuming 60% carbohydrates, 20% fat, and 20% protein.

9.26. A man (weight 165 lb) operates a bicycle-type exercise machine for $\frac{1}{2}$ hr. The measured torque is 10.2 ft-lb$_f$, and the speed is 2 rev/sec. His oxygen consumption rate over this period is 2600 cm^3/min, and his total water loss by respiration and perspiration is 0.68 lb.
a. What is the total amount of energy from the combustion of food in kcal?
b. How much work is done in kcal?
c. How much heat does the man give off to the surroundings by radiation, conduction, and convection?
d. What is the efficiency of converting chemical energy into work?

9.27. Process heating is needed at 350°F for a reactor, and steam at 220°F is available. (See Fig. 9-19.) A heat pump that uses water as the working fluid can be designed to deliver heat to the reactor at a temperature above 350°F. Fill in the missing design specifications for the heat pump. (*Hint:* Start with the compressor and work counterclockwise around the flow diagram. The valve is adiabatic (isenthalpic), the evaporator and condenser are isobaric, and the compressor is adiabatic. Depressurized water from the valve is a two-phase mixture of liquid and vapor. Obtain thermodynamic properties from the steam tables.) Calculate the coefficient of performance (C.O.P.) of the heat pump:
$$\text{C.O.P.} = Q_H/W.$$

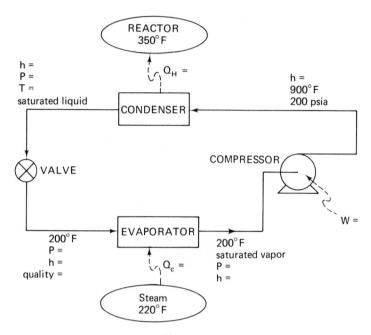

Figure 9-19

9.28. A heater using Dowtherm A (see the thermodynamic data below from Perry's handbook) supplies process heating at two temperatures. (See Fig. 9-20.) The high temperature (600°F) is controlled by the pressure in the vaporizer (43 psia), and the low temperature is controlled by a bypass loop which returns part of the cold liquid to the low-temperature heat exchanger. The following data were recorded during steady-state operation of the system: $T_1 = T_2$

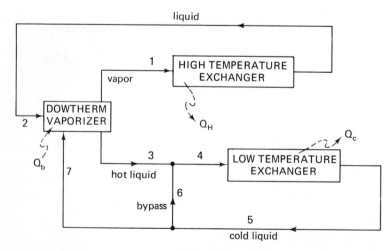

Figure 9-20

$= T_3 = 600°F,\; T_5 = T_6 = T_7 = 300°F,\; T_4 = 350°F,\; dQ_h/dt = 1.5 \times 10^6$ Btu/hr, $dQ_c/dt = 3.75 \times 10^6$ Btu/hr. Calculate the flow rates of all streams. (*Hint:* Write material and energy balances for each unit. For example, for the vaporizer,

$$F_2 h_2 + F_7 h_7 + \frac{dQ_b}{dt} = F_1 h_1 + F_3 h_3$$

Assume that streams 3 and 6 mix adiabatically. There are four independent energy balances.) Data for saturated Dowtherm A (73.5% diphenyloxide, 26.5% diphenyl):

Temperature (°F)	Pressure (psia)	Enthalpy (Btu/lb)	
		Liquid	Vapor
280	0.49	97.5	240
300	0.74	108	250
320	1.1	118	258
340	1.6	128	266
360	2.2	138	275
380	3.0	150	286
400	4.1	162	296
500	15	222	345
600	43	288	398
700	103	358	455

Material and Energy 10
Balances

In this chapter, all the skills that have been developed, particularly those pertaining to numerical methods, thermodynamics, and computer-based information systems, are assembled to make material and energy balances on chemical process units operating at steady state. Before analyzing the problem, we shall briefly review the material and energy balance equations.

10.1 Review of Material Balance Equations

The principle of conservation of mass, applied to a process unit operating at steady state, is

$$\sum_{i=1}^{N_s} F_i x_{ij} = 0 \tag{10.1}$$

where F_i is the signed molar flow rate of stream i. The sign convention is that F_i is positive if stream i enters the process unit, and negative if the stream leaves the process unit. The total number of mass streams in the summation is N_s. There is one equation of type (10.1) for each nonreacting component j [see Eqn. (6.4)].

For those components that participate in chemical reactions, Eqn. (10.1) does not apply because molecular species are not preserved. The principle of conservation of chemical elements is applied to those components which react chemically,

$$\sum_{i=1}^{N_s} \sum_{j=1}^{N_r} F_i x_{ij} m_{jk} = 0 \tag{10.2}$$

where m_{jk} is number of atoms in component j of element k [see Eqn. (7.10)]. There is one equation of type (10.2) for each element present in the reacting components, but all these equations may not be independent.

10.2 Review of Energy Balance Equation

The principle of conservation of energy for a process unit operating at steady state is [see Eqn. (9.28)]

$$\sum_{i=1}^{N_s} F_i h_i + \sum \frac{dQ_i}{dt} + \sum \frac{dW_i}{dt} = 0 \qquad (10.3)$$

Equation (10.3) is written in terms of number of moles: F_i is molar flow rate, and h_i is molar enthalpy. Each term in Eqn. (10.3) has units of energy per unit time.

dQ_i/dt in Eqn. (10.3) is rate of transfer of heat across the boundary of the process unit. dW_i/dt is rate of transfer of energy in the form of work across the boundary. All the energy streams (F_i, dQ_i/dt, and dW_i/dt) are signed according to the convention

Direction of Flow of Mass or Energy	Sign of Stream
Into process unit	$+$
Out of process unit	$-$

Thus, a positive value for dQ_i/dt means that heat enters the process from the surroundings. A positive value for dW_i/dt means that work is done on the process unit *by* the surroundings.

Heat flow across the boundary of the process unit occurs by the mechanisms of radiation and conduction. Work may be electrical or mechanical. Work done by the surroundings to force a mass stream into or out of the process unit is *not* written as a separate work term; flow work is taken into account automatically by the enthalpy of the mass stream.

It is important to prescribe the boundary of the process unit in order to identify its interactions with the environment. If there is more than one mass, heat, or work interaction, a summation according to Eqn. (10.3) is needed. Since Eqn. (10.3) is for steady state, there must be at least two mass streams (feed and product).

Enthalpy is measured at the point where the stream crosses the boundary of the process unit. Methods for computing enthalpy as a function of temperature, pressure, and composition are given in Chapter 9.

In summary, the terms in Eqn. (10.3) account for transport of energy across the process-unit boundary. Mechanisms of energy transport are

Term in Eqn. (10.3)	Mechanism for Transport of Energy
$F_i h_i$	Mass
dQ_i/dt	Heat
dW_i/dt	Work

Equation (10.3) states that *net* rate of transport of energy into the process unit is zero at steady state. Equation (10.1) [or (10.2) for reacting species] and Eqn. (10.3), taken together, stipulate that neither mass nor energy can accumulate within a process unit operated at steady state.

Example 10.1

Pure, superheated ammonia vapor, at 247 psia and 140°F, is condensed at constant pressure to saturated liquid ammonia. Flow rate of the ammonia is 1000 lb/hr. What rate of heat removal is needed to operate the condenser at steady state?

Solution:

The process-unit diagram is shown in Fig. 10-1. The material balance, Eqn. (10.1), is

$$F_1' = F_2'$$

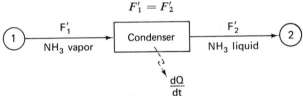

Figure 10-1

The energy balance, Eqn. (10.3), reduces to

$$F_1' h_1' - F_2' h_2' - \frac{dQ}{dt} = 0$$

Mass units (identified by a prime symbol) are used in anticipation of the fact that enthalpy of ammonia is tabulated in mass units. Notice the use of the sign convention: plus (+) for streams entering, and minus (−) for streams leaving the process unit.

Solving these two equations for dQ/dt,

$$\frac{dQ}{dt} = F_1'(h_1' - h_2')$$

Tabulated values of the enthalpy of ammonia are found in Perry's handbook:

State	T (°F)	P (psia)	h' (Btu/lb)
Superheated vapor	140	247	657.7
Saturated liquid	110	247	167.0

where the reference state ($h' = 0$) is saturated liquid ammonia at $-40°C$. The solution is

$$\frac{dQ}{dt} = (1000) \frac{lb}{hr} (657.7 - 167.0) \frac{Btu}{lb} = 4.91 \times 10^5 \text{ Btu/hr}$$

Solution of the previous example is simple because there are only a few variables. If the process unit has several multicomponent streams and equipment parameters, it is necessary to analyze the problem, determine the design variables, and devise a solution procedure. Analysis of the problem is discussed next.

10.3 Analysis of the Problem

Analysis of a material and energy balance problem is similar to that discussed in Ch. 6, as modified in Ch. 7 for reactors. When conservation of energy is imposed, Eqn. (10.3) is added to the list of equations describing the process unit.

Thermodynamic enthalpy (h_i) of each stream is needed in order to apply Eqn. (10.3). According to the phase rule of thermodynamics, molar enthalpy of a single-phase stream containing N_c components is a function of $N_c + 1$ intensive variables. A convenient set of intensive variables is temperature, pressure, and composition. For each stream,

$$h_i = h_i\{T, P, x_{i1}, x_{i2}, \ldots, x_{i,N_c-1}\} \tag{10.4}$$

These $N_c + 1$ variables are independent. The mole fraction of the N_cth component is not independent; it is fixed by the mole-fraction constraint equation for stream i:

$$x_{i1} + x_{i2} + \cdots + x_{i,N_c} = 1 \tag{10.5}$$

Equations describing the operation of a process unit may be classified into five groups:

1. Equipment constraints.
2. Material balance equations.
3. Mole-fraction constraint equations (one per stream).
4. Enthalpy equations (one per stream).
5. Energy balance equation (one per process unit).

Since enthalpy is a function of T and P in addition to composition, the variables for each stream are

Type of Variable	Number of Variables
Composition	N_c
T, P	2
Flow rate	1
Enthalpy	1

Therefore, for energy balance problems, there are $N_c + 4$ variables for each stream. The total number of variables for a process unit is

$$N_v = N_s(N_c + 4) + N_q + N_w + N_p \qquad (10.6)$$

N_q is number of heat terms, N_w is number of work terms, and the other quantities have the usual meaning [see Eqn. (6.5)].

As before, the number of design variables for a process unit is given by

$$N_d = N_v - N_e \qquad (10.7)$$

The analysis is illustrated next for a problem in which experimental values of enthalpy are available in the form of an enthalpy-concentration diagram.

Example 10.2 *Crystallizer*

A Swenson-Walker crystallizer (Fig. 10-2) recovers epsom salts (MgSO$_4 \cdot$ 7H$_2$O) from a concentrated aqueous solution of MgSO$_4$. Feed solution is fed into one end of the trough; crystals form and grow as the solution flows through the trough. Heat is removed by cooling water which flows through a water jacket welded to the outside of the trough. Heat removal is needed to cool the feed solution below saturation and thus provide the driving force for crystallization.

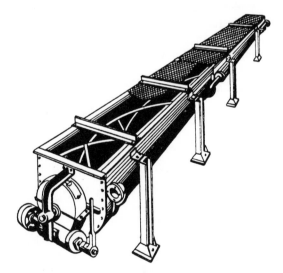

Figure 10-2 Swenson-Walker crystallizer. [J. H. Perry and C. H. Chilton, eds., *Chemical Engineers' Handbook*, 4th ed., McGraw-Hill, New York (1963), p. 17-17.]

Inside the trough, a screw conveyor continuously removes crystals from the sides of the trough and keeps the crystals in suspension for uniform growth. At the end of the trough, liquor and crystals are removed. The crystals are dried in a centrifuge, and liquor is recycled to the process.

Here, recycling of the liquor is ignored by studying the once-through operation of the crystallizer. The overall process diagram is shown in Fig. 10-3.

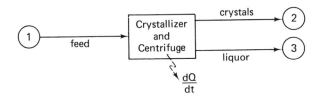

Figure 10-3

Apply the principles of conservation of material and energy to this process. Determine a convenient set of design variables, and devise a solution strategy.

Solution:

The components are

Compound	Number
$MgSO_4$	1
H_2O	2
$MgSO_4 \cdot 7H_2O$	3

1. Equations and constraints.
   a. Equipment constraints. It is assumed that the equilibrium amount of crystals of epsom salt is formed in the crystallizer. Therefore, liquor leaving the crystallizer is a saturated solution; the equilibrium conditions are

$$T_2 = T_{equil} \tag{1}$$

$$T_3 = T_{equil} \tag{2}$$

$$x_{31} = x_{31}\{T_{equil}\} \tag{3}$$

The first two equations impose thermal equilibrium upon the product streams. The third equation represents the equilibrium solubility of $MgSO_4$ in water as a function of temperature. This solubility relation, obtained from experimental data, is plotted in Fig. 10-4. The figure shows that concentration of $MgSO_4$ in the liquor, at equilibrium with $MgSO_4 \cdot 7H_2O$, varies from about 21% by weight at 35.7°F to 33% by weight at 118.8°F. This relationship is given by line bc, which is a plot of equilibrium temperature as a function of $MgSO_4$ concentration in the liquor. At temperatures above 118.8°F, other hydrates ($MgSO_4 \cdot 6H_2O$ and $MgSO_4 \cdot H_2O$) are more stable than the heptahydrate. The pressure is atmospheric for all streams. It is assumed that there is a complete separation of the mother liquor and the epsom salts ($x_{21} = x_{22} = x_{33} = 0$). The feed solution contains no crystals ($x_{13} = 0$).
   b. Material balance equations. There are two independent material balance equations. The chemical reaction is

$$MgSO_4(aq) + 7H_2O \rightleftharpoons MgSO_4 \cdot 7H_2O(s)$$

Element		
Mg	$F_1 x_{11} = F_2 + F_3 x_{31}$	(4)
H	$2F_1 x_{12} = 14F_2 + 2F_3 x_{32}$	(5)

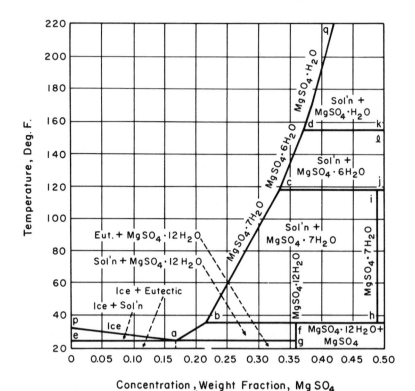

Figure 10-4 Phase diagram of $MgSO_4 \cdot H_2O$ system. [J. H. Perry and C. H. Chilton, eds., Chemical Engineers' Handbook, 4th ed., McGraw-Hill, New York (1963), p. 17-10.]

c. Mole-fraction constraint equations:

$$x_{11} + x_{12} = 1 \tag{6}$$

$$x_{31} + x_{32} = 1 \tag{7}$$

d. Equations (10.4) for enthalpy of each stream at atmospheric pressure are

$$h_1 = h_1\{T_1, x_{11}\} \tag{8}$$

$$h_2 = h_2\{T_2\} \tag{9}$$

$$h_3 = h_3\{T_3, x_{31}\} \tag{10}$$

These enthalpy functions, obtained from experimental data, are plotted on an enthalpy-concentration diagram in Fig. 10-5. The series of lines connects phases in equilibrium; these are called tie lines. The letters $a, b, c, \dots$ correspond to the letters used in Fig. 10-4 and identify the phases. Line hi in Fig. 10-5 is enthalpy of $MgSO_4 \cdot 7H_2O$, Eqn. (9). Line bc provides the enthalpy of the liquor, Eqn. (10). Notice that h_3 is actually a function of a single variable, either T_3 or x_{31}. This conclusion, apparent from Fig. 10-5, also follows from a combination of

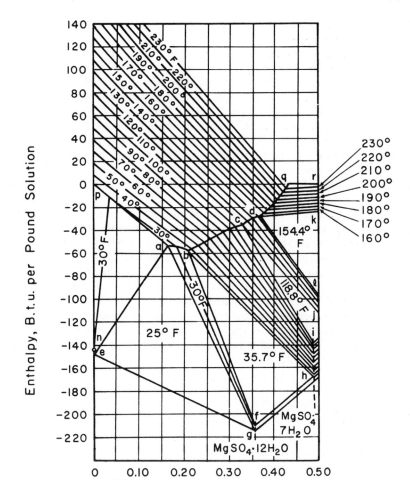

Figure 10-5 Enthalpy-concentration diagram of $MgSO_4 \cdot H_2O$ system. [J. H. Perry and C. H. Chilton, eds., *Chemical Engineers' Handbook*, 4th ed., McGraw-Hill, New York (1963), p. 17-10.]

Eqns. (2), (3), and (10). h_1, enthalpy of the unsaturated feed solution, is a function of two variables, as shown by Eqn. (8); h_1 is plotted in Fig. 10-5 as a function of concentration using temperature (30°, 40°, ..., 230°F) as a parameter.

e. The energy equation:

$$F_1 h_1 - F_2 h_2 - F_3 h_3 - \frac{dQ}{dt} = 0 \tag{11}$$

2. Number of variables: $N_v = 15$ (three flow rates, three temperatures, three enthalpies, four mole fractions, one heat flow rate, and one parameter).

The equipment parameter is the exit temperature (T_{equil}) of the crystals and mother liquor.

3. Design or decision variables: $N_d = N_v - N_e = 15 - 11 = 4$. The feed-stream variables and product temperature form the set F_1, x_{11}, T_1, and T_{equil}. This is the most convenient set of design variables.

4. Solution of equations. The quantity dQ/dt appears in Eqn. (11) only. The enthalpies (h_1, h_2, h_3) appear only in Eqns. (8)–(10). Therefore, the set of four variables dQ/dt, h_1, h_2, and h_3 appears in Eqns. (8)–(11) (the energy balance part of the problem) but not in Eqns. (3)–(7) (the material balance part of the problem). It follows that the material balance portion of the problem can be solved first; the result is then used to solve the energy balance. This breakdown of the problem into two parts simplifies the solution procedure.

The solution of the material balance part of the problem is easy. Equations (3), (6), and (7) are solved directly using the values of the design variables. The material balance equations (4) and (5) are in molar units, but design variables and enthalpy data are in mass units. One could convert design variables to molar units and, after solving the material balance equations in molar units, convert to mass units to solve the energy balance part of the problem. It is easier to reformulate the material balance equations in mass units by treating the hydrate as a mixture of fixed composition, containing α weight fraction $MgSO_4$ and $1 - \alpha$ weight fraction H_2O. Two material balance equations can be written, one for $MgSO_4$ and the other for H_2O,

$$MgSO_4: \quad F_1' x_{11}' = F_2' \alpha + F_3' x_{31}'$$

$$H_2O: \quad F_1' x_{12}' = F_2'(1 - \alpha) + F_3' x_{32}'$$

where α is determined by the weight fractions of $MgSO_4$ and H_2O in the hydrate ($MgSO_4 \cdot 7H_2O$). In 1 mole of hydrate there are 120.4 g of $MgSO_4$ and 7(18.02) g of H_2O. Consequently,

$$\alpha = \frac{120.4}{120.4 + 7(18.02)} = 0.4884$$

Given x_{31}' at T_{equil} (Fig. 10-4) and $x_{32}' = 1 - x_{31}'$, the two material balance equations may be solved simultaneously for the unknown mass flow rates F_2' and F_3'. The numerical solution is illustrated for the following values of the design variables:

$$F_1' = 500 \text{ lb/hr}$$

$$x_{11}' = 0.325 \quad \text{(weight fraction)}$$

$$T_1 = 160°F$$

$$T_{equil} = 70°F$$

Equation (3) yields $x_{31}' = 0.261$ (from Fig. 10-4). Simultaneous solution of the material balance equations gives

$$F_2' = 141 \text{ lb/hr}$$

$$F_3' = 359 \text{ lb/hr}$$

Values of enthalpy in Eqns. (8)–(10) are read from Fig. 10-5. Equation (11) gives

$$\frac{dQ}{dt} = F'_1 h'_1 - F'_2 h'_2 - F'_3 h'_3 = (500)(-6) - (141)(-154) - (359)(-48)$$
$$= 35,900 \text{ Btu/hr}$$

The solution is summarized:

Stream No.	F'_i (lb/hr)	T_i (°F)	P_i (atm)	h'_i (Btu/lb)	Weight Fraction MgSO₄	Weight Fraction H₂O
1	500	160	1	−6	0.325	0.675
2	141	70	1	−154	0.488	0.512
3	359	70	1	−48	0.261	0.739

Values of enthalpy needed to solve the energy balance for the crystallizer had been measured in previous laboratory experiments and were read directly from a graph.

When experimental values of enthalpy are not available, they may be estimated using the methods of Chapter 9 as illustrated in the following example.

Example 10.3   Combustion

The furnace described in Example 7.5 burns propane fuel:

$$C_3H_8 + 5O_2 \longrightarrow 3CO_2 + 4H_2O$$

The flow diagram of the furnace is shown in Fig. 10-6.

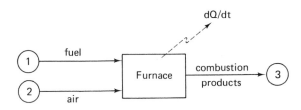

Figure 10-6

Assume, as before, that fuel is pure propane and that all the propane is consumed in the furnace. Values of design variables for the material balance are

$$F_1 = 1 \text{ g-mole/hr} \quad \text{(basis)}$$
$$\alpha = \text{air/fuel ratio} = 28$$

Calculate the heat supplied by this furnace (dQ/dt).

Solution:

The material balance was solved in Example 7.5:

Stream	F_i	Mole Fraction				
No. (i)	(g-mole/hr)	C_3H_8	O_2	CO_2	H_2O	N_2
1	1	1	0	0	0	0
2	28	0	0.21	0	0	0.79
3	30	0	0.0293	0.1	0.1333	0.7374

The component code is

Component	No. (j)
C_3H_8	1
O_2	2
CO_2	3
H_2O	4
N_2	5

1. Equations and constraints. The problem is reduced to an energy balance:

$$\boxed{F_1}h_1 + \boxed{F_2}h_2 - \boxed{F_3}h_3 - \frac{dQ}{dt} = 0 \tag{1}$$

Enthalpy equations (10.4) (in functional notation) are

$$h_1 = h_1\{T_1, P_1\} \tag{2}$$

$$h_2 = h_2\{T_2, P_2, \boxed{x_{22}}\} \tag{3}$$

$$h_3 = h_3\{T_3, P_3, \boxed{x_{33}}, \boxed{x_{34}}, \boxed{x_{35}}\} \tag{4}$$

Known quantities are circled.

2. Number of additional variables: $N_v = 10$ ($h_1, h_2, h_3, T_1, T_2, T_3, P_1, P_2, P_3, dQ/dt$).

3. Additional design or decision variables: $N_d = N_v - N_e = 10 - 4 = 6$. P_1, P_2, P_3, T_1, T_2, and T_3 are selected as design variables in accordance with the problem statement.

4. Solution of equations. The solution is straightforward: h_1, h_2, and h_3 are calculated using specified design variables, and then dQ/dt is given by Eqn. (1). Specifically, consider the following set of design variables:

$$P_1 = P_2 = P_3 = 1 \text{ atm}$$

$$T_1 = T_2 = 25°C = 298.15°K$$

$$T_3 = 871°C = 1144.15°K$$

Equations for calculating enthalpy of reacting, gaseous mixtures are (9.41) and (9.45). The assumption of a perfect gas is satisfactory because pressure is atmospheric. For stream 1,

$$h_1 = \Delta h_1^f + \int_{T_0}^{T_1} c_{p1}\, dT \tag{5}$$

$$= (1)(-24,820) + 0 = -24,820 \text{ cal/mole}$$

c_{p1} is molal specific heat of stream 1. Since the reference temperature is 25°C, the integral is zero. For stream 2,

$$h_2 = \sum_{j=1}^{N_c} x_{2j}\, \Delta h_j^f + \int_{T_0}^{T_2} \bar{c}_{p2}\, dT$$

$$= 0 + 0 = 0 \tag{6}$$

because heats of formation of N_2 and O_2 at 25°C are zero and $T_0 = T_2$. For stream 3,

$$h_3 = \sum_{j=2}^{N_c} x_{3j}\, \Delta h_j^f + \int_{T_0}^{T_3} \bar{c}_{p3}\, dT \tag{7}$$

The molal-average heat of formation is

$$\sum x_{3j}\, \Delta h_j^f = (0.0293)(0) + (0.1)(-94,050)$$

$$+ (0.1333)(-57,800) + (0.7374)(0)$$

$$= -17,110 \text{ cal/mole}$$

Molal-average specific heat at zero pressure is given (see Table 4.14) by

$$\bar{c}_{p3} = \sum_{j=2}^{N_c} x_{3j}(a_j + b_j T + c_j T^2 + d_j T^{-1/2})$$

$$= \bar{a}_3 + \bar{b}_3 T + \bar{c}_3 T^2 + \bar{d}_3 T^{-1/2} \tag{8}$$

Molal-average coefficients $(\bar{a}_3, \bar{b}_3, \bar{c}_3, \bar{d}_3)$ are calculated from coefficients for the pure gases given in Table 4.14:

Component	a_j	$b_j \times 10^2$	$c_j \times 10^5$	d_j
O_2	6.732	0.1505	−0.01791	0
CO_2	18.036	−0.004474	0	−158.08
H_2O	6.970	0.3464	−0.04833	0
N_2	6.529	0.1488	−0.02271	0
Molal avg.	7.744	0.1599	−0.02371	−15.81

Coefficients for propane are not included because there is no propane in the product stream. Substituting Eqn. (8) into (7) and integrating,

$$h_3 = \sum x_{3j}\, \Delta h_j^f + \bar{a}_3(T_3 - T_0) + \frac{\bar{b}_3}{2}(T_3^2 - T_0^2) + \frac{\bar{c}_3}{3}(T_3^3 - T_0^3)$$

$$+ 2\bar{d}_3(T_3^{1/2} - T_0^{1/2}) \tag{9}$$

Substituting $T_3 = 871°C = 1144.15°K$ and $T_0 = 25°C = 298.15°K$,

$h_3 = -17,110 + (7.744)(1144.15 - 298.15) + \frac{1}{2}(0.1599 \times 10^{-2})$

$(1144.15^2 - 298.15^2) + \frac{1}{3}(-0.02371 \times 10^{-5})$

$(1144.15^3 - 298.15^3) + 2(-15.81)(1144.15^{1/2} - 298.15^{1/2})$

$= -17,110 + 6551 + 975 - 116 - 524$

$= -10,224$ cal/mole

Finally, from Eqn. (1),

$$\frac{dQ}{dt} = F_1 h_1 + F_2 h_2 - F_3 h_3$$

$$= (1)(-24,820) + (28)(0) - (30)(-10,224)$$

$$= 281,900 \text{ cal/hr}$$

The molecular weight of propane is 44.1. Therefore, heat liberated per unit mass of propane is

$$\frac{1}{M}\frac{dQ/dt}{F_1} = \frac{(281,900)}{(44.1)(1)} = 6,390 \text{ cal/g}$$

In the previous example, after calculation of the enthalpy of each stream, the energy balance equation is solved for dQ/dt. An interesting complication arises when dQ/dt *is itself a design variable*, for example, in the calculation of an adiabatic flame temperature, illustrated next.

Example 10.4   Adiabatic Flame Temperature of Propane

Calculate the adiabatic flame temperature of propane. Assume, as in Examples 7.5 and 10.3, pure propane fuel burned with an air/fuel ratio of 28.

Solution:

Solution of the material balance part of the problem is the same as in Example 7.5. Energy balance equations are the same as in Example 10.3; using the same notation,

$$\boxed{F_1} h_1 + \boxed{F_2} h_2 - \boxed{F_3} h_3 - \frac{dQ}{dt} = 0 \qquad (1)$$

$$h_1 = h_1\{T_1, P_1\} \qquad (2)$$

$$h_2 = h_2\{T_2, P_2, \boxed{x_{22}}\} \qquad (3)$$

$$h_3 = h_3\{T_3, P_3, \boxed{x_{33}}, \boxed{x_{34}}, \boxed{x_{35}}\} \qquad (4)$$

There are, as before, 10 variables, 4 equations and 6 design variables. The new selection of design variables is $T_1, T_2, P_1, P_2, P_3, dQ/dt$.

Solution of the equations. This set of design variables calls for a new solution procedure. h_1 and h_2 are calculated using the specified design variables. Then h_3 is given by Eqn. (1):

$$h_3 = \frac{F_1 h_1 + F_2 h_2 - dQ/dt}{F_3} \qquad (5)$$

Finally, Eqn. (4) is solved for T_3. The difficulty is that Eqn. (4) cannot be solved explicitly for T_3; graphical methods, the method of successive substitutions, or Newton's method (see Ch. 11) may be used.

Specifically, consider the following values of design variables:

$$P_1 = P_2 = P_3 = 1 \text{ atm}$$

$$T_1 = T_2 = 25°C = 298.15°K$$

$$\frac{dQ}{dt} = 0 \quad \text{(adiabatic flame)}$$

As in Example 10.3,

$$h_1 = -24,820 \text{ cal/mole}$$

$$h_2 = 0$$

From Eqn. (5),

$$h_3 = \frac{F_1 h_1 + F_2 h_2 - dQ/dt}{F_3} = \frac{(1)(-24,820) + (28)(0) - 0}{30} = -827 \text{ cal/mole}$$

As in Example 10.3, the explicit formula for Eqn. (4) is

$$h_3 = \sum [x_{3j} \Delta h_j^f] + \bar{a}_3(T_3 - T_0) + \frac{\bar{b}_3}{2}(T_3^2 - T_0^2) + \frac{\bar{c}_3}{3}(T_3^3 - T_0^3)$$
$$+ 2\bar{d}_3(T_3^{0.5} - T_0^{0.5})$$

where

$$\sum x_{3j} \Delta h_j^f = -17,110 \text{ cal/mole}$$

$$\bar{a}_3 = 7.744 \text{ cal/mole-°K}$$

$$\bar{b}_3 = 0.1599 \times 10^{-2} \text{ cal/mole(°K)}^2$$

$$\bar{c}_3 = -0.02371 \times 10^{-5} \text{ cal/mole(°K)}^3$$

$$\bar{d}_3 = -15.81 \text{ cal/mole(°K)}^{0.5}$$

$$T_0 = 298.15°K$$

This equation contains only one unknown (T_3) and can be rearranged in the form

$$f\{T_3\} = \bar{a}_3(T_3 - T_0) + \frac{\bar{b}_3}{2}(T_3^2 - T_0^2) + \frac{\bar{c}_3}{3}(T_3^3 - T_0^3)$$
$$+ 2\bar{d}_3(T_3^{0.5} - T_0^{0.5}) + \sum [x_{3j} \Delta h_j^f] - h_3 = 0$$

Tabulating $f\{T_3\}$ at selected values of T_3,

T_3 (°K)	$f\{T_3\}$ (cal/mole)
2000	-1474
2100	-508
2200	466
2300	1446

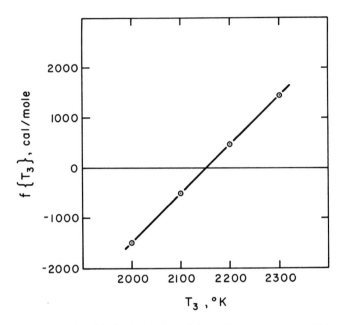

Figure 10-7 Graphical solution for adiabatic flame temperature (T_3).

These points are plotted in Fig. 10-7, from which it is found by interpolation that the solution ($f\{T_3\} = 0$) is

$$\text{adiabatic flame temperature} = T_3 = 2{,}152°\text{K}$$

In the previous example, the air/fuel ratio was somewhat higher than the stoichiometric ratio; as a result, combustion products contain some leftover oxygen. Theoretically, the hottest flame corresponds to stoichiometric ratios of oxygen and fuel, so that there is neither unburned fuel nor oxygen in the combustion products. In the next example, adiabatic flame temperatures for stoichiometric ratios of oxygen/fuel are compared for several different fuel gases.

Example 10.5   *Adiabatic Flame Temperature of Hydrocarbons*

Prepare a WATFIV program that computes the flame temperature for complete combustion in air of the hydrocarbon C_kH_l according to the reaction

$$C_kH_l + \left[k + \frac{l}{4}\right]O_2 \longrightarrow kCO_2 + \frac{l}{2}H_2O$$

Assume that the C_kH_l and O_2 are fed to the flame in stoichiometric ratio at room temperature and atmospheric pressure. Heat from the flame is dQ/dt; an adiabatic flame means $dQ/dt = 0$.

Use the program to compute the adiabatic flame temperature of hydrogen, methane, ethane, ethylene, acetylene, propane, and *n*-butane.

Solution:

See Fig. 10-8. The chemicals are

Component	No. (j)
C_kH_l	1
O_2	2
CO_2	3
H_2O	4
N_2	5

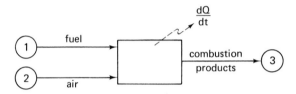

Figure 10-8

1. Equations and constraints.
    a. Material balance equations.
        (1) Reacting species:

$$\text{element C:} \qquad kF_1 = F_3x_{33} \tag{1}$$

$$\text{H:} \qquad lF_1 = 2F_3x_{34} \tag{2}$$

$$\text{O:} \quad 2F_2x_{22} = F_3(2x_{33} + x_{34}) \tag{3}$$

   (2) Inerts:

$$N_2: \quad F_2x_{25} = F_3x_{35} \tag{4}$$

b. Mole-fraction constraints:

$$x_{33} + x_{34} + x_{35} = 1 \tag{5}$$

c. Energy balance equation:

$$F_1h_1 + F_2h_2 - F_3h_3 - \frac{dQ}{dt} = 0 \tag{6}$$

d. Enthalpy equations:

$$h_1 = h_1\{T_1, P_1\} \tag{7}$$

$$h_2 = h_2\{T_2, P_2, x_{22}\} \tag{8}$$

$$h_3 = h_3\{T_3, P_3, x_{33}, x_{34}\} \tag{9}$$

2. Number of variables: $N_v = 18$ (three flow rates, three temperatures, three pressures, three enthalpies, five mole fractions, one heat term).
3. Design or decision variables: $N_d = N_v - N_e = 18 - 9 = 9$. $F_1, T_1, T_2, P_1, P_2, P_3, x_{22}, x_{25},$ and dQ/dt are selected in accordance with the problem statement.

4. Solution of the equations. For this set of design variables, Eqns. (1)–(5) can be solved independently of Eqns. (6)–(9). In other words, the material balance portion of the problem can be solved separately. When the five equations (1)–(5) are solved for the five unknowns x_{33}, x_{34}, x_{35}, F_2, and F_3 the result is

$$x_{33} = \frac{k}{\beta}$$

$$x_{34} = \frac{l}{2\beta}$$

$$x_{35} = \frac{[(1 - x_{22})/x_{22}][k + l/4]}{\beta}$$

$$F_3 = \beta F_1$$

$$F_2 = \frac{F_1}{x_{22}}\left(k + \frac{l}{4}\right)$$

where

$$\beta = k + \frac{l}{2} + \left(\frac{1 - x_{22}}{x_{22}}\right)\left(k + \frac{l}{4}\right)$$

$$= k + \frac{l}{2} + 3.76\left(k + \frac{l}{4}\right)$$

Notice that the three terms in the expression for β are number of moles of CO_2, H_2O, and N_2, respectively, per mole of fuel. Therefore, $\beta = F_3/F_1$. Equations for enthalpies in terms of standard heats of formation and specific heats are the same as in Example 10.3. For a reference temperature $T_0 = 25°C = 298.15°K$ at 1 atm,

$$h_1 = \Delta h_1^f + \int_{T_0}^{T_1} c_{p1}\, dT$$

$$= \Delta h_1^f$$

$$h_2 = \sum x_{2j}\, \Delta h_j^f + \int_{T_0}^{T_2} \bar{c}_{p2}\, dT$$

$$= 0$$

· The energy balance equation (6) gives h_3,

$$h_3 = \frac{h_1 F_1 + h_2 F_2 - (dQ/dt)}{F_3}$$

The last step is to solve Eqn. (9) for T_3. Using the same notation as in Example 10.4,

$$f\{T_3\} = \int_{T_0}^{T_3} \bar{c}_{p3}\, dT + \sum [x_{3j}\, \Delta h_j^f] - h_3 = 0 \qquad (10)$$

where

$$\bar{c}_{p3} = \bar{a}_3 + \bar{b}_3 T + \bar{c}_3 T^2 + \bar{d}_3 T^{-1/2} \qquad (11)$$

Equation (10) can be solved numerically using Newton's method,

$$T_3 = T_3^* - \frac{f\{T_3^*\}}{f'\{T_3^*\}}$$

where T_3^* is the guess value and

$$f'\{T_3\} = \bar{c}_{p3} \tag{12}$$

Convergence to a solution value is achieved when

$$\left| \frac{T_3 - T_3^*}{T_3^*} \right| \leq \epsilon$$

The WATFIV program (see Fig. 10-9)

1. Sets certain parameters and constants.
2. Reads values of design variables from a card.
3. Reads heats of formation and coefficients of zero-pressure specific heat for each compound.
4. Solves the material balance equations.
5. Computes h_1 and h_2 and coefficients of specific heat for the mixture.
6. Computes flame temperature iteratively using Newton's method.
7. Prints the results.

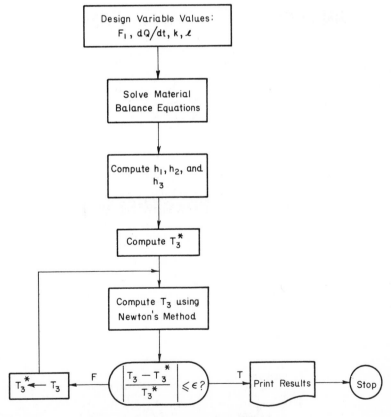

Figure 10-9 Flow diagram of algorithm.

Table of Symbols

Problem Symbol	Program Symbol	Definition	Units
a_j	A(J)	See Eqn. (8), Example 10.3	cal/gmole-°K
$\bar{a}$	AP	See Eqn. (8), Example 10.3	cal/gmole-°K
b_j	B(J)	See Eqn. (8), Example 10.3	cal/gmole-°K^2
$\bar{b}$	BP	See Eqn. (8), Example 10.3	cal/gmole-°K^2
c_j	C(J)	See Eqn. (8), Example 10.3	cal/gmole-°K^3
$\bar{c}$	CP	See Eqn. (8), Example 10.3	cal/gmole-°K^3
d_j	D(J)	See Eqn. (8), Example 10.3	cal/gmole-°K$^{1/2}$
$\bar{d}$	DP	See Eqn. (8), Example 10.3	cal/gmole-°K$^{1/2}$
$f\{T_3\}$	FUNC	See Eqn. (10)	cal/gmole
$f'\{T_3\}$	DERIV	See Eqn. (12)	cal/gmole-°K
F_i	F(I)	Molar flow rate of stream i	gmole/hr
h_i	H(I)	Molar enthalpy of stream i	cal/gmole
Δh_j^f	HF(J)	Molar enthalpy of formation of component j at the standard state (25°C, 1 atm)	cal/gmole
$\overline{\Delta h^f}$	HFP	Molal average enthalpy of formation of stream 3	cal/gmole
k	K	Number of carbon atoms in the fuel molecule	
k_{max}	KMAX	Maximum number of iterations by Newton's method	
l	L	Number of hydrogen atoms in the fuel molecule	
	NEWDAT	A logical variable: When .TRUE., heat of formation and specific heat data are read for all five components. When .FALSE., data are read for the fuel only.	
P_i	P(I)	Pressure of stream i	atm
dQ/dt	Q	Heat loss due to radiation	cal/hr
T_i	T(I)	Temperature of stream i	°K
T_3^*	T3STAR	Guess temperature for stream 3	°K
T_0	TO	Temperature at the reference state	°K
x_{ij}	X(I,J)	Mole fraction of component j in stream i	
β	BETA	F_3/F_1	
ϵ	EPS	Convergence tolerance	

Program Listing

```
C**    PROGRAM TO COMPUTE THE FLAME TEMPERATURE OF THE FUEL C(K)H(L),
C      WHERE K AND L REPRESENT THE NUMBER OF CARBON AND HYDROGEN ATOMS,
C      RESPECTIVELY.  THE FUEL AND OXYGEN ARE FED TO THE FLAME IN
C      STOICHIOMETRIC RATIO AT ROOM TEMPERATURE AND ATMOSPHERIC PRESSURE.
C      FUEL, OXYGEN, CARBON DIOXIDE, WATER AND NITROGEN HAVE COMPONENT
C      NUMBERS (J) = 1, 2, ..., 5, RESPECTIVELY.  FUEL, AIR, AND
C      COMBUSTION PRODUCT STREAMS ARE NUMBERED (I) = 1, 2, 3,
```

```
C      RESPECTIVELY.
C
       LOGICAL NEWDAT
       DIMENSION F(3), T(3), P(3), H(3), X(3,5), A(5), B(5), C(5), D(5)
       DIMENSION HF(5)
       NEWDAT = .TRUE.
       T0 = 298.15
C
C**    INITIALIZES ARRAYS CONTAINING MANY ZEROES
C
       DO 1 J = 1, 5
       DO 1 I = 1, 3
     1 X(I,J) = 0
C
C**    SETS VARIABLES EQUAL TO CONSTRAINED VALUES.
C
       X(2,2) = 0.21
       X(2,5) = 0.79
       X(1,1) = 1.0
       T(1) = 298.15
       T(2) = 298.15
       DO 2 I = 1, 3
     2 P(I) = 1.0
C
C**    READS DESIGN VARIABLE AND ITERATION VARIABLE VALUES.
C
     6 READ, F(1), Q, K, L
       WRITE (6,101)
       WRITE (6,102) F(1), Q, K, L
       READ, EPS, KMAX
       WRITE (6,103)
       WRITE (6,104) EPS, KMAX
C
C**    READS HEATS OF FORMATION AT 25.C AND ZERO PRESSURE SPECIFIC HEAT
C      COEFFICIENTS FOR EACH CHEMICAL (ALTHOUGH FUEL COEFFICIENTS ARE NOT
C      USED IN THE FLAME TEMPERATURE CALCULATION).  WHEN NEWDAT = .TRUE.,
C      READS DATA FOR ALL FIVE CHEMICALS.  WHEN NEWDAT = .FALSE., READS
C      DATA FOR THE FUEL ONLY.
C
       WRITE (6,105)
       IF (NEWDAT)  GO TO 20
       NCARD = 1
       GO TO 21
    20 NCARD = 5
    21 DO 3 J = 1, NCARD
       READ, HF(J), A(J), B(J), C(J), D(J)
     3 WRITE (6,106) J, HF(J), A(J), B(J), C(J), D(J)
C
C**    SOLVES MATERIAL BALANCE EQUATIONS.
C
       BETA = K + L/2.0 + 3.76*(K + L/4.0)
       X(3,3) = K/BETA
       X(3,4) = L/(2.0*BETA)
       X(3,5) = 3.76*(K + L/4.0)/BETA
       F(3) = F(1)*BETA
       F(2) = F(1)*(K + L/4.0)/X(2,2)
C
C**    COMPUTES FEED STREAM ENTHALPIES, PRODUCT STREAM HEAT OF FORMATION
C      AND PRODUCT STREAM SPECIFIC HEAT COEFFICIENTS.
C
       H(1) = HF(1)
       H(2) = 0
       HFP = 0
       AP = 0
       BP = 0
       CP = 0
       DP = 0
       EP = 0
       DO 4 J = 3,5
       HFP = HFP + X(3,J)*HF(J)
       AP = AP + X(3,J)*A(J)
       BP = BP + X(3,J)*B(J)
       CP = CP + X(3,J)*C(J)
     4 DP = DP + X(3,J)*D(J)
```

```
C
C**    COMPUTES PRODUCT STREAM ENTHALPY.
C
       H(3) = (F(1)*H(1) + F(2)*H(2) - Q)/F(3)
C
C**    COMPUTES THE FLAME TEMPERATURE, T(3), ITERATIVELY USING NEWTON'S
C      METHOD.  FIRST, A GUESS TEMPERATURE, T3STAR, IS COMPUTED ASSUMING
C      THAT BP = CP = DP = 0.
C
       T3STAR = (H(3) - HFP)/AP + T0
       WRITE (6,107)
       DO 5 KK = 1, KMAX
       FUNC = AP*(T3STAR - T0) + BP*(T3STAR**2 - T0**2)/2.0 + CP*
      1(T3STAR**3 - T0**3)/3.0 + 2.0*DP*(SQRT(T3STAR) - SQRT(T0)) + HFP
      1 - H(3)
       DERIV = AP + BP*T3STAR + CP*T3STAR**2 + DP/SQRT(T3STAR)
       T(3) = T3STAR - FUNC/DERIV
       IF (ABS((T(3) - T3STAR)/T3STAR) .LE. EPS)   GO TO 8
       WRITE (6,108) KK, T3STAR, T(3)
     5 T3STAR = T(3)
       WRITE (6,109)
       STOP

C
C**    PRINTS RESULTS.
C
     8 WRITE (6,110)
       DO 7 I = 1, 3
     7 WRITE (6,111) I, T(I), P(I), H(I), F(I), (X(I,J), J = 1,5)
       NEWDAT = .FALSE.
       GO TO 6
C
C**    INPUT AND OUTPUT FORMATS.
C
 101   FORMAT ('1F(1), Q, K, L = ', /)
 102   FORMAT (2F15.4, 2I10)
 103   FORMAT (//' EPS, KMAX = ', /)
 104   FORMAT (F15.4, I10)
 105   FORMAT (//' J, HF(J), A(J), B(J), C(J), D(J) = ', /)
 106   FORMAT (I10, F10.2, 4E12.4)
 107   FORMAT (//' K, T3STAR, T(3) = '/)
 108   FORMAT (I10, 2F15.4)
 109   FORMAT (//' KMAX EXCEEDED', //)
 110   FORMAT (//' STREAM NO. (I), T(I), P(I), H(I), F(I), X(I,1), X(I,2)
      1,..., X(I,5) = ',/)
 111   FORMAT (I10, F12.4, F6.2, F10.2, 6F9.4)
       END
```

Data

```
1.0, 0., 0, 2
0.0001, 25
0., 0., 0., 0., 0.
0., 0., 0., 0., 0.
-9.4052E4, 18.036, -4.474E-5, 0., -158.08
-5.7798E4, 6.97, 0.3464E-2, -0.04833E-5, 0.
0., 6.529, 0.1488E-2, -0.02271E-5, 0.
1.0, 0., 1, 4
0.0001, 25
-1.7889E4, 0., 0., 0., 0.
1.0, 0., 2, 6
0.0001, 25
-2.0236E4, 0., 0., 0., 0.
1.0, 0., 2, 4
0.0001, 25
 1.2496E4, 0., 0., 0., 0.
1.0, 0., 2, 2
0.0001, 25
 5.4194E4, 0., 0., 0., 0.
```

```
1.0, 0., 3, 8
0.0001, 25
-2.4820E4, 0., 0., 0., 0.
1.0, 0., 4, 10
0.0001, 25
-2.9812E4, 0., 0., 0., 0.
```

Computed Output

```
F(1), Q, K, L =

    1.0000          0.0000        0        2


EPS, KMAX =

    0.0001          25


J, HF(J), A(J), B(J), C(J), D(J) =

    1       0.00  0.0000E 00  0.0000E 00  0.0000E 00   0.0000E 00
    2       0.00  0.0000E 00  0.0000E 00  0.0000E 00   0.0000E 00
    3  -94052.00  0.1804E 02 -0.4474E-04  0.0000E 00  -0.1581E 03
    4  -57798.00  0.6970E 01  0.3464E-02 -0.4833E-06   0.0000E 00
    5       0.00  0.6529E 01  0.1488E-02 -0.2271E-06   0.0000E 00


K, T3STAR, T(3) =

    1    3301.4970      2536.8540
    2    2536.8540      2529.7120
```

```
STREAM NO. (I), T(I), P(I), H(I), F(I), X(I,1), X(I,2),..., X(I,5) =
```

					H_2	O_2	CO_2	H_2O	N_2
1	298.1499	1.00	0.00	1.0000	1.0000	0.0000	0.0000	0.0000	0.0000
2	298.1499	1.00	0.00	2.3810	0.0000	0.2100	0.0000	0.0000	0.7900
3	2529.7110	1.00	0.00	2.8800	0.0000	0.0000	0.0000	0.3472	0.6528

CH_4, C_2H_6, and C_2H_4 calculations are not included due to space limitations. See the table of flame temperatures below.

```
                         .
                         .
```

```
F(1), Q, K, L =

    1.0000          0.0000        2        2


EPS, KMAX =

    0.0001          25


J, HF(J), A(J), B(J), C(J), D(J) =

    1  54194.00  0.0000E 00  0.0000E 00  0.0000E 00  0.0000E 00


K, T3STAR, T(3) =

    1    3172.2290      2905.2070
    2    2905.2070      2904.6050
```

```
STREAM NO. (I), T(I), P(I), H(I), F(I), X(I,1), X(I,2),..., X(I,5) =
```

					C_2H_2	O_2	CO_2	H_2O	N_2
1	298.1499	1.00	54194.00	1.0000	1.0000	0.0000	0.0000	0.0000	0.0000
2	298.1499	1.00	0.00	11.9048	0.0000	0.2100	0.0000	0.0000	0.7900
3	2904.6050	1.00	4370.48	12.4000	0.0000	0.0000	0.1613	0.0806	0.7581

The n-C_3H_8 and n-C_4H_{10} results are not included but are tabulated below.

Discussion.   Tabulating the results, we have

Flame	Computed °K	Measured* °K	Error %
H_2	2530	2318	9.1
CH_4	2328	2148	8.4
C_2H_6	2382	2168	9.9
C_2H_4	2566	2248	14.1
C_2H_2	2905	2600	11.7
$n\text{-}C_3H_8$	2395	2200	8.9
$n\text{-}C_4H_{10}$	2400	2168	10.7

Notice that adiabatic flame temperatures of saturated hydrocarbons increase slowly with number of carbon atoms:

$$T_{CH_4} < T_{C_2H_6} < T_{C_3H_8} \cdots$$

A more striking variation is the increase of flame temperature with degree of unsaturation of the hydrocarbon molecules:

$$T_{C_2H_6} < T_{C_2H_4} < T_{C_2H_2}$$

Experimental flame temperatures are lower than values calculated in this example because of partial dissociation of the combustion products; the effect of this dissociation will be studied next.

10.4 Simultaneous Material and Energy Balances

A simultaneous material and energy balance means that equations for the material balance are coupled to equations for the energy balance.

For each example in the previous section, the material balance portion of the problem was solved first, independently of the energy balance. This is not always possible. Sometimes variables of the material balance equations (flow rates, compositions) are inextricably interwoven with variables of the energy balance equations (enthalpy, temperature, pressure, rate of heat transfer). As a result of this entanglement, the material and energy balances must be solved simultaneously.

Calculation of flame temperature provides an excellent example of how this entanglement arises. In Example 10.5, it was assumed that all the fuel is consumed and that the products are CO_2 and H_2O. However, there is partial dissociation of the CO_2 (forming CO and O_2) and of the H_2O (forming H_2 and O_2) at the temperature of the flame. These dissociations require energy, and therefore the actual adiabatic temperature of the flame is lower than values calculated in Example 10.5. Since degree of dissociation is a function of temperature, the composition of the combustion products is a function of

*J. H. Perry, ed., *Chemical Engineers' Handbook*, 3rd ed., McGraw-Hill, New York, 1950, p. 1589.

temperature. Therefore, equations for the material balance cannot be solved independently of the energy balance.

The way in which equations for the material balance and the energy balance are coupled is illustrated by the following example.

Example 10.6   *Adiabatic Flame Temperature of Hydrocarbons*

Prepare a WATFIV program that computes flame temperature for complete combustion in air of the gaseous hydrocarbon C_kH_l according to the reaction

$$C_kH_l + \left[k + \frac{l}{4}\right]O_2 \longrightarrow kCO_2 + \frac{l}{2}H_2O$$

Combustion products dissociate partially according to the reactions

$$CO_2 \rightleftharpoons CO + \tfrac{1}{2}O_2$$
$$H_2O \rightleftharpoons H_2 + \tfrac{1}{2}O_2$$

Assume that the dissociation reactions proceed to equilibrium; this is an excellent assumption at the temperature of the flame where reactions are fast. Assume, as before, that fuel and air are introduced at room temperature and atmospheric pressure and that the oxygen/fuel ratio is stoichiometric.

Use the program to calculate the adiabatic flame temperature of methane, ethane, ethylene, acetylene, propane, propylene, propyne, n-butane, 2-methylpropane, 1-butene, 1,2-butadiene, and 1,3-butadiene.

Solution:

See Fig. 10-10. The chemical code is

Component	No. (j)
C_kH_l	1
O_2	2
CO_2	3
H_2O	4
N_2	5
CO	6
H_2	7

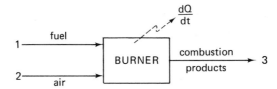

Figure 10-10

1. Equations and Constraints.
   a. Equipment constraints. The oxygen is in stoichiometric ratio to the fuel:

$$F_2 x_{22} = \left[k + \frac{l}{4}\right]F_1 \qquad (1)$$

Therefore, fuel is completely consumed ($x_{31} = 0$).

b. Chemical-equilibrium constraints. The dissociation reactions proceed to equilibrium. According to Eqn. (7.11):

$$\text{dissociation of } CO_2: \quad K_1 = \frac{x_{36}\sqrt{x_{32}}}{x_{33}} \qquad (2)$$

$$\text{dissociation of } H_2O: \quad K_2 = \frac{x_{37}\sqrt{x_{32}}}{x_{34}} \qquad (3)$$

These equations are based upon $P_3 = 1$ atm. Chemical equilibrium constants (K_1 and K_2) are functions of the temperature of the flame (T_3):

$$K_1 = K_1\{T_3\} \qquad (4)$$

$$K_2 = K_2\{T_3\} \qquad (5)$$

The explicit equation for the equilibrium constant in terms of standard thermochemical constants is given in Appendix IV.

c. Material balance equations
(1) Reacting species:

element   C: $kF_1 = F_3(x_{33} + x_{36})$ $\qquad (6)$

H: $lF_1 = 2F_3(x_{34} + x_{37})$ $\qquad (7)$

O: $2F_2 x_{22} = F_3(2x_{32} + 2x_{33} + x_{34} + x_{36})$ $\qquad (8)$

(2) Inerts:

$$N_2: \quad F_2 x_{25} = F_3 x_{35} \qquad (9)$$

d. Mole-fraction constraints:

$$x_{32} + x_{33} + x_{34} + x_{35} + x_{36} + x_{37} = 1 \qquad (10)$$

e. Energy balance equation:

$$F_1 h_1 + F_2 h_2 - F_3 h_3 - \frac{dQ}{dt} = 0 \qquad (11)$$

f. Constitutive equations for enthalpy:

$$h_1 = h_1\{T_1, P_1\} \qquad (12)$$

$$h_2 = h_2\{T_2, P_2, x_{22}\} \qquad (13)$$

$$h_3 = h_3\{T_3, P_3, x_{32}, x_{33}, x_{34}, x_{35}, x_{36}\} \qquad (14)$$

2. Number of variables: $N_v = 23$ (three flow rates, three temperatures, three pressures, three enthalpies, eight mole fractions, one heat flow rate, two parameters). The parameters are the chemical equilibrium constants, K_1 and K_2.

3. Design or decision variables: $N_d = N_v - N_e = 23 - 14 = 9$. $F_1, T_1, T_2, P_1, P_2, P_3, x_{22}, x_{25}$, and dQ/dt are selected as design variables in accordance with the problem statement.

4. Solution of the equations. It is instructive to compare these equations with those of the previous example. The increase in number of variables (five) is exactly balanced by an increase in the number of equations (five) so that the number of design variables is unchanged. The new feature is that the composition of the product stream is related to its temperature by Eqns. (2)–(5). This means that the equations for the material balance cannot be solved until T_3 is known, but T_3 cannot be calculated from the equations

for the energy balance until the composition of the product stream is known. Thus, the material and energy balances cannot be solved separately.

The equations can be solved in the following way. First, Eqn. (1) is solved for F_2. The set of 9 equations (2)–(10) contains 10 unknowns (F_3, T_3, K_1, K_2, x_{32}, x_{33}, x_{34}, x_{35}, x_{36}, x_{37}). This set of 9 equations in 10 unknowns may be reduced to a single equation in 2 unknowns using a reduction procedure based upon the stoichiometry of the reactions.

Since fuel and oxygen in the feed gases are present in stoichiometric proportions, it is convenient to pretend that combustion and dissociation reactions occur consecutively so that all the fuel and oxygen are consumed prior to dissociation of CO_2 and H_2O. Before dissociation there are k moles of CO_2 and $l/2$ moles of H_2O per mole of fuel. If we let α_1 be the fractional dissociation of CO_2 and α_2 be the fractional dissociation of H_2O, it is easy to tabulate the amount of gas dissociated and the amount remaining after dissociation:

	$CO_2 \rightleftharpoons CO + \frac{1}{2}O_2$			$H_2O \rightleftharpoons H_2 + \frac{1}{2}O_2$		
Moles before dissoc.	k	0	0	$\frac{l}{2}$	0	0
Moles dissoc. or formed	$k\alpha_1$	$k\alpha_1$	$\frac{1}{2}k\alpha_1$	$\frac{l}{2}\alpha_2$	$\frac{l}{2}\alpha_2$	$\frac{l}{4}\alpha_2$
Moles left after dissoc.	$k(1-\alpha_1)$	$k\alpha_1$	$\frac{1}{2}k\alpha_1$	$\frac{l}{2}(1-\alpha_2)$	$\frac{l}{2}\alpha_2$	$\frac{l}{4}\alpha_2$

The total number of moles after dissociation per mole of fuel, excluding nitrogen, is equal to $k(1 + \frac{1}{2}\alpha_1) + (l/2)(1 + \frac{1}{2}\alpha_2)$. The number of moles of nitrogen per mole of fuel is equal to

$$\left(\frac{1 - x_{22}}{x_{22}}\right)\left(k + \frac{l}{4}\right)$$

(see Example 10.5). Therefore,

$$\frac{F_3}{F_1} = k\left(1 + \frac{1}{2}\alpha_1\right) + \frac{l}{2}\left(1 + \frac{1}{2}\alpha_2\right) + \left(\frac{1 - x_{22}}{x_{22}}\right)\left(k + \frac{l}{4}\right) \quad (15)$$

and the mole fractions are

$$x_{32} = \left[\frac{k}{2}\alpha_1 + \frac{l}{4}\alpha_2\right]\frac{F_1}{F_3}$$

$$x_{33} = k(1 - \alpha_1)\frac{F_1}{F_3}$$

$$x_{34} = \frac{l}{2}(1 - \alpha_2)\frac{F_1}{F_3}$$

$$x_{35} = \left(\frac{1 - x_{22}}{x_{22}}\right)\left(k + \frac{l}{4}\right)\frac{F_1}{F_3}$$

$$x_{36} = k\alpha_1\frac{F_1}{F_3}$$

$$x_{37} = \frac{l}{2}\alpha_2\frac{F_1}{F_3}$$

These expressions for composition and flow rate of the product stream satisfy Eqns. (1) and (6)–(10). Division of Eqn. (2) by Eqn. (3) followed by substitution for x_{33}, x_{34}, x_{36}, and x_{37} gives an equation for α_2 in terms of α_1:

$$\alpha_2 = \frac{1}{1 + (K_1/K_2)[(1 - \alpha_1)/\alpha_1]} \qquad (16)$$

Next the expressions for x_{32}, x_{33}, and x_{36} are substituted into Eqn. (2) to obtain a single equation in two unknowns (T_3 and α_1),

$$K_1\{T_3\} = \frac{\alpha_1}{1 - \alpha_1}\sqrt{\left[\frac{k}{2}\alpha_1 + \frac{l}{4}\alpha_2\right]\frac{F_1}{F_3}} \qquad (17)$$

where (F_1/F_3) is obtained from Eqn. (15) and α_2 is obtained from Eqn. (16). Since T_3 is unknown, a guess value (T_3^*) is provided, and Eqn. (17) is solved for α_1 using values of K_1 and K_2 evaluated at T_3^*. For solution by Newton's method, Eqn. (17) is rewritten in the form

$$f\{\alpha_1\} = K_1\{T_3^*\} - \frac{\alpha_1}{1 - \alpha_1}\sqrt{\left(\frac{k}{2}\alpha_1 + \frac{l}{4}\alpha_2\right)\frac{F_1}{F_3}} = 0 \qquad (18)$$

Then

$$\alpha_1 = \alpha_1^* - \frac{f\{\alpha_1^*\}}{f'\{\alpha_1^*\}}$$

$f'\{\alpha_1^*\}$ is computed numerically. Convergence is achieved when

$$\left|\frac{\alpha_1 - \alpha_1^*}{\alpha_1^*}\right| \leq \epsilon$$

Convergence tolerance (ϵ) is specified in the program. Equilibrium constants of dissociation reactions (K_1 and K_2) are calculated from standard thermochemical data. For specific heat at zero pressure, we use the same equation as in the previous example:

$$c_{pj}^0 = a_j + b_j T + c_j T^2 + d_j T^{-0.5}$$

Coefficients are given in Table 4.14, and standard thermochemical data are in the *Handbook of Chemistry and Physics*:

Component	No.	a_j (cal/ mole-K)	$b_j \times 10^2$ (cal/ mole-K^2)	$c_j \times 10^5$ (cal/ mole-K^3)	d_j (cal/ mole-K$^{0.5}$)	Δh_{298}^f (cal/ mole)	Δg_{298}^f (cal/ mole)
O_2	2	6.732	0.1505	-0.01791	0	0	0
CO_2	3	18.036	-0.004474	0	-158.08	-94,050	-94,260
H_2O	4	6.970	0.3464	-0.04833	0	-57,800	-54,640
N_2	5	6.529	0.1488	-0.02271	0	0	0
CO	6	6.480	0.1566	-0.02387	0	-26,420	-32,810
H_2	7	6.424	0.1039	-0.007804	0	0	0

The equilibrium constant for each reaction is (see Appendix IV),

$$\ln (K\{T_3\}) = \frac{-\Delta G_0^\circ}{RT_0} + \frac{(\Delta H_0^\circ - I_0)(T_3 - T_0)}{RT_0 T_3} + \int_{T_0}^{T_3} \frac{I}{RT^2}\, dT \qquad (19)$$

where

$$I_0 = (\Delta a)T_0 + \frac{(\Delta b)}{2}T_0^2 + \frac{(\Delta c)}{3}T_0^3 + 2(\Delta d)T_0^{0.5}$$

$$\int_{T_0}^{T_3} \frac{I}{RT^2}\, dT = \frac{\Delta a}{R} \ln \frac{T_3}{T_0} + \frac{\Delta b}{2R}(T_3 - T_0) + \frac{\Delta c}{6R}(T_3^2 - T_0^2)$$
$$- \frac{4\Delta d}{R}(T_3^{-0.5} - T_0^{-0.5})$$

and
$$T_0 = 298.15°K$$

For the first reaction, $CO_2 \rightleftharpoons CO + \frac{1}{2}O_2$,

$$\Delta a = a_6 + \tfrac{1}{2}a_2 - a_3 = -8.190 \text{ cal/mole-K}$$
$$\Delta b = b_6 + \tfrac{1}{2}b_2 - b_3 = 0.2363 \times 10^{-2} \text{ cal/mole-K}^2$$
$$\Delta c = c_6 + \tfrac{1}{2}c_2 - c_3 = -0.03282 \times 10^{-5} \text{ cal/mole-K}^3$$
$$\Delta d = d_6 + \tfrac{1}{2}d_2 - d_3 = 158.08 \text{ cal/mole-K}^{0.5}$$
$$\Delta H_0^\circ = -26,420 + \tfrac{1}{2}(0) - (-94,050) = 67,630 \text{ cal}$$
$$\Delta G_0^\circ = -32,810 + \tfrac{1}{2}(0) - (-94,260) = 61,450 \text{ cal}$$

For the second reaction, $H_2O \rightleftharpoons H_2 + \frac{1}{2}O_2$,

$$\Delta a = a_7 + \tfrac{1}{2}a_2 - a_4 = 2.82 \text{ cal/mole-K}$$
$$\Delta b = b_7 + \tfrac{1}{2}b_2 - b_4 = -0.1672 \times 10^{-2} \text{ cal/mole-K}^2$$
$$\Delta c = c_7 + \tfrac{1}{2}c_2 - c_4 = 0.03157 \times 10^{-5} \text{ cal/mole-K}^3$$
$$\Delta d = d_7 + \tfrac{1}{2}d_2 - d_4 = 0$$
$$\Delta H_0^\circ = 0 + \tfrac{1}{2}(0) - (-57,800) = 57,800 \text{ cal}$$
$$\Delta G_0^\circ = 0 + \tfrac{1}{2}(0) - (-54,640) = 54,640 \text{ cal}$$

Having solved for the composition of the product stream at a guess temperature (T_3^*), Eqn. (11) gives the value of h_3 at T_3^*:

$$h_3 = \frac{F_1 h_1 + F_2 h_2 - (dQ/dt)}{F_3} \tag{20}$$

Enthalpies of each stream are calculated from its specific heat as in the previous example; the only change is an increase in the number of components in the product stream:

$$h_1 = \Delta h_1^f$$
$$h_2 = 0$$
$$h_3 = \sum_{j=2}^{7} x_{3j}\, \Delta h_j^f + \int_{T_0}^{T_3} \bar{c}_{p3}\, dT$$

or

$$f\{T_3\} = \sum_{j=2}^{7} x_{3j}\, \Delta h_j^f + \int_{T_0}^{T_3} \bar{c}_{p3}\, dT - h_3 = 0 \tag{21}$$

where

$$\int_{T_0}^{T_3} \bar{c}_{p3}\, dT = \bar{a}(T_3 - T_0) + \frac{\bar{b}}{2}(T_3^2 - T_0^2) + \frac{\bar{c}}{3}(T_3^3 - T_0^3)$$
$$+ 2\bar{d}(T_3^{0.5} - T_0^{0.5})$$

with

$$\bar{a} = \sum_{j=2}^{7} x_{3j} a_j \qquad \bar{c} = \sum_{j=2}^{7} x_{3j} c_j$$
$$\bar{b} = \sum_{j=2}^{7} x_{3j} b_j \qquad \bar{d} = \sum_{j=2}^{7} x_{3j} d_j$$

Note that x_{3j} and h_3 have been computed at the guess value for T_3. Equation (21) can be solved for T_3 using Newton's method,

$$T_3 = T_3^* - \frac{f\{T_3^*\}}{f'\{T_3^*\}}$$

where $f'\{T_3^*\}$ is calculated numerically. Convergence is achieved when

$$\left| \frac{T_3 - T_3^*}{T_3^*} \right| < \epsilon$$

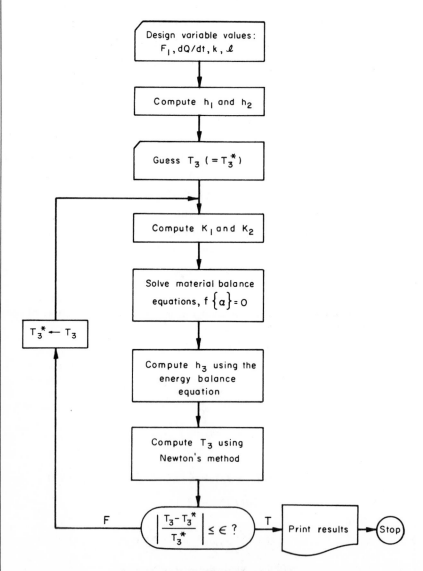

Figure 10-11 Flow diagram of algorithm.

In summary, the solution procedure is similar to that of the previous example in that Eqn. (21) must be solved for T_3; the complication is that composition and flow rate of the product stream are temperature-dependent variables. Figure 10-11 is a simplified flow diagram of the algorithm.

The WATFIV program (see Fig. 10-11)

1. Sets certain stream parameters and constants.
2. Reads values of design variables from a card.
3. Reads heats of formation, Gibbs free energy of formation, and coefficients of zero-pressure specific heat for each compound.
4. For each dissociation reaction, computes standard heat of reaction, standard Gibbs free energy of reaction, and coefficients for specific heat.
5. Reads a guess flame temperature, T_3^*.
6. Computes $f\{T_3^*\}$ and $f\{T_3^*(1 + \delta)\}$ for computation of $f'\{T_3^*\}$ to be used in Newton's method.
   a. Computes constants for each dissociation reaction, K_1 and K_2.
   b. Solves the material balance equations for α_1.
   c. Computes heat of formation and specific heat of product.
   d. Computes enthalpy of product.
7. Computes T_3 using Newton's method and checks for convergence.
8. Prints results when convergence criteria are satisfied; otherwise, sets $T_3^* \longleftarrow T_3$ and returns to step 6.

Table of Symbols

Problem Symbol	Program Symbol	Definition	Units
a_j	A(J)	See Eqn. (8), Example 10.3	cal/gmole-K
$\bar{a}$	AP	See Eqn. (8), Example 10.3	cal/gmole-K
Δa_i	AR(I)	See Eqn. (19) for dissociation reaction i, $i = 1, 2$	cal/gmole-K
b_j	B(J)	See Eqn. (8), Example 10.3	cal/gmole-K^2
$\bar{b}$	BP	See Eqn. (8), Example 10.3	cal/gmole-K^2
Δb_i	BR(I)	See Eqn. (19) for dissociation reaction i, $i = 1, 2$	cal/gmole-K^2
c_j	C(J)	See Eqn. (8), Example 10.3	cal/gmole-K^3
$\bar{c}$	CP	See Eqn. (8), Example 10.3	cal/gmole-K^3
Δc_i	CR(I)	See Eqn. (19) for dissociation reaction i, $i = 1, 2$	cal/gmole-K^3
d_j	D(J)	See Eqn. (8), Example 10.3	cal/gmole-K$^{1/2}$
$\bar{d}$	DP	See Eqn. (8), Example 10.3	cal/gmole-K$^{1/2}$
Δd_i	DR(I)	See Eqn. (19) for dissociation reaction i, $i = 1, 2$	cal/gmole-K$^{1/2}$
$f\{T_3^*\}$	FT3	See Eqn. (21)	cal/gmole
$f\{T_3^*(1 + \delta)\}$	FT3DEL	See Eqn. (21)	cal/gmole
$f'\{T_3^*\}$	DERIV	$(f\{T_3^*(1 + \delta)\} - f\{T_3^*\})/(T_3^*\delta)$	cal/gmole-K
$f\{\alpha_1^*\}$	FALF1	See Eqn. (18)	
$f\{\alpha_1^* + \delta\}$	FALF1D	See Eqn. (18)	
$f'\{\alpha_1^*\}$	DERIV	$(f\{\alpha_1^* + \delta\} - f\{\alpha_1^*\})/\delta$	

Problem Symbol	Program Symbol	Definition	Units
F_i	F(I)	Molar flow rate of stream i	gmole/hr
Δg_j^f	GF(J)	Molar Gibbs free energy of formation of component j at the standard state (25°C, 1 atm)	cal/gmole
$(\Delta G_0^\circ)_i$	GFR(I)	Gibbs free energy for dissociation reaction i, $i = 1, 2$; see Eqn. (19)	cal
h_i	H(I)	Molar enthalpy of stream i	cal/gmole
Δh_j^f	HF(J)	Molar heat of formation of component j at the standard state (25°C, 1 atm)	cal/gmole
$(\Delta H_0^\circ)_i$	HR(I)	Heat of reaction for dissociation reaction i, $i = 1, 2$; see Eqn. (19)	cal
$\overline{\Delta h^f}$	HFP	Molal average heat of formation of stream 3	cal/gmole
I_0	IO	See Eqn. (19)	cal/gmole
$\int_{T_0}^{T_3} \frac{I}{RT^2}\, dT$	INT	See Eqn. (19)	
k	K	Number or carbon atoms in the fuel molecule	
$k_{\max}$	KMAX	Maximum number of iterations by Newton's method	
$K_i\{T_3\}$	EQK(I)	Chemical-equilibrium constant for dissociation reaction i, $i = 1, 2$	
l	L	Number of hydrogen atoms in the fuel molecule	
$\ln(K\{T_3\})$	LOGK	See Eqn. (19)	
	NEWDAT	A logical variable: When .TRUE., heat of formation, free energy of formation, and specific heat data are read for all seven components. When .FALSE., data are read for the fuel only.	
P_i	P(I)	Pressure of stream i	atm
dQ/dt	Q	Heat loss due to radiation	cal/hr
R	R	Universal gas constant	cal/gmole-K
	ROUTE	A logical variable: When .TRUE., computes $f\{\alpha_1^*\}$. When .FALSE., computes $f\{\alpha_1^* + \delta\}$.	
	SWITCH	A logical variable: When .TRUE., computes $f\{T_3^*\}$. When .FALSE., computes $f\{T_3^*(1 + \delta)\}$.	
T_i	T(I)	Temperature of stream i	K
T_3^*	T3STAR	Guess temperature of stream 3	K
T_0	TO	Temperature at the standard state	K
x_{ij}	X(I,J)	Mole fraction of component j in stream i	

Problem Symbol	Program Symbol	Definition	Units
α_1	ALFA1	Fractional dissociation of CO_2	
α_1^*	ALFA1S	Guess fractional dissociation of CO_2	
α_2	ALFA2	Fractional dissociation of H_2O	
β	BETA	F_3/F_1	
δ	DELTA	Step size for numerical differentiation	
ϵ	EPS	Convergence tolerance	

Program Listing

```
C**   PROGRAM TO COMPUTE THE FLAME TEMPERATURE OF THE FUEL C(K)H(L),
C     WHERE K AND L REPRESENT THE NUMBER OF CARBON AND HYDROGEN ATOMS,
C     RESPECTIVELY.  COMBUSTION PRODUCTS DISSOCIATE ACCORDING TO THE
C     REACTIONS CO(2) = CO + (1/2)O(2) AND H(2)O = H(2) + (1/2)O(2).
C     BOTH REACTIONS ARE ASSUMED TO REACH EQUILIBRIUM AT THE FLAME TEMP-
C     ERATURE.  FUEL AND OXYGEN ARE FED IN STOICHIOMETRIC RATIO AT ROOM
C     TEMPERATURE AND ATMOSPHERIC PRESSURE.  FUEL, OXYGEN, CARBON
C     DIOXIDE, WATER, NITROGEN, CARBON MONOXIDE, AND HYDROGEN HAVE
C     COMPONENT NUMBERS (J) = 1,2,...,7, RESPECTIVELY.  FUEL, AIR, AND
C     COMBUSTION PRODUCT STREAMS ARE NUMBERED (I) = 1,2, AND 3,
C     RESPECTIVELY.
C
      REAL IO, INT, LOGK
      LOGICAL SWITCH, ROUTF, NEWDAT
      DIMENSION F(3), T(3), P(3), H(3), X(3,7), A(7), B(7), C(7), D(7)
      DIMENSION HF(7), GF(7), HR(2), GFR(2), AR(2), BR(2), CR(2), DR(2)
      DIMENSION EQK(2)
      NEWDAT = .TRUE.
      R = 1.9872
      T0 = 298.15
C
C**   INITIALIZES ARRAYS CONTAINING MANY ZEROES.
C
      DO 1 J = 1,7
      DO 1 I = 1,3
    1 X(I,J) = 0
C
C**   SETS VARIABLES EQUAL TO CONSTRAINED VALUES.
C
      X(2,2) = 0.21
      X(2,5) = 0.79
      X(1,1) = 1.0
      T(1) = 298.15
      T(2) = 298.15
      DO 2 I = 1,3
    2 P(I) = 1.0
C
C**   READS DESIGN VARIABLE AND ITERATION VARIABLE VALUES AND SETS A
C     GUESS VALUE FOR ALFA1S.
C
   19 READ, F(1), Q, K, L
      WRITE (6,101)
      WRITE (6,102) F(1), Q, K, L
      READ, EPS, DELTA, KMAX
      WRITE (6,103)
      WRITE (6,104) EPS, DELTA, KMAX
      ALFA1S = 0.2
C
C**   COMPUTES F(2) SO THAT OXYGEN IS FED IN STOICHIOMETRIC RATIO TO THE
C     FUEL.
C
```

```
      F(2) = ((K + L/4.)*F(1))/X(2,2)
C
C**   READS HEAT OF FORMATION AND GIBBS FREE ENERGY OF FORMATION AT
C     25.C AND ZERO PRESSURE SPECIFIC HEAT COEFFICIENTS (ALTHOUGH THE
C     COEFFICIENTS AND GIBBS FREE ENERGY OF FORMATION FOR THE FUEL ARE
C     NOT USED IN THE FLAME TEMPERATURE CALCULATION).  WHEN NEWDAT =
C     .TRUE., READS DATA FOR ALL SEVEN CHEMICALS.  WHEN NEWDAT =
C     .FALSE., READS DATA FOR THE FUEL ONLY.
C
      WRITE (6,105)
      IF (NEWDAT)  GO TO 20
      NCARD = 1
      GO TO 21
   20 NCARD = 7
   21 DO 3 J = 1, NCARD
      READ, HF(J), GF(J), A(J), B(J), C(J), D(J)
    3 WRITE (6,106) J, HF(J), GF(J), A(J), B(J), C(J), D(J)
C
C**   COMPUTES THE FEED STREAM ENTHALPIES.
C
      H(1) = HF(1)
      H(2) = 0
C
C**   FOR EACH DISSOCIATION REACTION (1 AND 2), COMPUTES STANDARD HEAT
C     OF REACTION, STANDARD GIBBS FREE ENERGY OF REACTION, AND CHANGE
C     IN COEFFICIENTS FOR SPECIFIC HEAT FOR REACTION.
C
      HR(1) = HF(6) + HF(2)/2.0 - HF(3)
      GFR(1) = GF(6) + GF(2)/2.0 - GF(3)
      AR(1) = A(6) + A(2)/2.0 - A(3)
      BR(1) = B(6) + B(2)/2.0 - B(3)
      CR(1) = C(6) + C(2)/2.0 - C(3)
      DR(1) = D(6) + D(2)/2.0 - D(3)
      HR(2) = HF(7) + HF(2)/2.0 - HF(4)
      GFR(2) = GF(7) + GF(2)/2.0 - GF(4)
      AR(2) = A(7) + A(2)/2.0 - A(4)
      BR(2) = B(7) + B(2)/2.0 - B(4)
      CR(2) = C(7) + C(2)/2.0 - C(4)
      DR(2) = D(7) + D(2)/2.0 - D(4)
C
C**   READS GUESS FLAME TEMPERATURE, T3STAR.  A GOOD GUESS IS THE
C     ADIABATIC FLAME TEMPERATURE ASSUMING NO DISSOCIATION OF CARBON
C     DIOXIDE OR WATER.
C
      READ, T3STAR
      WRITE (6,107) T3STAR
C
C**   BEGINS NEWTON'S METHOD ITERATIONS TO COMPUTE T(3).
C
      DO 4 KK = 1,KMAX
      WRITE (6,108) KK
C
C**   EVALUATES FT3 = F(T3STAR) WHEN SWITCH = .TRUE. AND FT3DEL =
C     F(T3STAR*(1.0 + DELTA)) WHEN SWITCH = .FALSE.  FT3 AND FT3DEL ARE
C     USED TO COMPUTE THE DERIVATIVE NUMERICALLY FOR NEWTON'S METHOD
C     ESTIMATION OF T(3).
C
      SWITCH = .FALSE.
   16 IF (SWITCH)  GO TO 5
      T3STAR = T3STAR*(1.0 + DELTA)
C
C**   COMPUTES THE EQUILIBRIUM CONSTANT FOR EACH DISSOCIATION REACTION
C     (1 AND 2).
C
    5 DO 6 I = 1,2
      I0 = AR(I)*T0 + (BR(I)/2.0)*T0**2 + (CR(I)/3.0)*T0**3 + 2.0*DR(I)*
     1SQRT(T0)
      INT = (AR(I)/R)*ALOG(T3STAR/T0) + (BR(I)/(2.0*R))*(T3STAR - T0) +
     1(CR(I)/(6.0*R))*(T3STAR**2 - T0**2) - (4.0 * DR(I)/R)*
     1(T3STAR**(-0.5) - T0**(-0.5))
      LOGK = -GFR(I)/(R*T0) + (HR(I) - I0)*(T3STAR - T0)/(R*T0*T3STAR)
     1+ INT
    6 EQK(I) = EXP(LOGK)
```

```
C
C**    SOLVES MATERIAL BALANCE EQUATIONS AT T3STAR.  BEGINS NEWTON'S
C      METHOD ITERATIONS TO COMPUTE ALFA1.
C
       WRITE (6,109)
       DO 7 KKK = 1,KMAX
C
C**    EVALUATES FALF1 = F(ALFA1S) WHEN ROUTE = .TRUE. AND FALF1D =
C      F(ALFA1S + DELTA) WHEN ROUTE = .FALSE.  FALF1 AND FALF1D ARE USED
C      TO COMPUTE THE DERIVATIVE NUMERICALLY FOR ESTIMATION OF ALFA1.
C      BETA = F(3)/F(1).
C
       ROUTE = .FALSE.
   11  IF (ROUTE)  GO TO 8
       ALFA1S = ALFA1S + DELTA
    8  ALFA2 = 1.0/(1.0 + (EQK(1)/EQK(2))*((1.0 - ALFA1S)/ALFA1S))
       BETA = K*(1.0 + ALFA1S/2.0) + (L/2.0)*(1.0 + ALFA2/2.0) +
      1(K + L/4.0)*(1.0 - X(2,2))/X(2,2)
       FUNC = EQK(1) - ALFA1S/(1.0 - ALFA1S) * SQRT(((K/2.0)*ALFA1S +
      1(L/4.0)*ALFA2)/BETA)
       IF (ROUTE)  GO TO 9
       FALF1D = FUNC
       ALFA1S = ALFA1S - DELTA
       ROUTE = .TRUE.
       GO TO 11
    9  FALF1 = FUNC
C
C**    ESTIMATES ALFA1 USING NEWTON'S METHOD.  CHECKS FOR CONVERGENCE.
C
       DERIV = (FALF1D - FALF1)/DELTA
       ALFA1 = ALFA1S - FALF1/DERIV
       IF (ABS((ALFA1 - ALFA1S)/ALFA1S) .LE. EPS)  GO TO 12
       WRITE (6,110) KKK, ALFA1S, ALFA1
    7  ALFA1S = ALFA1
       WRITE (6,111)
       STOP
C
C**    ALFA1 IS KNOWN AT T3STAR.  COMPUTES MOLE FRACTIONS AND FLOW RATES
C      OF THE PRODUCT STREAM.
C
   12  X(3,2) = ((K/2.0)*ALFA1 + (L/4.0)*ALFA2)/BETA
       X(3,3) = K*(1.0 - ALFA1)/BETA
       X(3,4) = (L/2.0)*(1.0 - ALFA2)/BETA
       X(3,5) = (K + L/4.0)*((1.0 - X(2,2))/X(2,2))/BETA
       X(3,6) = K*ALFA1/BETA
       X(3,7) = (L/2.0)*ALFA2/BETA
       F(3) = F(1)*BETA
C
C**    COMPUTES THE PRODUCT STREAM HEAT OF FORMATION AND SPECIFIC HEAT
C      COEFFICIENTS.
C
       HFP = 0
       AP = 0
       BP = 0
       CP = 0
       DP = 0
       DO 13 J = 2,7
       HFP = HFP + X(3,J)*HF(J)
       AP = AP + X(3,J)*A(J)
       BP = BP + X(3,J)*B(J)
       CP = CP + X(3,J)*C(J)
   13  DP = DP + X(3,J)*D(J)
C
C**    COMPUTES THE PRODUCT STREAM ENTHALPY AT T3STAR AND COMPUTES FUNC,
C      WHICH IS STORED IN FT3 OR FT3DEL DEPENDING UPON SWITCH.
C
       H(3) = (F(1)*H(1) + F(2)*H(2) - Q)/F(3)
       FUNC = HFP + AP*(T3STAR - T0) + (BP/2.0)*(T3STAR**2 - T0**2) +
      1(CP/3.0)*(T3STAR**3 - T0**3) + 2.0*DP*(SQRT(T3STAR) - SQRT(T0))) -
      1H(3)
       IF (SWITCH)  GO TO 14
       FT3DEL = FUNC
       T3STAR = T3STAR/(1.0 + DELTA)
       SWITCH = .TRUE.
       GO TO 16
   14  FT3 = FUNC
```

```
C
C**    ESTIMATES T(3) USING NEWTON'S METHOD. CHECKS FOR CONVERGENCE.
C
       DERIV = (FT3DEL - FT3)/(DELTA*T3STAR)
       T(3) = T3STAR - FT3/DERIV
       IF (ABS((T(3) - T3STAR)/T3STAR) .LE. EPS)  GO TO 17
       WRITE (6,112) KK, T3STAR, T(3)
     4 T3STAR = T(3)
       WRITE (6,113)
       STOP
C
C**    PRINTS RESULTS.
C
    17 WRITE (6,114)
       DO 18 I = 1,3
    18 WRITE (6,115) I, T(I), P(I), H(I), F(I), (X(I,J), J = 1,7)
       NEWDAT = .FALSE.
       GO TO 19
C
C**    INPUT AND OUTPUT FORMATS.
C
   101 FORMAT ('1F(1), Q, K, L = ',/)
   102 FORMAT (2F15.4, 2I10)
   103 FORMAT (//' EPS, DELTA, KMAX = ',/)
   104 FORMAT (2F15.4, I10)
   105 FORMAT (//' J, HF(J), GF(J), A(J), B(J), C(J), D(J) =',/)
   106 FORMAT (I10, 2F10.2, 4E12.4)
   107 FORMAT (//' GUESS FLAME TEMPERATURE, T3STAR = ', F10.2)
   108 FORMAT (////' ITERATION NO. TO DETERMINE T3STAR =', I5)
   109 FORMAT (//' MATERIAL BALANCE - KKK, ALFA1S, ALFA1 =',/)
   110 FORMAT (I10, 2F15.4)
   111 FORMAT (//' MATERIAL BALANCE DID NOT CONVERGE. KMAX EXCEEDED.'//)
   112 FORMAT (//' AFTER ITERATION NO.', I5, ', T3STAR AND T(3) =',
      12F12.2)
   113 FORMAT (//' ENERGY BALANCE DID NOT CONVERGE.  KMAX EXCEEDED.'//)
   114 FORMAT (////'      .....CONVERGENCE ACHIEVED......'///' STREAM NO.
      1 (I), T(I), P(I), H(I), F(I), X(I,1), X(I,2), ..., X(I,7) =',/)
   115 FORMAT (I10, 2F10.4, F10.2, 8F10.4)
       END
```

Data

```
        1.0, 0., 1, 4
        0.0001, 0.0001, 25
        -1.7889E4, 0., 0., 0., 0., 0.
        0., 0., 6.732, 0.1505E-2, -0.01791E-5, 0.
        -94052., -94260., 18.04, -0.004474E-2, 0., -158.08
        -57798., -54640., 6.97, 0.3464E-2, -0.04833E-5, 0.
        0., 0., 6.529, 0.1488E-2, -0.02271E-5, 0.
        -26420., -32810., 6.48, 0.1566E-2, -0.02387E-5, 0.
        0., 0., 6.424, 0.1039E-2, -0.007804E-5, 0.
        2328.
        1.0, 0., 2, 6
        0.0001, 0.0001, 25
        -2.0236E4, 0., 0., 0., 0., 0.
        2382.
        1.0, 0., 2, 4
        0.0001, 0.0001, 25
        1.2496E4, 0., 0., 0., 0., 0.
        2566.
        1.0, 0., 2, 2
        0.0001, 0.0001, 25
        54194., 0., 0., 0., 0., 0.
        2904.5
        1.0, 0., 3, 8
        0.0001, 0.0001, 25
        -2.4820E4, 0., 0., 0., 0., 0.
        2395.
```

```
1.0, 0., 3, 6
0.0001, 0.0001, 25
4879., 0., 0., 0., 0., 0.
2500.
1.0, 0., 3, 4
0.0001, 0.0001, 25
44319., 0., 0., 0., 0., 0.
2500.
1.0, 0., 4, 10
0.0001, 0.0001, 25
-2.9812E4, 0., 0., 0., 0., 0.
2400.
1., 0., 4, 10
0.0001, 0.0001, 25
-31452., 0., 0., 0., 0., 0.
2500.
1.0, 0., 4, 8
0.0001, 0.0001, 25
280., 0., 0., 0., 0., 0.
2500.
1.0, 0., 4, 6
0.0001, 0.0001, 25
39550., 0., 0., 0., 0., 0.
2500.
1.0, 0., 4, 6
0.0001, 0.0001, 25
26750., 0., 0., 0., 0., 0.
2500.
```

Computed Output   (for the acetylene fuel only)

```
F(1), Q, K, L =

     1.0000          0.0000          2          2

EPS, DELTA, KMAX =

     0.0001          0.0001          25

J, HF(J), GF(J), A(J), B(J), C(J), D(J) =

     1  54194.00      0.00  0.0000E 00  0.0000E 00  0.0000E 00  0.0000E 00

GUESS FLAME TEMPERATURE, T3STAR =     2904.50


ITERATION NO. TO DETERMINE T3STAR =    1

MATERIAL BALANCE - KKK, ALFA1S, ALFA1 =

          1          0.2000          0.8264
          2          0.8264          0.7189
          3          0.7189          0.6024
          4          0.6024          0.5256
          5          0.5256          0.5053
          6          0.5053          0.5042

MATERIAL BALANCE - KKK, ALFA1S, ALFA1 =

          1          0.5042          0.5040

AFTER ITERATION NO.    1, T3STAR AND T(3) =     2904.50     2595.92
```

```
ITERATION NO. TO DETERMINE T3STAR =    2

MATERIAL BALANCE - KKK, ALFA1S, ALFA1 =

           1        0.5040        0.3569
           2        0.3569        0.2821
           3        0.2821        0.2677
           4        0.2677        0.2673

MATERIAL BALANCE - KKK, ALFA1S, ALFA1 =

           1        0.2673        0.2671

AFTER ITERATION NO.    2, T3STAR AND T(3) =     2595.92        2598.91

ITERATION NO. TO DETERMINE T3STAR =    3

MATERIAL BALANCE - KKK, ALFA1S, ALFA1 =

           1        0.2671        0.2694

MATERIAL BALANCE - KKK, ALFA1S, ALFA1 =

           1        0.2694        0.2692

......CONVERGENCE ACHIEVED......

STREAM NO. (I), T(I), P(I), H(I), F(I), X(I,1), X(I,2), ..., X(I,7) =

  1   298.1499   1.0000   54194.00    1.0000    1.0000   0.0000   0.0000   0.0000   0.0000   0.0000   0.0000
  2   298.1499   1.0000       0.00   11.9048    0.0000   0.0000   0.2100   0.1151   0.0744   0.7900   0.0424
  3  2598.8660   1.0000    4266.82   12.7013    0.0000   0.0000   0.0233   0.0233   0.7405   0.7405   0.0043
```

Discussion.   Tabulating the results, we have

Flame	Measured °K	Theoretical, °K Dissociation	Neglecting Dissociation
CH_4	2148	2250	2328
C_2H_6	2168	2286	2382
C_2H_4	2248	2407	2566
C_2H_2	2600	2599	2905
C_3H_8	2200	2294	2395
C_3H_6	2208	2367	
C_3H_4		2483	
n-C_4H_{10}	2168	2297	2400
2-Methylpropane		2294	
1-Butene	2203	2354	
1,2-Butadiene		2439	
1,3-Butadiene		2409	

Because of heat losses by radiation and imperfect combustion, flame temperatures measured experimentally are somewhat lower than the theoretical values calculated in this example.

Coupling of material and energy balance equations also occurs in phase-equilibrium problems, as illustrated in the following example of an equilibrium-flash vaporizer.

Example 10.7   Multicomponent Flash

A preheated liquid feed containing two or more components (stream 1) is flashed to a lower pressure in a flash vaporizer to separate the light components (which concentrate in the vapor) from the heavy components (which concentrate in the liquid). Liquid and vapor streams are withdrawn continuously to maintain steady state. At the reduced pressure in the chamber there is partial vaporization of the liquid and therefore a lowering of its temperature. Baffles in the chamber remove drops of liquid from the vapor stream. Residence time in the chamber is sufficient to equilibrate the liquid and vapor product streams leaving the chamber.

Solve the material and energy balance for flashing a feed composed of N_c components in a well-insulated, adiabatic chamber. See Fig. 10-12.

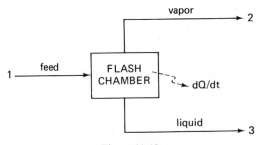

Figure 10-12

Solution:

1. Equations and constraints.
   a. Equations for phase equilibrium. Since product streams are in equilibrium,

   $$T_2 = T_3 \tag{1}$$

   $$P_2 = P_3 \tag{2}$$

   $$f_{2j}\{T_2, P_2, x_{21}, x_{22}, \ldots\} = f_{3j}\{T_3, P_3, x_{31}, x_{32}, \ldots\}$$
   $$(j = 1, 2, \ldots, N_c) \tag{3}$$

   f_{ij} means fugacity of component j in stream i, which is a function of temperature, pressure, and composition of the ith stream. Specific equations for fugacity are given in Appendix IV.
   b. Mole-fraction constraints:

   $$\sum_{j=1}^{N_c} x_{ij} = 1 \qquad (i = 2, 3) \tag{4}$$

   c. Material balance equations:

   $$F_1 x_{1j} = F_2 x_{2j} + F_3 x_{3j} \qquad (j = 1, 2, \ldots, N_c) \tag{5}$$

   d. Energy balance equation:

   $$F_1 h_1 - F_2 h_2 - F_3 h_3 - \frac{dQ}{dt} = 0 \tag{6}$$

   where dQ/dt is the rate of cooling of the chamber. For the adiabatic case under consideration, $dQ/dt = 0$.
   e. Constitutive equations for enthalpy:

   $$h_i = h_i\{T_i, P_i, x_{i1}, x_{i2}, \ldots\} \qquad (i = 1, 2, 3) \tag{7}$$

   Explicit equations for enthalpy are written below.
   The total number of equations is

phase equilibrium:	$N_c + 2$
mole fraction:	2
material balance:	N_c
energy balance:	1
enthalpy:	3
total:	$2N_c + 8$

2. Number of variables:

   $$N_v = N_s(N_c + 4) + N_q + N_w + N_p$$
   $$= 3(N_c + 4) + 1 + 0 + 0$$
   $$= 3N_c + 13$$

3. Design or decision variables:

   $$N_d = N_v - N_e$$
   $$= 3N_c + 13 - (2N_c + 8)$$
   $$= N_c + 5$$

In accordance with the problem statement, the set of $N_c + 5$ design variables is $\{F_1, T_1, P_1, x_{11}, x_{12}, \ldots, x_{1N_c}, P_2, dQ/dt\}$.

4. Solution of the equations. Equations (2) and (7) give P_3 and h_1. Equations (3), (4), and (5) are $2N_c + 2$ equations in $2N_c + 3$ unknowns $\{x_{21}, x_{22}, \ldots, x_{2N_c}, x_{31}, x_{32}, \ldots, x_{3N_c}, F_2, F_3, T_2\}$; therefore, the material balance is coupled to the energy balance by the variable T_2.

The solution procedure is similar to that for the adiabatic flame calculation. A guess value of T_2, called T_2^*, permits solution of Eqns. (3), (4), and (5), after which Eqns. (7) are solved for h_2 and h_3. The solution is that value of T_2^* that satisfies the energy balance, Eqn. (6).

Since the product consists of liquid and vapor in equilibrium, solution values for T_2 at the flash pressure are bounded by the bubble point temperature (T_{bub}) and the dew-point temperature (T_{dew}) of the feed:

$$T_{\text{bub}} < T_2 < T_{\text{dew}}$$

An explanation of bubble and dew points of mixtures and how to calculate them is taken up in the next example. The first guess for T_2 is

$$T_2^* = \tfrac{1}{2}(T_{\text{bub}} + T_{\text{dew}})$$

Suppose that pressure (P_2) is low enough (see Appendix IV) so that Eqn. (3) becomes

$$P_2 x_{2j} = [P_j^s\{T_2\}][\gamma_j\{T_2, x_{31}, x_{32}, \ldots\}]x_{3j}$$
$$= P_j^s \gamma_j x_{3j} \qquad (j = 1, 2, \ldots, N_c) \tag{8}$$

Recall that $T_2 = T_3$. P_j^s is vapor pressure of the jth liquid and γ_j is its activity coefficient in the liquid phase (stream 3). In terms of k-values, Eqn. (8) is

$$k_j = \frac{x_{2j}}{x_{3j}} \qquad (j = 1, 2, \ldots, N_c) \tag{9}$$

where

$$k_j = \frac{P_j^s \gamma_j}{P_2} = \frac{[P_j^s\{T_2\}][\gamma_j\{T_2, x_{31}, x_{32}, \ldots\}]}{P_2} \tag{10}$$

k-values are computed from a guess value for T_2 and liquid composition $(x_{31}, x_{32}, \ldots)$. Then the flash equation, derived by combining Eqns. (4), (5), and (9), is solved for $\alpha = F_3/F_2$ (see Example 6.8):

$$f\{\alpha\} = \sum_{j=1}^{N_c} \frac{x_{1j}(1 - k_j)}{\alpha + k_j} = 0 \tag{11}$$

After solving Eqn. (11) for α, F_2 and F_3 are computed by

$$F_2 = \frac{F_1}{1 + \alpha}$$
$$F_3 = F_1 - F_2$$

Then (see Example 6.8),

$$x_{2j} = \frac{F_1}{F_2}\left(\frac{k_j x_{1j}}{\alpha + k_j}\right)$$

and

$$x_{3j} = \frac{x_{2j}}{k_j}$$

Convergence on mole fractions in the liquid is checked by

$$\left| \frac{x_{3j} - x_{3j}^*}{x_{3j}^*} \right| \leq \epsilon \qquad (j = 1, 2, \dots, N_c)$$

If the inequality is not satisfied, the method of successive substitutions is used to get the next guess values:

$$x_{3j}^* \longleftarrow x_{3j} \qquad (j = 1, 2, \dots, N_c)$$

Upon convergence of the material balance at T_2^*, enthalpies of product streams are computed at T_2^* (specific equations to be discussed). Finally, the energy balance equation (6) is used to compute $f\{T_2^*\}$, where $f\{T_2\}$ is defined by

$$f\{T_2\} = F_1 h_1 - F_2 h_2 - F_3 h_3 - \frac{dQ}{dt} = 0 \qquad (12)$$

f is zero at the solution value for T_2. Newton's method is used to get the next guess value for T_2,

$$T_2 \longleftarrow T_2^* - \frac{f\{T_2^*\}}{f'\{T_2^*\}}$$

where the derivative f' is computed numerically. Occasionally, Newton's method extrapolates outside of the two-phase region to $T_2 < T_{bub}$ or to $T_2 > T_{dew}$. If this happens, then the next guess for T_2 is positioned midway between T_2 and T_{bub} or T_{dew}:

$$T_2 \longleftarrow \frac{T_2^* + T_{bub}}{2} \qquad (T_2 < T_{bub})$$

$$T_2 \longleftarrow \frac{T_2^* + T_{dew}}{2} \qquad (T_2 > T_{dew})$$

Convergence to a solution value is achieved when

$$\left| \frac{T_2 - T_2^*}{T_2^*} \right| < \epsilon$$

A flow diagram of the algorithm for solving the material and energy balance and phase-equilibrium equations is shown in Fig. 10-13. Specifically, consider the following five-component mixture ($N_c = 5$):

Component	No. (j)
Neopentane (2,2-dimethylpropane)	1
Carbon tetrachloride	2
Cyclohexane	3
Benzene	4
Ethylbenzene	5

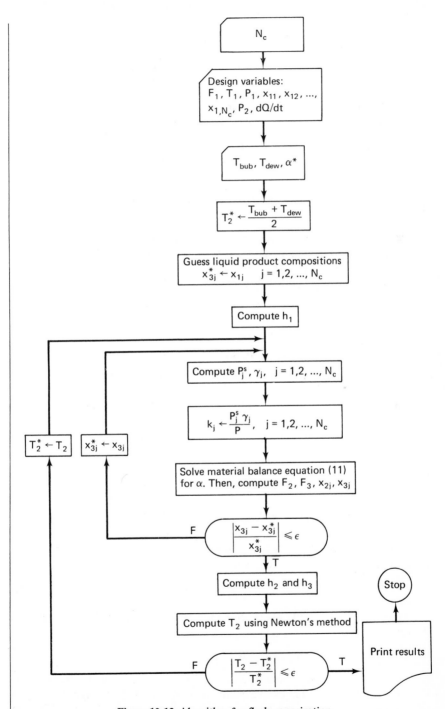

Figure 10-13 Algorithm for flash vaporization.

421

Properties of these substances (see Table 4.1) are

	T_b (°K)	λ at T_b (cal/mole)	T_c (°K)	P_c (atm)
Neopentane	282.65	5438	433.8	31.6
Carbon tetrachloride	349.85	7140	556.4	45.0
Cyclohexane	353.85	7204	553	40.0
Benzene	353.25	7353	562	48.6
Ethylbenzene	409.35	8600	619.6	38.0

where λ is latent heat of vaporization of the liquid at its normal boiling point (T_b).

Vapor Pressure. The vapor pressure for each component in the liquid can be computed as a function of temperature using the Riedel correlation (R. C. Reid and T. K. Sherwood, *Properties of Gases and Liquids*),

$$\log_{10} P_j^s = \log_{10} P_{c_j} - 0.1183\varphi_j\{T_{r_j}\} + 7 \log_{10} T_{r_j} - (\alpha_j - 7)\psi_j\{T_{r_j}\} \quad (13)$$

where

$$\varphi_j\{T_{r_j}\} = \frac{36}{T_{r_j}} + 42 \ln T_{r_j} - 35 - T_{r_j}^6$$

$$\psi_j\{T_{r_j}\} = 0.0364\varphi_j - \log_{10} T_{r_j}$$

The coefficient α_j is the Riedel factor; values for these chemicals are

Chemical	α_j
Neopentane	6.771
Carbon tetrachloride	6.742
Cyclohexane	6.844
Benzene	6.848
Ethylbenzene	7.330

Liquid-Phase Activity Coefficients. For a liquid mixture containing N_c components, there are $[(N_c)(N_c - 1)]/2$ binary pairs. It is assumed that excess Gibbs free energy for each *binary* liquid is given by Eqn. (6) in Appendix IV terminated after the first coefficient,

$$\frac{\Delta g_{jk}^e}{RT} = x_j x_k C_{jk} \quad (14)$$

where each binary coefficient (C_{jk}) is a function of temperature according to the empirical equation

$$C_{jk} = A_{jk} + \frac{B_{jk}}{T} \quad (15)$$

and A_{jk} and B_{jk} are constants, different for each binary liquid pair. We make the assumption that Gibbs free energy of a mixture of N_c components may be calculated in terms of the behavior of the binary systems of which it is composed according to the pairwise-additive equation:

$$\frac{\Delta g^e}{RT} = \sum_{j=1}^{N_c} \sum_{\substack{k=1 \\ (k>j)}}^{N_c} C_{jk} x_j x_k \qquad (16)$$

Substitution of this equation for Δg^e into Eqn. (5) of Appendix IV yields an equation for the activity coefficient of each component:

$$\ln \gamma_j = \sum_{\substack{k=1 \\ j \neq k}}^{N_c} C_{jk} x_k (1 - x_j) - \sum_{\substack{m=1 \\ (j \neq m) \\ (j \neq n) \\ (n>m)}}^{N_c} \sum_{n=1}^{N_c} C_{mn} x_m x_n \qquad (17)$$

For example, for a ternary mixture ($N_c = 3$),

$$\ln \gamma_1 = C_{12} x_2 (1 - x_1) + C_{13} x_3 (1 - x_1) - C_{23} x_2 x_3$$

where x_j means mole fraction of the jth component—the stream number (3) is omitted for clarity.

The following experimental data have been measured for the various pairs in the five-component mixture:

Liquid Pair	A_{jk}	B_{jk} (°K)
1–2	0.018	149
1–3	0	88
1–4	0	274
1–5	0	274
2–3	−0.125	71
2–4	−0.045	53
2–5	−0.045	53
3–4	−0.797	394
3–5	−0.797	394
4–5	0	0

Enthalpy.   Enthalpy of the vapor (stream 2) is given by Eqn. (2) in Appendix IV and (9.45):

$$h_2 = \sum_{j=1}^{5} x_{2j} \left[\int_{T_0}^{T_{bj}} c_{pj}^{liq} \, dT + \lambda_{T_{bj}} + \int_{T_{bj}}^{T_3} c_{pj}^{\circ} \, dT \right] \qquad (18)$$

The reference state is pure liquid at T_0, for which we choose the temperature of the feed ($T_0 = T_1$). T_{bj} is normal boiling point of the jth component and $\lambda_{T_{bj}}$ is its heat of vaporization at the normal boiling point. c_{pj}° is zero-pressure specific heat of the jth component. Coefficients of Eqn. (4.32) are

	(cal/ mole-°K) a_j	(cal/ mole-°K^2) $b_j \times 10^2$	(cal/ mole-°K^3) $c_j \times 10^5$	(cal/ mole-°K^4) $d_j \times 10^9$
Neopentane	−3.865	13.305	−8.018	18.83
Carbon tetrachloride	12.24	3.4	−2.995	8.828
Cyclohexane	−15.935	16.454	−9.203	19.27
Benzene	−8.650	11.578	−7.54	18.54
Ethylbenzene	−8.398	15.935	−10.003	23.95

c_{pj}^{liq} is specific heat of liquid given by

$$c_{pj}^{\text{liq}} = a_j + b_j T \qquad (19)$$

Constants for these substances are

	a_j (cal/mole-°K)	$b_j \times 10^2$ (cal/mole-°K^2)
Neopentane	21.20	6.6
Carbon tetrachloride	27.25	1.4
Cyclohexane	15.04	7.6
Benzene	15.82	5.6
Ethylbenzene	15.04	5.6

These constants for liquids (a_j and b_j) should not be confused with the constants for specific heats of the gases (c_p°). Deviations of the vapor (stream 2) from the perfect gas law are neglected because its pressure is atmospheric.

From Eqn. (1) in Appendix IV for enthalpy of the liquid streams,

$$h_1 = \sum_{j=1}^{5} x_{1j}\left[\int_{T_0}^{T_1} c_{pj}^{\text{liq}}\, dT\right] + \Delta h^m\{T_1, x_{11}, x_{12}, \ldots\} = \Delta h^m\{T_1, x_{11}, x_{12}, \ldots\}$$

$$(20)$$

because $T_0 = T_1$.

$$h_3 = \sum_{j=1}^{5} x_{3j}\left[\int_{T_0}^{T_3} c_{pj}^{\text{liq}}\, dT\right] + \Delta h^m\{T_3, x_{31}, x_{32}, \ldots\} \qquad (21)$$

Δh^m is heat of mixing when the liquid mixture is formed isothermally from the pure liquids.

Heat of mixing of the liquid may be obtained from Gibbs free energy by the Gibbs-Helmholtz equation,

$$\Delta h^m = -T^2 \frac{\partial}{\partial T}\left[\frac{\Delta g^e}{T}\right]$$

pressure and composition being held constant for the differentiation. Specifically, it follows from Eqns. (14)–(16) that heat of mixing for stream 1 is

$$\frac{\Delta h^m}{R} = \sum_{\substack{j=1 \\ (k>j)}}^{N_c} \sum_{k=1}^{N_c} B_{jk} x_{1j} x_{1k}$$

and for stream 3 is

$$\frac{\Delta h^m}{R} = \sum_{\substack{j=1 \\ (k>j)}}^{N_c} \sum_{k=1}^{N_c} B_{jk} x_{3j} x_{3k}$$

$$(22)$$

Interaction coefficients (B_{jk}) were given earlier in connection with the liquid-phase activity coefficients.

WATFIV Program

A WATFIV program implements the algorithm in Fig. 10-13. Estimation programs for each property are stored in the property information system library. These are listed in Table 10.1. Data records are stored for each pure substance and data records for mixtures contain the binary constants A_{jk} and B_{jk}. Subroutine ACTIVE activates the information system, as described in Ch. 5.

TABLE 10.1
PROPERTY ESTIMATION PROGRAMS*

Estimation Program	Property	Algorithm	Data Required
ZPHBP	Enthalpy at zero pressure relative to vapor at boiling point	$h = a(T - T_b) + \dfrac{b}{2}(T^2 - T_b^2)$ $+ \dfrac{c}{3}(T^3 - T_b^3) + \dfrac{d}{4}(T^4 - T_b^4)$	T_b, a, b, c, d
HLIQTO	Enthalpy change for heating a liquid from T_0 to T	$h = a(T - T_0) + \dfrac{b}{2}(T^2 - T_0^2)$	T_0, a, b
HVAP	Enthalpy of vapor mixture	Equation (18), using ZPHBP and HLIQTO	$T_{bj}, \lambda_{T_{bj}}, j = 1, 2, \ldots, N_c$
HMIX	Heat of mixing	Equation (22)	Binary constants, B_{jk}
HLIQ	Enthalpy of liquid mixture	Equation (21), using HLIQTO and HMIX	
RIEDEL	Vapor pressure	Equation (13)	T_c, P_c, α (Riedel factor)
ACOEF	Liquid-phase activity coefficients	Equations (15) and (17)	Binary constants, A_{jk} and B_{jk}

*Units are °K, atm, cal, and gmole.

425

Table of Symbols

Problem Symbol	Program Symbol	Definition	Units
	DSUM	$f'\{\alpha^*\}$, first derivative of Eqn. (11)	
F_i	F(I)	Molar flow rate of stream i	gmole/hr
	FSUM	$f\{\alpha^*\}$; see Eqn. (11)	
$f\{T_2\}$	FUNC	See Eqn. (12)	cal/hr
$f\{T_2^*\}$	FT2	See Eqn. (12)	cal/hr
$f\{T_2^*(1+\delta)\}$	FT2DEL	See Eqn. (12)	cal/hr
$f'\{T_2^*\}$	DERIV	$(f\{T_2^*(1+\delta)\} - f\{T_2^*\})/(T_2^*\delta)$	cal/hr-°K
h_i	H(I)	Enthalpy of stream i	cal/gmole
k_j	KEQ(J)	Vapor-liquid equilibrium constant	
$k_{\max}$	KMAX	Maximum number of iterations	
N_c	NC	Number of components	
P_i	P(I)	Pressure of stream i	atm
P_j^s	PSAT(J)	Vapor pressure of component j	atm
dQ/dt	Q	Heat loss	cal/hr
	SWITCH	A logical variable: When .TRUE., computes $f\{T_2^*\}$. When .FALSE., computes $f\{T_2^*(1+\delta)\}$.	
T_{bub}	TBUB	Bubble-point temperature	°K
T_{dew}	TDEW	Dew-point temperature	°K
T_i	T(I)	Temperature of stream i	°K
T_2^*	T2STAR	Guess temperature of stream 2	°K
x_{ij}	X(I,J)	Mole fraction of component j in stream i	
x_{3j}^*	X3STAR(J)	Guess mole fraction of component j in stream 3	
	XPROP(J)	Mole fraction of component j in a mixture	
α	ALPHA	F_3/F_2	
α^*	ALPHAS	Guess value for α	
γ_j	GAMMA(J)	Liquid-phase activity coefficient for component j	
δ	DELTA	Step size for numerical differentiation	
ϵ	EPS	Convergence tolerance	

Program Listing

```
C**    PROGRAM TO COMPUTE TEMPERATURE AND COMPOSITION OF N-COMPONENT
C      VAPOR AND LIQUID PRODUCTS LEAVING A FLASH DRUM.  LIQUID FEED TEMP-
C      ERATURE, PRESSURE, FLOW RATE, AND COMPOSITIONS ARE READ FROM CARDS
C      AS DESIGN VARIABLES, AS WELL AS FLASH DRUM PRESSURE AND RATE OF
C      HEAT LOSS.   STREAM 1 IS FEED, 2 VAPOR PRODUCT, AND 3 LIQUID
C      PRODUCT.  ENTHALPIES, VAPOR PRESSURES, AND LIQUID-PHASE ACTIVITY
C      COEFFICIENTS ARE COMPUTED FOR ANY N-COMPONENT MIXTURE BY THE
C      UNIVERSITY OF PENNSYLVANIA PROPERTY INFORMATION SYSTEM.   IDENTITY
C      OF THE COMPONENTS AND COMPUTATION METHODS ARE SPECIFIED AS DATA.
C
       LOGICAL SWITCH
       REAL KEQ(5)
       DIMENSION T(3), P(3), H(3), F(3), X(3,5), X3STAR(5), PSAT(5)
       DIMENSION GAMMA(5), XPROP(5)
C
C**    ACTIVATES THE UNIVERSITY OF PENNSYLVANIA PROPERTY INFORMATION
C      SYSTEM.
C
```

```
          CALL ACTIVE
C
C**    READS AND PRINTS THE NUMBER OF COMPONENTS (NC), DESIGN VARIABLE
C      VALUES, BUBBLE POINT, DEW POINT, A GUESS FOR ALPHA, AND ITERATION
C      PARAMETERS.
C
     1    READ, NC
          WRITE (6,101) NC
          READ, P(2), Q
          WRITE (6,103) P(2), Q
          WRITE (6,104)
          READ, T(1), P(1), F(1), (X(1,J), J = 1, NC)
          WRITE (6,106) T(1), P(1), F(1), (X(1,J), J = 1, NC)
          READ, TBUB, TDEW, ALPHAS
          WRITE (6,107) TBUB, TDEW, ALPHAS
          READ, KMAX, EPS, DELTA
          WRITE (6,108) KMAX, EPS, DELTA
C
C**    SETS PRESSURE AND GUESSES FOR TEMPERATURE, T2STAR, AND LIQUID
C      PRODUCT MOLE FRACTIONS, X3STAR(J).
C
          P(3) = P(2)
          T2STAR = (TBUB + TDEW)/2.0
          DO 4 J = 1, NC
     4    X3STAR(J) = X(1,J)
C
C**    PROPERTY INFORMATION SYSTEM COMPUTES ENTHALPY OF FEED.
C
          DO 5 J = 1, NC
     5    XPROP(J) = X(1,J)
          H(1) = PPCF(402, T(1), P(1), XPROP)
C
C**    BEGINS NEWTON'S METHOD ITERATIONS TO COMPUTE T(2).
C
          DO 7 K = 1, KMAX
          WRITE (6,110) K
C
C**    EVALUATES FT2 = F(T2STAR) WHEN SWITCH = .TRUE. AND FT2DEL =
C      F(T2STAR*(1.0 + DELTA)) WHEN SWITCH = .FALSE.  FT2 AND FT2DEL ARE
C      USED TO COMPUTE THE DERIVATIVE NUMERICALLY FOR NEWTON'S METHOD
C      ESTIMATION OF T(2).
C
          SWITCH = .FALSE.
    20    IF (SWITCH)  GO TO 8
          T2STAR = T2STAR*(1.0 + DELTA)
C
C**    SOLVES THE MATERIAL BALANCE EQUATIONS AT T2STAR.
C
     8    DO 9 KK = 1, KMAX
C
C**    PROPERTY INFORMATION SYSTEM COMPUTES VAPOR PRESSURES AND LIQUID-
C      PHASE ACTIVITY COEFFICIENTS.
C
          CALL PPCS(216, T2STAR, P(2), X3STAR, PSAT)
          CALL PPCS(302, T2STAR, P(2), X3STAR, GAMMA)
C
C**    COMPUTES K-VALUES AND SOLVES F(ALPHA) = 0 FOR ALPHA USING
C      NEWTON'S METHOD, WHERE ALPHA = F(3)/F(2).
C
          DO 10 J = 1, NC
    10    KEQ(J) = PSAT(J)*GAMMA(J)/P(2)
          WRITE (6,111)
          DO 11 KKK = 1, KMAX
          FSUM = 0
          DSUM = 0
          DO 12 J = 1, NC
          PROD = X(1,J)*(1.0 - KEQ(J))/(ALPHAS + KEQ(J))
          FSUM = FSUM + PROD
    12    DSUM = DSUM - PROD/(ALPHAS + KEQ(J))
          ALPHA = ALPHAS - FSUM/DSUM
          WRITE (6,112) ALPHAS, ALPHA
          IF (ABS((ALPHA - ALPHAS)/ALPHAS) .LE. EPS)  GO TO 13
    11    ALPHAS = ALPHA
          WRITE (6,113)
          STOP
```

```
C
C**   COMPUTES F(2), F(3), X(2,J), AND X(3,J) AND CHECKS FOR CONVERGENCE
C     OF THE MATERIAL BALANCE EQUATIONS.
C
   13 F(2) = F(1)/(1.0 + ALPHA)
      F(3) = F(1) - F(2)
      DO 14 J = 1, NC
      X(3,J) = (F(1)/F(2))*X(1,J)/(ALPHA + KEQ(J))
   14 X(2,J) = KEQ(J)*X(3,J)
      DO 15 J = 1, NC
      IF (ABS((X(3,J) - X3STAR(J))/X3STAR(J)) .LE. EPS)  GO TO 15
      GO TO 16
   15 CONTINUE
      GO TO 25
   16 DO 9 J = 1, NC
    9 X3STAR(J) = X(3,J)
      WRITE (6,114)
C
C**   PROPERTY INFORMATION SYSTEM COMPUTES PRODUCT STREAM ENTHALPIES.
C
   25 DO 17 J = 1, NC
   17 XPROP(J) = X(2,J)
      H(2) = PPCF(401, T2STAR, P(2), XPROP)
      DO 18 J = 1, NC
   18 XPROP(J) = X(3,J)
      H(3) = PPCF(402, T2STAR, P(3), XPROP)
C
C**   COMPUTES FUNC WHICH IS STORED IN FT2 OR FT2DEL DEPENDING UPON
C     SWITCH.
C
      FUNC = F(1)*H(1) - F(2)*H(2) - F(3)*H(3) - Q
      IF (SWITCH)  GO TO 19
      FT2DEL = FUNC
      T2STAR = T2STAR/(1.0 + DELTA)
      SWITCH = .TRUE.
      GO TO 20
   19 FT2 = FUNC
C
C**   ESTIMATES T(2) USING NEWTON'S METHOD. CHECKS FOR CONVERGENCE.
C
      DERIV = (FT2DEL - FT2)/(DELTA*T2STAR)
      T(2) = T2STAR - FT2/DERIV
      IF (ABS((T(2) - T2STAR)/T2STAR) .LE. EPS)  GO TO 21
      WRITE (6,115) K, T2STAR, T(2)
      IF (T(2) .LE. TBUB)  T(2) = (TBUB + T2STAR)/2.0
      IF (T(2) .GE. TDEW)  T(2) = (TDEW + T2STAR)/2.0
    7 T2STAR = T(2)
      WRITE (6,116)
      STOP
C
C**   PRINTS RESULTS.
C
   21 T(3) = T(2)
      WRITE (6,117)
      DO 22 I = 1, 3
   22 WRITE (6,118) I, T(I), P(I), H(I), F(I), (X(I,J), J = 1, NC)
      GO TO 1
C
C**   INPUT AND OUTPUT FORMATS.
C
  101 FORMAT ( ' NUMBER OF COMPONENTS = ', I5,//)
  103 FORMAT (' P(2), Q =',//, 2F10.2,//)
  104 FORMAT (' STREAM NO. 1 - T(1), P(1), F(1), X(1,1), X(1,2),...,X(1,
     1NC) =',/)
  106 FORMAT (3F9.2, 5F9.4,/9(27X, 5F9.4))
  107 FORMAT (//' TBUB, TDEW, ALPHAS =',//, 2F10.2, F10.4)
  108 FORMAT (//' KMAX, EPS, DELTA, =',//, I10, 2F10.5)
  110 FORMAT (////' ITERATION NO. TO DETERMINE T2STAR =', I5)
  111 FORMAT (//' INTERMEDIATE VALUES OF ALPHAS AND ALPHA ='/)
  112 FORMAT (2F12.6)
  113 FORMAT (//' NO CONVERGENCE FOR ALPHA.  KMAX EXCEEDED.'//)
  114 FORMAT (//' MATERIAL BALANCE DID NOT CONVERGE.  KMAX EXCEEDED.'//)
```

```
115  FORMAT (//' AFTER ITERATION NO.' I5,', T2STAR AND T(2) =',
    1 2F12.2)
116  FORMAT (//' ENERGY BALANCE DID NOT CONVERGE. KMAX EXCEEDED.'//)
117  FORMAT (///' ......CONVERGENCE ACHIEVED......'///' STREAM NO. (I),
    1 T(I), P(I), H(I), F(I), X(I,1), X(I,2),..., X(I,NC) ='/)
118  FORMAT (I5, 3X, 3F10.2, F10.3/ 10(20X, 5F10.4))
     END
```

Data

The current list of chemicals and key words that identify the estimation programs are read from cards by subroutine ACTIVE.

```
           PERSONAL DATA BASE = D. S. POZNANOVIC

           CURRENT LIST OF CHEMICALS
             NEOPENTANE,
             CARBON TETRACHLORIDE,
             CYCLOHEXANE,
             BENZENE,
             ETHYLBENZENE;

           KEY WORDS
             PROPERTY = 216, PROGRAM = RIEDEL;
             PROPERTY = 302, PROGRAM = ACOEF;
             PROPERTY = 401, PROGRAM = HVAP;
             PROPERTY = 402, PROGRAM = HLIQ;
             PROPERTY = 406, PROGRAM = ZPHBP;
             PROPERTY = 463, PROGRAM = HLIQTO;
             PROPERTY = 422, PROGRAM = HMIX;

           END
```

This card deck is followed by the data deck for the flash program:

```
    5
    1.0, 0.
    400.58, 10.0, 100.0, 0.35, 0.1, 0.1, 0.1, 0.35
    303.51, 379.46, 1.0
    20, 0.0001, 0.00001
```

Computed Output

```
NUMBER OF COMPONENTS =      5

P(2), Q =

    1.00       0.00

STREAM NO. 1 - T(1), P(1), F(1), X(1,1), X(1,2),...,X(1,NC) =

  400.58    10.00   100.00    0.3500    0.1000    0.1000    0.1000    0.3500


TBUB, TDEW, ALPHAS =

  303.51    379.46    1.0000

KMAX, EPS, DELTA, =

    20   0.00010    0.00001
```

Intermediate values of T_2^*, α^*, and x_{3j}^* are not shown. Three iterations for T_2, 34 for α, and 18 for x_{3j} were required.

......CONVERGENCE ACHIEVED......

STREAM NO. (I), T(I), P(I), H(I), F(I), X(I,1), X(I,2),..., X(I,NC) =

1	400.58	10.00	4088.57	100.000			
		0.3500	0.1000	0.1000	0.1000	0.3500
2	339.75	1.00	7292.48	44.415			
		0.6954	0.0846	0.0865	0.0780	0.0554
3	339.75	1.00	1528.40	55.585			
		0.0740	0.1123	0.1108	0.1175	0.5854

Discussion

The calculated result satisfies the material and energy balance equations and thermodynamic equations for equilibrium of liquid and vapor.

The effectiveness of a single stage in separating the lightest and heaviest components depends on the difference in their boiling points: The greater the difference, the better the separation. In this example, the difference in boiling points of ethylbenzene and neopentane is 126°C. The single-stage flash achieves a partial separation: Vapor is rich in the light component (neopentane), and liquid is rich in the heavy component (ethylbenzene). The middle cut (carbon tetrachloride, cyclohexane, and benzene) splits about evenly between liquid and vapor.

Example 10.9 shows how staging in a distillation column gives a much better separation of the same feed.

The temperature of a pure liquid rises as it is heated at constant pressure until it reaches its boiling point, the temperature at which vaporization begins. If heating continues, the temperature remains fixed at the boiling point as long as liquid is present.

Mixtures do not have boiling points because the temperature of liquid and vapor rises during vaporization at constant pressure. Instead of a boiling point, each mixture is characterized by its bubble point and dew point. Bubble and dew points, like boiling point, depend on pressure. Liquid mixtures form their first bubble of vapor when the temperature is raised to the *bubble point*. Vapor mixtures form the first drop of liquid when temperature is lowered to the *dew point*. At intermediate temperatures above the bubble point and below the dew point, liquid and vapor phases coexist in equilibrium. The next example shows how to calculate the bubble and dew point of a mixture.

Example 10.8   Bubble and Dew Point

Calculate the bubble and dew point for a mixture of N_c components.

Solution:

1. Equations and constraints. At equilibrium the temperature and pressure are equal in both phases, liquid and vapor. In addition the condition for

equilibrium of each component is equality of fugacity in both phases:

$$f_j^{\text{vap}}\{T, P, y_1, y_2, \ldots\} = f_j^{\text{liq}}\{T, P, x_1, x_2, \ldots\} \qquad (j = 1, 2, \ldots, N_c) \quad (1)$$

The specific equation for fugacity depends on the pressure, nonideality of the liquid phase, etc. Mole fraction constraints are

$$\sum_{j=1}^{N_c} y_j = 1 \tag{2}$$

and

$$\sum_{j=1}^{N_c} x_j = 1 \tag{3}$$

where x refers to liquid and y refers to vapor.

2. Number of variables: $N_v = 2N_c + 2 \ (T, P, x_1, x_2, \ldots, y_1, y_2, \ldots)$.
3. Design or decision variables:

$$
\begin{aligned}
N_d &= N_v - N_e \\
&= (2N_c + 2) - (N_c + 2) \\
&= N_c
\end{aligned}
$$

For the bubble-point calculation, liquid composition is known, and the N_c design variables are

$$x_1, x_2, \ldots, x_{N_c-1}, P$$

For the dew-point calculation, vapor composition is known, and the design variables are

$$y_1, y_2, \ldots, y_{N_c-1}, P$$

4. Solution of the equations. Bubble and dew points are calculated for N_c components that form a nonideal liquid solution. Pressure is assumed to be atmospheric or lower so that the vapor behaves like a perfect gas; therefore, Eqn. (4) of Appendix IV applies:

$$Py_j = P_j^s \gamma_j x_j = P_j^s\{T\}\gamma_j\{T, x_1, x_2, \ldots\}x_j \qquad (j = 1, 2, \ldots, N_c) \tag{4}$$

Introducing k-values,

$$k_j = \frac{y_j}{x_j} \tag{5}$$

where

$$k_j = \frac{P_j^s \gamma_j}{P} = \frac{P_j^s\{T\}\gamma_j\{T, x_1, x_2, \ldots\}}{P} \qquad (j = 1, 2, \ldots, N_c) \tag{6}$$

Bubble point. Equations (2), (5), and (6) are combined to give a single equation in one unknown (T):

$$f\{T\} = \sum_{j=1}^{N_c} k_j x_j - 1 = \sum_{j=1}^{N_c} k_j\{T, \boxed{P}, \boxed{x_1}, \boxed{x_2}, \ldots\}\boxed{x_j} - 1 = 0 \tag{7}$$

The first guess for temperature, T^*, is the molal average of the boiling points (at pressure P) of the pure liquids.

Dew point. Equations (5) are substituted into Eqn. (3):

$$f\{T\} = \sum_{j=1}^{N_c} \frac{\boxed{y_j}}{k_j} - 1 = 0 \tag{8}$$

Equations (8) and (6) are solved simultaneously. Unknowns are dew point, T, and liquid mole fractions $(x_1, x_2, \ldots)$. Raoult's law $[x_j = Py_j/P_j^s]$ is used to make a first guess of the mole fractions (x_j^*).

The algorithm is summarized in Fig. 10-14. Note that z_j represents liquid composition for bubble-point calculations and vapor composition for dew-point calculations.

Specifically, let the mixture consist of the following substances,

Component	Mole Fraction, z_j
Neopentane	0.35
Carbon tetrachloride	0.10
Cyclohexane	0.10
Benzene	0.10
Ethylbenzene	0.35

and calculate bubble and dew points at 1 atm. Specific equations for vapor pressure and liquid-phase activity coefficients of these substances are given in Example 10.7.

WATFIV Program

A WATFIV program implements the algorithm in Fig. 10-14. Estimation programs and data records for each property are summarized in Table 10.1.

Table of Symbols

Most symbols are defined by Example 10.7. Only new symbols are listed here.

Problem Symbol	Program Symbol	Definition	Units
$f\{T\}$	FUNC	See Eqns. (7) and (8)	
$f\{T^*\}$	FT	See Eqns. (7) and (8)	
$f\{T^*(1 + \delta)\}$	FTDEL	See Eqns. (7) and (8)	
P	P	Pressure	atm
T	T	Bubble- or dew-point temperature	°K
T^*	TSTAR	Guess temperature	°K
z_j	Z(J)	Liquid mole fractions at bubble point; vapor mole fractions at dew point	

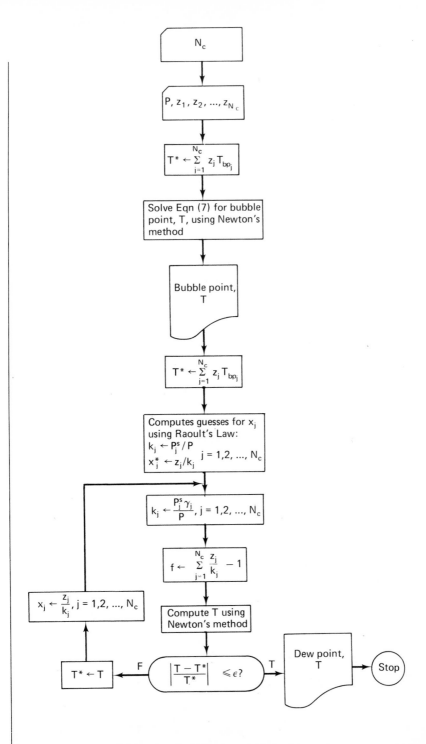

Figure 10-14 Algorithm for bubble and dew points.

433

Program Listing

```
C
C**    PROGRAM TO COMPUTE THE BUBBLE AND DEW POINT OF AN N-COMPONENT
C      MIXTURE.
C
       LOGICAL SWITCH
       REAL KEQ(5)
       DIMENSION Z(5), PSAT(5), GAMMA(5), XSTAR(5)
C
C**    ACTIVATES THE UNIVERSITY OF PENNSYLVANIA PROPERTY INFORMATION
C      SYSTEM.
C
       CALL ACTIVE
C
C**    READS AND PRINTS THE NUMBER OF COMPONENTS (NC), VALUES OF DESIGN
C      VARIABLES, AND ITERATION PARAMETERS.
C
       READ, NC
       WRITE (6,101) NC
       READ, P, (Z(J), J = 1, NC)
       WRITE (6,102) P, (Z(J), J = 1, NC)
       READ, KMAX, EPS, DELTA
       WRITE (6,103) KMAX, EPS, DELTA
C
C**    COMPUTES GUESS TEMPERATURE, TSTAR.  PROPERTY INFORMATION SYSTEM
C      RETRIEVES BOILING POINTS, DEG.K.
C
       SUM = 0
       DO 1 J = 1, NC
       TBP = PURE (217, 0., P, J)
    1  SUM = SUM + Z(J)*TBP
       TSTAR = SUM
       SAVETS = SUM
       WRITE (6,104) TSTAR
C
C**    BEGINS NEWTON'S METHOD ITERATIONS TO COMPUTE BUBBLE POINT.
C
       DO 2 K = 1, KMAX
C
C**    EVALUATES FT = F(TSTAR) WHEN SWITCH = .TRUE. AND FTDEL = F(TSTAR*
C      (1.0 + DELTA)) WHEN SWITCH = .FALSE.  FT AND FTDEL ARE USED TO
C      COMPUTE THE DERIVATIVE NUMERICALLY FOR NEWTON'S METHOD ESTIMATION
C      OF T.
C
       SWITCH = .FALSE.
    3  IF (SWITCH)  GO TO 4
       TSTAR = TSTAR*(1.0 + DELTA)
C
C**    PROPERTY INFORMATION SYSTEM COMPUTES VAPOR PRESSURES AND LIQUID-
C      PHASE ACTIVITY COEFFICIENTS.
C
    4  CALL PPCS (216, TSTAR, 0., Z, PSAT)
       CALL PPCS (302, TSTAR, 0., Z, GAMMA)
C
C**    COMPUTES K-VALUES AND EVALUATES FUNC, WHICH IS STORED IN FT OR
C      FTDEL DEPENDING UPON SWITCH.
C
       SUM = - 1.0
       DO 5 J = 1, NC
       KEQ(J) = PSAT(J)*GAMMA(J)/P
    5  SUM = SUM + KEQ(J)*Z(J)
       FUNC = SUM
       IF (SWITCH)  GO TO 6
       FTDEL = FUNC
       TSTAR = TSTAR/(1.0 + DELTA)
       SWITCH = .TRUE.
       GO TO 3
    6  FT = FUNC
C
C**    ESTIMATES T USING NEWTON'S METHOD.  CHECKS FOR CONVERGENCE.
C
```

```
          DERIV = (FTDEL - FT)/(DELTA*TSTAR)
          T = TSTAR - FT/DERIV
          IF (ABS((T - TSTAR)/TSTAR) .LE. EPS)  GO TO 7
          WRITE (6,105) K, TSTAR, T
     2    TSTAR = T
          WRITE (6,106)
          STOP
C
C**  PRINTS RESULTS.
C
     7    WRITE (6,107) T
C
C**  BEGINS DEW POINT CALCULATIONS.  COMPUTES GUESSES FOR LIQUID MOLE
C    FRACTIONS, XSTAR(J), USING RAOULT'S LAW.  PROPERTY INFORMATION
C    SYSTEM COMPUTES VAPOR PRESSURES.
C
          TSTAR = SAVETS
          CALL PPCS (216, TSTAR, 0., Z, PSAT)
          DO 8 J = 1, NC
          KEQ(J) = PSAT(J)/P
     8    XSTAR(J) = Z(J)/KEQ(J)
C
C**  BEGINS NEWTON'S METHOD ITERATIONS TO COMPUTE DEW POINT.
C
          DO 9 K = 1, KMAX
C
C**  EVALUATES FT = F(TSTAR) WHEN SWITCH = .TRUE. AND FTDEL = F(TSTAR*
C    (1.0 + DELTA)) WHEN SWITCH = .FALSE.
C
          SWITCH = .FALSE.
    13    IF (SWITCH)  GO TO 10
          TSTAR = TSTAR*(1.0 + DELTA)
C
C**  PROPERTY INFORMATION SYSTEM COMPUTES VAPOR PRESSURES AND LIQUID-
C    PHASE ACTIVITY COEFFICIENTS.
C
    10    CALL PPCS (216, TSTAR, 0., Z, PSAT)
          CALL PPCS (302, TSTAR, 0., XSTAR, GAMMA)
C
C**  COMPUTES K-VALUES AND EVALUATES FUNC, WHICH IS STORED IN FT OR
C    FTDEL DEPENDING UPON SWITCH.
C
          SUM = -1.0
          DO 11 J = 1, NC
          KEQ(J) = PSAT(J)*GAMMA(J)/P
    11    SUM = SUM + Z(J)/KEQ(J)
          FUNC = SUM
          IF (SWITCH)  GO TO 12
          FTDEL = FUNC
          TSTAR = TSTAR/(1.0 + DELTA)
          SWITCH = .TRUE.
          GO TO 13
    12    FT = FUNC
C
C**  ESTIMATES T USING NEWTON'S METHOD.  CHECKS FOR CONVERGENCE.
C    ADJUSTS XSTAR(J).
C
          DERIV = (FTDEL - FT)/(DELTA*TSTAR)
          T = TSTAR - FT/DERIV
          IF (ABS((T - TSTAR)/TSTAR) .LE. EPS)  GO TO 14
          WRITE (6,108) K, TSTAR, T, (XSTAR(J), J = 1, NC)
          TSTAR = T
          DO 9 J = 1, NC
     9    XSTAR(J) = Z(J)/KEQ(J)
C
C**  PRINTS RESULTS.
C
    14    WRITE (6,109) T, (Z(J)/KEQ(J), J = 1, NC)
          STOP
C
C**  INPUT AND OUTPUT FORMATS.
C
```

```
101   FORMAT ('1', 'NUMBER OF COMPONENTS = ', I5//)
102   FORMAT (' P, Z(1),..., Z(NC) = '//6F10.5//)
103   FORMAT (' KMAX, EPS, DELTA = '//I10, 2F10.5//)
104   FORMAT (' GUESS TEMPERATURE, TSTAR = 'F10.2///' BUBBLE POINT ITERA
     1TIONS, TSTAR AND T'//)
105   FORMAT (I10, 2F10.2)
106   FORMAT (' NO CONVERGENCE FOR T.  KMAX EXCEEDED.')
107   FORMAT (//' BUBBLE POINT = ', F10.2//' DEW POINT ITERATIONS, TSTAR
     1, T, XSTAR(1),..., XSTAR(NC)'//)
108   FORMAT (I10, 2F9.2, 5F9.5)
109   FORMAT (//' DEW POINT = ', F10.2//' X(1),..., X(NC) = '//5F10.5)
      END
```

Data

The card deck containing the current list of chemicals and key words that identify estimation programs is the same as in Example 10.7. It is followed by data for the bubble- and dew-point program:

```
5
1.0, 0.35, 0.1, 0.1, 0.1, 0.35
20, 0.0001, 0.00001
```

Computed Output

```
NUMBER OF COMPONENTS =     5

P, Z(1),..., Z(NC) =

 1.00000   0.35000   0.10000   0.10000   0.10000   0.35000

KMAX, EPS, DELTA =

     20  0.00010   0.00001

GUESS TEMPERATURE, TSTAR =    347.90

BUBBLE POINT ITERATIONS, TSTAR AND T

       1   347.89     317.93
       2   317.92     305.65
       3   305.65     303.49

BUBBLE POINT =    303.51

DEW POINT ITERATIONS, TSTAR, T, XSTAR(1),..., XSTAR(NC)

       1   347.89   365.79   0.05399   0.10617   0.12001   0.11832   2.70885
       2   365.79   376.76   0.00707   0.09943   0.05965   0.14127   3.23437
       3   376.76   379.23   0.00308   0.04978   0.03037   0.07441   1.48144
       4   379.23   379.46   0.00947   0.04137   0.03643   0.05138   0.94695

DEW POINT =    379.46

X(1),..., X(NC) =

 0.01443   0.04085   0.04001   0.04737   0.85733
```

Below 303.51°K the mixture is all liquid, and above 379.46°K the mixture is all vapor (at 1 atm). In the flash vaporization of Example 10.7, a feed with this composition was flashed at 1 atm and the product was 44% vapor (mole percentage) at 339.75°K.

Material and energy balances must be solved simultaneously when the heat load is a design variable. Previous examples of adiabatic chemical reaction and adiabatic flash vaporization show how the equations are interlocked. In staged operations such as distillation, material and energy balances must be solved simultaneously for each stage. In addition, calculations for different stages are interlocked by countercurrent flow so that the whole set of material and energy balances, one for each stage, must be solved simultaneously. Thus, staged operations introduce a new dimension of complexity into the solution of material and energy balances.

A distillation column is one of the most important applications of staged operations in chemical engineering. Material and energy balances for a distillation column are studied in the next example, which shows how to set up the equations and determine the design variables. Solution methods, which include graphical and iterative techniques, are discussed in textbooks on staged operations.*

Example 10.9

A distillation tower is shown in Fig. 1-3, and its operation is explained briefly in Ch. 1. Set up material and energy balance equations for each stage, and determine the number of design variables for the distillation column.

Let the feed be a multicomponent mixture which the column separates into a distillate (substances with low boiling points) and bottoms (substances with high boiling points). If the feed is a binary mixture, it is sometimes possible to get a nearly perfect separation of the feed into its pure constituents. If the feed contains three or more components, only one product stream (distillate or bottoms) can be a pure substance.

Assume that the condenser provides just enough coolant to condense all the vapor to liquid at its bubble point, which is then split into two streams: distillate product and reflux. The condenser is then called a total condenser (in a partial condenser, some of the distillate is vapor).

Each stage is assumed to reach equilibrium with respect to heat and mass transfer between outgoing streams. Real distillation columns do not attain equilibrium in each stage, but the equilibrium stage concept enables one to define an efficiency that can be correlated with actual behavior of the column.

Assume that the number of trays in the column is known so that the problem is to calculate the flow rate and composition of the product. This is called the simulation problem. (A different problem, called the design problem, arises when

*C. J. King, *Separation Processes*, McGraw-Hill, New York, 1971. P. L. T. Brian, *Staged Cascades in Chemical Processing*, Prentice-Hall, Englewood Cliffs, N.J., 1972. B. D. Smith, *Design of Equilibrium Stage Processes*, McGraw-Hill, New York, 1963.

the product composition is a design variable and the problem is to calculate the number of trays.)

Solution:

Each tray of the distillation column has two feed streams and two product streams, arranged in a countercurrent flow pattern of liquid flowing downward and vapor rising upward [see Fig. 1-3(b)]. The schematic is shown in Fig. 10-15.

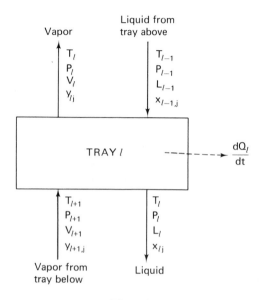

Figure 10-15

Product streams from each tray are at the same temperature and pressure in accordance with the assumption of equilibrium mentioned previously. y_{lj} means mole fraction of component j in the vapor (V) leaving tray l; x_{lj} means mole fraction of component j in the liquid (L) leaving tray l. Trays are numbered from top to bottom as shown in Fig. 10-16.

Notice that the schematic for tray l is modified for the feed tray, the top tray (condenser), and the bottom tray (reboiler). The feed tray has one more stream entering, and the reboiler receives no vapor from below. The condenser receives no liquid from above, and the composition of distillate (and reflux) is the same as that of vapor from the second tray. Even though there is no vapor leaving a total condenser, it is necessary to calculate the composition of vapor in equilibrium with reflux liquid in order to calculate its bubble-point temperature.

1. Equations and constraints.
   a. Equilibrium constraints. Product streams from tray l have the same temperature and pressure (T_l, P_l). The phase-equilibrium constraints are Eqn. (3) in Appendix IV, one for each component:

$$f_{lj}^{\text{vap}}\{T_l, P_l, y_{l1}, y_{l2}, \ldots, y_{l,N_c-1}\} = f_{lj}^{\text{liq}}\{T_l, P_l, x_{l1}, x_{l2}, \ldots, x_{l,N_c-1}\}$$

$$(j = 1, 2, \ldots, N_c)$$

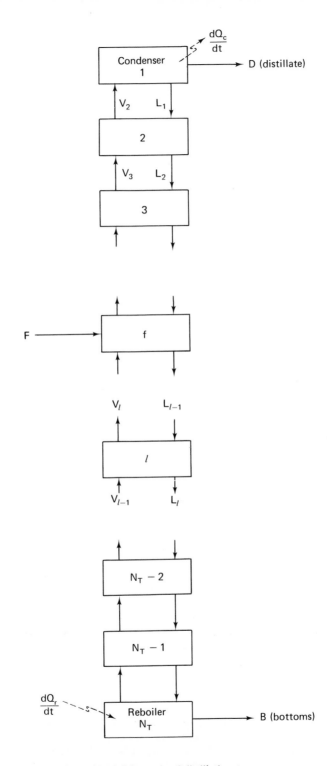

Figure 10-16 Schematic of distillation tower.

439

N_c is the number of components in the feed stream to the column. The specific form of the fugacity equations depends on the pressure and the nonideality of the liquid mixture; see Eqn. (4) in Appendix IV.

b. Material balance equations:

$$V_{l+1}y_{l+1,j} + L_{l-1}x_{l-1,j} = V_l y_{lj} + L_l x_{lj} \qquad (j = 1, 2, \ldots, N_c)$$

This equation is modified for the feed tray, condenser, and reboiler:

feed tray: $\quad V_{f+1}y_{f+1,j} + L_{f-1}x_{f-1,j} + Fz_j = V_f y_{fj} + L_f x_{fj}$

$$(j = 1, 2, \ldots, N_c)$$

condenser: $\quad y_{2j} = x_{1j}$ $\qquad\qquad\qquad (j = 1, 2, \ldots, N_c - 1)$

$$V_2 = L_1 + D$$

reboiler: $\quad L_{N_T-1}x_{N_T-1,j} = V_{N_T}y_{N_T,j} + Bx_{N_T,j}$

$$(j = 1, 2, \ldots, N_c)$$

where f is the number of the feed tray, N_T is the total number of trays (see Fig. 10-16), and z_j is mole fraction of component j in the feed stream. Flow rates (L, V, F, D, B) are in units of moles per unit time.

c. Energy balance equations:

$$V_{l+1}h_{V_{l+1}} + L_{l-1}h_{L_{l-1}} = V_l h_{V_l} + L_l h_{L_l} + \frac{dQ_l}{dt}$$

Modifications for the feed tray, condenser, and reboiler are

feed tray: $\quad V_{f+1}h_{V_{f+1}} + L_{f-1}h_{L_{f-1}} + Fh_F = V_f h_{V_f} + L_f h_{L_f} + \frac{dQ_f}{dt}$

condenser: $\quad V_2 h_{V_2} = (L_1 + D)h_{L_1} + \frac{dQ_c}{dt}$

reboiler: $\quad L_{N_T-1}h_{L_{N_T-1}} = V_{N_T}h_{V_{N_T}} + Bh_B - \frac{dQ_r}{dt}$

where h is molar enthalpy. dQ_c/dt is rate of heat transfer from the condenser to its cooling water or refrigerant; dQ_r/dt is rate of heat transfer from steam or some other heating fluid to the reboiler. Although there is an allowance for possible heat loss from the other trays, the best operating conditions are adiabatic ($dQ_l/dt = dQ_f/dt = 0$).

d. Reflux ratio. Liquid returned from the condenser to the column is called reflux, the amount of which affects the performance of the column. Reflux ratio (R) is defined as the ratio of reflux (L_1) to that removed as product:

$$R = \frac{L_1}{D}$$

For a given number of trays, increasing the reflux ratio increases the purity of the product but at the expense of higher operating costs for heating and cooling larger volumes of internal flow.

e. Mole-fraction constraints. For each of $2N_T - 2$ internal streams there is one equation:

$$\sum_{j=1}^{N_c} x_j = 1$$

or

$$\sum_{j=1}^{N_c} y_j = 1$$

In addition there is an equation for the equilibrium vapor in the condenser (composition of vapor needed to calculate the bubble point of the liquid) and for the bottoms (B). The composition of the feed is known, and the composition of distillate (D) is the same as L_1. Therefore, there is a total of $(2N_T - 2) + 1 + 1 = 2N_T$ equations.

f. Constitutive equations for enthalpy. An equation for molar enthalpy is written for each of $2N_T - 2$ internal streams and the bottoms stream as a function of their temperature, pressure, and composition. The specific form of the equation depends on whether the stream is liquid or gas. Enthalpy of the feed is assumed to be known; molar enthalpy of distillate is the same as that of L_1. Therefore, there is a total of $(2N_T - 2) + 1 = 2N_T - 1$ constitutive equations for enthalpy.

We can now count the total number of equations for N_c components and a column of N_T trays:

Type of Equation	No.
Equilibrium constraints	$N_T N_c$
Material balance	$N_T N_c$
Energy balance	N_T
Reflux ratio	1
Mole fraction constraints	$2N_T$
Enthalpy	$2N_T - 1$
Total	$2N_T N_c + 5N_T$

For example, for a column of 15 trays ($N_T = 15$) and a ternary mixture ($N_c = 3$), there are

$$2(15)(3) + 5(15) = 165 \text{ equations}$$

to be solved simultaneously.

2. Number of variables.

a. Streams. $2N_T N_c + 6N_T - 1$

Disregarding the feed stream, there are $2N_T - 2$ internal streams plus distillate and bottoms, a total of $2N_T$ streams. Variables for these streams are $2N_T$ flow rates, N_T temperatures, N_T pressures, $2N_T N_c$ compositions, and $2N_T - 1$ enthalpies.

b. Feed stream (flow rate, temperature, pres- $N_c + 4$
   sure, composition, and quality)
c. Rate of heat transfer (dQ/dt) N_T
d. Reflux ratio (R) 1
e. Number of trays (N_T) 1
f. Location of feed tray (f) 1

$$N_v = 2N_T N_c + 7N_T + N_c + 6$$

3. Design variables:

$$N_d = N_v - N_e$$
$$= 2N_T N_c + 7N_T + N_c + 6 - (2N_T N_c + 5N_T)$$
$$= 2N_T + N_c + 6$$

For the simulation problem, a convenient set is

Type of Variable	No. of Variables
Distillate flow rate, D	1
Reflux rate, R	1
Rate of heat transfer, dQ/dt (except for reboiler and condenser)	$N_T - 2$
Pressure, P	N_T
Feed stream (flow rate, temperature, pressure, composition, quality)	$N_c + 4$
Number of trays, N_T	1
Location of feed tray, f	1
Total	$2N_T + N_c + 6$

4. Solution of the equations. We shall use a computer program prepared by Seader* and based upon the Wang-Henke method† to solve the equations. The program solves for the unknown product composition and reboiler heating load given the number of trays, distillate flow rate, and reflux ratio. Values of design variables are

a. Feed stream:

$$F = 100 \text{ lb-moles/hr} \quad \text{(basis)}$$

$$z_1 = 0.35 \quad \text{(neopentane)}$$

$$z_2 = 0.10 \quad \text{(carbon tetrachloride)}$$

$$z_3 = 0.10 \quad \text{(cyclohexane)}$$

$$z_4 = 0.10 \quad \text{(benzene)}$$

$$z_5 = 0.35 \quad \text{(ethylbenzene)}$$

*J. Christensen, ed., *Stagewise Computations—Computer Programs for Chemical Engineering Education*, Aztec Publishing Co., Houston, 1972.
†J. C. Wang and G. E. Henke, "Tridiagonal Matrix for Distillation," *Hydrocarbon Processing*, 45(8), 155 (1966).

$$T = 86.6°F = 303.51°K \quad \text{(bubble point)}$$

$$P = 1 \text{ atm}$$

condition of feed: 100% saturated liquid

b. Distillate flow rate, $D = 36$ lb-moles/hr.
c. Reflux ratio, $R = 3$.
d. Rate of heat transfer, $dQ/dt = 0$ (adiabatic operation for all trays except reboiler and condenser).
e. Pressure, $P = 1$ atm for every tray. (Actually a small pressure drop from tray to tray is required to maintain the upward flow of vapor.)
f. Number of trays, $N_T = 11$.
g. Location of feed tray, $f = 6$.

Properties of pure substances such as specific heat, heat of vaporization, vapor pressure, normal boiling point, critical temperature, and critical pressure and properties of liquid mixtures such as enthalpy and free energy of mixing are given in Example 10.7. The same example gives the equations for calculating enthalpies of liquid and vapor streams and for calculating activity coefficients in the liquid mixture. Computed results are shown in Fig. 10-17.

Calculated results satisfy equations for equilibrium on each tray, and they satisfy the steady-state material and energy balance equations for any tray or combination of trays, including the entire column.

The driving force for the distillation is heating in the reboiler, which could be provided by condensing steam at atmospheric pressure (212°F). Cooling water for the condenser is supplied at a temperature of 40°–45°F.

The column splits the lightest and heaviest components: All the ethylbenzene is recovered in the bottoms, and all the neopentane appears in the distillate. Distillate is nearly pure neopentane, and most of the middle cut (carbon tetrachloride, cyclohexane, benzene) appears in the bottoms under these operating conditions.

Calculated results are for an idealized column that reaches equilibrium with respect to heat and mass transfer in every tray. This separation in a real column would require more trays and more heat energy (in the form of steam).

The Wang-Henke method begins with guesses for temperature and flow rates on each tray. k-values for vapor-liquid equilibrium on each tray are used to eliminate vapor composition variables. The set of material balance equations is then linear in liquid compositions. For each component, coefficients of the material balance equations form a tridiagonal matrix that is inverted to solve for liquid compositions on each tray. Since flow rates and k-values are guess values, mole fractions calculated for each tray do not necessarily sum to unity. If mole fractions do not sum to unity, they are forced to do so by normalization, and then the bubble-point temperature is calculated for each tray. Vapor compositions are calculated at the bubble point. Enthalpies are computed for each stream. Then a material and energy balance, one for each tray, is used to solve consecutively for vapor and liquid flow rates connecting the trays. The cycle is repeated until convergence of temperature and flow rates is achieved on each tray. For this particular example, the program required 35 iterations to obtain results accurate to four significant figures. Computer time on an IBM 370/168 is 105 sec.

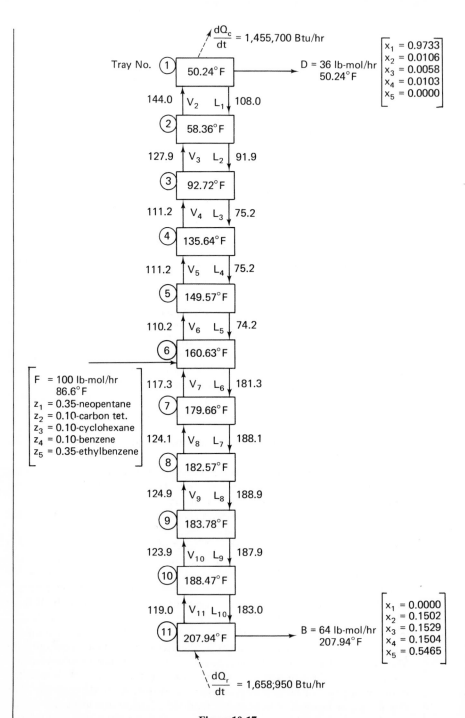

Figure 10-17

	D	V_2	V_3	V_4	V_5	V_6	V_7	V_8	V_9	V_{10}	V_{11}
Temperature, °F	50.24	58.36	92.72	135.64	149.57	160.63	179.66	182.57	183.78	188.47	207.94
Flow rate, lb-moles/hr	36	144.00	127.95	111.17	111.15	110.15	117.28	124.06	124.94	123.91	118.96
Mole fraction											
Neopentane	0.9733	0.9733	0.8435	0.5173	0.3704	0.3496	0.0567	0.0070	0.0008	0.0001	0.0000
Carbon tet.	0.0106	0.0106	0.0609	0.1832	0.2328	0.2273	0.3277	0.3415	0.3383	0.3265	0.2845
Cyclohexane	0.0058	0.0058	0.0452	0.1537	0.2077	0.2132	0.3106	0.3287	0.3320	0.3276	0.2903
Benzene	0.0103	0.0103	0.0504	0.1454	0.1853	0.1835	0.2660	0.2811	0.2835	0.2807	0.2557
Ethylbenzene	0.0000	0.0000	0.0000	0.0004	0.0038	0.0264	0.0390	0.0417	0.0454	0.0651	0.1695

	L_1	L_2	L_3	L_4	L_5	L_6	L_7	L_8	L_9	L_{10}	B
Temperature, °F	50.24	58.36	92.72	135.64	149.57	160.63	179.66	182.57	183.78	188.47	207.94
Flow rate, lb-moles/hr	108.00	91.95	75.17	75.15	74.15	181.28	188.06	188.94	187.91	182.96	64
Mole fraction											
Neopentane	0.9733	0.7929	0.3003	0.0827	0.0476	0.0367	0.0046	0.0006	0.0001	0.0000	0.0000
Carbon tet.	0.0106	0.0805	0.2653	0.3388	0.3322	0.2650	0.2764	0.2745	0.2664	0.2375	0.1502
Cyclohexane	0.0058	0.0605	0.2240	0.3041	0.3136	0.2549	0.2689	0.2713	0.2681	0.2422	0.1529
Benzene	0.0103	0.0661	0.2098	0.2687	0.2674	0.2252	0.2366	0.2384	0.2363	0.2189	0.1504
Ethylbenzene	0.0000	0.0000	0.0006	0.0057	0.0392	0.2182	0.2135	0.2152	0.2291	0.3014	0.5465

PROBLEMS

10.1. An aqueous solution at $100°F$ containing 30% $MgSO_4$ by weight is cooled until it is a solid mass. Read the heat of solidification from Fig. 10-5 and compare it with the heat of solidification of pure water at $32°F$ (144 Btu/lb).

10.2. Heat liberated by the combustion of propane is calculated in Example 10.3 for combustion products at $1600°F$. Calculate the heat evolved in Btu/lb of propane for the same air/fuel ratio if the combustion products are gaseous carbon dioxide and liquid water at $77°F$.

10.3. Calculate the adiabatic flame temperature of hydrogen burned in air using the same assumptions as in Example 10.6: stoichiometric (2-to-1) ratio of hydrogen to oxygen, feed gases at $25°C$ and 1 atm. Notice that the algorithm prepared in Example 10.6 for combustion of hydrocarbons breaks down for hydrogen (why?). What fraction of water vapor is decomposed at the temperature of the flame?

10.4. Carbon monoxide is consumed in the manufacture of chemical intermediates such as phosgene, diisocyanate, and ethyl acrylate. Carbon monoxide can be produced by the reforming of natural gas, as shown in Fig. 10-18. Natural gas (mostly methane) is mixed with steam and reacted at high temperature to produce carbon monoxide and hydrogen:

$$CH_4 + H_2O \rightleftharpoons CO + 3H_2$$

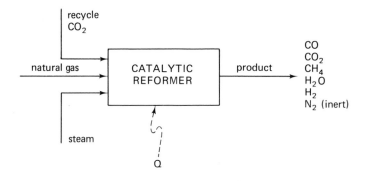

Figure 10-18

A catalyst is required. Carbon monoxide also reacts with water according to the shift reaction

$$CO + H_2O \rightleftharpoons CO_2 + H_2$$

Carbon dioxide is recycled (see Fig. 10-18) to shift the equilibrium in favor of a higher yield of carbon monoxide. Composition of the natural gas is

	Mole %
CH_4	96.0
CO_2	0.8
N_2	3.2

One mole (basis) of natural gas is mixed with 1.445 moles of steam and 0.191 mole of recycle carbon dioxide. The reformer is operated at 4.4 atm; feed and product are at the same pressure. Steam feed is at its saturation temperature (4.4 atm). Carbon dioxide and natural gas enter at 77°F, and the product temperature is 1500°F. Assume that both reactions are at equilibrium (1500°F), and calculate the composition of the product stream. Then calculate the heat load (Q), which is supplied by burning a portion of the natural gas. Obtain thermochemical data from the *Handbook of Chemistry and Physics* and specific heat data from Table 4.14.

10.5. The Avis Chemical Rocket Company builds reliable but expensive rocket engines. In an effort to cut costs without sacrificing performance, one of their engineers proposes adding excess hydrogen to the feed of their hydrogen-oxygen rocket. Rockets using excess hydrogen have a cooler flame but deliver more thrust per pound of fuel because the low-molecular-weight hydrogen is accelerated to a higher exhaust velocity. (See Fig. 10-19.) For a feed rate of 100 lb of oxygen per minute and a hydrogen-to-oxygen fuel ratio (molar) of $r = F_1/F_2 = 5$, calculate the composition, flow rate, and temperature of the rocket exhaust flame. Equipment constraints are adiabatic rocket engine, fuel temperature 25°C, fuel pressure 300 psia, and exhaust pressure 1 atm. For ease of calculation, assume perfect gas behavior for feed and exhaust gases and that specific heats are constants, independent of temperature:

Figure 10-19

	c_p (cal/mole-°K)
H_2	7.2
O_2	8.3
H_2O	9.8

Assume complete consumption of oxygen and neglect dissociation of water. Standard enthalpy of formation of water from its elements at 25°C is $-57,800$ cal/mole (gaseous state).

10.6. A catalytic reactor is operated adiabatically to carry out the reversible reaction

$$A + B \rightleftharpoons C + D \qquad \text{(all substances gaseous)}$$

Tests show that the reactor gives the equilibrium yield of products. Feed flow rate is 100 moles/hr; its composition is 40% A, 40% B, and 20% E (mole percentages). Feed enters at 25°C and the reactor is operated at atmospheric pressure. (See Fig. 10-20.) Set up the equations to solve for product composition and temperature. Write explicit equations for enthalpy and the equilibrium constant, and show that the number of equations matches the number of unknowns before attempting to solve. Thermochemical data are

Gas	c_p° (cal/mole-°K)	ΔH_{298}° (cal/mole)	ΔG_{298}° (cal/mole)
A	16	15,000	14,000
B	16	0	0
C	16	−22,000	−14,000
D	16	0	0
E	16	0	0

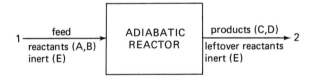

Figure 10-20

10.7. Prepare a program that computes the adiabatic flame temperature for complete combustion in air of the organic compound $C_kH_lO_mN_n$ according to the reaction

$$C_kH_lO_mN_n + \left[k + \frac{l}{4} - \frac{m}{2} + \frac{n}{2}\right]O_2 = k\,CO_2 + \frac{l}{2}H_2O + n\,NO$$

Assume that the oxygen (in air) is fed to the flame in stoichiometric proportion, that the organic compound is completely consumed, and that fuel and air feed are at 25°C, 1 atm. Neglect dissociation of combustion products. Use the program to calculate flame temperatures of

State at 25°C

N_2H_4 (hydrazine)	Liquid
CH_4 (methane)	Gas
CH_3OH (methanol)	Liquid
CH_3CH_2OH (ethanol)	Liquid
HCN	Gas
H_2NCONH_2 (urea)	Solid
CH_3COOH (acetic acid)	Liquid
CH_3CN (acetonitrile)	Liquid
C_6H_5OH (phenol)	Liquid
HCHO (formaldehyde)	Gas
CH_3COCH_3 (acetone)	Liquid

Standard enthalpies of formation of these substances are tabulated in Perry's handbook and the *Handbook of Chemistry and Physics*.

10.8. A gaseous mixture of benzene (1) and ethylbenzene (2) is partially condensed to obtain a liquid richer in ethylbenzene. The feed to the partial condenser (see Fig. 10-12) is

$F_1 = 100$ moles/hr   (basis)

$x_{11} = 0.75$ (mole fraction of benzene)

$x_{12} = 0.25$ (mole fraction of ethylbenzene)

$T_1 = 200°C$

$P_1 = 1.5$ atm

The partial condenser is operated at 100°C and atmospheric pressure. Calculate the cooling load (dQ/dt) necessary for the partial condensation and the composition of the enriched liquid. Thermodynamic data are

	Benzene	Ethyl-benzene
Normal boiling point, °C	80.1	136.2
Latent heat of vapor. at N.B.P., cal/mole	7350	8600
Critical temperature, °C	289	346.4
Critical pressure, atm	48.6	38
c_p, liquid, cal/mole-°K	34.5	47.8
c_p, vapor, cal/mole-°K	27.6	42.0

For ease of calculation, assume perfect gas vapor, ideal liquid solution, and constant specific heat (in table) for liquid and vapor. Vapor pressures are tabulated in the *Handbook of Chemistry and Physics*.

10.9. A liquid mixture of neopentane (2,2-dimethylpropane) and carbon tetrachloride at 65.6°C and 10 atm is flashed adiabatically to atmospheric pressure. The feed is 70% neopentane and 30% carbon tetrachloride (mole percentages). Since neopentane is more volatile than carbon tetrachloride, the vapor

product from the flash unit will be considerably richer in neopentane. Calculate the composition and flow rates of equilibrium liquid and vapor product
at steady state. Thermodynamic data (vapor pressure, specific heat, activity
coefficients, etc.) are reported in Example 10.7. Assume a basis of 100
moles/hr for the feed.

10.10. Pyrolysis of dichloroethane (see Fig. 3-5) yields the following mixture,

	Mole Fraction
HCl (hydrogen chloride)	0.375
C_2H_3Cl (vinyl chloride)	0.375
$C_2H_4Cl_2$ (1,2-dichloroethane)	0.250

which is then separated by two distillation columns in series. The mixture is
fed to the first column at a pressure of 12 atm. Assuming an ideal liquid
mixture and perfect gas, calculate the bubble-point temperature at 12 atm.
Vapor pressures of HCl and $C_2H_4Cl_2$ are in the *Handbook of Chemistry and
Physics*. For C_2H_3Cl,

$T(°C)$	Vapor Pressure (mm Hg)
−25	470
0	1293
25	2943

10.11. Calculate the bubble point and dew point at atmospheric pressure for the
following mixture of hydrocarbons using the program in Example 10.8:

Compound	Mole Fraction	T_b (°F)	T_c (°F)	Acentric Factor, ω	P_c (psia)
2-Methylpropane	0.009	10.89	274.96	0.185	529.1
n-Butane	0.032	31.1	305.62	0.201	550.7
2,2-Dimethylpropane	0.102	49.1	321.08	0.197	464.0
2-Methylbutane	0.205	82.13	369	0.222	483
n-Pentane	0.298	96.93	385.5	0.254	489.5
2,2-Dimethylbutane	0.190	121.53	420.1	0.237	450.7
2,3-Dimethylbutane	0.111	136.38	440.2	0.250	455.4
2-Methylpentane	0.028	140.59	435.7	0.282	440.1
3-Methylpentane	0.015	145.91	448.2	0.274	453.1
n-Hexane	0.010	155.73	454.1	0.301	440.0

Since these are all saturated hydrocarbons, it may be assumed that they
form an ideal liquid solution. Calculate vapor pressures using the Riedel
correlation described in Example 10.7. The Riedel factor (α) is related to the
acentric factor (ω) by the equation (Reid and Sherwood, *op. cit.*)

$$\omega = 0.203(\alpha - 7) + 0.242$$

Solution of Single Equations   **11**

There are two distinct stages in the creation of a new chemical process: synthesis and analysis. Synthesis is the development of a new idea and requires imagination. Analysis confirms or rejects the feasibility of new ideas by subjecting them to careful scrutiny to see if they obey or contradict the laws of physics and chemistry.

Analysis of a process requires

1. Development of various equations based upon conservation and other principles.
2. Solution of these equations for unknown variables such as flow rate, temperature, and pressure.

Analysis of chemical processes using appropriate conservation principles is the subject matter of previous chapters. In this and the next two chapters, several effective methods for solving equations with and without the help of a digital computer are introduced. These methods are used throughout the text. A more comprehensive study of numerical methods of solving equations can be found in *Applied Numerical Methods* by B. Carnahan, H. A. Luther, and J. O. Wilkes, Wiley, New York, 1969, and *Applied Nonlinear Programming* by D. Himmelblau, McGraw-Hill, New York, 1972.

Methods of solving a single equation of the form

$$f\{x\} = 0 \qquad (11.1)$$

are presented in this chapter.

11.1 Graphical Methods

Graphical methods for solving a single equation containing one unknown are useful and, besides, provide some insight into the behavior of the function. First the equation is written in the form $f\{x\} = 0$. Then the function is plotted on rectangular coordinates; $f\{x\}$ is the ordinate and x is the abscissa. Values of x at which $f\{x\}$ crosses the x-axis are the solution values. For example, in Fig. 11-1, there are three solution values $(\alpha_1, \alpha_2, \alpha_3)$ of $f\{x\}$. Usually only one of the solutions has physical significance, and the others are discarded.

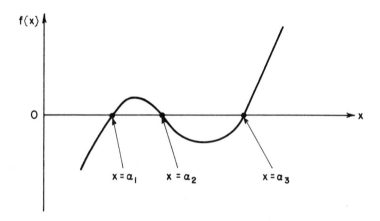

Figure 11-1 Graphical method.

Example 11.1

van der Waals' equation (4.9),

$$P = \frac{RT}{v - b} - \frac{a}{v^2}$$

relates the pressure, P, of a gas to absolute temperature, T, and molar volume, v. Individual gas constants (a and b) are given by Eqns. (4.12) and (4.13).

Determine the molar volume, v, of nitrogen at $t = -100°C$ and $P = 50$ atm. For nitrogen, $a = 1.351 \times 10^6$ atm-(cm³/gmole)²; $b = 38.64$ cm³/gmole.

Solution:

van der Waals' equation is rearranged:

$$f\{v\} = P - \frac{RT}{v - b} + \frac{a}{v^2} = 0$$

A table is prepared for $P = 50$ atm, $T = 173.15°K$, $R = 82.06$ cm³-atm/mole-°K:

v (cm³/gmole)	$f\{v\} = P - \dfrac{RT}{v-b} + \dfrac{a}{v^2}$ (atm)
100	−46.4
150	−17.5
200	−4.3
250	4.4
300	10.6
400	19.1

These points are plotted in Fig. 11-2 and connected by a smooth curve. The solution (root) is read directly from the graph: $v = 222$ cc/gmole. When higher accuracy is required, the procedure is repeated using an expanded scale in the region close to the solution value.

The graphical method finds solution values in the domain investigated ($100 < v < 400$). van der Waals' equation is cubic in volume, and therefore there are three solutions, two of which are complex numbers. In this case there is only one real solution. The experimental value of molar volume at $-100°C$ and 50 atm. is 232 cc/gmole.*

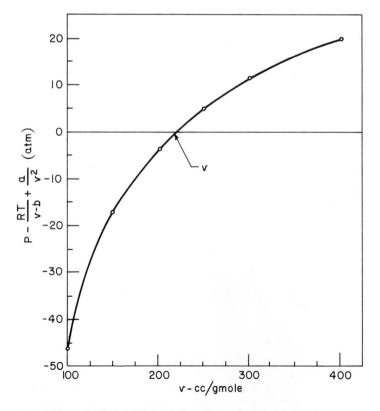

Figure 11-2 Graphical solution of van der Waals' equation.

*F. Din, *Thermodynamic Functions of Gases, Vol. 3*, Butterworths, London (1961).

Graphical methods can also be used to solve a set of two equations in two unknowns.†

11.2 Method of Successive Substitutions

Successive substitutions is a numerical method for solution of single equations of the form

$$x = F\{x\} \tag{11.2}$$

Example 11.2

Rearrange van der Waals' equation in a form suitable for application of the method of successive substitutions.

Solution:

Three examples are

$$v = F\{v\} = \frac{RT}{P + (a/v^2)} + b$$

$$v = \bar{F}\{v\} = -\frac{Pv^3}{a} + \frac{RTv^2}{a} + \frac{bPv^2}{a} + b$$

$$v = G\{v\} = \frac{RT}{P} + \frac{ab}{Pv^2} - \frac{a}{Pv} + b$$

The method of successive substitutions (sometimes called trial and error) begins with a guess solution value, $x^{(1)}$. The superscript 1 denotes the first of many values assigned to x during the iterative procedure for finding a solution value. The function in Eqn. (11.2) is used to obtain a second value $x^{(2)}$ as follows:

$$x^{(2)} = F\{x^{(1)}\}$$

If $x^{(2)}$ and $x^{(1)}$ do not agree within a prespecified tolerance, ϵ, such that

$$\left| \frac{x^{(2)} - x^{(1)}}{x^{(1)}} \right| \leq \epsilon$$

the method is repeated using $x^{(2)}$ as the next guess solution value; that is,

$$x^{(3)} = F\{x^{(2)}\}$$

and, in general, the method of successive substitutions is

$$x^{(k+1)} = F\{x^{(k)}\} \qquad (k = 1, 2, \ldots) \tag{11.3}$$

A solution value is accepted when the convergence criterion is satisfied:

†J. B. Rosenbach and E. A. Whitman, *College Algebra*, 3rd ed., Ginn, Boston, 1949, p. 180.

$$\left| \frac{x^{(k+1)} - x^{(k)}}{x^{(k)}} \right| \le \epsilon \qquad (11.4)$$

If the solution value approaches zero, the criterion $|x^{(k+1)} - x^{(k)}| \le \epsilon$ is adopted to avoid division by zero.

Example 11.3

Use the method of successive substitutions to solve van der Waals' equation for the molar volume, v, of nitrogen at $t = -100°C$ and $P = 50$ atm (conditions matching Example 11.1).

Solution:

The first functional form in Example 11.2 is selected:

$$v = F\{v\} = \frac{RT}{P + (a/v^2)} + b$$

In the notation of Eqns. (11.3) and (11.4),

$$v^{(k+1)} = F\{v^{(k)}\} = \frac{RT}{P + [a/(v^{(k)})^2]} + b \qquad (k = 1, 2, \ldots)$$

and

$$\left| \frac{v^{(k+1)} - v^{(k)}}{v^{(k)}} \right| \le \epsilon$$

A guess solution value $v^{(1)}$ is required; for example, $v^{(1)} = 10,000$ cc/gmole. A convergence tolerance of 0.001 is selected. The following table summarizes the iterations:

k	$v^{(k)}$ (cm³/gmole)	$F\{v^{(k)}\} = v^{(k+1)}$ (cm³/gmole)	$\left\|\frac{v^{(k+1)} - v^{(k)}}{v^{(k)}}\right\|$
1	10,000	322.7	0.9677
2	322.7	264.3	0.1811
3	264.3	243.5	0.0785
4	243.5	233.9	0.0397
5	233.9	228.9	0.0215
6	228.9	226.1	0.0120
7	226.1	224.6	0.0069
8	224.6	223.7	0.0039
9	223.7	223.2	0.0023
10	223.2	222.9	0.0013
11	222.9	222.7	0.0008

When $k = 11$, the convergence tolerance is satisfied; that is,
$$|(222.7 - 222.9)/222.9| = 0.0008 < 0.001.$$
The solution is $v = 222.7$ cm³/gmole.

Not all equations can be solved rapidly using the method of successive substitutions. In fact, some functions $F\{x\}$ do not permit convergence to a solution.

Example 11.4

For Example 11.3, use the functional form

$$v = \bar{F}\{v\} = -\frac{Pv^3}{a} + \frac{RTv^2}{a} + \frac{bPv^2}{a} + b$$

and try to solve for v by successive substitutions.

Solution:

Successive iterations are tabulated:

k	$v^{(k)}$ (cm³/gmole)	$\bar{F}\{v^{(k)}\} = v^{(k+1)}$ (cm³/gmole)	$\left\lvert \dfrac{v^{(k+1)} - v^{(k)}}{v^{(k)}} \right\rvert$
1	10,000	-3.581×10^7	3582.5
2	-3.581×10^7	1.700×10^{18}	4.747×10^{10}

This iterative sequence is diverging instead of converging to a solution. The method of successive substitutions fails in this case.

Applying the calculus, it can be shown* that for convergence to a solution value using successive substitutions,

$$|F'\{x\}| < 1 \tag{11.5}$$

for any x near the solution value. When Eqn. (11.5) is not satisfied, divergence may occur.

Example 11.5

For $F\{v\}$ and $\bar{F}\{v\}$ in Examples 11.3 and 11.4, evaluate the derivatives at $v = 10,000$ cc/gmole.

Solution:

$$F'\{v\} = \frac{2aRT}{v^3[P + (a/v^2)]^2}$$

$$= \frac{2(1.351 \times 10^6)(82.06)(173.15)}{(10^4)^3\{50 + [(1.351 \times 10^6)/(10^4)^2]\}^2}$$

$$= 1.53 \times 10^{-5} < 1 \qquad \textit{convergence}$$

$$\bar{F}'\{v\} = \frac{-3Pv^2}{a} + \frac{2RTv}{a} + \frac{2bPv}{a}$$

$$= \frac{-3(50)(10^4)^2 + 2(82.06)(173.15)(10^4) + 2(38.64)(50)(10^4)}{1.351 \times 10^6}$$

$$= -10,900$$

$$|\bar{F}'\{v\}| = 10,900 > 1 \qquad \textit{divergence}$$

*B. Carnahan, H. A. Luther, and J. O. Wilkes, *Applied Numerical Methods*, Wiley, New York, 1969, p. 168.

A sufficient condition for convergence is that the absolute value of the slope of $F\{x\}$, $|F'\{x\}|$, is less than unity. Figure 11-3 illustrates the method of successive substitutions graphically for two functions $F_1\{x\}$ and $F_2\{x\}$. In Fig. 11-3(a), $|F_1'\{x\}| < 1$; hence, convergence occurs. In Fig. 11-3(b), $|\bar{F}_2'\{x\}| > 1$, and divergence occurs; that is, successive values of $x^{(k)}$ move away from the solution value, α.

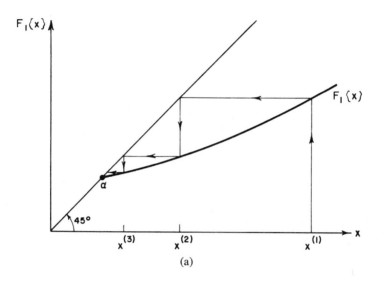

(a)

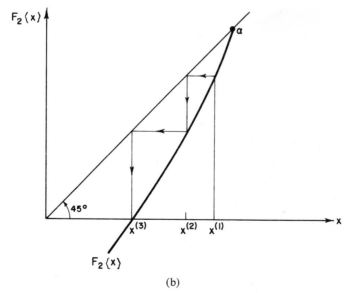

(b)

Figure 11-3 Graphical illustration of the method of successive substitutions. (a) Convergence: $|F_1'\{x\}| < 1$. (b) Divergence: $|F_2'\{x\}| > 1$.

In summary, the method of successive substitutions is an iterative procedure that repeatedly uses a guess value to obtain better estimates for the solution. Let the guess value for each iteration be x^*; then

$$x \longleftarrow F\{x^*\} \tag{11.6}$$

where x is the improved estimate of the solution and convergence is achieved when

$$\left| \frac{x - x^*}{x^*} \right| \leq \epsilon \tag{11.7}$$

If convergence is not achieved, x becomes x^* for the next iteration.

Example 11.6

Prepare a WATFIV program for solution of van der Waals' equation by successive substitutions (see Example 11.3).

Solution:

The algorithm requires as data the constants (a, b, R), operating conditions (T and P), iteration parameters (ϵ, k_{max}), and a guess for specific volume (v^*). If the guess value is a physically impossible value in the range $v^* \leq 0$, the program automatically uses the perfect gas law ($v^* = RT/P$) for the first estimate. See Fig. 11-4 for the corresponding flow diagram.

Flow Diagram

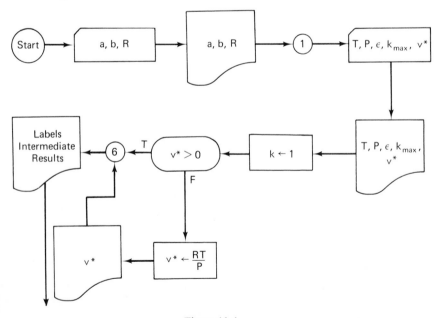

Figure 11-4

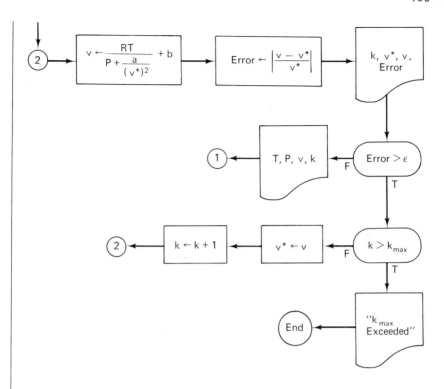

Figure 11-4 (Continued)

Table of Symbols

Problem Symbol	Program Symbol	Definition	Units
a	A	van der Waals' constant	atm(cc/gmole)^2
b	B	" " " "	cc/gmole
Error	ERR	$\left\|\dfrac{v - v^*}{v^*}\right\|$	
k	K	Iteration counter	
k_{max}	KMAX	Maximum iterations allowable	
P	P	Pressure	atm
R	R	Universal gas constant	cc-atm/gmole-°K
T	T	Absolute temperature	°K
v	V	Molar volume	cc/gmole
v^*	VSTAR	Guess molar volume	cc/gmole
ϵ	EPSI	Convergence tolerance	

Program Listing

```
C**    PROGRAM TO DETERMINE THE SPECIFIC VOLUME, V, OF A GAS USING VAN
C      DER WAAL'S EQUATION OF STATE WHEN THE GAS PRESSURE, P, AND TEMP-
C      ERATURE, T, ARE KNOWN.  THE IDEAL GAS LAW IS USED TO PROVIDE GUESS
C      VSTAR WHEN VSTAR IS READ  = 0.  THE METHOD OF SUCCESSIVE SUBSTITU-
C      TIONS IS USED.
C
C**    READS AND PRINTS GAS CONSTANTS.
C
       READ, A, B, R
       WRITE (6,15)
       WRITE (6,21) A, B, R
C
C**    READS AND PRINTS TEMPERATURE, PRESSURE, CONVERGENCE DATA, AND
C      GUESS SPECIFIC VOLUME.
C
   1   READ, T, P, EPSI, KMAX, VSTAR
       WRITE (6,16)
       WRITE (6,22) T, P, EPSI, KMAX, VSTAR
       K = 1
       IF (VSTAR .GT. 0) GO TO 6
C
C**    USES IDEAL GAS LAW TO ESTIMATE VSTAR.
C
       VSTAR = R*T/P
       WRITE (6,17)
       WRITE (6,23) VSTAR
C
C**    BEGINS THE METHOD OF SUCCESSIVE SUBSTITUTIONS.
C
   6   WRITE (6,18)
   2   V = (R*T)/(P+A/(VSTAR*VSTAR))+B
       ERR = ABS((V-VSTAR)/VSTAR)
C
C**    PRINTS INTERMEDIATE VALUES AND CHECKS CONVERGENCE.
C
       WRITE (6,24) K, VSTAR, V, ERR
       IF (ERR .GT. EPSI) GO TO 3
C
C**    CONVERGENCE HAS BEEN OBTAINED.  PRINTS RESULTS.
C
       WRITE (6,19)
       WRITE (6,25) T, P, V, K
       GO TO 1
C
C**    CHECKS THAT K (NO. OF ITERATIONS) HAS NOT EXCEEDED KMAX.
C
   3   IF (K .GE. KMAX) GO TO 5
       VSTAR = V
       K = K+1
       GO TO 2
C
C**    PRINTS ERROR COMMENT WHEN KMAX IS EXCEEDED.
C
   5   WRITE (6,20)
C
C**    INPUT/OUTPUT FORMAT STATEMENTS.
C
  15   FORMAT (//, ' A, B, R =',/)
  16   FORMAT (//, ' T, P, EPSI, KMAX, VSTAR =',/)
  17   FORMAT (//, ' IDEAL GAS LAW VSTAR =',/)
  18   FORMAT (//, ' K, VSTAR, V, ERR =',/)
  19   FORMAT (//, ' T, P, V, K =',/)
  20   FORMAT (1H0, ' KMAX EXCEEDED')
  21   FORMAT (1X, 1F12.2, 2F10.4)
  22   FORMAT (1X, 3F10.4, 1I5, 1F12.2)
  23   FORMAT (1X, 1F10.4)
  24   FORMAT (1X, 1I5, 3F12.4)
  25   FORMAT (1X, 3F10.4, 1I5)
       END
```

Data   1.351E6, 38.64, 82.06
                               173.15,50.,0.001,20,1.0E4

Computed Output

A, B, R =

   1351000.00   38.6400   82.0600

T, P, EPSI, KMAX, VSTAR =

   173.1500   50.0000   0.0010   20   10000.00

K, VSTAR, V, ERR =

1	10000.0000	322.7368	0.9677
2	322.7368	264.2800	0.1811
3	264.2800	243.5440	0.0785
4	243.5440	233.8754	0.0397
5	233.8754	228.8516	0.0215
6	228.8516	226.1003	0.0120
7	226.1003	224.5511	0.0069
8	224.5511	223.6653	0.0039
9	223.6653	223.1544	0.0023
10	223.1544	222.8582	0.0013
11	222.8582	222.6860	0.0008

T, P, V, K =

   173.1500   50.0000   222.6860   11

11.3 Wegstein's Method

Wegstein's method has a lesser tendency to diverge, and when it converges, the rate is faster than the method of successive substitutions. The equation is first rearranged in the form $x = F\{x\}$. Let $x^{(1)}$ be the initial guess value; then the second point is

$$x^{(2)} = F\{x^{(1)}\}$$

So far the method is the same as successive substitutions. When the convergence criterion, Eqn. (11.4), is not satisfied, the third point is computed according to the formula

$$x^{(3)} = tF\{x^{(2)}\} + (1 - t)x^{(2)}$$

where

$$t = \frac{1}{1 - s}$$

and

$$s = \frac{F\{x^{(2)}\} - F\{x^{(1)}\}}{x^{(2)} - x^{(1)}}$$

Figure 11-5 illustrates the method graphically for a function $F\{x\}$ whose derivative (absolute value) is greater than unity. Observe that $x^{(3)}$ is at the point where the 45° line intersects the secant of curve $F\{x\}$ from $x^{(1)}$ to $x^{(2)}$. s is the slope of the secant.

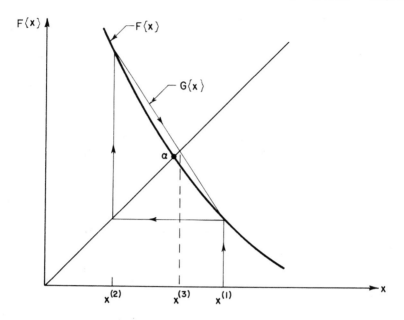

Figure 11-5 Graphical illustration of Wegstein's method.

In general, Wegstein's method is

$$x^{(k+1)} = tF\{x^{(k)}\} + (1-t)x^{(k)} \qquad (k = 2, 3, \ldots) \qquad (11.8)$$

where

$$t = \frac{1}{1-s}$$

and

$$s = \frac{F\{x^{(k)}\} - F\{x^{(k-1)}\}}{x^{(k)} - x^{(k-1)}}$$

Only the first iteration is carried out using the method of successive substitutions.

Equation (11.8) is derived from the equation for the secant line through the point $(x^{(2)}, F\{x^{(2)}\})$:

$$G\{x\} = F\{x^{(2)}\} + s(x - x^{(2)})$$

At its intersection with the 45° line,

$$G\{x^{(3)}\} = x^{(3)} = F\{x^{(2)}\} + s(x^{(3)} - x^{(2)})$$

Rearranging,

$$x^{(3)} = \frac{1}{1-s}F\{x^{(2)}\} - \frac{s}{1-s}x^{(2)}$$

Defining

$$t = \frac{1}{1-s}$$

It follows that

$$x^{(3)} = tF\{x^{(2)}\} + (1 - t)x^{(2)}$$

and, in general,

$$x^{(k+1)} = tF\{x^{(k)}\} + (1 - t)x^{(k)} \qquad (k = 2, 3, \ldots) \qquad (11.8)$$

As shown in Fig. 11-5, Wegstein's method interpolates for the next value when $x^{(k+1)}$ lies between the points $x^{(k)}$ and $x^{(k-1)}$. This is the case when $-\infty < s < 0$ and $0 < t < 1$. At the limit $s = -\infty$, $t = 0$ and $x^{(k+1)} = x^{(k)}$. At $s = 0$, $t = 1$ and $x^{(k+1)} = F\{x^{(k)}\}$, which is the method of successive substitutions. Therefore, for $0 < t < 1$, t may be viewed as a linear interpolation fraction between no change in the guess value at one extreme and the method of successive substitutions at the other extreme.

Wegstein's method extrapolates to get the next value when $x^{(k+1)}$ does not lie between $x^{(k)}$ and $x^{(k-1)}$. This is the case when $0 < s < \infty$ and $-\infty < t < 0$, or $1 < t < \infty$. At $s = 1$, t is undefined, and Wegstein's extrapolation does not work. Hence, most computer programs limit the degree of extrapolation by setting $t = t_{\max}$ when $t > t_{\max}$ and $t = -t_{\max}$ when $t < -t_{\max}$. A typical value of $t_{\max}$ is 10.

Example 11.7

Use Wegstein's method to solve van der Waals' equation for the molar volume, v, of nitrogen at $t = -100°C$ and $P = 50$ atm (conditions matching Examples 11.1 and 11.3).

Solution:

The first iteration is identical to that in Example 11.3:

$$v^{(2)} = F\{v^{(1)}\} = \frac{RT}{P + [a/(v^{(1)})^2]} + b$$

From Eqn. (11.8),

$$v^{(k+1)} = tF\{v^{(k)}\} + (1 - t)v^{(k)} \qquad (k = 2, 3, \ldots)$$

where

$$t = \frac{1}{1 - s}$$

and

$$s = \frac{F\{v^{(k)}\} - F\{v^{(k-1)}\}}{v^{(k)} - v^{(k-1)}}$$

As in Example 11.3, $v^{(1)} = 10,000$ cc/gmole, and a convergence tolerance of 0.001 is adopted. The following table summarizes the computations by Wegstein's method:

k	$v^{(k)}$	$F\{v^{(k)}\}$	s	t	$v^{(k+1)}$	$\left\| \dfrac{v^{(k+1)} - v^{(k)}}{v^{(k)}} \right\|$
1	10,000	322.7			322.7	0.9677
2	322.7	264.3	0.006	1.006	263.9	0.1822
3	263.9	243.4	0.355	1.551	232.1	0.1207
4	232.1	227.9	0.487	1.950	223.9	0.0353
5	223.9	223.3	0.561	2.278	222.5	0.0062
6	222.5	222.5	0.581	2.384	222.4	0.0003

In each iteration, extrapolation is used to accelerate convergence. After the first iteration using successive substitutions, only 5 iterations are required to achieve a convergence tolerance of 0.001. This should be compared with 11 iterations for the method of successive substitutions and 4 iterations for Newton's method (see Example 11.9).

Wegstein's method is a convenient method for machine calculations. The program must save $x^{(k-1)}$ and $F\{x^{(k-1)}\}$ as well as $x^{(k)}$. The program in Example 11.6 requires only a few alterations to solve the problem by Wegstein's method instead of successive substitutions.

11.4 Newton's Method

Newton's method usually converges more rapidly than successive substitutions. Let the equation be written in the form

$$f\{x\} = 0 \tag{11.1}$$

and let $x^{(1)}$ be the first guess value. The new value $x^{(2)}$ is at the point where the tangent to the curve $f\{x\}$ intersects the abscissa. Figure 11-6(a) shows a graph of $f\{x\}$ versus x. $f'\{x^{(1)}\}$ is the slope of the tangent to the curve $f\{x\}$ at $x^{(1)}$. The intersection of the tangent line with the abscissa, $\bar{x}$, is illustrated in Fig. 11-6(b) and can be calculated using the definition of the slope,

$$\text{slope} = \tan\theta = f'\{x^{(1)}\} = \frac{f\{x^{(1)}\} - 0}{x^{(1)} - \bar{x}}$$

Rearranging,

$$\bar{x} = x^{(1)} - \frac{f\{x^{(1)}\}}{f'\{x^{(1)}\}}$$

Newton's method is based upon the fact that $\bar{x}$ is usually (but not always) closer to the solution (α) than $x^{(1)}$, so that $\bar{x}$ becomes the next guess value ($x^{(2)}$),

$$x^{(2)} = x^{(1)} - \frac{f\{x^{(1)}\}}{f'\{x^{(1)}\}}$$

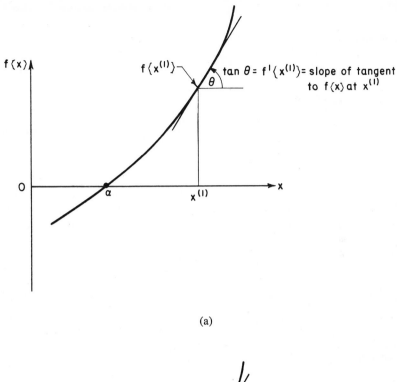

(a)

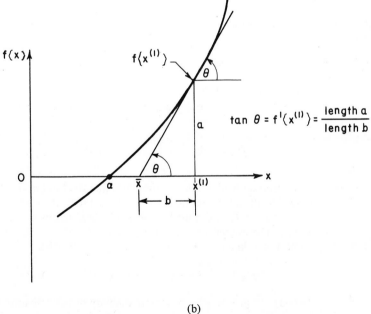

(b)

Figure 11-6 Graphical illustration of Newton's method: (a) slope of tangent; (b) extrapolation.

and, in general,

$$x^{(k+1)} = x^{(k)} - \frac{f\{x^{(k)}\}}{f'\{x^{(k)}\}} \qquad (k = 1, 2, \ldots) \qquad (11.9)$$

Convergence is achieved when

$$\left| \frac{x^{(k+1)} - x^{(k)}}{x^{(k)}} \right| \leq \epsilon \qquad (11.10)$$

is satisfied.

For each iteration ($k = 1, 2, \ldots$) all quantities on the right-hand side of Eqn. (11.9) are known or can be calculated. The derivative $f'\{x^{(k)}\}$ can be evaluated analytically by differentiating $f\{x\}$ with respect to x to obtain the derivative (df/dx) at $x^{(k)}$ or numerically by approximating the derivative with the formula

$$f'\{x^{(k)}\} = \frac{f\{x^{(k)} + \delta\} - f\{x^{(k)}\}}{\delta}$$

where δ is very small:

$$\delta \ll |x^{(k+1)} - x^{(k)}|$$

Example 11.8

Evaluate the derivative of the function $f\{x\} = x^3 - x^2 + 2x$ analytically and numerically at $x = 2$.

Solution:

1. Analytically. The derivative is

$$f'\{x\} = 3x^2 - 2x + 2$$

At $x = 2$,

$$f'\{2\} = 3(2)^2 - 2(2) + 2 = 10$$

2. Numerically. A value for δ must be selected. Accuracy increases as δ decreases (the true derivative value is approached in the limit as $\delta \longrightarrow 0$), but additional significant figures must be maintained to evaluate the small difference $f\{x + \delta\} - f\{x\}$. δ must be sufficiently large to avoid roundoff error due to fixed computer word length. Typically, only seven significant figures can be stored in a computer word. Let $\delta = 0.001$. Then

$$f'\{2\} = \frac{f\{2.001\} - f\{2\}}{0.001} = 10.005$$

δ is small enough to give an accurate approximation of the derivative but not small enough to generate significant roundoff error.

The next example shows how Newton's method converges more rapidly than successive substitutions.

Example 11.9

Use Newton's method to solve van der Waals' equation for the molar volume, v, of nitrogen at $t = -100°C$ and $P = 50$ atm (conditions matching Example 11.1).

Solution:

van der Waals' equation is written in the form of Eqn. (11.1):

$$f\{v\} = \left(P + \frac{a}{v^2}\right)(v - b) - RT = 0$$

The derivative is

$$f'\{v\} = \frac{df}{dv} = P - \frac{a}{v^2}\left[1 - \frac{2b}{v}\right]$$

Substituting in Eqn. (11.9),

$$v^{(k+1)} = v^{(k)} - \frac{[P + a/(v^{(k)})^2][v^{(k)} - b] - RT}{P - [a/(v^{(k)})^2][1 - (2b/v^{(k)})]} \qquad (k = 1, 2, \ldots)$$

As in Example 11.3, let $v^{(1)} = 10,000$ cc/gmole. A convergence tolerance of 0.001 is assumed. The following table summarizes the computations:

k	$v^{(k)}$	$v^{(k+1)}$	$\left\| \dfrac{v^{(k+1)} - v^{(k)}}{v^{(k)}} \right\|$
1	10000	317.5	0.9682
2	317.5	230.4	0.2744
3	230.4	222.6	0.0341
4	222.6	222.4	0.0005

The convergence tolerance is satisfied when $k = 4$. Note that 11 iterations are needed to obtain the same result by successive substitutions (Example 11.3) and 6 iterations are needed for Wegstein's method (Example 11.7).

Newton's method usually requires only one-half or one-third as many iterations as the method of successive substitutions. However, Newton's method requires evaluation of the function's derivative and therefore has more computations per iteration. Newton's method diverges less frequently than the method of successive substitutions.

In summary, Newton's method is an iterative procedure that repeatedly uses a guess value to obtain better estimates for the solution value. If x^* is the guess value, then the improved estimate (x) is

$$x \longleftarrow x^* - \frac{f\{x^*\}}{f'\{x^*\}} \tag{11.11}$$

and convergence is achieved when

$$\left|\frac{x - x^*}{x^*}\right| \le \epsilon$$

Like successive substitutions, Newton's method is well suited for digital computation. In fact, programs for the two methods are nearly identical. Only one program statement need be modified to switch from successive substitutions (Example 11.6) to Newton's method (Example 11.10).

Example 11.10

Prepare a WATFIV program for solution of van der Waals' equation using Newton's method (see Example 11.9).

Solution:

The flow diagram of the program is the same as Example 11.6, except for the calculation of v from the last guess value v^*:

$$v \longleftarrow v^* - \frac{[P + a/(v^*)^2][v^* - b] - RT}{P - [a/(v^*)^2][1 - (2b/v^*)]}$$

The symbols are the same as Example 11.6, and the program listing is as follows.

Program Listing

```
C**    PROGRAM TO DETERMINE THE SPECIFIC VOLUME, V, OF A GAS USING VAN
C      DER WAAL'S EQUATION OF STATE WHEN THE GAS PRESSURE, P, AND TEMP-
C      ERATURE, T, ARE KNOWN.  THE IDEAL GAS LAW IS USED TO PROVIDE GUESS
C      VSTAR WHEN VSTAR IS READ = 0.  NEWTON'S METHOD IS USED.
C
C**    READS AND PRINTS GAS CONSTANTS.
C
       READ, A, B, R
       WRITE (6,15)
       WRITE (6,21) A, B, R
C
C**    READS AND PRINTS TEMPERATURE, PRESSURE, CONVERGENCE DATA, AND
C      GUESS SPECIFIC VOLUME.
C
   1   READ, T, P, EPSI, KMAX, VSTAR
       WRITE (6,16)
       WRITE (6,22) T, P, EPSI, KMAX, VSTAR
       K = 1
       IF (VSTAR .GT. 0) GO TO 6
C
C**    USES IDEAL GAS LAW TO ESTIMATE VSTAR.
C
       VSTAR = R*T/P
       WRITE (6,17)
       WRITE (6,23) VSTAR
C
C**    BEGINS NEWTON'S METHOD.
C
   6   WRITE (6,18)
   2   V = VSTAR-((P+A/VSTAR**2)*(VSTAR-B)-R*T)/(P-A*(1.0-2.0*B/VSTAR)
      1/VSTAR**2)
       ERR = ABS((V-VSTAR)/VSTAR)
C
C**    PRINTS INTERMEDIATE VALUES AND CHECKS CONVERGENCE.
C
       WRITE (6,24) K, VSTAR, V, ERR
       IF (ERR .GT. EPSI) GO TO 3
C
C**    CONVERGENCE HAS BEEN OBTAINED.  PRINTS RESULTS.
C
```

```
      WRITE (6,19)
      WRITE (6,25) T, P, V, K
      GO TO 1
C
C**   CHECKS THAT K (NO. OF ITERATIONS) HAS NOT EXCEEDED KMAX.
C
   3  IF (K .GE. KMAX) GO TO 5
      VSTAR = V
      K = K+1
      GO TO 2
C
C**   PRINTS ERROR COMMENT WHEN KMAX IS EXCEEDED.
C
   5  WRITE (6,20)
C
C**   INPUT/OUTPUT FORMAT STATEMENTS.
C
  15  FORMAT (//, ' A, B, R =',/)
  16  FORMAT (//, ' T, P, EPSI, KMAX, VSTAR =',/)
  17  FORMAT (//, ' IDEAL GAS LAW VSTAR =',/)
  18  FORMAT (//, ' K, VSTAR,V, ERR =',/)
  19  FORMAT (//, ' T, P, V, K =',/)
  20  FORMAT (1H0, ' KMAX EXCEEDED')
  21  FORMAT (1X, 1F12.2, 2F10.4)
  22  FORMAT (1X, 3F10.4, 1I5, 1F12.2)
  23  FORMAT (1X, 1F10.4)
  24  FORMAT (1X, 1I5, 3F12.4)
  25  FORMAT (1X, 3F10.4, 1I5)
      END
```

Data

```
                1.351E6, 38.64, 82.06
                173.15,50.,0.001,20,1.0E4
```

Computed Output

```
        A, B, R =

          1351000.00    38.6400    82.0600


        T, P, EPSI, KMAX, VSTAR =

          173.1500    50.0000    0.0010    20    10000.00


        K, VSTAR,V, ERR =

            1   10000.0000    317.5313    0.9682
            2     317.5313    230.4099    0.2744
            3     230.4099    222.5532    0.0341
            4     222.5532    222.4454    0.0005


        T, P, V, K =

          173.1500    50.0000  222.4454    4
```

11.5 Half-Interval Method

The half-interval method solves an equation of the form

$$f\{x\} = 0$$

when the solution is known to lie within an interval bounded by x_l on the

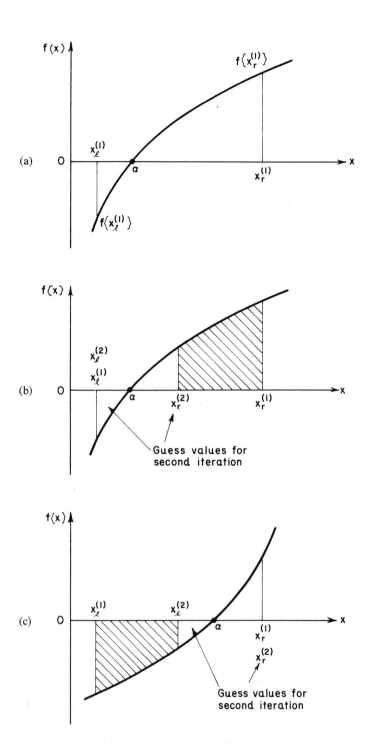

Figure 11-7 Half-interval method.

left and x_r on the right. If there is only one solution on the interval, then $f\{x_l\}$ and $f\{x_r\}$ have opposite signs, as shown in Fig. 11-7(a).

The procedure is to select a guess value x^* midway between $x_l^{(1)}$ and $x_r^{(1)}$. If $f\{x^*\}$ has the same sign as $f\{x_r^{(1)}\}$, as in Fig. 11-7(b), then $x_r^{(2)} \leftarrow x^*$, $x_l^{(2)} \leftarrow x_l^{(1)}$ defines the new interval for the next iteration. If, on the other hand, $f\{x^*\}$ has the same sign as $f\{x_l^{(1)}\}$, as in Fig. 11-7(c), then $x_l^{(2)} \leftarrow x^*$, $x_r^{(2)} \leftarrow x_r^{(1)}$ defines the new interval. In either case, each iteration reduces the size of the interval containing the solution by half. The number of iterations (N) necessary to reduce the size of the interval containing the solution by a factor of $1/\gamma$ times the original interval is

$$N = -1.44 \ln \gamma \qquad (11.12)$$

because $\gamma = (1/2)^N$. No convergence test is required because the number of iterations is preset by the desired accuracy and Eqn. (11.12).

Example 11.11

Use the half-interval method to solve van der Waals' equation for the molar volume, v, of nitrogen at $t = -100°C$ and $P = 50$ atm (conditions matching Example 11.1).

Solution:

The equation is

$$f\{v\} = \left(P + \frac{a}{v^2}\right)(v - b) - RT = 0$$

An interval containing the solution is selected: $v_l^{(1)} = 10$ cc/gmole and $v_r^{(1)} = 10,000$ cc/gmole. The uncertainty in v is set at 0.1 cc/gmole, so that $\gamma = 10^{-5}$ and

$$N = -1.44 \ln (10^{-5}) = 16.58$$

$$= 17$$

The following table summarizes the computations:

k	$v_l^{(k)}$	$v_r^{(k)}$
1	10	10,000
2	10	5,005
3	10	2,508
4	10	1,259
5	10	634.3
6	10	322.2
7	166.1	322.2
8	166.1	244.1
9	205.1	244.1
10	205.1	224.6
11	214.9	224.6
12	219.8	224.6
13	222.2	224.6

k	$v_i^{(k)}$	$v_r^{(k)}$
14	222.2	223.4
15	222.2	222.7
16	222.2	222.4
17	222.2	222.3
18	222.2	222.2

PROBLEMS

11.1. Consider the equation $f\{x\} = x^3 - 3x + 1 = 0$.
  a. Plot $f\{x\}$ versus x on graph paper and make rough estimates of the roots.
  b. Find successive substitution algorithms of the form

$$x^{(k+1)} = F\{x^{(k)}\}$$

  that will satisfy the convergence criterion

$$|F'\{x\}| < 1$$

  c. Select a starting guess for one of the roots from part a and carry out the first five iterations of a convergent algorithm for successive substitution.
  d. Find an algorithm for solving the equation by Newton's method.

11.2. The function $x^3 - 4x^2 + 5x - 2 = 0$ has roots at 1 and 2.
  a. With the equation in the form

$$x = -0.2x^3 + 0.8x^2 + 0.4$$

  can the method of successive substitutions locate one or both of these roots [show which one(s)]? Within what region surrounding the root 2 must a guess value lie for convergence to be achieved? Do three successive substitutions starting with a guess value $x^* = 1.8$.
  b. To which root will Newton's method converge for a guess value $x^* = 1.5$? Carry out the first three iterations.
  c. How many roots does this equation have?

11.3. The specific heat of chloroethene

$$\begin{array}{cc} H & Cl \\ | & | \\ H-C&=C-H \end{array}$$

vapor at low pressure is a function of absolute temperature:

$$c_p^0 = 2.401 + 0.0427T - 2.751 \times 10^{-5}T^2 + 6.797 \times 10^{-9}T^3$$

At what temperature (°K) is $c_p^0 = 28.3$ cal/mole-°K? Use the following solution procedure:
  a. Estimate a guess temperature T^* by ignoring the nonlinear terms.
  b. At T^*, rearrange the equation into a form that will allow convergence using the method of successive substitutions.
  c. Carry out five iterations. Is the convergence tolerance $\epsilon = 0.001$ satisfied by five iterations?

d. Carry out five iterations using Wegstein's method. Is the convergence tolerance satisfied in five iterations?

11.4. The Redlich-Kwong equation of state gives the approximate relation among pressure, volume, and temperature for gases. The equation is

$$\left[P + \frac{a}{T^{1/2}v(v+b)}\right][v - b] = RT$$

For 1-butene the constants are

$$a = 261.7 \text{ liter}^2\text{-atm}(°K)^{1/2}/\text{mole}^2$$

$$b = 0.0752 \text{ liter/mole}$$

$$R = 0.08206 \text{ liter-atm/mole-}°K = \text{gas constant}$$

These constants give P in atm for v in liter/mole and T in °K.

a. For $P = 40.8$ atm and $T = 250°C$, determine the specific volume of 1-butene using graphical methods.

b. Write the Redlich-Kwong equation in a form suitable for application of the method of successive substitutions.

c. Write the Redlich-Kwong equation in a form suitable for application of Newton's method. Carry out the first three iterations beginning with $v^* = 1.0$ liter/mole.

11.5. For the equation

$$M(e^\theta - 1) = \theta$$

use the half-interval method to determine θ for $M = 0.6$. (*Hint:* The root lies in the range $0.5 < \theta < 1.5$.) Locate the root within an uncertainty of 0.001. How many iterations are necessary?

Simultaneous Linear Equations

12

Equations

Solution methods for single equations are described in Ch. 11. Often, analysis of a chemical process leads to a set of simultaneous equations. This chapter is devoted to the special case of simultaneous linear equations, which can be solved by the methods of matrix algebra. The Gauss-Jordan method is presented because it is easy to program for an arbitrary number of equations. The more difficult problem of solving simultaneous nonlinear equations is taken up in Ch. 13.

12.1 Independent Equations

Let us consider the following set of simultaneous, nonlinear equations:

$$x_1 x_2 + 3x_3 - 14 = 0$$
$$x_1^2 + 2x_2 - 9(x_3)^{1/2} + 13 = 0 \qquad (12.1)$$
$$4x_1 + 2x_2 + x_3 - 16 = 0$$

For a set of solution values to exist (there may be more than a single set), the *number of unknowns must equal the number of equations* and the equations must be *independent*. A set of l equations are *dependent* when a set of constants $c_1, c_2, \ldots, c_l$, not all zero, exist such that

$$c_1(\text{Eqn}_1) + c_2(\text{Eqn}_2) + \cdots + c_l(\text{Eqn}_l) = 0$$

otherwise the l equations are *independent*. Equations (12.1) are independent.

Example 12.1

Are the equations

$$x_1 x_2 + 3x_3 - 14 = 0 \tag{1}$$

$$(1 - 2x_2 - x_3)x_1 + 3x_2 - 6x_3 + 31 = 0 \tag{2}$$

$$x_1 + 3x_2 - x_1 x_3 + 3 = 0 \tag{3}$$

independent? Why?

Solution:

$$-2(\text{Eqn}_1) - \text{Eqn}_2 + \text{Eqn}_3 = 0$$

Therefore the equations are dependent.

In Example 12.1, there are two independent equations and three unknowns. A third independent equation is required in order to solve for the three unknowns.

12.2 Gauss-Jordan Reduction

An equation is linear when it is composed of terms containing one and only one unknown raised to the first power. For example, of the three equations (12.1), the first two equations are nonlinear, and the third equation is linear in the unknowns (x_1, x_2, x_3).

The Gauss-Jordan reduction algorithm is one method for solving sets of simultaneous linear equations. Take, for example, the following set of three simultaneous linear equations:

$$-2x_1 + 7x_2 - 4x_3 = 4$$

$$3x_1 + 5x_2 - 5x_3 = 1 \tag{12.2}$$

$$8x_1 - 2x_2 - x_3 = 3$$

The first step in the algorithm is to form an $m \times n$ augmented coefficient matrix, where m = number of equations and $n = m + 1$. The augmented coefficient matrix for Eqns. (12.2) is

$$\mathbf{C} = (c_{ij}) = \begin{bmatrix} -2 & 7 & -4 & 4 \\ 3 & 5 & -5 & 1 \\ 8 & -2 & -1 & 3 \end{bmatrix}$$

Note that each row contains coefficients of one equation. The equations may be stacked in any order, subject to a restriction to be mentioned later. Each column contains the coefficients of one of the unknowns except the nth column, which is reserved for constants on the right-hand side of the equations.

Example 12.2

Set up the augmented coefficient matrix for the following set of simultaneous linear equations:

$$-2x_1 + x_3 + 0.5x_4 = 3$$
$$7x_2 - 5x_3 + x_4 = 10$$
$$x_1 - 2x_2 + 4x_3 - 9x_4 = 8$$
$$x_2 + 3x_4 = -5$$

Solution:

$$\mathbf{C} = (c_{ij}) = \begin{bmatrix} -2 & 0 & 1 & 0.5 & 3 \\ 0 & 7 & -5 & 1 & 10 \\ 1 & -2 & 4 & -9 & 8 \\ 0 & 1 & 0 & 3 & -5 \end{bmatrix}$$

Note that when a variable does not occur in an equation, its coefficient is zero and hence a zero appears in the augmented coefficient matrix.

The next step is to select the first *pivot element*. Using the *diagonal pivot strategy*, pivot elements are selected from among the diagonal elements of the coefficient matrix, c_{kk}, as follows. The first pivot element is the uppermost diagonal element, c_{11}; hence, $k = 1$. The row in which the pivot element lies is the *pivot row*, and the column in which the pivot element lies is the *pivot column*. For the first pivot element, c_{11}, the pivot row is 1 and the pivot column is 1. Succeeding pivot elements will be selected from the diagonal elements so that the pivot row $= k$ and the pivot column $= k$, where $k = 2, 3, \ldots, m$, in order.

After selecting the first pivot element, c_{11}, a three-step procedure is followed:

1. Normalize the pivot row. All elements in the pivot row are divided by the pivot element.
2. Zero the pivot column. For each row, i, in the matrix, excluding the pivot row, the element in the pivot column, c_{ik}, is used to multiply the elements of the pivot row, and the products formed are subtracted individually from the corresponding elements in row i (i.e., $c_{ij} \leftarrow c_{ij} - c_{ik} \cdot c_{kj}$ for each element j in row i). This procedure is repeated one row at a time for all rows in the matrix except the pivot row.
3. Move to the next pivot element. When $k \leq m$, steps 1 and 2 are repeated for each new pivot element.

Example 12.3

Find the solution for the simultaneous linear equations (12.2) using the Gauss-Jordan method.

Solution:

The augmented coefficient matrix is rewritten with the first pivot element, c_{11}, encircled:

$$\begin{bmatrix} \boxed{-2} & 7 & -4 & 4 \\ 3 & 5 & -5 & 1 \\ 8 & -2 & -1 & 3 \end{bmatrix}$$

Upon normalization of the pivot row (step 1), the matrix becomes

$$\begin{bmatrix} ① & -7/2 & 2 & -2 \\ 3 & 5 & -5 & 1 \\ 8 & -2 & -1 & 3 \end{bmatrix}$$

Step 2 is applied successively to rows 2 and 3:

$$\begin{bmatrix} ① & -7/2 & 2 & -2 \\ 0 & 31/2 & -11 & 7 \\ 0 & 26 & -17 & 19 \end{bmatrix}$$

Note that zeros now appear in the pivot column. The new pivot element is c_{22}:

$$\begin{bmatrix} 1 & -7/2 & 2 & -2 \\ 0 & ⟨31/2⟩ & -11 & 7 \\ 0 & 26 & -17 & 19 \end{bmatrix}$$

Step 1 is repeated,

$$\begin{bmatrix} 1 & -7/2 & 2 & -2 \\ 0 & ① & -22/31 & 14/31 \\ 0 & 26 & -17 & 19 \end{bmatrix}$$

and step 2 is applied for rows 1 and 3:

$$\begin{bmatrix} 1 & 0 & -15/31 & -13/31 \\ 0 & ① & -22/31 & 14/31 \\ 0 & 0 & 45/31 & 225/31 \end{bmatrix}$$

The last pivot element is c_{33}:

$$\begin{bmatrix} 1 & 0 & -15/31 & -13/31 \\ 0 & 1 & -22/31 & 14/31 \\ 0 & 0 & ⟨45/31⟩ & 225/31 \end{bmatrix}$$

Step 1 is repeated,

$$\begin{bmatrix} 1 & 0 & -15/31 & -13/31 \\ 0 & 1 & -22/31 & 14/31 \\ 0 & 0 & ① & 5 \end{bmatrix}$$

and step 2 is applied for rows 1 and 2:

$$\begin{bmatrix} 1 & 0 & 0 & 2 \\ 0 & 1 & 0 & 4 \\ 0 & 0 & \textcircled{1} & 5 \end{bmatrix}$$

The algorithm is complete. In the square portion of the augmented coefficient matrix we find the identity matrix, and in the nth column we find the *solution values* $x_1 = 2$, $x_2 = 4$, and $x_3 = 5$.

It can be shown that the Gauss-Jordan method obeys the rules of algebra for solving linear equations. The set of solution values is called the solution vector **X**, where

$$\mathbf{X} = \begin{bmatrix} x_1 \\ x_2 \\ x_3 \end{bmatrix} = \begin{bmatrix} 2 \\ 4 \\ 5 \end{bmatrix}$$

Observe that the solution vector is found in the nth column of the $m \times n$ augmented coefficient matrix upon completion of the Gauss-Jordan reduction algorithm.

In addition to the requirements that the equations be linear and independent, an additional condition is imposed when using Gauss-Jordan reduction. Since pivot elements are selected from diagonal positions and are divisors in the normalization step, they must all be nonzero. Therefore, the equations must be arranged such that zeroes are not generated on the principal diagonal of the augmented coefficient matrix.

12.3 Computer Program for Solution of Linear Equations

The repetitive nature of the Gauss-Jordan algorithm makes it easy to program on a computer. The number of equations that can be solved is limited by computer storage. $m \times (m + 1)$ computer words are required to store the augmented coefficient matrix for a set of m equations. One hundred equations require approximately 10,000 words, which is well within the storage capacity of most machines.

Example 12.4

Prepare a WATFIV subroutine named SIMUL that solves a set of m linear equations. SIMUL should accept as one of its arguments the augmented coefficient matrix and return to the calling program the solution vector obtained by Gauss-Jordan reduction.

As a check, solve Eqns. (12.2).

Solution:

The algorithm follows the Gauss-Jordan reduction procedure described above. Nested iteration statements involving row, column, and pivot element counters (i, j, k) are used to carry out each step.

See Figs. 12-1 and 12-2 for the flow diagrams.

Table of Symbols

Problem Symbol	Program Symbol	Definition
Main		
$\mathbf{C}$	C	Coefficient matrix—order $m \times n$
i	I	Row counter
j	J	Column counter
m	M	No. of rows in $\mathbf{C}$ matrix
n	N	No. of columns in $\mathbf{C}$ matrix
$\mathbf{X}$	X	Solution vector
Subroutine SIMUL		
k	K	Pivot row
Pivi	PIVI	Row i element in the pivot column k, c_{ik}
Pivot	PIVOT	c_{kk}

Flow Diagrams

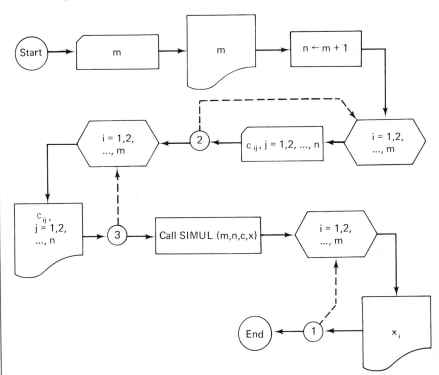

Figure 12-1 Main program.

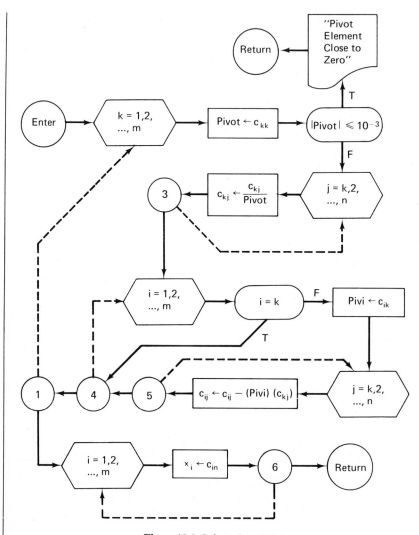

Figure 12-2 Subroutine SIMUL.

Program Listings

Main Program

```
C
C**    PROGRAM TO SOLVE M SIMULTANEOUS LINEAR EQUATIONS.  PROGRAM
C      FIRST READS AND PRINTS THE COEFFICIENT MATRIX.  THEN SUBROUTINE
C      SIMUL IS CALLED TO SOLVE SET OF SIMULTANEOUS EQUATIONS.
```

```
C       SIMUL RETURNS M SOLUTION VALUES IN THE X VECTOR.  FINALLY,
C       THE PROGRAM PRINTS THE SOLUTION VALUES.
C
        DIMENSION C(10,11), X(10)
        REAL*8 C
C
C**     READ AND PRINT M AND COEFFICIENT MATRIX.
C
        READ, M
        WRITE (6,10) M
        N = M+1
        DO 2 I = 1,M
    2   READ, (C(I,J), J = 1,N)
        WRITE (6,11)
        DO 3 I = 1,M
    3   WRITE (6,13) (C(I,J), J = 1,N)
C
C**     SOLVE EQUATIONS.
C
        CALL SIMUL (M, N, C, X)
C
C**     PRINT SOLUTION VALUES.
C
        WRITE (6,12)
        DO 1 J = 1,M
    1   WRITE (6,14) X(J)
C
C**     INPUT AND OUTPUT FORMATS.
C
   10   FORMAT ('1','M =', I5)
   11   FORMAT (//,' COEFFICIENT MATRIX =',/)
   12   FORMAT (//,' SOLUTION VECTOR ='/)
   13   FORMAT (8F10.4)
   14   FORMAT (F15.4)
        STOP
        END
```

Subroutine SIMUL

```
        SUBROUTINE SIMUL (M, N, C, X)
        IMPLICIT REAL*8 (A-H,O-Z)
        REAL*4 X
C
C**     SIMUL USES THE GAUSS-JORDAN REDUCTION METHOD,
C       DIAGONAL PIVOT STRATEGY, TO SOLVE M SIMULTANEOUS
C       LINEAR EQUATIONS.  THE COEFFICIENT MATRIX IS AN
C       M BY N (M+1) MATRIX SUPPLIED BY THE USER.  X
C       IS A VECTOR OF M SOLUTION VALUES PREPARED BY
C       SIMUL.
C
        DIMENSION C(10,11), X(10)
C
C**     SELECTS PIVOT ELEMENT
C
        DO 1 K = 1,M
        PIVOT = C(K,K)
C
C**     CHECKS THAT PIVOT ELEMENT IS NON-ZERO
C
        IF (DABS(PIVOT) .LE. 0.001) GO TO 2
C
C**     NORMALIZES PIVOT ROW
C
        DO 3 J = K,N
    3   C(K,J) = C(K,J)/PIVOT
C
C**     ZEROS PIVOT COLUMN
C
```

```
           DO 4 I = 1,M
           IF (I .EQ. K)   GO TO 4
           PIVI = C(I,K)
           DO 5 J = K,N
       5   C(I,J) = C(I,J) - PIVI*C(K,J)
       4   CONTINUE
       1   CONTINUE
C
C**    SET UP SOLUTION VECTOR X
C
           DO 6 J = 1,M
       6   X(J) = C(J,N)
           RETURN
C
C**    ERROR COMMENT
C
       2   WRITE (6,100) K
     100   FORMAT (' PIVOT ELEMENT', I5, ' IS CLOSE TO ZERO')
           RETURN
           END
```

Data

```
                    3
                    -2.0,  7.0,  -4.0,  4.0
                    3.0,  5.0,  -5.0,  1.0
                    8.0,  -2.0,  -1.0,  3.0
```

Computed Output

```
               M =    3

               COEFFICIENT MATRIX =

                   -2.0000      7.0000     -4.0000      4.0000
                    3.0000      5.0000     -5.0000      1.0000
                    8.0000     -2.0000     -1.0000      3.0000

               SOLUTION VECTOR =

                    2.0000
                    4.0000
                    5.0000
```

A somewhat more complicated program is needed to reorder the rows of the coefficient matrix when zeros are generated in the pivot elements.

PROBLEMS

12.1. Solve the following equations:

$$3x_1 + 2x_2 + 5x_3 = 12$$
$$-x_1 + x_2 - 3x_3 = -2$$
$$2x_1 - 3x_2 + x_3 = -3$$

Find the determinant of the coefficient matrix.

12.2. Use the Gauss-Jordan reduction algorithm to solve the following set of equations:

$$-2x_1 + x_2 - 3x_3 = 2$$
$$4x_1 - x_2 + 5x_3 = -2$$
$$3x_1 + 2x_2 - x_3 = 2$$

12.3. Figure 12-3 shows one model which has been postulated to explain calcium metabolism in man. Q_i represents the quantity of i in a compartment and R_{ij} the rate of transport to i from j. Suppose that a man has been living with the steady-state conditions given by $Q_1 = 2.4$ g, $Q_2 = 2.3$ g, $Q_3 = 5000$ g, $R_{41} = 0.072$ g/day, $R_{51} = 0.23$ g/day, $R_{31} = 0.356$ g/day, and $R_{21} = 1.89$ g/day. R_{10} is suddenly changed to 0.5 g/day at time zero, and a set of differential equations may be solved to express the quantity of material in a compartment at any given time thereafter. The solutions to these equations are

$$Q_1 = 3.98 - 0.7627C_1e^{-1.755t} - 0.5251C_2e^{-0.1284t} + 0.00026C_3e^{-0.00003t}$$

$$Q_2 = 3.82 + 0.6436C_1e^{-1.755t} - 0.5965C_2e^{-0.1284t} + 0.000249C_3e^{-0.00003t}$$

$$Q_3 = 8290 + 0.0645C_1e^{-1.755t} + 0.607C_2e^{-0.1284t} + C_3e^{-0.00003t}$$

Use the Gauss-Jordan method to find the value of the constants C_1, C_2, and C_3.

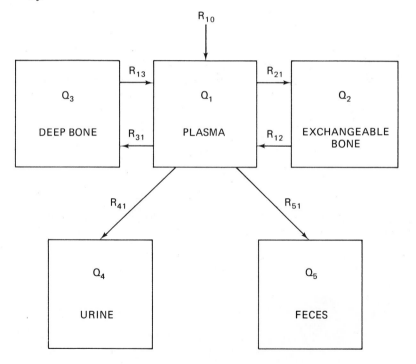

Figure 12-3

Simultaneous Nonlinear Equations 13

If a set of simultaneous equations is nonlinear, then the methods of matrix algebra described in Ch. 12 do not apply. Solution of sets of simultaneous nonlinear equations by the method of successive substitutions, Newton's method, and other techniques is the subject of this chapter. Consider, for example, the following set of nonlinear equations:

$$x_1^{1/2} + x_2 x_3 = 33$$
$$x_1^2 + x_2^2 + x_3^2 = 81 \qquad (13.1)$$
$$(x_1 x_2)^{1/3} + x_3^{1/2} = 4$$

It is convenient to use a functional notation to represent m simultaneous equations (m unknowns):

$$f_1\{x_1, x_2, \ldots, x_m\} = 0$$
$$f_2\{x_1, x_2, \ldots, x_m\} = 0$$
$$\vdots \qquad (13.2)$$
$$f_m\{x_1, x_2, \ldots, x_m\} = 0$$

For Eqns. (13.1), for example,

$$f_1\{x_1, x_2, x_3\} = (x_1)^{1/2} + x_2 x_3 - 33 = 0$$
$$f_2\{x_1, x_2, x_3\} = x_1^2 + x_2^2 + x_3^2 - 81 = 0$$
$$f_3\{x_1, x_2, x_3\} = (x_1 x_2)^{1/3} + (x_3)^{1/2} - 4 = 0$$

The method of adjusting guess values of unknowns toward desired solution values is not usually obvious. A proper adjustment of guess values for all the unknowns decreases, simultaneously, the values of all the functions toward the desired value of zero:

$$|f_i\{x_1, x_2, \ldots, x_m\}| \longrightarrow 0 \qquad (i = 1, 2, \ldots, m) \qquad (13.3)$$

Sometimes equation-solving methods inadvertently adjust guess values to emphasize a subset of the equations. Although $|f_i|$ decreases for those equations in the subset, $|f_i|$ increases or remains unchanged for the remaining equations. When this occurs, convergence is not achieved, and the correct solution values are not obtained. These difficulties are magnified as the number of simultaneous equations increases.

13.1   Precedence-Ordering Methods

Some sets of nonlinear equations contain equations that

1. Can be solved for an unknown variable irrespective of the other equations, and they are therefore solved first.
2. Contain an unknown variable that does not occur in any other equation, and they are therefore solved for that variable after all other equations have been solved.

A precedence-ordering method is an algorithm that identifies type 1 equations to be solved first and type 2 equations to be solved last and that simplifies the remaining equations so as to reduce or eliminate the need for costly iteration. Several articles describing precedence-ordering methods have been written by D. V. Steward, D. F. Rudd et al., and S. Soylemez and W. D. Seider.* The basic steps are as follows:

1. Equations containing only one unknown variable are solved first using methods in Ch. 11.
2. When an unknown variable occurs in only one equation, the equation is solved for this variable last, after all other unknowns in the equation have been determined. The equation is entered last in the ordered list of equations.
3. Remaining equations (if any) containing only two unknowns are assembled. Select an equation that can be rearranged to express one

*D. V. Steward, "On An Approach to Techniques for the Analysis of the Structure of Large Systems of Equations", *SIAM Rev.*, *4*, No. 4, 321 (Oct. 1962). D. V. Steward, "Partitioning and Tearing Systems of Equations," *SIAM Numer. Anal.*, *2*, No. 2, 345 (1965). W. Lee, J. H. Christensen, and D. F. Rudd, "Design Variable Selection To Simplify Process Calculations," *A.I.Ch.E. J.*, *12*, No. 6, 1104 (Nov. 1966). S. Soylemez and W. D. Seider, "A New Technique for Precedence-Ordering Chemical Process Equations Sets," *A.I.Ch.E. J.*, *19*, No. 5, 934 (Sept. 1973).

unknown, the output variable, explicitly in terms of the other. This expression is substituted in all remaining equations that contain the output variable. The equation is placed in the ordered list of equations just above the equations to be solved last (from step 2).

4. Steps 1–3 are repeated for the remaining equations when applicable. Otherwise, select an equation containing three variables that can be rearranged to express one unknown explicitly in terms of the other two. As in step 3, this expression is substituted in all equations containing the output variable, and the equation is placed above the equations to be solved last in the ordered list of equations. If an equation containing three variables cannot be found, equations containing four or more variables are sought.

5. Step 4 is repeated until (a) no additional equations remain, or (b) each remaining equation cannot be rearranged to provide an explicit expression for an output variable in terms of the other unknowns (this occurs when expressions for the unknown are implicit or too complicated, e.g., the solution of a cubic equation).

6. Equations in step 5(b) are solved using an iterative, simultaneous-equation-solving procedure, or a guess value is provided for one of the unknowns and steps 1–5 are repeated for the "torn" equations. These methods are described next.

Example 13.1

Use precedence-ordering to solve the equations

	N_u (number of unknowns)	
$x_1 x_2 + x_6 x_4 = 18$	4	(1)
$x_2 + x_5 + x_6 = 12$	3	(2)
$x_1 + \ln\left(\dfrac{x_2}{x_4}\right) = 3$	3	(3)
$x_3^2 + x_3 = 2$	1	(4)
$x_2 + x_4 = 4$	2	(5)
$x_3(x_3 + x_6) = 7$	2	(6)

Solution:

Step 1 is to locate equations with one unknown ($N_u = 1$). Equation (4) falls in this category and can be solved for x_3 using the quadratic formula

$$x_3 = \frac{-1 \pm \sqrt{1+8}}{2} = 1 \quad \text{and} \quad -2$$

The equations are rewritten to reflect the fact that x_3 is no longer unknown (the circle, $\textcircled{x_3}$, is a notation indicating that x_3 has been determined in a prior step). Note that N_u is adjusted where appropriate.

$$
\begin{array}{lcr}
 & N_u & \\
x_1 x_2 + x_6 x_4 = 18 & 4 & (1) \\
x_2 + x_5 + x_6 = 12 & 3 & (2) \\
x_1 + \ln\left(\dfrac{x_2}{x_4}\right) = 3 & 3 & (3) \\
x_2 + x_4 = 4 & 2 & (5) \\
\textcircled{x_3}\,(\textcircled{x_3} + x_6) = 7 & 1 & (6)
\end{array}
$$

Again, according to step 1,

$$ x_6 = \frac{7}{\textcircled{x_3}} - \textcircled{x_3} $$

Rewriting the equations,

$$
\begin{array}{lcr}
 & N_u & \\
x_1 x_2 + \textcircled{x_6}\,x_4 = 18 & 3 & (1) \\
x_2 + x_5 + \textcircled{x_6} = 12 & 2 & (2) \\
x_1 + \ln\left(\dfrac{x_2}{x_4}\right) = 3 & 3 & (3) \\
x_2 + x_4 = 4 & 2 & (5)
\end{array}
$$

Each equation in this reduced set contains more than one unknown. Hence, we proceed to step 2 in the algorithm.

A table of the number of equations in which each unknown occurs (N_0) is prepared:

Unknown	N_0
x_1	2
x_2	4
x_4	3
x_5	1

When an unknown occurs in only one equation ($N_0 = 1$), the equation is solved for this unknown after all other unknowns in the equation have been determined. Equation (2) falls in this category, since x_5 appears in this equation and no other. Equation (2) is solved for x_5 after Eqns. (1), (3), and (5) are solved for x_1, x_2, x_4. The reduced set of equations is

$$
\begin{array}{lcr}
 & N_u & \\
x_1 x_2 + \textcircled{x_6}\,x_4 = 18 & 3 & (1) \\
x_1 + \ln\left(\dfrac{x_2}{x_4}\right) = 3 & 3 & (3) \\
x_2 + x_4 = 4 & 2 & (5)
\end{array}
$$

and the accompanying "table of unknowns" is

Unknown	N_0
x_1	2
x_2	3
x_4	3

Steps 1 and 2 have been exhausted. Proceeding to step 3, it is observed that Eqn. (5) contains two unknowns and can be rearranged to give an explicit expression for x_2 in terms of x_4:

$$x_2 = 4 - x_4$$

This expression is substituted for x_2 in the remaining equations. The reduced set of equations is

$$x_1(4 - x_4) + \widehat{x_6}\,x_4 = 18 \qquad \overset{N_u}{2} \qquad (1)$$

$$x_1 + \ln\left(\frac{4 - x_4}{x_4}\right) = 3 \qquad 2 \qquad (3)$$

and the table of unknowns is

Unknown	N_0
x_1	2
x_4	2

Since steps 1 and 2 are exhausted, step 3 is repeated. Both Eqns. (1) and (3) contain two unknowns. Arbitrarily, we select Eqn. (1) and rearrange, expressing x_1 in terms of x_4,

$$x_1 = \frac{18 - \widehat{x_6}\,x_4}{4 - x_4}$$

and substitute it into Eqn. (3):

$$\frac{18 - \widehat{x_6}\,x_4}{4 - x_4} + \ln\left(\frac{4 - x_4}{x_4}\right) = 3 \qquad (3)$$

This is a single equation to be solved numerically for x_4.

The order of solution of the equations is summarized in Table 13.1. Notice that each equation is assigned an *output variable*. The order of solution in the table is consistent with the above discussion. A set of solution values for these equations is $x_1 = 3$, $x_2 = 2$, $x_3 = 1$, $x_4 = 2$, $x_5 = 4$, $x_6 = 6$. What is another set of solution values?

TABLE 13.1
ORDERED EQUATIONS

Solution Order	Eqn. No.	Output Variable	Equation
1	4	x_3	$x_3^2 + x_3 = 2$
2	6	x_6	$x_6 = \dfrac{7}{x_3} - x_3$
3	3	x_4	$\dfrac{18 - x_6 x_4}{4 - x_4} + \ln\left(\dfrac{4 - x_4}{x_4}\right) = 3$
4	1	x_1	$x_1 = \dfrac{18 - x_6 x_4}{4 - x_4}$
5	5	x_2	$x_2 = 4 - x_4$
6	2	x_5	$x_5 = 12 - x_2 - x_6$

Frequently, in step 3 of the algorithm, equations with only two unknowns do not exist, or if they do, one of the two unknowns cannot be expressed explicitly in terms of the other. The latter situation occurs in implicit equations such as

$$\ln\{x_1 x_2\} = \sqrt{\frac{x_1}{x_2}}$$

When either situation arises, step 4 of the algorithm is to seek equations with three unknowns ($N_u = 3$) and select an equation that can be rearranged to provide an explicit expression for one unknown in terms of the other two. An additional example of precedence ordering of equations is given in Appendix I.

13.2 Tearing Method

It is not always feasible or convenient to use steps 3–5 (rearrangement and substitution) of the algorithm for precedence-ordering of equations. An alternative approach is the tearing method. Given m simultaneous nonlinear equations, the tearing method is to guess values for l of the unknowns. Then any subset of $m - l$ equations in which each of the remaining $m - l$ unknowns occurs at least once is solved for these unknowns. If care is taken to select $m - l$ equations that can be solved without iteration, the problem reduces to the iterative solution of l simultaneous equations. It is said that l equations are "torn" from the initial set, and the l variables are called *tear variables*. The tearing method is illustrated in the following example.

Example 13.2

Use the tearing method to solve the equations

$$x_1 x_3 - x_4 = 1 \tag{1}$$

$$x_2^2 x_3^2 + x_4 = 17 \tag{2}$$

$$x_1 + x_2 = 6 \tag{3}$$

$$\ln\{x_3 x_4^2\} + x_3 x_4^2 = 1 \tag{4}$$

Solution:

Since Eqn. (4) cannot be solved explicitly for either variable, it is solved iteratively. The tear variable can be x_3 or x_4, but x_3 is preferred because it simplifies solution of Eqns. (1)–(3). Equation (4) is torn from the set to be solved iteratively for x_3:

$$f\{x_3\} = \ln\{x_3 x_4^2\} + x_3 x_4^2 - 1 = 0 \tag{4}$$

For each guess value of the tear variable, x_3^*, Eqns. (1)–(3) are solved for x_1, x_2, and x_4. These equations are ordered using the algorithm of Sec. 13.1:

Solution Order	Eqn. No.	Output Variable	Equation
1	2	x_2	$x_2 = [1 + \sqrt{73 - 24x_3^*}]/2x_3^*$
2	1	x_4	$x_4 = (6 - x_2)x_3^* - 1$
3	3	x_1	$x_1 = 6 - x_2$

The expression for x_2 is the positive root of the quadratic equation $(x_3^*)^2 x_2^2 - x_3^* x_2 + 6x_3^* - 18 = 0$. The negative root corresponds to another solution vector.

Equation (4) is solved iteratively using the half-interval method (see Ch. 11). The following table summarizes the calculations beginning with $x_l = 0.0001$ and $x_r = 3$:

k	x_3	x_1	x_2	x_4
1	1.5000	3.6391	2.3609	4.4587
2	0.7500	0.3893	5.6107	−0.7080
3	1.1250	2.5412	3.4588	1.8589
4	0.9375	1.6767	4.3233	0.5719
5	1.0313	2.1473	3.8527	1.2144
6	0.9844	1.9230	4.0770	0.8929
7	1.0078	2.0377	3.9623	1.0536
8	0.9961	1.9810	4.0190	0.9733
9	1.0020	2.0095	3.9905	1.0134
10	0.9990	1.9953	4.0047	0.9933
11	1.0005	2.0024	3.9976	1.0034
12	0.9998	1.9988	4.0012	0.9984
13	1.0001	2.0006	3.9994	1.0009
14	0.9999	1.9997	4.0003	0.9996
15	1.0000	2.0002	3.9998	1.0003
16	1.0000	2.0000	4.0000	0.9999
17	1.0000	2.0001	3.9999	1.0001
18	1.0000	2.0000	4.0000	1.0000

Values of x_3 are tabulated at the center of the preceding interval. The half-interval method is used because convergence was not achieved using Newton's method.

Several examples of the tearing method for solution of material and energy balance equations are given in Ch. 10.

13.3 Iterative Methods Without Partial Derivatives

The Gauss-Jacobi method and Wegstein's method are two well-known iterative methods that do not involve evaluation of partial derivatives. They are multidimensional analogs of the method of successive substitutions and Wegstein's method in Chap. 11.

Gauss-Jacobi method

For the Gauss-Jacobi method, the equations must be expressed in the functional form

$$x_1 = F_1\{x_1, x_2, \ldots, x_m\}$$
$$x_2 = F_2\{x_1, x_2, \ldots, x_m\}$$
$$\vdots \qquad\qquad (13.4)$$
$$x_m = F_m\{x_1, x_2, \ldots, x_m\}$$

Guess solution values $(x_1^{(1)}, x_2^{(1)}, \ldots, x_m^{(1)})$ are used to compute $F_1, F_2, \ldots,$ F_m. These function values are then assigned to $x_1^{(2)}, x_2^{(2)}, \ldots, x_m^{(2)}$ as follows:

$$x_1^{(2)} \longleftarrow F_1\{x_1^{(1)}, x_2^{(1)}, \ldots, x_m^{(1)}\}$$
$$x_2^{(2)} \longleftarrow F_2\{x_1^{(1)}, x_2^{(1)}, \ldots, x_m^{(1)}\}$$
$$\vdots$$
$$x_m^{(2)} \longleftarrow F_m\{x_1^{(1)}, x_2^{(1)}, \ldots, x_m^{(1)}\}$$

If convergence to a solution is achieved,

$$\left| \frac{x_j^{(2)} - x_j^{(1)}}{x_j^{(1)}} \right| < \epsilon \qquad j = 1, 2, \ldots, m$$

where the convergence tolerance, ϵ, is small enough to provide the desired accuracy. Otherwise, the method is reapplied with new guess solution values, $x_1^{(2)}, x_2^{(2)}, \ldots, x_m^{(2)}$. In general, for the kth iteration,

$$x_1^{(k+1)} \longleftarrow F_1\{x_1^{(k)}, x_2^{(k)}, \ldots, x_m^{(k)}\}$$
$$x_2^{(k+1)} \longleftarrow F_2\{x_1^{(k)}, x_2^{(k)}, \ldots, x_m^{(k)}\}$$
$$\vdots \qquad\qquad (k = 1, 2, \ldots) \qquad (13.5)$$
$$x_m^{(k+1)} \longleftarrow F_m\{x_1^{(k)}, x_2^{(k)}, \ldots, x_m^{(k)}\}$$

where the convergence criterion is

$$\left|\frac{x_j^{(k+1)} - x_j^{(k)}}{x_j^{(k)}}\right| < \epsilon \quad (j = 1, 2, \ldots, m; k = 1, 2, \ldots) \quad (13.6)$$

As in the method of successive substitutions, satisfactory convergence to a solution depends on the functions. When there is convergence, the rate is usually slow.

Example 13.3

Use the Gauss-Jacobi method to solve Eqns. (13.1).

Solution:

The functional form selected is

$$x_1 = F_1\{x_1^*, x_2^*, x_3^*\} = \frac{[4 - (x_3^*)^{1/2}]^3}{x_2^*}$$

$$x_2 = F_2\{x_1^*, x_2^*, x_3^*\} = [81 - (x_1^*)^2 - (x_3^*)^2]^{1/2}$$

$$x_3 = F_3\{x_1^*, x_2^*, x_3^*\} = \frac{33 - (x_1^*)^{1/2}}{x_2^*}$$

where the asterisks denote guess values of the solution.

Four sets of initial guess values for x_1^*, x_2^*, and x_3^* are selected to study the possibility of multiple solutions and the convergence properties of the Gauss-Jacobi method:

No.	x_1^*	x_2^*	x_3^*
1	2	10	5
2	4	10	5
3	4	3	5
4	8	2	1

A convergence tolerance of 0.0001 is selected. The following tables summarize the Gauss-Jacobi calculations:

1. $x_1^* = 2$, $x_2^* = 10$, $x_3^* = 5$:

k	$x_1^{(k)}$	$x_2^{(k)}$	$x_3^{(k)}$
1	2	10	5
2	0.5488	7.2111	3.1586
3	1.5229	8.4096	4.4735
4	0.7964	7.6595	3.7773
5	1.1354	8.1300	4.1919
6	0.9157	7.8828	3.9279
7	1.0427	8.0457	4.0649
8	0.9704	7.9617	3.9747
9	1.0144	8.0163	4.0211

k	$x_1^{(k)}$	$x_2^{(k)}$	$x_3^{(k)}$
10	0.9901	7.9876	3.9910
11	1.0049	8.0057	4.0068
12	0.9967	7.9960	3.9968
13	1.0017	8.0020	4.0022
14	0.9989	7.9987	3.9989
15	1.0006	8.0007	4.0007
16	0.9996	7.9996	3.9996
17	1.0002	8.0002	4.0002
18	0.9999	7.9999	3.9999
19	1.0001	8.0001	4.0001
20	1.0000	8.0000	4.0000

2. $x_1^* = 4$, $x_2^* = 10$, $x_3^* = 5$:

k	$x_1^{(k)}$	$x_2^{(k)}$	$x_3^{(k)}$
1	4	10	5
2	0.5488	6.3246	3.1000
3	1.7755	8.4314	5.1006
4	0.6265	7.1994	3.7559
5	1.2178	8.1548	4.4738
6	0.8212	7.7138	3.9114
7	1.0722	8.0639	4.1606
8	0.9341	7.9082	3.9639
9	1.0254	8.0259	4.0507
10	0.9780	7.9712	3.9855
11	1.0091	8.0099	4.0158
12	0.9929	7.9909	3.9945
13	1.0032	8.0037	4.0050
14	0.9977	7.9971	3.9980
15	1.0011	8.0013	4.0016
16	0.9992	7.9991	3.9993
17	1.0004	8.0005	4.0005
18	0.9998	7.9997	3.9997
19	1.0001	8.0002	4.0002
20	0.9999	7.9999	3.9999
21	1.0000	8.0001	4.0001
22	1.0000	8.0000	4.0000

3. $x_1^* = 4$, $x_2^* = 3$, $x_3^* = 5$:

k	$x_1^{(k)}$	$x_2^{(k)}$	$x_3^{(k)}$
1	4	3	5
2	1.8295	6.3246	10.3333
3	Divergence occurred		

4. $x_1^* = 8$, $x_2^* = 2$, $x_3^* = 1$:

k	$x_1^{(k)}$	$x_2^{(k)}$	$x_3^{(k)}$
1	8	2	1
2	13.5000	4.0000	15.0858
3	Divergence occurred		

Discussion: Convergence is achieved for cases 1 and 2 where the initial guess values are close to the solution values. However, divergence occurs for cases 3 and 4 where the initial guess values are farther away from the solution values.

Wegstein's method

The multidimensional Wegstein's method usually requires fewer iterations and is less likely to diverge compared to the Gauss-Jacobi method. As before, the equations are expressed in the form $x_i = F_i\{x_1, x_2, \ldots, x_m\}$, $i = 1, 2, \ldots, m$, and

$$x_1^{(2)} = F_1\{x_1^{(1)}, x_2^{(1)}, \ldots, x_m^{(1)}\}$$
$$x_2^{(2)} = F_2\{x_1^{(1)}, x_2^{(1)}, \ldots, x_m^{(1)}\}$$
$$\vdots$$
$$x_m^{(2)} = F_m\{x_1^{(1)}, x_2^{(1)}, \ldots, x_m^{(1)}\}$$

When the convergence criteria, Eqns. (13.6), have not been satisfied, candidate solution values for each subsequent iteration are computed using Eqn. (11.8), rewritten for simultaneous equations:

$$x_i^{(k+1)} = t_i F_i\{x_1^{(k)}, x_2^{(k)}, \ldots, x_m^{(k)}\} + (1 - t_i)x_i^{(k)} \qquad (i = 1, 2, \ldots, m, \\ k = 2, 3, \ldots) \tag{13.7}$$

where

$$t_i = \frac{1}{1 - s_i}$$

and

$$s_i = \frac{F_i\{x_1^{(k)}, x_2^{(k)}, \ldots, x_m^{(k)}\} - F_i\{x_1^{(k-1)}, x_2^{(k-1)}, \ldots, x_m^{(k-1)}\}}{x_i^{(k)} - x_i^{(k-1)}}$$

As in the one-dimensional case, most computer programs limit the degree of extrapolation by setting $t_i = t_{max}$ when $t_i > t_{max}$ and $t_i = -t_{max}$ when $t < -t_{max}$. A typical value of t_{max} is 10.

Example 13.4

Use Wegstein's method to solve Eqns. (13.1) beginning with the guess solution values in Example 13.3. Compare the results.

Solution:

As in Example 13.3, the equations are expressed in the form

$$x_1 = F_1\{x_1^*, x_2^*, x_3^*\} = \frac{[4 - (x_3^*)^{1/2}]^3}{x_2^*}$$

$$x_2 = F_2\{x_1^*, x_2^*, x_3^*\} = [81 - (x_1^*)^2 - (x_3^*)^2]^{1/2}$$

$$x_3 = F_3\{x_1^*, x_2^*, x_3^*\} = \frac{33 - (x_1^*)^{1/2}}{x_2^*}$$

The same four sets of initial guess values, x_1^*, x_2^*, and x_3^*, are used. The convergence tolerance is 0.0001. The following tables summarize calculations by Wegstein's method:

1. $x_1^* = 2$, $x_2^* = 10$, $x_3^* = 5$:

k	$x_1^{(k)}$	$x_2^{(k)}$	$x_3^{(k)}$
1	2	10	5
2	0.5488	7.2111	3.1586
3	1.1317	8.0494	3.9257
4	1.0727	8.0288	3.9509
5	1.0071	8.0113	4.0171
6	0.9842	7.9905	3.9884
7	0.9977	7.9999	4.0007
8	0.9991	7.9999	4.0003
9	1.0000	7.9999	4.0000
10	1.0000	7.9999	4.0000

2. $x_1^* = 4$, $x_2^* = 10$, $x_3^* = 5$:

k	$x_1^{(k)}$	$x_2^{(k)}$	$x_3^{(k)}$
1	4	10	5
2	0.5488	6.3246	3.1000
3	1.4538	7.6638	4.0745
4	1.2154	7.8265	4.1120
5	0.9396	7.9256	4.0997
6	0.9733	7.9815	4.0414
7	0.9971	7.9833	3.9775
8	1.1316	8.0116	4.0098
9	1.0092	7.9961	3.9959
10	1.0024	7.9980	3.9985
11	1.0004	8.0000	4.0004
12	0.9993	7.9998	4.0001
13	0.9999	7.9999	4.0001
14	1.0000	7.9999	4.0001

3. $x_1^* = 4$, $x_2^* = 3$, $x_3^* = 5$:

k	$x_1^{(k)}$	$x_2^{(k)}$	$x_3^{(k)}$
1	4	3	5
2	1.8295	6.3246	10.3333
3	Divergence occurred		

4. $x_1^* = 8$, $x_2^* = 2$, $x_3^* = 1$:

k	$x_1^{(k)}$	$x_2^{(k)}$	$x_3^{(k)}$
1	8	2	1
2	13.5000	4.000	15.0858
3	Divergence occurred		

Discussion: Wegstein's method accelerates convergence for cases 1 and 2. Both successive substitutions and Wegstein's method diverge for cases 3 and 4.

Wegstein's method usually reduces by one-half the number of iterations needed to achieve convergence by the Gauss-Jacobi method. In some cases, Wegstein's method converges but the Gauss-Jacobi method diverges.

13.4 Iterative Methods with Partial Derivatives

The number of iterations required for convergence can be reduced by methods that use partial derivatives. However, any decrease in number of iterations must be weighed against an increase in computing time for evaluating derivatives.

Newton-Raphson method

The set of m simultaneous equations is expressed in the form

$$f_1\{x_1, x_2, \ldots, x_m\} = 0$$
$$f_2\{x_1, x_2, \ldots, x_m\} = 0$$
$$\vdots \qquad (13.2)$$
$$f_m\{x_1, x_2, \ldots, x_m\} = 0$$

To begin the algorithm, one provides a complete set of guess solution values, $x_1^*, x_2^*, \ldots, x_m^*$. Unless by coincidence the guess values correspond to the solution vector, substitution into Eqns. (13.2) generates values for some or all of $f_1, f_2, \ldots, f_m$ that differ from zero. The objective is to obtain improved guess values of the solution such that $f_1, f_2, \ldots, f_m$ all approach zero.

Partial derivatives evaluated at the guess solution,

$$\frac{\partial f_1}{\partial x_1}\bigg|_*, \frac{\partial f_1}{\partial x_2}\bigg|_*, \ldots, \frac{\partial f_1}{\partial x_m}\bigg|_*,$$

enable one to predict values of functions in the neighborhood of the guess values by extrapolation. Prediction formulas are based upon a Taylor's series expansion terminated after the first derivative:

$$f_1\{x_1, x_2, \ldots, x_m\} \simeq f_1\{x_1^*, x_2^*, \ldots, x_m^*\} + (x_1 - x_1^*)\frac{\partial f_1}{\partial x_1}\bigg|_*$$

$$+ (x_2 - x_2^*)\frac{\partial f_1}{\partial x_2}\bigg|_* + \cdots + (x_m - x_m^*)\frac{\partial f_1}{\partial x_m}\bigg|_*$$

$$f_2\{x_1, x_2, \ldots, x_m\} \simeq f_2\{x_1^*, x_2^*, \ldots, x_m^*\} + (x_1 - x_1^*)\frac{\partial f_2}{\partial x_1}\bigg|_*$$

$$+ (x_2 - x_2^*)\frac{\partial f_2}{\partial x_2}\bigg|_* + \cdots + (x_m - x_m^*)\frac{\partial f_2}{\partial x_m}\bigg|_*$$

$$\vdots$$

$$f_m\{x_1, x_2, \ldots, x_m\} \simeq f_m\{x_1^*, x_2^*, \ldots, x_m^*\} + (x_1 - x_1^*)\frac{\partial f_m}{\partial x_1}\bigg|_*$$

$$+ (x_2 - x_2^*)\frac{\partial f_m}{\partial x_2}\bigg|_* + \cdots + (x_m - x_m^*)\frac{\partial f_m}{\partial x_m}\bigg|_*$$

Observe that each function must be expanded. The set of extrapolation formulas may be written in abbreviated notation,

$$f_i\{x_1, x_2, \ldots, x_m\} \simeq f_i\{x_1^*, x_2^*, \ldots, x_m^*\} + (x_1 - x_1^*)\frac{\partial f_i}{\partial x_1}\bigg|_*$$

$$+ (x_2 - x_2^*)\frac{\partial f_i}{\partial x_2}\bigg|_* + \cdots + (x_m - x_m^*)\frac{\partial f_i}{\partial x_m}\bigg|_*$$

$$(13.8)$$

where i denotes the function number ($i = 1, 2, \ldots, m$).

Example 13.5

Consider the first equation in the set of Eqns. (13.1):

$$f_1\{x_1, x_2, x_3\} = (x_1)^{1/2} + x_2 x_3 - 33 = 0$$

Evaluate this function and its partial derivatives at the guess solution $x_1^* = 4$, $x_2^* = 3$, $x_3^* = 5$. Use Eqn. (13.8) ($i = 1$) to estimate the value of the function at $x_1 = 4.5$, $x_2 = 3.5$, $x_3 = 5.5$. Compare with the true value.

Solution:

$$f_1\{x_1^*, x_2^*, x_3^*\} = (x_1^*)^{1/2} + (x_2^*)(x_3^*) - 33$$
$$= (4)^{1/2} + (3)(5) - 33$$
$$= -16$$

(since $f_1\{x_1^*, x_2^*, x_3^*\} \neq 0$, x_1^*, x_2^*, x_3^* is not a solution.) The first partial derivatives are

$$\frac{\partial f_1}{\partial x_1} = \frac{1}{2x_1^{1/2}}, \quad \frac{\partial f_1}{\partial x_2} = x_3, \quad \frac{\partial f_1}{\partial x_3} = x_2$$

Values of derivatives at the guess solution are

$$\left.\frac{\partial f_1}{\partial x_1}\right|_* = \frac{1}{2(4)^{1/2}} = 0.25, \quad \left.\frac{\partial f_1}{\partial x_2}\right|_* = 5, \quad \left.\frac{\partial f_1}{\partial x_3}\right|_* = 3$$

The estimated value of the function at $x_1 = 4.5$, $x_2 = 3.5$, $x_3 = 5.5$ is

$$f_1\{4.5, 3.5, 5.5\} \simeq -16 + (4.5 - 4)(0.25) + (3.5 - 3)(5) + (5.5 - 5)(3)$$
$$\simeq -11.875$$

The actual value is

$$f_1\{4.5, 3.5, 5.5\} = (4.5)^{1/2} + (3.5)(5.5) - 33$$
$$= -11.63$$

The estimate is within 2% of the actual value of the function.

In the previous example, a Taylor series expansion is used to estimate the value of the function at points close to the guess solution. The Newton-Raphson method is just the reverse: Given a guess solution, the known value of each function at the real solution (zero) is used to estimate a new (and, hopefully, better) guess solution. Equation (13.8) is set equal to zero:

$$0 \simeq f_1\{x_1^*, x_2^*, \ldots, x_m^*\} + (x_1 - x_1^*)\left.\frac{\partial f_1}{\partial x_1}\right|_* + (x_2 - x_2^*)\left.\frac{\partial f_1}{\partial x_2}\right|_* + \cdots$$
$$+ (x_m - x_m^*)\left.\frac{\partial f_1}{\partial x_m}\right|_*$$

$$0 \simeq f_2\{x_1^*, x_2^*, \ldots, x_m^*\} + (x_1 - x_1^*)\left.\frac{\partial f_2}{\partial x_1}\right|_* + (x_2 - x_2^*)\left.\frac{\partial f_2}{\partial x_2}\right|_* + \cdots$$
$$+ (x_m - x_m^*)\left.\frac{\partial f_2}{\partial x_m}\right|_*$$

$$\vdots$$

$$0 \simeq f_m\{x_1^*, x_2^*, \ldots, x_m^*\} + (x_1 - x_1^*)\left.\frac{\partial f_m}{\partial x_1}\right|_* + (x_2 - x_2^*)\left.\frac{\partial f_m}{\partial x_2}\right|_* + \cdots$$
$$+ (x_m - x_m^*)\left.\frac{\partial f_m}{\partial x_m}\right|_*$$

where $x_1, x_2, \ldots, x_m$ are new solution values. These equations are abbreviated,

$$0 \simeq f_i\{x_1^*, x_2^*, \ldots, x_m^*\} + (x_1 - x_1^*)\frac{\partial f_i}{\partial x_1}\bigg|_* + (x_2 - x_2^*)\frac{\partial f_i}{\partial x_2}\bigg|_* + \cdots$$

$$+ (x_m - x_m^*)\frac{\partial f_i}{\partial x_m}\bigg|_* \tag{13.9}$$

where i denotes the function number $= 1, 2, \ldots, m$. These m equations are *linear* in m unknowns $(x_1, x_2, \ldots, x_m)$ and can be solved using the Gauss-Jordan reduction algorithm. Convergence to a set of solution values is achieved when

$$\left|\frac{x_j - x_j^*}{x_j^*}\right| < \epsilon \tag{13.10}$$

for $j = 1, 2, \ldots, m$.

The augmented coefficient matrix for the linear equations (13.9) is

$$\begin{bmatrix} \dfrac{\partial f_1}{\partial x_1}\bigg|_* & \dfrac{\partial f_1}{\partial x_2}\bigg|_* & \cdots & \dfrac{\partial f_1}{\partial x_m}\bigg|_* & \gamma_1 \\[2mm] \dfrac{\partial f_2}{\partial x_1}\bigg|_* & \dfrac{\partial f_2}{\partial x_2}\bigg|_* & \cdots & \dfrac{\partial f_2}{\partial x_m}\bigg|_* & \gamma_2 \\[2mm] \vdots & \vdots & & \vdots & \vdots \\[2mm] \dfrac{\partial f_m}{\partial x_1}\bigg|_* & \dfrac{\partial f_m}{\partial x_2}\bigg|_* & \cdots & \dfrac{\partial f_m}{\partial x_m}\bigg|_* & \gamma_m \end{bmatrix}$$

where

$$\gamma_i = -f_i^* + x_1^*\frac{\partial f_i}{\partial x_1}\bigg|_* + x_2^*\frac{\partial f_i}{\partial x_2}\bigg|_* + \cdots + x_m^*\frac{\partial f_i}{\partial x_m}\bigg|_*, \qquad i = 1, 2, \ldots, m$$

All coefficients in the matrix are known at the guess values. Upon completion of the Gauss-Jordan algorithm, the augmented coefficient matrix is transformed to the identity matrix and vector of new guess solution values, that is,

$$\begin{bmatrix} 1 & 0 & 0 & 0 & \cdots & & x_1 \\ 0 & 1 & 0 & 0 & & & x_2 \\ 0 & 0 & 1 & 0 & & & x_3 \\ 0 & 0 & 0 & 1 & & & x_4 \\ & & \vdots & & \vdots & & \vdots \\ & & \vdots & & \vdots & & \vdots \\ 0 & 0 & 0 & 0 & \cdots & 1 & x_m \end{bmatrix}$$

identity matrix (mth degree)   new guess solution values

Example 13.6

Use the Newton-Raphson method to solve Eqns. (13.1):

$$(x_1)^{1/2} + x_2 x_3 = 33$$
$$x_1^2 + x_2^2 + x_3^2 = 81 \qquad\qquad (13.1)$$
$$(x_1 x_2)^{1/3} + (x_3)^{1/2} = 4$$

Try $x_1^* = 2$, $x_2^* = 10$, $x_3^* = 5$ as the initial guess values.

Solution:

The equations are

$$f_1\{x_1, x_2, x_3\} = (x_1)^{1/2} + x_2 x_3 - 33 = 0$$
$$f_2\{x_1, x_2, x_3\} = x_1^2 + x_2^2 + x_3^2 - 81 = 0$$
$$f_3\{x_1, x_2, x_3\} = (x_1 x_2)^{1/3} + x_3^{1/2} - 4 = 0$$

The augmented coefficient matrix is

$$\begin{bmatrix} \left(\dfrac{1}{2(x_1^*)^{1/2}}\right) & x_3^* & x_2^* & \gamma_1 \\[2ex] 2x_1^* & 2x_2^* & 2x_3^* & \gamma_2 \\[2ex] \left(\dfrac{(x_2^*)^{1/3}}{3(x_1^*)^{2/3}}\right) & \left(\dfrac{(x_1^*)^{1/3}}{3(x_2^*)^{2/3}}\right) & \left(\dfrac{1}{2(x_3^*)^{1/2}}\right) & \gamma_3 \end{bmatrix}$$

where

$$\gamma_1 = x_2^* x_3^* - \frac{(x_1^*)^{1/2}}{2} + 33$$

$$\gamma_2 = (x_1^*)^2 + (x_2^*)^2 + (x_3^*)^2 + 81$$

$$\gamma_3 = -\frac{(x_1^* x_2^*)^{1/3}}{3} - \frac{(x_3^*)^{1/2}}{2} + 4$$

The following table summarizes successive applications of the Newton-Raphson method with $\varepsilon = 0.0001$. The calculation is described in the next example.

k	x_1^*	x_2^*	x_3^*	f_1^*	f_2^*	f_3^*
1	2	10	5	18.4142	48.0000	0.9505
2	0.7084	8.3416	4.0334	1.4871	5.3527	−0.1837
3	0.9636	8.0185	3.9932	0.0014	0.1711	−0.0247
4	0.9995	8.0002	3.9999	−0.0003	0.0017	−0.0003
5	1.0000	8.0000	4.0000	0.0000	0.0000	0.0000

The number of iterations should be compared with Example 13.3 (Gauss-Jacobi) and with Example 13.4 (Wegstein's method): Newton's method converges faster for this example.

Partial derivatives in the coefficient matrix may be calculated numerically; for example,

$$\left.\frac{\partial f_2}{\partial x_1}\right|_* \simeq \frac{f_2\{(x_1^* + \delta), x_2^*, \ldots, x_m^*\} - f_2\{x_1^*, x_2^*, \ldots, x_m^*\}}{\delta}$$

Example 13.7

Prepare a WATFIV program to solve Eqns. (13.1) using the Newton-Raphson method (see Example 13.6).

Solution:

The program is to solve m nonlinear equations in m unknowns. The main program (see Fig. 13-1) reads the guess solution x_i^* ($i = 1, 2, \ldots, m$) and sets up the coefficient matrix using numerical differentiation. Function values are calculated using the subprogram FUNC (see Fig. 13-2). Each set of equations requires a different FUNC subprogram. The linear equations are solved for new solution values using the subprogram SIMULI*, which is similar to the program of Example 12.4. Convergence is checked using Eqn. (13.10) and, when satisfied, solution values are printed; otherwise, new solution values replace the previous ones, and the next Newton-Raphson iteration is executed.

Observe that double-precision variables and arithmetic are required for numerical estimation of partial derivatives and Gauss-Jordan reduction of the simultaneous linear equations. Single-precision variables often eliminate significant digits and lead to spurious results.

Flow Diagram

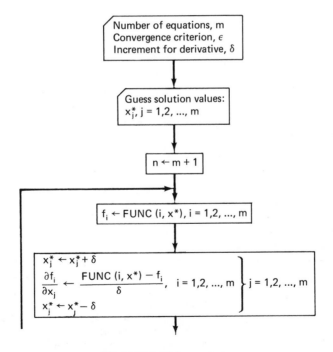

Figure 13-1 Main program.

*B. Carnahan, H. A. Luther, and J. O. Wilkes, *Applied Numerical Methods*, Wiley, New York, 1969, p. 290.

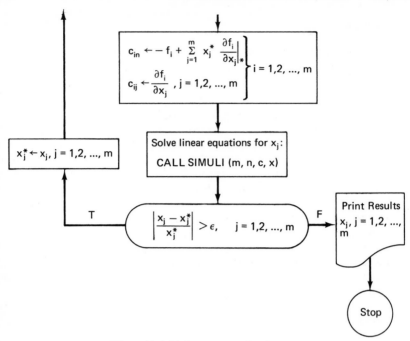

Figure 13-1 Main program (Continued).

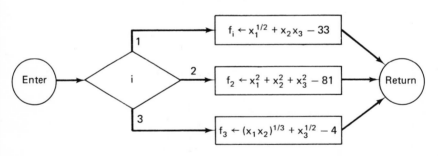

Figure 13-2 Subprogram FUNC.

Table of Symbols

Problem Symbol	Program Symbol	Definition
Main		
C	C	Coefficient matrix—order $m \times n$
f	F	Vector containing value for each function at the guess solution values
i	I	Subscript representing ith equation; also row counter (coefficient matrix)
j	J	Subscript representing jth unknown variable; also column counter (coefficient matrix)

Problem Symbol	Program Symbol	Definition
k	K	Iteration counter
k_{max}	KMAX	Maximum number of iterations
m	M	No. of equations; no. of rows in $\mathbf{C}$ matrix
n	N	$m + 1$; no. of columns in $\mathbf{C}$ matrix
x	X	Vector of new solution values
x^*	XS	Vector of guess solution values
δ	DELTA	Increment for partial derivative
ϵ	EPSI	Convergence criterion
$\dfrac{\partial f_i}{\partial x_j}$	DERIV (I, J)	Table of partial derivatives
γ_i	GAM (I)	Vector containing as elements $(i = 1, 2, \ldots, m)$, $$-f_i^* + x_1^* \left.\frac{\partial f_i}{\partial x_1}\right|_* + x_2^* \left.\frac{\partial f_i}{\partial x_2}\right|_* + \cdots + x_m^* \left.\frac{\partial f_i}{\partial x_m}\right|_*$$
Function FUNC		
i	I	Equation number
x	X	Vector of unknown variable values

Program Listings

Main Program

```
C
C**    GENERAL PROGRAM TO SOLVE M SIMULTANEOUS NON-LINEAR EQUATIONS
C      USING THE NEWTON-RAPHSON METHOD.  FUNC(I,X) EVALUATES THE ITH
C      EQUATION USING VALUES OF INDEPENDENT VARIABLES STORED IN A VECTOR.
C
       IMPLICIT REAL*8 (A-H,O-Z)
       REAL*8 C(11,11), F(10), DERIV(10,10), GAM(10), X(10), XS(10),
      1ERR(10)
C
C**    READS AND PRINTS DATA
C
       READ, M
       WRITE (6,101)
       PRINT, M
       READ, EPSI, DELTA, KMAX
       WRITE (6,103)
       WRITE (6,107) EPSI, DELTA, KMAX
       READ, (XS(J), J = 1,M)
       WRITE (6,102)
       WRITE (6,106) (XS(J), J = 1,M)
       N = M + 1
C
C**    CARRY OUT ITERATIVE NEWTON-RAPHSON METHOD.
C
       DO 10 K = 1,KMAX
C
C**    EVALUATES FUNCTIONS AT GUESS VALUES.
C
       DO 11 I = 1,M
   11  F(I) = FUNC(I,XS)
C
C**    ESTIMATES DERIVATIVES NUMERICALLY.
C
       DO 1 J = 1,M
       XS(J) = XS(J) + DELTA
       DO 12 I = 1,M
   12  DERIV(I,J) = (FUNC(I,XS) - F(I))/DELTA
    1  XS(J) = XS(J) - DELTA
C
C**    CALCULATES GAM
C
```

```
          DO 2 I = 1,M
          GAM(I) = -F(I)
          DO 2 J = 1,M
      2   GAM(I) = GAM(I) + XS(J)*DERIV(I,J)
C
C**   SETS UP COEFFICIENT MATRIX.
C
          DO 3 I = 1,M
          C(I,N) = GAM(I)
          DO 3 J = 1,M
      3   C(I,J) = DERIV(I,J)
C
C**   SOLVES LINEAR EQUATIONS.
C
          CALL SIMULI (M, N, C, X)
C
C**   CHECKS FOR CONVERGENCE
C
          DO 4 J = 1,M
          ERR(J) = DABS((X(J) - XS(J))/XS(J))
          IF (ERR(J) .GE. EPSI) GO TO 5
      4   CONTINUE
C
C**   PRINTS SOLUTION VALUES.
C
          WRITE (6,104)
          DO 7 J = 1,M
      7   WRITE (6,106) X(J)
          STOP
C
C**   SETS NEW GUESS VALUES, XS, EQUAL TO SOLUTION VALUE CANDIDATES, X.
C
      5   DO 6 J = 1,M
      6   XS(J) = X(J)
          WRITE (6,106) (XS(J), J = 1,M)
     10   CONTINUE
C
C**   KMAX HAS BEEN EXCEEDED.   PRINTS ERROR MESSAGE.
C
          WRITE (6,105)
          STOP
C
C**   INPUT AND OUTPUT FORMAT STATEMENTS.
C
    101   FORMAT ( ' M =',/)
    102   FORMAT (//, ' GUESS SOLUTION VALUES XS(J) = ',/)
    103   FORMAT (//,' EPSI, DELTA, KMAX =',/)
    104   FORMAT (//,' SOLUTION VALUES X(J) =',/)
    105   FORMAT (//,' KMAX EXCEEDED')
    106   FORMAT (' ', 8F15.4)
    107   FORMAT (' ', 2F15.6, 1I12)
          END
```

Subprogram FUNC

```
          FUNCTION FUNC (I,X)
C
C**   FUNCTION SUBPROGRAM TO EVALUATE M NON-LINEAR EQUATIONS.
C
          REAL*8 X(10), FUNC
          GO TO (1,2,3), I
      1   FUNC = X(1)**0.5 + X(2)*X(3) - 33.0
          RETURN
      2   FUNC = X(1)*X(1) + X(2)*X(2) + X(3)*X(3) - 81.0
          RETURN
      3   FUNC = (X(1)*X(2))**(1.0/3.0) + X(3)**0.5 - 4.0
          RETURN
          END
```

Data

```
3
1.0E-4, 1.0E-5, 25
2.0, 10.0, 5.0
```

Computed Output

```
M =

        3


EPSI, DELTA, KMAX =

    0.00010           0.00001              25


GUESS SOLUTION VALUES XS(J) =

        2.0000        10.0000       5.0000
        0.7084         8.3416       4.0334
        0.9636         8.0185       3.9932
        0.9995         8.0002       3.9999
        1.0000         8.0000       4.0000


SOLUTION VALUES X(J) =

        1.0000
        8.0000
        4.0000
```

Discussion

Convergence is fast for this particular initial guess value (2, 10, 5). However, convergence does not occur for the other guess values [(4, 10, 5), (4, 3, 5), (8, 2, 1)] in Example 13.3.

The Jacobian of a set of m equations in m unknowns is a determinant defined by

$$
J = \begin{vmatrix}
\dfrac{\partial f_1}{\partial x_1}\bigg|_* & \dfrac{\partial f_1}{\partial x_2}\bigg|_* & \cdots & \dfrac{\partial f_1}{\partial x_m}\bigg|_* \\[2mm]
\dfrac{\partial f_2}{\partial x_1}\bigg|_* & \dfrac{\partial f_2}{\partial x_2}\bigg|_* & \cdots & \dfrac{\partial f_2}{\partial x_m}\bigg|_* \\
\cdot & \cdot & & \cdot \\
\cdot & \cdot & & \cdot \\
\cdot & \cdot & & \cdot \\
\dfrac{\partial f_m}{\partial x_1}\bigg|_* & \dfrac{\partial f_m}{\partial x_2}\bigg|_* & \cdots & \dfrac{\partial f_m}{\partial x_m}\bigg|_*
\end{vmatrix}
= \left(\dfrac{\partial f_i}{\partial x_j}\right)
\quad
\begin{array}{l}
(i = 1, 2, \ldots, m, \\
\; j = 1, 2, \ldots, m)
\end{array}
\tag{13.11}
$$

This array appears in the augmented coefficient matrix for solving Eqns. (13.9). It can be shown that a necessary condition for a unique solution is that the Jacobian be nonzero. Divergence can occur even when the Jacobian is nonzero but there are several optimization techniques, such as the method of steepest descent* and Marquardt's method,* that are designed to reduce the tendency toward divergence. Table 13.2 shows solutions for 4 sets of guess values. It is interesting that different methods may locate different solutions even when they begin searching at the same point.

TABLE 13.2
SOLUTION OF EQUATIONS (13.1) USING THE METHOD OF STEEPEST
DESCENT AND MARQUARDT'S METHOD

	Guess Values			Solution		
	x_1^*	x_2^*	x_3^*	x_1	x_2	x_3
Method of Steepest						
Descent	2	10	5	1	8	4
	4	10	5	1	8	4
	4	3	5	0.393	4.027	8.039
	8	2	1	0.393	4.027	8.039
Marquardt's Method	2	10	5	1	8	4
	4	10	5	1	8	4
	4	3	5	0.393	4.027	8.039
	8	2	1	1	8	4

PROBLEMS

13.1. Use the methods of Section 13.1 to solve the nonlinear equations:

$$x_1^{1/2} + x_2 x_3 = 33$$
$$x_1 + x_3 = 5$$
$$(x_1 x_2)^{1/3} + x_3^{1/2} = 4$$

13.2. Precedence order the following equations:

$$x_1^2(1 - x_2) = 2$$
$$x_3 + x_5 x_6 = -2$$
$$x_4 + x_4^2 = 3$$
$$x_3(x_5 + x_6) + \ln x_6 = 2$$
$$x_1 x_5^{1/2} + x_4 = 10$$
$$x_1 + x_3 + x_5 = 3$$

13.3. Consider the following two simultaneous equations:

$$x_1 + x_2 = 5$$
$$x_1^2 - x_1 x_2 = -3$$

*D. Himmelblau, *Applied Nonlinear Programming*, McGraw-Hill, New York, 1972.
E. J. Henley and E. M. Rosen, *Material and Energy Balance Computations*, Wiley, N.Y. (1969).

Use the Newton-Raphson method to solve these equations with guess values $x_1^* = 0$, $x_2^* = 1$. Show the complete method including the matrix of partial derivatives, etc. Carry out the calculations for 4 iterations. Note that these equations can be reduced to a single quadratic equation.

Appendices

Solution of Material Balance Equations for Chemical Reactor

I

Equations (1)–(6) in Example 7.10 are ordered for solution using the methods in Sec. 13.1. The six equations to be solved are

$$\boxed{K'} = \frac{x_{23}^2}{x_{21}x_{22}^3} \tag{I.1}$$

$$x_{21} + x_{22} + x_{23} + x_{24} + x_{25} = 1 \tag{I.2}$$

$$2\,\boxed{F_1}\boxed{x_{11}} + \boxed{F_1}\boxed{x_{13}} = 2F_2 x_{21} + F_2 x_{23} \tag{I.3}$$

$$2\,\boxed{F_1}\boxed{x_{12}} + 3\,\boxed{F_1}\boxed{x_{13}} = 2F_2 x_{22} + 3F_2 x_{23} \tag{I.4}$$

$$\boxed{F_1}\boxed{x_{14}} = F_2 x_{24} \tag{I.5}$$

$$\boxed{F_1}\boxed{x_{15}} = F_2 x_{25} \tag{I.6}$$

Design variables are circled. These equations can be written more compactly by defining various constants:

$$\alpha_1 = \boxed{F_1}\left(2\,\boxed{x_{11}} + \boxed{x_{13}}\right)$$

$$\alpha_2 = \boxed{F_1}\left(2\,\boxed{x_{12}} + 3\,\boxed{x_{13}}\right)$$

$$\alpha_3 = \boxed{F_1}\boxed{x_{14}}$$

$$\alpha_4 = \boxed{F_1}\boxed{x_{15}}$$

so that

$$\boxed{K'} = \frac{x_{23}^2}{x_{21}x_{22}^3} \tag{I.1}$$

$$x_{21} + x_{22} + x_{23} + x_{24} + x_{25} = 1 \tag{I.2}$$

$$2F_2 x_{21} + F_2 x_{23} = \boxed{\alpha_1} \tag{I.3}$$

$$2F_2 x_{22} + 3F_2 x_{23} = \boxed{\alpha_2} \tag{I.4}$$

$$F_2 x_{24} = \boxed{\alpha_3} \tag{I.5}$$

$$F_2 x_{25} = \boxed{\alpha_4} \tag{I.6}$$

Equations (5) and (6) have only two unknowns, and the rest have more than two. We select x_{24} and x_{25} as output variables. Rearranging,

$$x_{24} = \frac{\boxed{\alpha_3}}{F_2} \tag{I.5}$$

$$x_{25} = \frac{\boxed{\alpha_4}}{F_2} \tag{I.6}$$

After substitution, the four remaining equations are

$$\boxed{K'} = \frac{x_{23}^2}{x_{21} x_{22}^3} \tag{I.1}$$

$$x_{21} + x_{22} + x_{23} + \frac{\boxed{\alpha_3}}{F_2} + \frac{\boxed{\alpha_4}}{F_2} = 1 \tag{I.2}$$

$$2F_2 x_{21} + F_2 x_{23} = \boxed{\alpha_1} \tag{I.3}$$

$$2F_2 x_{22} + 3F_2 x_{23} = \boxed{\alpha_2} \tag{I.4}$$

All remaining equations have at least three unknowns. We select x_{21} and x_{22} as output variables for Eqns. (3) and (4), respectively:

$$x_{21} = \frac{\boxed{\alpha_1} - F_2 x_{23}}{2F_2} \tag{I.3}$$

$$x_{22} = \frac{\boxed{\alpha_2} - 3F_2 x_{23}}{2F_2} \tag{I.4}$$

After substitution, the two remaining equations are

$$\boxed{K'} = \frac{16 x_{23}^2}{[(\boxed{\alpha_1}/F_2) - x_{23}][(\boxed{\alpha_2}/F_2) - 3x_{23}]^3} \tag{I.1}$$

$$\frac{\boxed{\alpha_1} - F_2 x_{23}}{2F_2} + \frac{\boxed{\alpha_2} - 3F_2 x_{23}}{2F_2} + x_{23} + \frac{\boxed{\alpha_3}}{F_2} + \frac{\boxed{\alpha_4}}{F_2} = 1 \tag{I.2}$$

The second equation may be rearranged to give

$$2F_2(x_{23} + 1) = \boxed{\beta} \tag{I.2}$$

where

$$\beta = \boxed{\alpha_1} + \boxed{\alpha_2} + 2(\boxed{\alpha_3} + \boxed{\alpha_4})$$

Equations (1) and (2) have two unknowns. Equation (2) can be rearranged most easily; x_{23} is selected as the output variable:

$$x_{23} = \frac{\textcircled{β}}{2F_2} - 1 \tag{I.2}$$

After substitution, we are left with Eqn. (1) containing one unknown (F_2):

$$\textcircled{K'} = 16F_2^2 \frac{(\textcircled{γ_1} - F_2)^2}{(\textcircled{γ_2} + F_2)(\textcircled{γ_3} + 3F_2)^3} \tag{I.1}$$

where

$$\gamma_1 = \frac{\textcircled{β}}{2}$$

$$\gamma_2 = \textcircled{α_1} - \frac{\textcircled{β}}{2}$$

$$\gamma_3 = \textcircled{α_2} - \frac{3\textcircled{β}}{2}$$

Equation (1) may be solved iteratively for F_2 using Newton's method, for example.

The ordered equations are listed in Table I.1.

TABLE I.1
ORDERED EQUATIONS

Solution Order	Eqn. No.	Output Variable	Equation
1	1	F_2	$16F_2^2(\gamma_1 - F_2)^2 = K'(\gamma_2 + F_2)(\gamma_3 + 3F_2)^3$
2	2	x_{23}	$x_{23} = \frac{\beta}{2F_2} - 1$
3	3	x_{21}	$x_{21} = \frac{\alpha_1 - F_2 x_{23}}{2F_2}$
4	4	x_{22}	$x_{22} = \frac{\alpha_2 - 3F_2 x_{23}}{2F_2}$
5	5	x_{24}	$x_{24} = \frac{\alpha_3}{F_2}$
6	6	x_{25}	$x_{25} = \frac{\alpha_4}{F_2}$

where

$$\alpha_1 = F_1(2x_{11} + x_{13}) \qquad \beta = \alpha_1 + \alpha_2 + 2[\alpha_3 + \alpha_4]$$

$$\alpha_2 = F_1(2x_{12} + 3x_{13}) \qquad \gamma_1 = \frac{\beta}{2}$$

$$\alpha_3 = F_1 x_{14} \qquad \gamma_2 = \alpha_1 - \frac{\beta}{2}$$

$$\alpha_4 = F_1 x_{15} \qquad \gamma_3 = \alpha_2 - \frac{3\beta}{2}$$

Periodic Table of the Elements*

KEY TO CHART

Atomic Number → **50** → Oxidation States
Symbol → **Sn** +2
Atomic Weight → 118.69 +4
Electron Configuration → 18 18 4

1a	2a	3b	4b	5b	6b	7b	8	8	8	1b	2b	3a	4a	5a	6a	7a	0	Orbit
1 H +1 −1 1.008₀																	**2** He 0 4.00260 2	K
3 Li +1 6.94 2 1	**4** Be +2 9.01218 2 2											**5** B +3 10.81 2 3	**6** C +2 +4 −4 12.011 2 4	**7** N +1 +2 +3 +4 +5 −1 −2 −3 14.0067 2 5	**8** O −2 15.9994 2 6	**9** F −1 18.9984 2 7	**10** Ne 0 20.17₉ 2 8	K L
11 Na +1 22.9898 2 8 1	**12** Mg +2 24.305 2 8 2											**13** Al +3 26.9815 2 8 3	**14** Si +2 +4 −4 28.086 2 8 4	**15** P +3 +5 −3 30.9738 2 8 5	**16** S +4 +6 −2 32.06 2 8 6	**17** Cl +1 +5 +7 −1 35.453 2 8 7	**18** Ar 0 39.948 2 8 8	K L M
19 K +1 39.102 8 8 1	**20** Ca +2 40.08 8 8 2	**21** Sc +3 44.9559 8 9 2	**22** Ti +2 +3 +4 47.90 8 10 2	**23** V +2 +3 +4 +5 50.941₄ 8 11 2	**24** Cr +2 +3 +6 51.996 8 13 1	**25** Mn +2 +3 +4 +7 54.9380 8 13 2	**26** Fe +2 +3 55.847 8 14 2	**27** Co +2 +3 58.9332 8 15 2	**28** Ni +2 +3 58.71 8 16 2	**29** Cu +1 +2 63.546 8 18 1	**30** Zn +2 65.37 8 18 2	**31** Ga +3 69.72 8 18 3	**32** Ge +2 +4 72.59 8 18 4	**33** As +3 +5 −3 74.9216 8 18 5	**34** Se +4 +6 −2 78.96 8 18 6	**35** Br +1 +5 −1 79.904 8 18 7	**36** Kr 0 83.80 8 18 8	L M N

Transition Elements

Group 8

Transition Elements

512

Period 5 (Rb–Xe)

Z	Sym	Oxidation	Atomic weight	Shells (M N O)
37	Rb	+1	85.467₈	18 8 1
38	Sr	+2	87.0₂	18 8 2
39	Y	+3	88.9059	18 9 2
40	Zr	+4	91.22	18 10 2
41	Nb	+3 +5	92.9064	18 12 1
42	Mo	+6	95.94	18 13 1
43	Tc	+4 +6 +7	98.9062	18 13 1
44	Ru	+3	101.07	18 15 1
45	Rh	+3	102.9055	18 16 1
46	Pd	+2 +4	106.4	18 18 0
47	Ag	+1	107.868	18 18 1
48	Cd	+2	112.40	18 18 2
49	In	+3	114.82	18 18 3
50	Sn	+2 +4	118.69	18 18 4
51	Sb	+3 +5 -3	121.75	18 18 5
52	Te	+4 +6 -2	127.60	18 18 6
53	I	+1 +5 +7 -1	126.9045	18 18 7
54	Xe	0	131.30	18 18 8

Period 6 (Cs–Rn)

Z	Sym	Oxidation	Atomic weight	Shells (N O P)
55	Cs	+1	132.9055	18 8 1
56	Ba	+2	137.34	18 8 2
57*	La	+3	138.9055	18 9 2
72	Hf	+4	178.49	32 10 2
73	Ta	+5	180.947₉	32 11 2
74	W	+6	183.85	32 12 2
75	Re	+4 +6 +7	186.2	32 13 2
76	Os	+3 +4	190.2	32 14 2
77	Ir	+3 +4	192.22	32 15 2
78	Pt	+2 +4	195.09	32 16 2
79	Au	+1 +3	196.9665	32 18 1
80	Hg	+1 +2	200.59	32 18 2
81	Tl	+1 +3	204.37	32 18 3
82	Pb	+2 +4	207.2	32 18 4
83	Bi	+3 +5	208.9806	32 18 5
84	Po	+2 +4	(209)	32 18 6
85	At	-1	(210)	32 18 7
86	Rn	0	(222)	32 18 8

Period 7 (Fr–105)

Z	Sym	Oxidation	Atomic weight	Shells (O P Q)
87	Fr	+1	(223)	18 8 1
88	Ra	+2	(226)	18 8 2
89**	Ac	+3	(227)	18 9 2
104			—	32 10 2
105				

*Lanthanides (N O P)

Z	Sym	Oxidation	Atomic weight	Shells
58	Ce	+3 +4	140.12	20 8 2
59	Pr	+3	140.9077	21 8 2
60	Nd	+3	144.24	22 8 2
61	Pm	+3	(145)	23 8 2
62	Sm	+2 +3	150.4	24 8 2
63	Eu	+2 +3	151.96	25 8 2
64	Gd	+3	157.25	25 9 2
65	Tb	+3	158.9254	27 8 2
66	Dy	+3	162.50	28 8 2
67	Ho	+3	164.9303	29 8 2
68	Er	+3	167.26	30 8 2
69	Tm	+3	168.9342	31 8 2
70	Yb	+2 +3	173.04	32 8 2
71	Lu	+3	174.97	32 9 2

**Actinides (O P Q)

Z	Sym	Oxidation	Atomic weight	Shells
90	Th	+4	232.0381	18 10 2
91	Pa	+5 +4	231.0359	20 9 2
92	U	+4 +5 +6	238.029	21 9 2
93	Np	+4 +5 +6	237.0482	22 9 2
94	Pu	+3 +4 +5 +6	(244)	24 8 2
95	Am	+3 +4 +5 +6	(243)	25 8 2
96	Cm	+3	(247)	25 9 2
97	Bk	+3 +4	(247)	27 8 2
98	Cf	+3	(251)	28 8 2
99	Es	+3	(254)	29 8 2
100	Fm		(257)	30 8 2
101	Md		(256)	31 8 2
102	No		(254)	32 8 2
103	Lr	+3	(254)	32 9 2

Numbers in parentheses are mass numbers of most stable isotope of that element.

*R. C. Weast, ed., *Handbook of Chemistry and Physics*, 55th ed., Chemical Rubber Publishing Company, Cleveland, 1974–1975.

FORTRAN *Dialects*

WATFOR (WATerloo FORtran) and WATFIV, dialects of the FOR-
TRAN language, were developed by the Computing Center at the University
of Waterloo. These compilers offer

1. Extremely fast translation of programs prepared by students.
2. Excellent *run-time diagnostics* or error messages.

Subtle differences between these programs are described by B. Carnahan
and J. O. Wilkes in Ch. 3 of their textbook *Digital Computing and Numerical
Methods*, Wiley, New York, 1973.

One difference that appears in most of the programs in this text is that
format-free input is permitted in WATFOR and WATFIV but *not* in FOR-
TRAN. The format-free READ statement is

READ, L

where *L* is the normal FORTRAN input list. Examples are

READ, N, ALPHA, X(1)

The data items appear on a card separated by either a comma or blanks or
both. The comma must immediately follow the final character in the preceding entry.

Phase and Chemical Equilibria

IV

Several important thermodynamic equations that are used in this book to calculate equilibrium states of reacting and nonreacting mixtures are summarized here for convenience. The derivation of these equations may be found in the following textbooks:

J. M. Smith and H. C. Van Ness, *Introduction to Chemical Engineering Thermodynamics*, McGraw-Hill, N. Y. (1975).

J. M. Prausnitz, *Molecular Thermodynamics of Fluid-Phase Equilibria*, Prentice-Hall, Englewood Cliffs, N. J. (1969).

K. Denbigh, *The Principles of Chemical Equilibrium*, Cambridge University Press, London (1966).

Enthalpy of Liquid Mixtures

Molar enthalpy of a liquid mixture of composition $x_1, x_2, \ldots, x_{N_c}$ at temperature T is given by

$$h_{\text{mix}} = \sum_{j=1}^{N_c} h_j x_j + \Delta h^m \qquad (\text{IV.1})$$

Summation is over the liquids contained in the mixture. Δh^m is the enthalpy change, called heat of mixing, when one mole of solution is formed isothermally by mixing the pure liquids. Heat of mixing is a function of temperature and composition of the liquid. h_j is molar enthalpy of each pure liquid at T, the calculation of which requires data on the specific heat of each liquid and

515

its standard heat of formation [cf. Eqn. (9.41)]. If the liquids are nonreacting, it is customary to set heat of formation equal to zero and let the reference state be the pure liquid at temperature T_0.

Enthalpy of Perfect Gas Mixtures

Molar enthalpy of a perfect gas mixture of composition $y_1, y_2, \ldots, y_{N_c}$ and at temperature T is given by Eqn. (9.45). The assumption of a perfect gas is usually satisfactory when pressure does not exceed a few atmospheres. If the gases are nonreacting and the reference state is the pure liquid at temperature T_0:

$$h_{\text{mix}} = \sum_{j=1}^{N_c} y_j \left\{ \int_{T_0}^{T_{b_j}} c_{p_j}^{\text{liq}} \, dT + \lambda_{T_{b_j}} + \int_{T_{b_j}}^{T} c_{p_j}^{\circ} \, dT \right\} \qquad (IV.2)$$

The first term within the braces is the enthalpy change for heating a pure liquid from the reference temperature (T_0) to its normal boiling point (T_b). The second term, λ_{T_b}, is enthalpy of vaporization of the liquid at its normal boiling point. The last term is for heating the gas at low pressure from its normal boiling point to temperature T.

Vapor-Liquid Equilibria

If a two-phase mixture of liquid and vapor is at equilibrium, then

$$f_j^{\text{liq}} = f_j^{\text{vap}} \qquad (IV.3)$$

for every component of the mixture. Specifically, if the pressure is low ($P \leq 1$ atm)

$$P_j^s \gamma_j x_j = P y_j \qquad (IV.4)$$

where x_j and y_j are mole fractions of jth component in the liquid and gas phases, respectively. γ is the activity coefficient in the liquid mixture, which is a function of temperature and liquid composition. The vapor pressure of each component, P^s, is a function of temperature only. For ideal liquid mixtures $\gamma = 1$ by definition. Nonideality of a liquid mixture may be expressed in terms of excess Gibbs free energy (Δg^e), which has the useful mathematical property that all of the activity coefficients may be calculated from it by differentiation:

$$\ln \gamma_j = \left[\frac{\partial \left(\frac{n \Delta g^e}{RT} \right)}{\partial n_j} \right]_{T, P, n_k}, \quad j = 1, 2, \ldots, N_c; \, j \neq k, \qquad (IV.5)$$

n is total number of moles in the liquid and n_k means that differentiation is performed with all mole numbers except n_j held constant. Δg^e is a function of temperature and composition of the liquid. For an ideal liquid mixture, $\Delta g^e = 0$ and $\gamma_j = 1$.

A useful empirical expression for Δg^e is the Redlich-Kister* equation for a binary liquid mixture:

$$\frac{\Delta g^e}{RT} = x_1 x_2 \sum_{i=1}^{m} C_i (x_1 - x_2)^{i-1} \tag{IV.6}$$

$$= x_1 x_2 [C_1 + C_2(x_1 - x_2) + \cdots + C_m(x_1 - x_2)^{m-1}]$$

Coefficients C_i are functions of temperature but independent of composition.

Chemical Equilibria

The chemical equilibrium constant, K, for a reacting mixture of perfect gases is:

$$K = \left[\frac{P}{P^\circ}\right]^{\Sigma v_j} \prod \{y_j^{v_j}\} \tag{IV.7}$$

P° is the reference pressure (1 atm) and may be omitted if P is measured in atmospheres. The symbol $\prod$ stands for repeated multiplication of y_j terms, each raised to the v_j power. For the jth component participating in the reaction, y_j is its mole fraction in the equilibrium mixture and v_j is its stoichiometric coefficient in the balanced chemical reaction. K is a function of T only and may be calculated from standard thermochemical data by the equation:

$$\ln K = \frac{-\Delta G_0^\circ}{RT_0} + \frac{(\Delta H_0^\circ - I_0)(T - T_0)}{RT_0 T} + \int_{T_0}^{T} \frac{I}{RT^2} dT \tag{IV.8}$$

The reference temperature (T_0) at which thermochemical properties (ΔG_0° and ΔH_0°) are tabulated is conventionally 25°C (298.15°K). I, which is a function of temperature, is the indefinite integral of the polynomial for Δc_p°:

$$I = \int \Delta c_p^\circ \, dT \tag{IV.9}$$

Δc_p° is specific heat of products minus specific heat of reactants [Eqn. (9.43)] at the limit of low pressure (perfect-gas state). See Example 10.6 for a typical calculation of K.

---

*O. Redlich and A.T. Kister, "Algebraic Representation of Thermodynamic Properties and the Classification of Solutions" *Ind. Eng. Chem.* 40, 345 (1948).

Index